THE LIFE AND LEGACY OF
M. E. ENSMINGER

by

M. E. ENSMINGER, B.S., M.A., Ph.D.

with added anecdotes by A. H. Ensminger, B.Sc.H.E., M.S.

Around the World
the Best-Known Animal Scientist
of the Twentieth Century

Published by
AGRISERVICES FOUNDATION
through Interstate Publishers, Inc., Danville, Illinois

THE LIFE AND LEGACY OF

M. E. ENSMINGER

Library of Congress Control Number: 00-135313

ISBN 0-8134-3119-0

Order from:

The Interstate Publishers, Inc.
P.O. BOX 50, DANVILLE, IL 61834-0050
PH: 800-843-4774 • FAX: 217-446-9706

PROLOGUE

When I finally had time to think after downsizing and subsequent disbursement of our many possessions (which took over a year), I realized that I had no alternative but to finalize Dr. E's autobiography which he had completed during his last two or three years. I did not realize just what that decision would mean to me. I was concerned that it would be very sad to relive our 57 years together and I might become depressed. Strangely, it had the opposite effect. I feel very happy and gratified to be doing this.

For his many friends around the world, I do not need to tell you what he accomplished, but, for those readers, students, and stockmen who never met him, I am including here the very excellent eulogy that Dr. James Oldfield, Oregon State University, published in the Journal of Animal Science.

Some people's achievements cause them to become legends in their time, and the American Society of Animal Science has had its share, one of whom was Marion E. (Gene) Ensminger. "Doc E," as he was affectionately called, dedicated his life to the extension of knowledge about animal agriculture, which he accomplished by writing 22 books and countless articles and by organizing and conducting a series of International Stockmen's Schools, and, later, International Ag-Tech Schools. Several of his books have been translated into foreign languages.

His preparation began early. His first paper was published in 1934, when he was the first manager of the Dixon Springs Experiment Station operated by the University of Illinois. Subsequently, he wrote over 500 journal papers, bulletins, and circulars and three syndicated agricultural columns. In 1937, he returned to university work, which he followed for 25 years, at the University of Massachusetts, the University of Minnesota, and Washington State University (WSU). Moving with the times, Dr. Ensminger presided over the renaming of his department at WSU, from Animal Husbandry to Animal Science. He initiated a doctoral program in the animal sciences at WSU and also began an ambitious program of extension, the International Stockmen's School, which he operated from Pullman for 20 years and later moved to Arizona and Texas.

In 1941, Dr. Ensminger married Audrey Helen Watts of Winnipeg, Canada, whom he met at the University of Minnesota, and the two formed an enduring team. Mrs. Ensminger brought degrees from the University of Manitoba, and later WSU, to their publishing ventures. The Ensmingers have one son, John, who is in the publishing business in New York.

Dr. Ensminger maintained close ties to the livestock industries and was widely sought as a consultant. He served on the board of the American Southdown Breeders' Association from 1949 to 1962, and, while at WSU, he developed Hilltop Stables, which was recognized as one of the best light-horse facilities in the nation. This was done entirely through gift and grant funds, something that was unusual at the time but is now becoming commonplace.

His consultancies led to his election as the first president of the American Society of Agricultural Consultants, which honored him with its Appreciation Award in 1977. They also led to his appointment to the National Board of Field Advisors to the Small Business Administration in Washington, D.C.

Perhaps the brightest jewel in his crown was his organizing and conducting of scientific and cultural exchanges in technical agriculture, which began in 1966. These so-called ag-tech schools ultimately involved the Ensmingers in 70 countries, but emphasis was placed on work in China, Cuba, Russia, and the Ukraine. In China, he enrolled 560 agriculturists in schools held at Beijing, Huhehot, Wuhan, and Guilin. These were the first such efforts by foreigners in over 25 years. Similarly, his schools in Cuba in 1995, attended by 493 in Camaguey and Havana, were the first in more than 30 years. Ag-tech schools in Stavropol, Russia and Kiev in the Ukraine were held in 1995 under joint sponsorship by Iowa State University. The staff for these schools was drawn from five countries in addition to the United States, and the enrollees totaled 670.

Highly technical information at these schools was dispensed with a blend of efficiency and friendly informality. A stickler for punctuality, Dr. E. began each school program by vigorously ringing a large brass school bell. He signaled the close of each lecture with similar directness, and woe betide the instructor who let his classes drag on! At the close of his Russian schools, faculty and enrollees joined hands and sang "Auld Lang Syne," which had been translated into Russian for the occasion. His many friends will remember breakfasts at the Ensminger home before a day of meetings. Doc. E would announce these the night before: "Breakfast will be at 7 in the morning. Not 5 minutes before and not 5 minutes after. Seven." And so it was. He liked things to be on time.

An important avenue for his work, both in the United States and overseas, was the Agriservices Foundation, which Dr. Ensminger organized at Clovis, California in 1964. The Foundation was governed by a board of 20 distinguished agriculturists, drawn from academia as well as production agriculture. Its stated objective was to foster and support programs of education, research, and development for the effective application of science and technology to the practice of agriculture for the benefit of mankind. Agriservices Foundation never received a penny of government money. It was largely supported by royalties from the sale of the Ensmingers' books in the United States. Any royalties on foreign sales were waived to ensure wider access to the books.

Dr. Ensminger had many ties to the American Society of Animal Science. He arranged for the design of the Society's logo, which is still in use, and he organized and raised funding for its first careers brochure. He served as president of the Society's Western Section in 1958 and was a member of the ASAS's Executive Committee and vice-president in 1959. He was honored with the Society's Distinguished Teaching Award in 1960 and was elected a Fellow in 1979. In 1996, he received the Bouffault International Animal Agriculture Award, for which the citation identified him as "one of the world's great humanitarians."

Dr. Ensminger's awards are too numerous to list in this brief sketch, but some seem particularly appropriate to his lifetime dedication to animal agriculture education. These include the People-to-People Appreciation Award in 1968; an Honorary Professorship at Wuhan University in 1984; a Gold Medal and Outstanding Achievement Award from the University of Minnesota in 1991; an Honorary Doctor of Laws degree from the University of the Ukraine in 1994, and an Honorary Doctor of Humane Letters degree from Iowa State University in 1996. Washington State University named its Ensminger Beef Cattle Research Center for him in 1984, and Iowa State University dedicated its Marion Eugene Ensminger and Audrey Helen Ensminger International Room, in Kildee Hall, in the fall of 1998. He was proud to have his portrait in oils hung in the famed Saddle and Sirloin Club collection, in Lexington, Kentucky in 1985, because he felt it recognized the application of academic learning in agricultural practice.

Truly, Gene Ensminger's visions had broad horizons, and he liked to observe that the world was his classroom. There are not many who can be said to have made a measurable difference in this world, but he was one of them. Through his efforts to improve practices of food production, he has improved the quality of the lives of literally millions of people, and on the precept that "a hungry man listens not to reason," he contributed significantly to world peace. Not bad, for a Missouri farm boy.

J. E. Oldfield

TABLE OF CONTENTS

1908–1923	When I Was Born—How It Used to Be Done	1
1923–1926	The Search for a Better Life	11
1926–1932	Over-privileged College Days	17
1933–1937	After College — During the Great Depression	25
1937–1940	The University of Massachusetts	37
1940–1941	The University of Minnesota: Two Fabulous Accomplishments — a Bride and a Ph.D.	45
1941–1962	Washington State University Life Was Never Boring	53
1962	Time to Move Along to a Different Life	101
	Consultants Agriservices and the American Society of Agricultural Consultants	113
	About Agriservices Foundation	123
1963–1972	Twenty-two Horse Science (Farrier) Schools	143
1964–1981	Twenty-four More Successful International Schools	149
	Dr. E — the Author	163
1966	A Global Perspective — the USSR And Europe We Saw	177
1968	The South America and Mexico We Saw	191
1970	The South Pacific We Saw	209
1971	Around the World We Saw	225
1972	The North Sea Countries We Saw	247
1972	The China We Saw	269
1973	The Africa We Saw	281
1974	The King Ranch and Mexico We Saw	305
1974	The Japan, South Korea and China We Saw	311

1976 The Guatemala We Saw 327
1976 & 1978 The Cuba We Saw 331
1977 The King Ranch and Guadalajara, Mexico We Saw . . . 339
1977 The China We Saw. 345
1983 The China We Saw. 357
1984 The China We Saw. 379
1993 Ag-Tech Schools in Ukraine and Russia 391
1995 Ag-Tech Schools in Havana and Camaguey, Cuba . . . 407
1996 Ag-Tech School in Kiev, Ukraine 419
1997 The Tianshan Mountains, Urumqi, China We Saw . . . 423
Awards 429
Epilogue. 439

1908–1923
WHEN I WAS BORN – HOW IT USED TO BE DONE

When I arrived at Stover, Missouri, U.S.A., in 1908, the world needed much fixin'. It still does. But it has been fun tinkering with it along the way. This is my saga of the 20th century from my end of the log.

The Family Tree

Jacob Ensminger, my father, was the youngest of eight children. He was born July 19, 1876, in Morgan County, Missouri. His father (my grandfather), John Ensminger, was one of the most progressive farmers of his day. He and Grandma Ensminger (Lucy Ann) were members of the Methodist Episcopal Church South. The name Ensminger is of German origin. In 1633, the Ensmingers came from Alsace-Lorraine, a 125- x 25-mile strip of land lying between France (on the west) and Germany (on the east). Alsace is the magical land of *foie gras* (fat goose liver), asparagus, and sauerkraut; and it's the home of the famed annual schnackelballer (snail) race, and of the "making ugly faces" contest.

Ella Ora Belt, my mother, was next to the youngest of nine children. She was born August 27, 1885. Her father, John William Belt (my grandfather), was a hard-shell Baptist minister, who could recite chapter after chapter from the Bible. Grandmother Belt (Virginia) was a southern belle from the state of Virginia; she smoked a pipe and used snuff. The Belts came from England, and settled in Virginia.

Jacob Ensminger and Ella Ora Belt were united in marriage on January 24, 1906 in the home of the bride, at Stover, Missouri. To this union was born seven children, of which I was number two.

John and Lucy Ensminger.

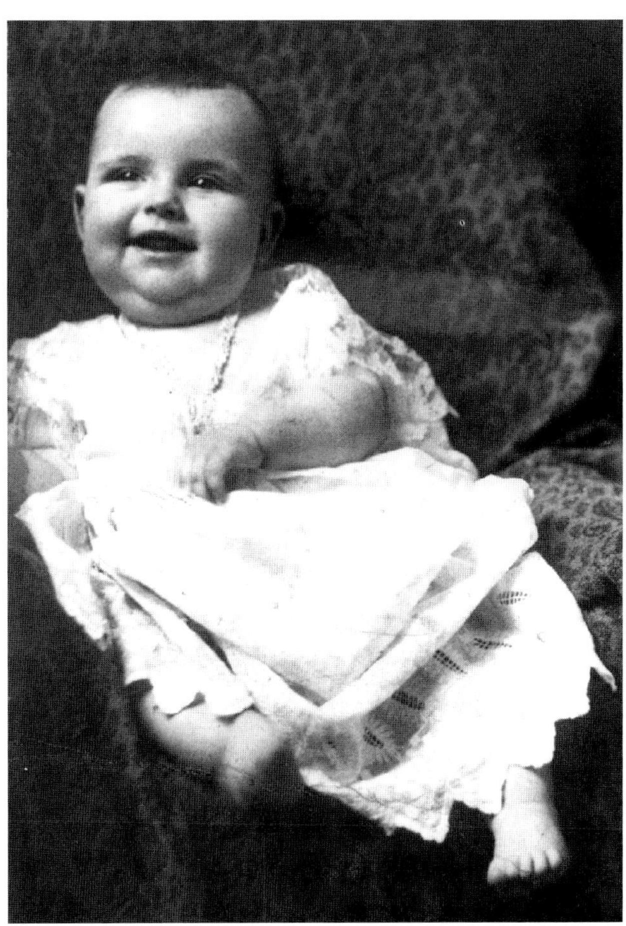

Marion Eugene Ensminger—a happy, chubby, baby boy—was born May 28, 1908.

Stover, Missouri — Vintage 1908

On the year of my birth, Stover boasted of a population of 400, a post office, a combined grade and high school, a bank, a Baptist church, two general stores, a restaurant, a blacksmith shop, a produce store (which bought and sold chickens, eggs, and wool), a feed store (for grain and hay), and a livery stable (consisting of a horse-and-buggy rental service, and stallions and jacks standing for public breeding services), and the family homes of those operating the town businesses. Theft, dope, and other crimes were unheard of; houses were never locked at night.

For the first four years of my life, our family lived in town; but father divided his time between buying and selling livestock, hay and grain, and farming.

I Had to Prove that I Was Born

In that day and age, births were not always recorded. Years later, I became painfully aware of this fact when I needed a birth certificate in order to secure a passport. I had to prove that I was born! Fortunately, three of the old timers (the required number) were willing to certify that unto Jacob and Ella Ensminger a baby boy was born on May 28, 1908, following which my birth was belatedly recorded.

Jacob and Ella Ora Ensminger with their first three children, *left to right:* Marion Eugene, Jacob Douglas (being held), and Harry Edward.

Today, some folks would say that I was disadvantaged as a boy. In terms of modern conveniences, automation, travel, and money, perhaps I was. But, in terms of the finer things of life, I count my blessings. Indeed, a severe case of nostalgia comes over me as I relive my childhood.

Discipline

Dad and Mother believed in the axiom: "Spare the rod, and spoil the child." Around our place, the trees didn't have limbs until they were 30 feet high (the limbs were used for switches), and a razor strap was used for administering punishment (spanking the buttocks), as well as for sharpening a straight-edge. I'm glad it was that way.

I Took the Raw Egg and Blackberry Cure for Diphtheria

In that era, there were few vaccines, and still fewer treatments for ailments, with the result that childhood diseases took a heavy toll. At age four, I had diphtheria. I couldn't be hospitalized, because there wasn't a hospital in the entire county. So, a sign reading "*Quarantine: Keep Out*" was hung on the front door of our house; and I was isolated from my brothers by being put to bed in a separate room. My parents heard of an English nurse who had just arrived in St. Louis and was looking for work. So, they engaged her services. She was a great nurse—and a strict disciplinarian. I have never known whether my doctor or my nurse was responsible for my diet consisting primarily of raw eggs and blackberry juice. To this day, I cannot bear the thought of either of these foods. Only Uncle John, my father's elder brother, came to see me. Each morning, he stood outside the house and visited with me through a slightly raised window. I looked forward to Uncle John's visits. In addition to being a pleasant person, he brought a surprise gift each morning; among them, crayons, blocks, tin soldiers, and a picture book.

The Medicine Man of Old

In frontier America, including Stover, Missouri, we looked forward to the visits of the medicine man—the doc—who, amid tom-toms and torch lights, plied his trade and provided entertainment. His show on the road was held in a tent, which he moved from village to village. His potent snake oil and tiger's milk cure-all were "smuggled out of the sacred tombs of ancient Egypt." Silk-hatted and suave, between music numbers, doc made his pitch:

> Ladies and gentlemen! Boils and bunions, fevers and fits, gout and gas—these have plagued mankind since life began. But no more! No more for those of you, who for a mere pittance, avail yourselves of this marvelous cure—the guarded secret of health and long life!

Asafetida for Warding Off Diseases

During epidemics of colds and flu, Dad and Mother warded off such diseases by suspending a bag of asafetida around our necks, carefully tucked under the shirt or blouse; where it could be smelled but not seen. Believe it or not, it worked. We didn't know why in that day and age, but, years later, after the completion of a doctorate degree, I discovered the reason for its effectiveness. Because it "stunk" to high heaven, it warded off people, and with it their contagious diseases.

Goose Grease for Croup

Dad and Mother had a treatment for croup. It consisted of a generous application of goose grease all over the chest. It made you feel so miserable, that you forgot all about having the croup.

The Little Brown Pills

The little brown pills that Dr. Newton and Dr. Snavely doled out were unbelievably versatile—they prescribed them for everything. Not only that, you didn't need a prescription. They had them in their little satchel. So, they would fill a little paper container, put your name on it, and write "one tablet before each meal." Then, to impart added assurance, they would tear off one corner of the package and take one pill in your presence. When Dr. Snavely's farm family patients were deathly sick, he traveled by horse-and-buggy to see them, day or night, fair or foul weather.

The house in Stover where we lived and where both Doug and Leonard were born.

I Started to School at Age Four

At 5½ years of age, my older brother, Harry, started to school in grade one (kindergarten was unknown). Even though I was only four years old, I went to school with Harry. The rotund and affable school superintendent, Mr. Steth, must have thought that I looked a bit young to be in school. So, he asked: "Gene, why are you here?" My reply: "I must take care of Harry." The shock generated by my reply, rather than the logic of it, must have resulted in

Hawcreek School, the one-room country school where I learned the three Rs and the big D. Photo taken after the school had been closed for several years.

Mr. Steth raising no more questions about my presence in school.

The First Automobile That I Saw

We lived on a hillside in Stover; so, I have a vivid recollection of an ancient Rheo chugging up the hill, with the occupants getting out and pushing it.

In 1913 (when I was five years old) my parents bought a farm about two miles from Stover, to which we moved. At that time, I had three brothers—Harry, Douglas, and Leonard. In 1916, a fifth son, Garnet Atwell, was born. My two precious sisters came along later, Aileen in 1921 and Ella Mae in 1926.

Hawcreek School, Where I Learned the Three Rs and the Big D

Our move to the farm placed us in the Hawcreek School District, the school of which was named after a nearby creek and located about two miles to the west of our house. Grades one through seven were taught by a bachelor lady named Franky Pontas. Miss Pontas lived in Stover, and traveled the four miles each morning and afternoon by horse (named Gay) and buggy. At Hawcreek School, Miss Pontas drilled us in the three Rs—reading, "riting," and "rithmetic." Additionally, she added a big D; she was a rigid *disciplinarian*. Even whispering would result in a student having to stand in the corner of the room (sometimes all four corners were filled).

Corporal punishment was never administered or necessary. *The reason*: all students were told by their parents that if they ever got a whipping in school, they would get a harder one at home. And that wasn't idle chatter! The different grades were seated in sections, thereby facilitating recitations. When the school wasn't too crowded, the seats in the front of the room were reserved for recitations. Protocol for answering the call of nature consisted in raising your hand and, upon acknowledgment by the teacher, asking: "Please, may I be excused?" There were 15-minute recess periods in each the mid-forenoon and the mid-afternoon, and a one-hour lunch period. During the recess periods and following lunch, students participated in games such as fox and geese, farmer in the dell, and baseball. During the fall and winter, we built "leaf houses" from fallen oak leaves in the adjacent wooded area. Occasionally, a brave boy would throw stones at the hornet nests suspended from the trees, then run for cover. Except during inclement weather, the students walked to school, with each one carrying a dinner pail and a satchel of books. On the way home, invariably Earl Houchen, a neighbor boy who used a gallon syrup bucket to carry his very considerable lunch, would give away any left-over sandwiches because, said he: "If I do not come home with an empty pail, my mom won't fill it tomorrow."

Near the end of the seventh grade, those students who wished to go to school in Stover for the eighth grade and high school were given a special qualifying examination. I took it, and passed. But, my starting school at age four to take care of my brother Harry returned to haunt me. I was told that I was too young to go into the eighth grade in Stover the next year; and that I must remain at Hawcreek School one more year. I accepted the decision as a closed subject and complied with it.

My evaluation of Franky Pontas and the one-room country school: The training that I received in the three Rs, along with the big D, prepared me well for my career. I wish that every boy and girl in America could have the same opportunity.

The School Lunch Program

The finest school lunch program ever devised didn't have any federal aid. It wasn't even formulated by a nutritionist. It evolved at Hawcreek School, a one- room country school near Stover, Missouri. It was correlated by Franky Pontas, the teacher. It consisted of each student bringing his or her syrup pail well-filled with sandwiches (usually, meat, eggs, homemade butter, or homemade jam) made with whole wheat bread, which was augmented by a vegetable soup made from farm-fresh ingredients and heated on the wood-burning stove that warmed the one-room school.

Molasses

If you haven't sopped the pans of freshly made molasses, you haven't lived! Fortunately, the community molasses mill was adjacent to Hawcreek School. It consisted of a pair of steel rollers powered by a team of horses or mules that went round and round, squeezing the sap from the cane; and of iron pans about 3 ft x 10 ft and 8 in. deep for boiling the sap down, heated by wood. Each fall, the molasses-making season lasted about a month; and most days there were pans to be sopped during the noon

Making sorghum molasses as it used to be done near Hawcreek School. (Photo by J. C. Allen & Son, Inc., West Lafayette, IN)

hour or the recess periods. Not only was the molasses finger-licking good, but it was good for you, for, unlike white sugar, the minerals were still there.

Selling Garden Seed

During this period, the Henry Field Garden Seed Company of Shenandoah, Iowa, put out a catalogue, showing big and beautiful vegetables and flowers produced from their seeds. Henry Field was "folksy." He told about each member of his big family. I also recall that he had Spotted Poland China hogs, for the summer comfort of which he built elevated quarters with an inclined ramp providing access for the porkers. Mr. Field claimed that the hogs enjoyed a cool breeze on the elevated platform. Then, came the sales pitch: By selling a specified number of packages of seed, the seller would receive one free package of choice. I found that I could sell. So, for three or four years, I sold garden seed to our neighbors each spring. The fun was in the selling; I gave the free garden seeds to Grandpa Belt.

Grades 8 and 9 in Stover

In 1921 and 1922, I was enrolled in grades 8 and 9 in Stover. With one exception, these were uneventful years. I won the mile race in the track meet that was held during graduation festivities in the spring of 1921, at the time of my completing the ninth grade. Training consisted of running the two miles each morning and each afternoon as I went to and from school.

The Tornado

The 1916 tornado devastated us. Anyone less resolute than Dad and Mother wouldn't have made it. Dad was away from home; he had gone to see his ailing brother, John, at Eldon, Missouri. Mother and the five boys, ranging from Harry—age nine, to Garnett—six weeks old, along with a hired man and a hired girl, were in the house. Every building on the place but a smokehouse was flattened (and the roof was blown off the latter). The hired girl, Lizzie, was carried into the pasture with one side of the house, and the hired man, Henry, was knocked out by a brick from the chimney which hit him on the head . Leonard and I crawled under a bed. One by one, we found our way to the roofless smokehouse. Garnett had stopped breathing, so mother revived him by pumping his arms up and down and using mouth-to-mouth resuscitation. We counted off! Harry was missing! We started the search, but soon Harry showed up. Miraculously, he was the only one who was not bruised or cut; when he came to, he was under an apple tree about one-fourth mile from the house. He never knew how he got there. Dad returned the next day. The neighbors took us in, and gave us shelter and food. The rebuilding started immediately. A sheet-iron roof was put on the old smokehouse, so that the hired man and the older boys could live there. The construction of the house and the barn followed. They are both still standing. On the side of the barn, proud but faint, the follow-

The barn and house that my parents built following the 1916 tornado. *Left,* the gambrel-roofed barn and *right*, the house.

ing sign can still be read: J. Ensminger & Sons, Duroc Breeders, Stover, Missouri.

Grandpa and Grandma Belt Came to Live with Us

In 1917, Grandmother Belt was in failing health. At that time, there were no rest homes and no Social Security. Besides, they couldn't afford to pay for special care even if it had been available. So, they came to live with us on the farm near Stover. A large room in our house was readied for them. Grandfather Belt divided most of his time between studying the Bible and gardening. I have vivid memories of his long graces before our family meals, his challenging the Baptist minister from his pew if he disagreed with his sermon, and his rainy day (when he couldn't work in the garden) discourses on the Bible as he sat in his favorite rocking chair on the screened porch. Grandpa and Grandma lived with us until they passed away; Grandpa died on June 24, 1924, and Grandma died on August 25, 1925.

The Baptist Church

My parents were members of the Southern Baptist Church in Stover. It was a place of worship, without any social fringes. Ministers changed frequently. Usually, they had part-time jobs on the side. I recall that one was a paper hanger. Their meager pay was usually augmented by the congregation with canned fruits and vegetables, along with fresh meat when the brethren did farm slaughtering. But they were devout men of God; in that day and age, scandal among ministers was unknown. Baptism was by immersion in Haw Creek.

I was baptized in this creek, known as Haw Creek. Sometimes, we had to delay baptisms until it rained and the creek had sufficient water for immersion.

The Vegetable Garden, Plus Greens

When we were growing up, Granddad Belt had a huge vegetable garden—at least two acres in size. Additionally, it was supplemented by poke, lambs quarter, and dandelion greens—gathered from the wild, foods rich in minerals and vitamins.

Buying and Selling Animals

Dad bought, and shipped by rail, all classes of livestock, primarily to the St. Louis National Stockyards. Occasionally, some of the animals were shipped to Chicago, and I recall that a few shipments of finished cattle were sent on-foot (live) by boat to England. Remember that there wasn't much in the way of refrigeration on boats in that day and age. So, animals going abroad were generally shipped on-foot.

Dad had an uncanny eye for determining the weight of animals. Even when he knew that an owner had scales on the place, he would dollar them off (so much per head) if the seller wished to do so. This meant that he had to be extremely accurate in estimating weights.

In selling animals in that day and age, a man's word was his bond. No contracts were signed, but no one ever defaulted—a deal was a deal, and a man's word was his bond.

Hollow-Tail

Our cattle used to get what Father diagnosed as "hollow-tail" in the spring of the year. After wintering on huge stacks of wheat and oat straw through which they ate tunnels (which were made to order for playing hide-and-seek), some cattle would go down. The malady was called hollow-tail, and dad had the cure for it—and it worked. The cure: About midway down the tail, split the hide with a knife in four places around the circumference and for a length of about three inches. Fill the slashes with generous quantities of hot pepper, then bandage securely. Almost miraculously, the cows would get up

When I was a boy on the Missouri farm, jobs, home, family, school, and church were a way of life not found in any other segment of American society. Farm families toiled together, for this was their land. Activities for farm families often centered around church and school. Ice cream socials, fish fries, and pie suppers not only raised money, but they brought people together for fun and fellowship. All these became a part of me as I broke ground with a walking plow (commonly known as a "foot burner") while chickens feasted on the worms (*upper left)*; shocked wheat behind a binder (*center right*); operated a bundle wagon and fed sheaves of grain into a separator powered by a steam engine (*center left*); and enjoyed a festive dinner (it was never called lunch) with the threshing crew (*lower right*). (Photos by J. C. Allen & Son, Inc., West Lafayette, IN)

and go to the far corner of the pasture, getting away from the mistreatment. There they would eat the first sprigs of spring grass; and in no time at all they were well. We now know that the straw stacks were deficient in protein, vitamin A, and certain minerals, which the green grass provided. But the hot pepper cure worked! It forced the cows to change their diet, from straw to green grass.

Farmer at Age Nine

With the help of Dock and Kate (a smart span of Missouri mules, who accommodated each other by alternating between working and being lazy), I started plowing corn at the age of nine; one little Ensminger drove, perched atop the cultivator on a bag of straw, and the other guided the shovels. Between times (while resting the mules), we had clod fights. By the age of 13, I could turn the sod with a "foot-burner" (a walking plow), shock bundles behind a seven-foot grain binder, cut and shock corn with either a knife or a two-row cutter pulled by a mule, operate a bundle wagon with a threshing crew, and pitchfork hay from a windrow onto a wagon or stack. I attribute my lifelong stamina to such work, which I loved. Were boys age 9 to 13 to repeat this type of work today, their parents would likely be hauled into court for violating a multitude of child labor laws.

The Threshing Crew

Threshing wheat, oats, and barley was work—plus a festive occasion. Sometimes, the grain was bound in bundles, shocked in the field to dry, then stacked. But, weather permitting and a threshing machine being available, the grain was hauled directly from the shocks in the field to the separator, which was powered by a steam engine. The neighbors swapped help. Usually, anywhere from 20 to 30 hands were involved in operating the engine and separator (including the water wagon), the bundle wagons, and in hauling grain. Additionally, the ladies swapped help, too; and they vied with each other for the coveted reputation of serving the best food to the threshing crew. No banquet ever compared with those marvelous home cooked meals. In the German community where we grew up, a hefty snack was also served in the middle of both the forenoon and the afternoon.

Fitting and Showing Livestock

There is no higher achievement than that of breeding, fitting, and showing a champion: an animal representing an ideal produced through intelligent breeding; fitted to the height of perfection; and trained, thoroughly groomed, and properly paraded before the judge. At ages 11 to 13, it was our happy privilege to show steers and hogs. We always exhibited at the Missouri State Fair, Sedalia; and sometimes at other state and county shows, also. Travel to and from the shows was in a railroad car; and we bunked in one end of the car, with feed decked above us. The railroad only provided one free attendant pass per car. So, we gave that to the youngest boy. The rest of us bummed—it was more fun that way. Occasionally, an unfriendly brakeman would kick us bums off when the train was stopped. At such times, we sat nearby until the train started again, then climbed aboard—for, according to rules, the train crew could not kick a bum off a moving train.

At the fair, we slept near the animals, either in an empty pen or in the alley. Eating at the fair was fun, too. Dad and Mother would come for the day of the show, and bring a bountiful supply of food. One old-time showman, Mr. Hollingsworth, always brought a five-gallon can of homemade buttermilk for the Ensminger boys. Each morning, we ordered pancakes at a fairgrounds stand; a tent with benches in the open along three sides, with food preparation and dish washing in a little tent to the back. Usually the cook used a hot plate at the front of the stand, all the time spieling "come and get 'em while they're

At age 13, I showed steers and hogs at the Missouri State Fair. (Photo of a State Fair by J. C. Allen & Son, Inc., West Lafayette, IN)

hot." One morning after ordering our pancakes, the small son of the chef came running out from the tent to the back, yelling to his dad: "The old woman washing dishes got mad and used the dishwater to mix the pancakes." At that moment, we lost our appetites and sneaked out.

Shinny

Today, it's called hockey; and, for the most part, it's a spectator sport—with professionals playing the game and people watching it.

Our shinny merely consisted of tin cans and curved sticks that we made. It didn't cost any money, nor did it require ice. Best of all, we were participants, and not spectators. And did we have fun!

Our Annual Vacation and Hunt

Mention of the word *coonhound* produces goose pimples on me, for some of the happiest recollections of my childhood were the annual one-week vacations and all-night coon, opossum, and raccoon hunts with Uncle Charley, Aunt Cenia, and our cousins—Arthur, Thelma, Cleo, and Milton—in the Ozarks of Missouri. Generally, Uncle Charley provided transportation for us in a big wagon, as he hauled stock or grain to market and returned with supplies.

Circa 1935. *Left to right:* Gene, Garnett, Mother, Aileen, and Dad. Ella Mae is in front.

Redbone Coonhound barking-up, or giving voice, to treed coon. (Courtesy Moran's Midnight Kennels, Inc., Duquesne, PA)

I live again the thrill of those hunts with cousin Arthur as the coonhounds worked their trails with skill and determination when they trailed bloodhound-fashion, entirely by scent, with noses to the ground, "barking up," or giving voice, the moment the quarry was treed. We didn't really catch that many, but it was all for the camaraderie of the hunt.

Mother and Dad Were Truly Great in Adversity

During the Great Depression, which for American farmers lasted throughout the 1920s and the 1930s, my parents lost everything. But they were too proud to take the bankrupt law. Instead, they asked their creditors to give them time. Later, they paid off every penny. Not only that, Dad had signed a note for his older brother, John, who, due to poor health, defaulted! So, Dad paid that off, too. What a legacy to leave to their children and grandchildren!

A bad case of nostalgia comes over me when I relive my childhood on the Missouri farm, where work was fun and fun was work. Indeed, much of what America immortalizes as ideal living had its roots on farms during the first third of the 1900s.

I did all the things pictured above. I made apple cider (*upper left*); slopped the pigs from swill barrels (*lower left*); scoop-shoveled ear corn to two- and three-year-old steers, with hogs feasting behind them (*upper right*); and drove hogs to market (*lower right*). (Photos by J. C. Allen & Son, Inc., West Lafayette, IN)

1923–1926
THE SEARCH FOR A BETTER LIFE

In 1923, in search of more fertile farmland and a better life, my parents decided to move to a rented farm near Raymore, Missouri. So, the Stover farm was sold. At age 15, assisted by brother Leonard who was age 12, I was given the responsibility for the shipment in a railroad car of a mixed load of horses, mules, hogs, and furniture. Although the distance was only about 150 miles, we made an overnight rest stop en route in compliance with the 36-hour law, which required that animals shipped by rail be unloaded and fed and watered en route at not to exceed 36-hour intervals. The railroad car was docked at Raymore, from which point brother Leonard and I trailed the animals a distance of about two miles to our new farm. The rest of the family—consisting of Father and Mother; brothers Harry, Doug, and Garnett; sister Aileen (age 2); and Grandfather and Grandmother Belt—made the trip by automobile.

The Raymore Farm

The Raymore farm was owned by Judge Long, a Kansas City judge, from whom my parents rented it. It had a large two-story farm house, framed by tall black walnut trees; and a large barn with a hay mow, one wing of which was a dairy barn equipped with stanchions and a concrete floor with a gutter for cleaning. With its menagerie of animals, our farm would have qualified as *Old Macdonald's Farm*. We operated a Grade A dairy; and we had beef cattle, hogs, sheep, chickens, and turkeys. Also, we produced corn, wheat, oats, and hay, using horses and mules for power. Each of the five Ensminger boys was completely responsible for his unit. I took care of the purebred Duroc swine herd and worked with all the animals.

Morning Came Early, and Night Came Late

Four a.m. was chore time! It was all right for us to play basketball or go to a country pie-supper the night before, *provided* we answered Dad's early morning call. Lantern in hand, the cows were fed and hand-milked; the horses were groomed and fed; the pigs were slopped; the beef cattle and sheep were given their hay and silage; and grain was scattered in the litter for the chickens.

During the last round of the barn at night, I learned the marvels and mysteries of barnyard talk. The animals kept up a running conversation with me as I gave a handful of hay to one still-hungry cow, treated a favorite horse to an apple, took a last look at a litter of newborn pigs, closed the gate on the sheep corral, and shut the poultry house door after the chickens had all gone to roost. It was a sign language, but it spoke louder than words; it told me how the animals felt and what they wanted. Every movement and every sound conveyed a message of well-being, distress, or disease. Lack of interest, dull eyes, sluggishness, rough coat, poor appetite, and/or abnormal droppings spelled trouble; sometimes, it called for an all-night vigil with a colicky animal. Extreme nervousness, uneasiness, and milk in the teats told me of an approaching birth and that I should be on the job that night.

No Gasoline/No Car

That first year on the Raymore farm, we didn't have enough money to buy gasoline for a gas-guzzling Studebaker automobile. So, we traveled to town and church in a big wagon drawn by mules.

Grades 10, 11, and 12/ 4-H Club and FFA

Without my realizing it at the time, much of my career was molded in Raymore and Belton, Missouri, during the period 1923 to 1926. The better life that my parents sought for their children was here and now.

While I was enrolled in the 10th and 11th grades, in the Raymore High School, I had a truly great English teacher named Marietta Davis. Prior to moving to the farm near Raymore, I attended one year of high school at Stover, at which time my grammar was terrible. In conversation, the natives "backed the hill up." But, Marietta Davis patiently taught me correct grammar. As a result, I facetiously say that, "When I don't feel well, I go into my study and write until I feel better." Think of this: Had it not been for my great English instructor, Marietta Davis, I might never have written books. *The reason:* As a perfectionist, I would have done something else, rather than write substandard books. Through the years, I sent Marietta Davis complimentary copies of several of my books; and again and again I thanked her for inspiring me to write.

On October 27, 1993—69 years after Marietta Davis started me on a writing career involving 500 feature articles and 21 books—I received a letter from Marietta Davis' daughter, Mrs. Thomas A. (Bettie T.) Moore, reading as follows:

> I am the daughter of Marietta Davis. In 1987, I informed you of Mother's passing. Subsequently, I have finally sorted through all of Mother's belongings. She was very proud of you and your accomplishments; and she was flattered by your complimentary letters and copies of your books. Mother had special keepsakes from her teaching career. Among them, were pictures and news clippings of your mother, when she was selected "Missouri's Mother of the Year" in 1956, and you and your brothers and sisters. I am sure that you have better copies of these, but I am sending them to you because they show what you and your family meant to her. Just before Mother passed away, she tried several times to write a tribute to you. But her health was deteriorating, with the result that she destroyed several copies because they were not up to her writing standards.

Think of the personal touch that this great English teacher imparted!

Also, when she was overloaded or had to be away, another teacher, Miss Clehouse, often asked me to teach her math course. As a result, I became addicted to teaching!

Ira Drymon, our county extension agent, got me to join the 4-H Club. At the end of the first year, I was awarded the Thomas E. Wilson Scholarship (named after the founder of Wilson and Company, Chicago meat packer), which provided an all-expense trip to Chicago to attend the National 4-H Congress and see the great International Livestock show. While visiting the Stockyards Inn, I stood in awe and reverence as I viewed the portraits in the Saddle and Sirloin Club of the all-time greats from Europe and the United States, enshrined for their contributions to

Ira Drymon—the noted Thoroughbred breeder in Kentucky.

the livestock industry; oblivious that one day my portrait would join them. Later, Mr. Drymon became a noted Thoroughbred breeder in Kentucky. When the immortal Man O' War died, he gave the eulogy over NBC.

During this period of time, Mr. J. L. "Mule" Campbell (nicknamed "Mule" when he was a basketball star at the University of Missouri) taught vocational agriculture (later called FFA) at the Belton, Missouri High School, about two miles to the west of our farm. From time to time, Mr. Campbell would

The Missouri champion vocational livestock judging team of 1926, *left to right:* Ralph Groh, Scott Keeney, Gene Ensminger, with teacher J. L. Campbell (back row).

drop by our farm for a visit and to see our livestock. Because Raymore didn't offer any courses in agriculture, I decided to transfer to Belton for my last year of high school. My transportation was a five-gaited American Saddlebred mare. During the year, Mr. Campbell taught a livestock judging course, from which he selected a team of five students to compete in a statewide judging contest sponsored by the University of Missouri, at Columbia. I made the team, and I was the high point individual in the entire contest at the University of Missouri. I graduated Valedictorian from Belton High School in the spring of 1926.

The American Royal

After moving to Raymore, Missouri, I showed hogs at the great American Royal Livestock Show in Kansas City. The first year that I exhibited there, Andy Patterson, the affable manager of the show, came to my exhibit to see me. His message:

> Gene: Mr. J. C. Penney, of J. C. Penney Stores, will come here tomorrow morning to see the show. He is interested in both animals and 4-H Club boys and girls. Will you please escort him through all the animal exhibits at the American Royal?

I was delighted to do so.

The next morning, Mr. Patterson brought Mr. Penney to my exhibit and introduced me, following which I spent a delightful three hours showing him exhibit after exhibit. Mr. Penney was very polite and alert, and very knowledgeable about the breeds of livestock. At the end of my guided tour, he thanked me profusely and departed. Little did I realize that JC Penney stores would become Americana in the decades to come.

How to Go to College with No Money

During and following the Great Depression, many parents didn't want their children to go to college, primarily because they needed their labor and wages at home. Not so with my parents. Their greatest concern was how to send the older children to college. To their great relief, we solved that dilemma by informing Dad and Mother that we would get student jobs and work our way through college. In addition, three of us, Doug, Leonard, and myself, put ourselves through graduate school and received Ph.Ds.

In 1926, I was awarded the Missouri Ruralist Trophy for 4-H Pig and Poultry Club Leadership.

Three Great Summers (1926, 1927, and 1928) on the Farm

Following my graduation from high school, I had three great summers on our farm, with the rest of our closely knit family. Also, on Sundays, I taught a Sunday School class in the Baptist Church at Belton.

After graduating from the Belton High School in the spring of 1926, I helped Dad on the Raymore farm that summer, prior to entering the University of Missouri.

During my freshman year at the University, my parents made another move. The judge who owned the Raymore farm had urgent need for it as a rendezvous with his girl friend, who was a Cotswold (an old English long wool breed) sheep fancier and "farmerette."

So, Dad and Mother rented, and moved to, the Slaughter Farm near Hickman Mills, Missouri. Here, they operated a sizable dairy, produced feed for the

My Belton High School graduation picture in the spring of 1926.

cows, and had a flock of layers. Also, father farmed some of the land owned by the Truman family. Because father needed help, I returned to the farm during the summers of 1927 and 1928. While plowing corn, I met a county judge by the name of Harry Truman. To earn extra money for returning to college, I worked at night for 25 cents per hour in a nearby oil filling station which was owned by his sister, Mary Truman. At that time, it never occurred to me that one day Mr. Truman would be the president of the United States; Miss Mary would be the sister of a U.S. president; and that years later I would be invited to have lunch with the Truman family on the occasion of the unveiling of the Thomas Hart Bentley Mural in the Truman Library at Independence, Missouri.

I Was a Product of the Great Depression!

During his 1928 campaign for the presidency, Herbert Hoover, the son of an Iowa blacksmith, promised to help the nation's farmers. They had endured a severe depression for nearly a decade, and many had lost their farms. To fulfill his promise, he called a special session of Congress in April, 1929. In June, Congress passed the Agricultural Marketing Act. It established the Federal Farm Board, which promoted farm cooperatives and purchased farm surpluses. The Congress also passed the Smoot-Hawley bill, which raised tariffs on farm products to reduce foreign competition. But the United States had been building up to a crash for a long time! Buying on credit had become a way of life, thousands of people borrowed money to pay for stocks, and stock prices soared to record heights.

In October, 1929, the Wall Street stock market crashed. The Great Depression arrived with a vengeance. Fortunes were wiped out, thousands of workers lost their jobs, banks failed, bread lines formed, and apple carts appeared on city streets. Meanwhile, down on the farm, a severe drought produced the "Dust Bowl," which centered in Oklahoma, causing thousands of people to flee the land and travel west.

In his 1932 re-election bid, Hoover was defeated by Franklin D. Roosevelt, who promised a New Deal. During Roosevelt's first two terms in office, efforts were made to stimulate the economy by the National Recovery Administration (which was subsequently declared unconstitutional by the Supreme Court), federal relief, the Civilian Conservation Corps (CCC), the Farm Credit Administration, the Home Owners Loan Corporation, the Works Progress Administration (WPA), the Resettlement Administration (a federal agency formed to aid impoverished farmers during the depression), and the Public Works Administration (PWA). Yet, at the end of the 1930s, unemployment was estimated at 17.2 %.

In other countries, the depression had even more profound effects; it shook the foundations of capitalism and the society based on it. The economic sluggishness in the United States and elsewhere persisted until early in the 1940s, at which time the massive military expenditures of World War II provided the stimulus that ended the depression in the United States and elsewhere.

Although people of all walks of life were affected by the Great Depression of the 1930s, U.S. farmers endured a chronic depression throughout the 1920s—10 years earlier than the rest of the nation. Thus, they were caught up in a depression for 20 long years. As a result, prior to entering the University of Missouri in the fall of 1926, and even during my first year in college, I did much soul searching relative to my choice of a career.

I liked the business world. I liked the field of

medicine, but scholarships and student employment were not available in the Medical School at the University of Missouri. I also considered the ministry, which many of my friends urged that I pursue. A fleeting thought was given to law, which was a respected profession in that era. Finally, the Lord and I had a long visit, out of which we decided that I should enroll in animal science (it was always my first love) at the University of Missouri.

The following facets of my career seemed to develop automatically: I wanted to be a humanitarian in the area of world food, hunger, and malnutrition, and I wanted to write books and conduct international schools with the whole world as my classroom.

Not only that, the Lord endowed me with a love, and whatever talent I may have, for writing; and with a distinct and commanding voice for conducting international schools.

Once these decisions were made, I never deviated from my course, no matter how attractive the offer. I have been happy with the choice.

The Legacy of Our Parents

Our parents didn't leave material things to their seven children. Instead, they inspired each of us to use our talents for the benefit of mankind. All of us can be proud of our heritage.

Jacob Ensminger died May 5, 1941 and Ella died October 5, 1973; both were buried in Morgan County, Missouri, near Stover.

The lifestyles, standards, work ethics, and old time religion established by those who tilled the soil were good examples for the rest of America—and for the entire world.

I did all the things shown in the following pictures while growing up on the Missouri farm. I forked hay onto a wagon to take it to the hay mow. (Photo courtesy, J. C. Allen & Son, West Lafayette, IN)

I stationed cans of milk roadside to be picked up by the milk truck. (Photo courtesy, J. C. Allen & Son, West Lafayette, IN)

My personal tributes to dad and mother are recorded in two of my books:

The dedication of *Animal Science* reads as follows:

> To the Memory of my father, the late
> Jacob Ensminger, who was my first instructor
> in animal science and the best stockman
> I have ever known, this book is dedicated.

The dedication of *Dairy Cattle Science* reads as follows:

> To Ella Ensminger, my mother and
> Missouri's Mother-of-the-Year in 1956, who
> encouraged me to Keep on Keeping on.

This blessed assurance the seven Ensminger children have relative to Dad and Mother: What great angels we have in heaven!

I mowed hay with a sickle bar, and, after it dried in the swath, raked it with a dump rake. (Photo courtesy, J. C. Allen & Son, West Lafayette, IN)

I provided milk that was delivered in horse-drawn milk wagons, in quart glass bottles, to the doorsteps of urban consumers. (Photos courtesy, The Bettman Archive)

When I was a boy on the Missouri farm, many notables of the world took pride in their animals. Cornelius K. G. Billings—Chicago utilities heir and self-styled "American Horse King"—hosted a horseback dinner in Louis Sherry's plush restaurant in New York City. The 36 guests, attired in white ties and tails and gingerly astride their favorite mounts, drank and ate to the merriment of music, while their steeds munched oats and costumed lackeys cleaned up behind them. Miniature tables were attached to the saddle pommels, and apprehensive waiters dressed in riding attire, served drink after drink, and course after course. Only one guest fell off his horse. (Photo by Byron, The Byron Collection; Courtesy, Museum of the City)

1926–1932
OVER-PRIVILEGED COLLEGE DAYS

On August 27, 1926, the second of my two precious sisters was born. Dad and Mother accorded her five brothers the honor of naming her. So, we went into a separate room for a closed session. Very soon, we agreed that baby sister should be named Ella Mae (the "Ella" being after Mother). I served as spokesman for the brothers and announced her name. The very next day, brother Harry and I departed for the University of Missouri, at Columbia.

Brother Harry and I Had Jobs Awaiting Us

Earlier in the summer of 1926, Mr. J. L. Campbell, the Belton, Missouri, vocational agricultural teacher, had taken brother Harry and me in his car to Columbia for the purpose of securing jobs; so, we landed in Columbia with jobs awaiting us.

Harry worked in a boarding house, operated by a woman whose boarders and roomers consisted of a curious mixture of brick layers and students. Unfortunately, the stress and work resulted in Harry becoming ill and having to return home. Later, Harry graduated from a business college, following which he was very successful in construction and municipal work.

During my job-hunting trip earlier in the summer, I applied for work at the college farm. But, at the time, all jobs were filled by upperclassmen, who had seniority. So, I was put on the waiting list. But, with only $2.50 left after enrolling as a freshman, I had to work in order to eat and buy books. So, I worked for Mr. McAllister, who operated McAllister's Cafeteria and McAllister's Market (a grocery store). Mr. and Mrs. McAllister lived on a farm just outside the city limits, where they kept hogs, for which city garbage was collected and fed. On this farm, they had a separate one-room shack for the hired man, which was my sleeping quarters. Mr. McAllister asked for my schedule. When I wasn't in class, he scheduled me for work throughout the day—early to late. I "hopped" tables at the cafeteria for my meals; then, he paid me 25 cents per hour for work at the grocery store, and for assisting with hauling garbage when my help was needed. At night, the fleas ate me up; I couldn't sleep. I had no time for study. Fortunately, before I encountered scholastic or health problems, I got a call from the Animal Husbandry Department offering me two part-time jobs; taking care of the swine breeding unit and feeding steers in the long shed, at 25 cents per hour.

I gave Mr. McAllister ample notice, thanked him profusely, said goodbye to those hungry fleas, and moved to town. I couldn't afford living in a boarding house; so, I teamed up with Earl Cassida, a graduate student majoring in physiology of reproduction. Together, we rented an apartment consisting of an upstairs bedroom in which there were two desks for study, and a porch equipped with a hot plate and a small refrigerator, which served as our kitchen and dining room. We bought dishes and "silverware" at Woolworth's. Earl married at the end of our first year, and I inherited all the silverware and dishes. The next year, I continued to batch alone. Subsequently, Earl Cassida completed his Ph.D. degree, joined the staff of the University of Wisconsin, and became one of the great animal physiologists of the world.

Because of lack of money, I went without breakfast. Harry Ball, MU Dairy Herdsman from 1918 to 1959, a kindly, dedicated man who took much interest in students, heard of my plight. So, early one morning when I was feeding the swine and steers, he hailed me and asked that I accompany him over to the milk room at the dairy barn. There, he opened the refrigerator box and showed me a special can of milk that he kept for the *cats*. I got the message! Because of college regulations, Harry Ball couldn't give milk to me, but he could feed the cats that he kept for controlling the mouse population. Upon Harry Ball's retirement in 1955, I was asked to contribute to a *Book of Letters* for him. In addition to the usual congratulating him on a job well done, and wishing him health and happiness in the years ahead, I thanked Harry for letting me be one of his *cats*.

My Two Part-time Jobs at the College Farm

The *Swine Unit* was used for two purposes: physiology of reproduction studies under the direction of Dr. Fred McKenzie, and nutrition studies under the direction of Dr. A. G. Hogan; two well known and highly respected scientists. The *Long Shed* was used for steer feeding experiments under the supervision of Professors Hubert Moffett and Jimmie Comfort, in the Animal Husbandry Department. I alone was responsible for the care of the *Swine Unit*. But, I shared responsibility for the cattle unit with another aggie, J. C. McLean. Feeding time was 4:00 a.m. and 4:00 p.m. At the *Swine Unit*, I used a wheelbarrow for cleanup work, and a scoop shovel for mixing the several rations. The cattle work was less demanding. Usually, it involved feeding silage along with concentrate rations that were mixed mechanically at the *College Feed Unit* and delivered to the *Long Shed*. Deep bedding was used at the cattle shed, and the corrals were cleaned by the farm crew at the end of each experiment. Both the swine and the cattle were individually weighed monthly. I held these two good jobs for five years, until I had completed both B.S. (1931) and M.S. (1932) degrees. During the Christmas vacation period, I stayed and took care of my animals. In their freshman year, some of the other students caring for experimental animals went home during the Christmas holidays without arranging for someone to take their places. Thereupon, Professor E. A. Trowbridge, head of the Animal Husbandry Department, administered a never-to-be-forgotten lesson. He hired other people to replace the vacationing caretakers on a permanent basis; so, when they returned to school they didn't have jobs.

During the summer months when I needed full-time work in order to earn enough money to stay in school, I arranged for someone to take my place. But usually few animal experiments were conducted during the summer months.

Brothers Douglas and Leonard Joined Me at the University of Missouri

During my junior year, brother Doug (number three of our family of seven children) enrolled in the University of Missouri; and during my senior year, brother Leonard (number four) joined us. Because of my contacts, I was able to secure desirable student employment on the campus for both of them. I got brother Doug two jobs: caring for white laboratory rats used in nutrition studies conducted by Dr. A. G. Hogan, and energy (calorimetry) experiments conducted by famed Dr. Samuel Brody. For brother Leonard, I secured employment in the soils department. Both Doug and Leonard were good students. But Leonard, a straight "A" student, flunked freshman English! Because I didn't want an "F" to mar Leonard's scholastic record, I decided to intercede. I made an appointment and visited with the English instructor. *My proposal:* That the professor give brother Leonard further assignments, followed by another examination. The professor readily agreed. Brother Leonard was given a "bundle" of assignments, followed by another examination; he received a final grade of "C." Subsequently, brother Doug completed a Ph.D. degree at Cornell University in Rural Sociology and became a world-renowned rural sociologist. Brother Leonard completed a doctorate at the University of Illinois, in soils, followed by a long and distinguished career as Chairman of Agronomy at Auburn University, Auburn, Alabama.

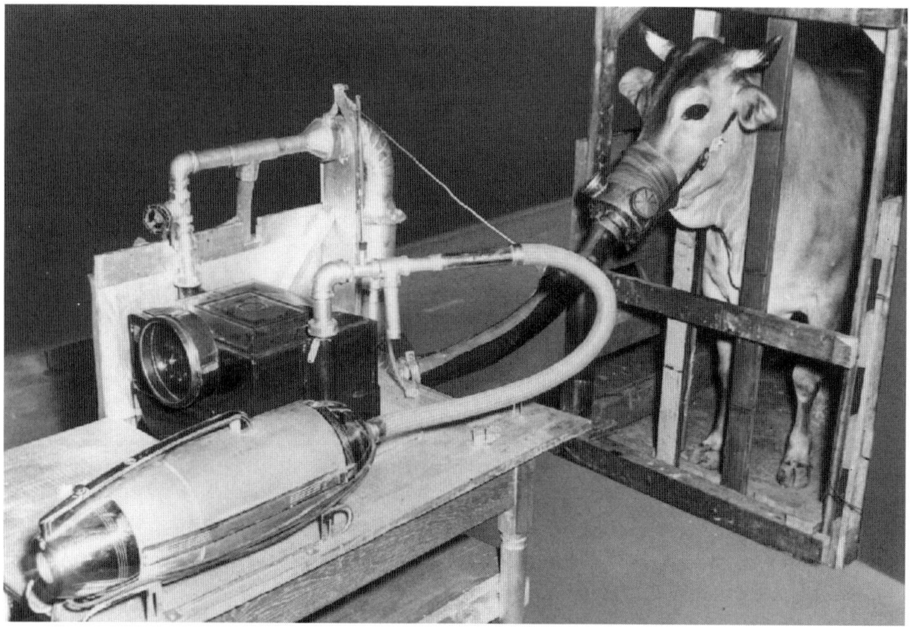

Energy (calorimetry) experiment conducted by famed scientist Dr. Samuel Brody.

The University of Missouri in the Roaring Twenties

The roaring twenties rocked the University of Missouri!

During my freshman year, a pre-Kinsey "Sex Questionnaire" that the Sociology Department of the University of Missouri sent out to a sampled list of students, shook the rafters of the alumns, the Board of Regents, and the legislators. Generally speaking, the students were supportive of the questionnaire. The president of the student body called campus-wide meetings of the students in the big auditorium in Jesse Hall. The students threatened to march to the State Capitol in Jefferson City in support of the questionnaire. The questionnaire brought down the presidency of the University.

But that wasn't all! A sorority girl was kicked out of school because she was caught having sex with her boyfriend in the parlor of the sorority house. Later, it leaked out that 17 sorority sisters of the booted one admitted that they had done the same thing. Soon, the campus buzz words were "We 17"; and little poems headed "We 17" appeared in the student newspaper.

Also smoking cigarettes characterized the "smart set" of college girls during this period.

In the College of Agriculture, the monthly meeting of the aggies ended with a "dirty story contest." This prompted Dean F. B. Mumford to come before the aggies and issue a stern warning to clean up their meeting, or face being banned.

Scholarship

At the University of Missouri, I majored in animal science, and minored in English and journalism. I liked all of my course work in animal science, including the related fields of zoology, botany, chemistry, physics, and mathematics. I also liked my courses in English, journalism, and public speaking. I was a member of the livestock, dairy, and meats judging teams, all of which competed in national contests. Also, I served as president of the Block and Bridle Club (the animal science club); and as a staff member of the *College Farmer*, the College of Agriculture magazine.

Improving My Social Graces

In order to improve my social graces, I joined the Alpha Gamma Sigma fraternity in my junior year. Earl Allen, a very finished senior in the fraternity, coached a small group of green country boys, including me. Among other things, Earl told us that we should never leave the spoon in our coffee cup; that pouring and blowing coffee (pouring some of the hot coffee into a saucer, then cooling it by blowing) was frowned upon; showed us the proper way to leave our knife and fork on our plate at the end of a meal; coached us on how to ask a beautiful girl for a date; and showed us how to dance.

My Green Suit

By my junior year, I had saved up enough money (working at 25 cents per hour) to buy my first suit. So, I went shopping in downtown Columbia and bought what I thought was a blue suit. Proudly, I wore it to the Burral Bible class the very next Sunday only to be greeted with "Gene, where did you get that green suit?" I am color blind. Having worn the suit, I couldn't return it to the clothing store; so, I continued to wear my first suit. At the end of my senior year, some joker alluded to my green suit in the

My green suit.

metropolitan paper, *The Columbia Missourian*, under "A Year Ago Today" column as follows:

> A year ago today, Gene Ensminger started wearing his green suit.

Cultural Events

For cultural improvement, beginning in my junior year, I ushered at concerts and other similar events because I couldn't afford a ticket. Among the great ones whom I heard were: Galli-Curci, the great Italian soprano; John McCormack, the most famous of Irish tenors; and Edna St. Vincent Millay, the Pulitzer prize poet who recited some of her works.

The Burral Bible Class

At that time, an all-denominational group known as the Burral Bible class, named after its first teacher, Jessie Burral, met each Sunday morning on the campus of Stephens College, a girls' college founded in 1833. It averaged an attendance of about 1,000 each Sunday morning, with attendees from the University of Missouri, and from the two girls' colleges in Columbia—Stephens College and Christian College. In addition to a fine message delivered by an outstanding teacher, the Burral class always had great music. Additionally, there was much student participation, including ushering, announcements, reading the scripture, prayers, and brief messages. The Burral class had many activities, including a special "Can Day," in which the stage was piled high with gifts of canned goods for the poor; a large lighted Christmas tree on the front lawn, around which the Burral class sang Christmas carols; and the publication of a magazine, *The Grail*.

I decided to become active in the Burral class for two reasons: because of my farm background, I was bashful, and I choked up when I was called upon to speak; and although I had never had any difficulty believing in the hereafter, I was beginning to find some of the here and now unbelievable. So, I told Jessie Burral that I would like to help where and when needed. I started as an usher, but I ended up as president of the Burral class when I was a senior. In the meantime Jessie Burral had retired. She was succeeded by Nellie Lee Holt, whom President Wood of Stephens College had trained for the job by sending her on a world tour for two years to meet, and spend time with, the great leaders of the day, including Ramsay Macdonald, the prime minister of England; and Mohandas K. Gandhi of India.

The YMCA

The same two reasons that prompted me to become active in the Burral Bible class caused me to become active in the college YMCA. So, I told Earl Gordon, the director, of my interest in helping when and where needed. He lost no time in appointing me chairman of the "Finance Committee," and in having me perform other services. During my senior year, I was elected president of the University of Missouri YMCA. Additionally, I was elected chairman of the Southwest Field Council of the YMCA, which included the five states of Missouri, Arkansas, Texas, Oklahoma, and Kansas. What an experience that was!

Educated Jealousies

During my junior and senior years, I experienced the viciousness of jealousies, with educated jealousies being the worst. At that time, the Agricultural Club on the campus was dominated by a bunch of puritans and dreamers who passed a club rule to the effect that no one, including friends, could ask anyone to vote for a nominee for office.

The two most important and prestigious events sponsored by the Ag Club at the time were the *Farmer's Fair*, held each spring, which consisted of a mile long parade through the main street of Columbia, followed by an open house at the College Farm; and *Barnwarming*, held each October in the campus gymnasium, which, for the dance, was transformed into a wonderland with only the dance floor recognizable. It was the dance of the year at the University of Missouri!

As a senior, I was nominated for, and elected, assistant manager of the Farmer's Fair. The assistant manager automatically became the manager during his senior year, but at the next meeting of the Ag Club following my election, some student accused one of my fraternity brothers of asking him to vote for me, and my election was ruled null and void; and a new assistant manager was elected.

Ahead of Barnwarming, a queen was elected. I didn't have a steady girlfriend, but because of my activities I knew many students on the campus. So, on the night when the aggies met to elect a queen, I escorted to the meeting and nominated for queen, Peggy Goodwin, a vivacious and beautiful girl from Macon, Missouri. One by one, in alphabetical order, the nominees for Barnwarming Queen were introduced by the president of the Ag Club as they paraded across the stage. Peggy Goodwin brought the house down and was elected by a wide margin. But, following the election, some student accused my brother, Doug, of asking him to vote for Peggy Goodwin. So, in a secret session, the officers of the club changed the vote and made the second choice queen. Again, the puritans and dreamers of the Ag Club prevailed, and again an educated jealousy protruded its forked tongue.

Subsequent to the above incidents, I came across an advertisement which was placed by Cadillac in 1915, which I framed and hung in my office. From time to time, I find consolation in reading this advertisement. It follows.

> THE PENALTY OF LEADERSHIP
>
> In every field of human endeavor, he that is first must perpetually live in the white light of publicity. Whether the leadership be vested in a man or in a manufactured product, emulation and envy are ever at work. In art, in literature, in music, in industry, the reward and the punishment are always the same. The reward is widespread recognition; the punishment, fierce denial and detraction. When a man's work becomes a standard for the whole world, it also becomes a target for the shafts of the envious few. If his work be merely mediocre, he will be left severely alone. If he achieves a masterpiece, it will set a million tongues a-wagging. Jealousy does not protrude its forked tongue at the artist who produces a commonplace painting. Whatsoever you write, or paint, or play, or sing, or build, no one will strive to surpass, or to slander you, unless your work be stamped with the seal of genius . . . . The leader is assailed because he is a leader. In the effort to equal or to excel, the follower seeks to depreciate and to destroy. But he only confirms once more the superiority of that which he strives to supplant. There is nothing new in this. It is as old as the world and as old as the human passions—envy, fear, greed, ambition, and the desire to surpass. And it all avails nothing. If the leader truly leads, he remains—the leader. Master poet, master painter, master workman—each in his turn is assailed, and each holds his laurels through the ages. That which is good or great makes itself known, no matter how loud the clamor of denial. That which deserves to live—lives.

Professor E. A. Trowbridge's Dictum of Me

Professor E. A. Trowbridge was head of Animal Husbandry at the University of Missouri during my student days. At the end of my senior year, a friend of mine divulged his dictum of me. It follows.

> Gene Ensminger is an innovator and a worker. I hope that whatever he sets out to do is right, because he will do it.

I accepted Professor Trowbridge's evaluation of me as a high compliment because I have always made certain that whatever I set out to do is right in the eyes of both my fellow mortals and the Lord. Indeed, when I climb the golden ladder I shall feel honored if I have earned the epitaph—

> He was a maverick who made his dreams come true.

My Ringside Seat in the History of Minerals and Vitamins

It was my happy privilege to have a ringside seat to, and even be a small part of, the discoveries of minerals, vitamins, and other nutrients—discoveries that largely came through animal research, and which led to greater health and happiness for millions of people.

Throughout history, mineral, vitamin, and other deficiencies have been the major cause of disease, morbidity, and death. Pellagra, scurvy, and beriberi decimated armies, ships' crews, and nations; they even reshaped the course of history. But the cause and cure for these diseases was not understood until the 20th century when the biological approach in experiments—the use of laboratory animals (largely white rats and mice, guinea pigs, chickens, pigeons, and dogs)—was ushered in. Their diets were made up of relatively pure nutrients (proteins, carbohydrates, fats, and minerals)—using casein or albumen, lard, and pure carbohydrate such as dextrin. Deficiencies followed. Then it was discovered that dramatic cures resulted when minute amounts of a mineral or a vitamin were added. Details of a few of these discoveries are noteworthy:

Vitamin A

In 1913, Elmer V. McCollum and Marguerite Davis of the University of Wisconsin, and Thomas B. Osborne and Lafayette B. Mendel of the Connecticut Experiment Station, working independently and using white rats, discovered vitamin A. It is noteworthy that Miss Marguerite Davis, a young biologist who had just obtained her bachelor's degree from the

University of California, volunteered to do the rat work for Dr. McCollum without salary.

Vitamin C

Scurvy, now known to be caused by a deficiency of vitamin C, was a dreaded disease in ancient times. It was once common among sailors who ate little except bread and salt meat while on long voyages. In 1497, when Vasco de Gama, a Portuguese navigator, sailed around the cape of Good Hope, 100 of his crew of 160 men perished of scurvy on the voyage.

In 1926, as a student at the University of Missouri, working for Dr. A. G. Hogan, pioneer nutritionist, I did some of the early vitamin C studies. In the process of conducting my experiments, I hand-squeezed loads of oranges at 4:00 a.m. Everything went well until the Columbia, Missouri, police suspicioned that I was violating the Prohibition Act, and making moonshine liquor. To keep out of jail, one wintry morning, I told the police the story of scurvy, and explained that orange juice contained a factor that would prevent the dreaded disease. Although not fully convinced as to the difference between making moonshine liquor and conducting a scientific experiment on scurvy, I narrowly averted a ride in the paddy wagon that morning.

Nicotinic Acid (Niacin) and Pellagra

In the early 1900s, there were around 100,000 cases of pellagra per year in the United States, and up to 10,000 deaths per year. A similar disease in dogs was called *blacktongue*. In 1937, Dr. Conrad Elvehjem (a biochemist whom I knew, who later became president of the University of Wisconsin) and his colleagues at the University of Wisconsin, in experiments with dogs, identified the antiblacktongue factor as nicotinic acid (niacin) and nicotinamide (niacinamide).

Comparative Slaughter Technique for Determining Net Energy

In 1926, the technique for determining energy storage and heat production was first employed by Dr. H. H. Mitchell (whom I knew) and co-workers, of the University of Illinois. In comparative slaughter studies, a part of the experimental animals were slaughtered at each the beginning and the end of the experiment, with the calorie content of the carcasses analyzed and the increased energy determined by difference in caloric content at the beginning and the end.

Minerals

In the 20th century, various minerals were found to be required by animals and man as indicated by the dates of the discoveries which follow: Phosphorus, 1918; copper, 1925; magnesium, manganese, and molybdenum, 1931; zinc, 1934; and cobalt, 1935. But it was not until 1948 that it was discovered that cobalt functions as a component of vitamin B-12. After developing isolation equipment to shield animals on ultrapure diets from contamination by minute amounts of mineral elements in the environment, the essentiality of selenium was discovered in 1957, and of chromium in 1959. Then, as recently as 1972, it was found that fluorine and silicon are essential.

Amino Acids

In studies conducted from 1935 to 1955, Dr. W. C. Rose (whom I also knew) and co-workers at the University of Illinois were the first to determine the essentiality of the amino acids and the minimum requirements of each. Using rats, Rose found that 10 different amino acids must be supplied in adequate amounts in the food to support the normal growth of young rats; and using his graduate students in nitrogen balance studies, Rose found that only eight of these amino acids were essential for the maintenance of nitrogen equilibrium in fully grown young men. Subsequently, it was shown that a ninth amino acid (histidine) is essential for human infants and, in long term studies, for adults as well.

Yes, I was there! I had a ringside seat for the discovery of most of the minerals, vitamins, amino acids, and a host of other nutrients essential for humans and farm animals.

Four Unique Summers Plus One Unique Year

During the summers of 1929, 1930, 1931, and 1932, and one great year in 1933, I had unique employment experiences—experiences which proved to be invaluable to me throughout my 65-year career.

Field Agent for the University of Missouri (MU) in Summers of 1929 and 1930

Throughout most of the 1920s, U.S. agriculture was in a depression. As a result, enrollment in the College of Agriculture of the University of Missouri had gone down and down. Farm families couldn't afford to send their sons to college (few girls were enrolled in agricultural colleges in that day and age).

Dean F. B. Mumford of the MU College of Agriculture, conceived the idea of having a presently enrolled ag student serve as field agent for the college to recruit high school graduates to come to the college. The dean offered me the job, which I readily accepted in order to earn money so that I could stay in school. Also, I recognized that it would be a fabulous experience. The rest of the story: The dean selected as my "chariot" a Model T Ford that the Soils Department of the University had retired (the dean didn't want that I display any signs of prosperity). The dean's brief and crisp instructions to me were: comb the rural areas of Missouri; search, find, and get the best and the brightest agricultural students to enroll in the MU College of Agriculture; secure employment in Columbia for those needing financial assistance (which was most of them), but require that each of them needing employment submit to me five letters of recommendation; and give Associate Dean Shirkey a progress report each week. I was assigned a cubicle and a desk adjacent to Dean Shirkey's office.

The "how to do it" was left up to me. I decided that I could best locate potential enrollees in each hamlet by visiting with the superintendent of the school, the vocational agricultural instructor, or the county extension agent. Some invited me to address local groups that were meeting at the time of my visit. After evolving with a list of potential enrollees, my next challenge was to find them. Some were walking behind plows, others were harvesting crops, and still others were exhibiting at the local fair. Rain or shine, gravel or dirt roads (sometimes getting stuck), I found them—bloodhound fashion. Wherever possible, I visited with the entire family. At night, I slept in low-cost hotels and motels (one night, the bedbugs ate me up). Generally, I returned to Columbia each Friday night; then, I worked all day Saturday hunting jobs—on the campus and in downtown Columbia, fitting the boys and the jobs to each other. For example, Ralph, a little south Missourian who chewed tobacco would not be suitable for hopping tables in a sorority house; so, I had him work for me at the college farm (the chaw of tobacco bulging his cheek didn't bother the swine). Although Dean Shirkey was my immediate supervisor, Dean Mumford, who was very stern, kept me on a short leash. I shall always remember two incidents in which the dean was involved.

Incident No. 1: At 11:00 o'clock one morning, Dean Mumford *told* (he didn't ask) me that he wanted that I accompany him to, and address, the Chamber of Commerce that day. He explained that he was responsible for the speaker; that the scheduled speaker couldn't be there for some reason, so I would substitute. The dean wanted that I tell about my work as field agent, and solicit jobs for the incoming students. So, I collected my thoughts and accompanied the dean to the luncheon. Following the luncheon, the dean introduced me, and I addressed the Chamber of Commerce.

Incident No. 2: Late one Thursday night, I arrived back in Columbia and parked the Model T in the lot back of the Alpha Gamma Sigma fraternity house of which I was a member. Associate Dean Shirkey had instructed me to use the parking lot back of the fraternity, rather than park the car on the street in front of the Ag Building—the other alternative. The campus garage was always closed when I arrived back in Columbia late at night. So, early Friday morning, I left the Model T in the fraternity house parking lot and walked to my little office on the campus for the purpose of organizing the flood of five letters of recommendation that each applicant for a job had submitted.

About the middle of the morning one of the professors on the campus came to Dean Mumford's office and told him of his urgent need for a car that day. Thereupon, the dean came to my desk and inquired: "Ensminger, where is the Model T?" "It's parked back of the Alpha Gamma Sigma fraternity," I responded. This brought a stern rebuke from the dean: "You cannot do that." I froze—speechless. But, I scrammed and brought the Model T to the professor, who was waiting in front of the Ag Building.

Upon regaining my composure, I went into Dean Shirkey's office and told him what had happened. Dean Shirkey, who was a very easy person with whom to visit, responded: "Why didn't you tell Dean Mumford that I told you to park the car where you did, instead of on the street?" My answer: "I couldn't." Dean Shirkey understood. Thereupon, he admonished me not to worry about the incident, and stated that he would background Dean Mumford.

In the fall of 1929, many of the students whom I had recruited during the summer, and for whom I had found part-time work, enrolled. So, enrollment was up and Dean Mumford was pleased. Then and there, he asked that I again serve as field agent in the summer of 1930; of course, with the same Model T serving as my mode of transportation.

Following graduation, many of these poor farm boys whom I recruited and found jobs for, in the summers of 1929 and 1930, went on to become great scientists and agricultural leaders throughout America in the decades ahead. Their success was my greatest reward.

Teaching at Northwest Missouri State University in Summers of 1931 and 1932

I served as an instructor at this institution at Marysville, Missouri, during two summers. In the summer of 1931, Dr. Roy Kinnard took leave of absence; and I was asked to take his place. In the summer of 1932, Dr. Carl Schowengerdt took leave; and I was invited to take his place. In addition to teaching courses in my major field, animal science, this gave me an opportunity to teach courses in soils, forage crops, horticulture, and poultry production. Additionally, I was responsible for the University's small orchard, and for the trees and shrubs on the campus, including the gardens surrounding the president's house. Mrs. Lampkin, the president's wife, bless her, could find more bugs on her flowers and shrubs than I was aware existed. I learned far more than the students because I had to do an enormous amount of studying in preparing my lectures and laboratories.

Among my students in one course the first year, was Al Hedges, the University's football star. Al was a "C" student. But in the final examination, he made an "A." I knew that he had gotten a copy of the examination in advance, perhaps from the University's mimeographing room. So, in the final class period, without mentioning Al's name, I mentioned the obvious. Further, I promised that if the guilty person would come to my office during the next hour, make a confession, and promise never to do such a thing again, I would give him/her a grade of "C" based on previous work, and that I would not reveal the name of the person.

Immediately following the class period, Al came in and confessed that he and others had stolen, at night, the final examination questions of several courses from the University's mimeographing room. Al was truly remorseful—he wept bitterly. So, I gave him a final grade of "C" and considered the incident closed. But that afternoon I was called into the president's office. President Lampkin advised me that several students had broken into the mimeographing room and stolen final examination questions, and that he had been informed that I knew the identity of one of the culprits. So, the president pressured me for the name of the student involved in my course. Thereupon, I told the president that I had promised the student that I would not reveal his/her name if he/she would confess, and promise never again to do such a thing. So, I would keep my word, and not reveal the name of the student. The president left no doubt that he didn't agree with my stand, and that he felt that I should reveal the name of the culprit.

I left his office fully expecting to receive a letter saying that I was fired. But, no such letter ever came—and I carried on. In my judgment, getting this football star to confess, and be truly remorseful, was far more effective than kicking him out of school.

Soil Erosion Station, Bethany, Missouri, Year of 1933

With the election of Franklin D. Roosevelt in 1932, new programs designed to provide employment and stimulate the economy popped up like toadstools after a rain. Hugh H. Bennett seized the opportunity to sell the Soil Conservation Program to President Roosevelt. At this time, a new Soil Erosion Station was established at Bethany, Missouri, with R. E. Uhland as superintendent. It provided employment for me at a minimum hourly wage, along with an opportunity to learn new skills in a fast-growing program during the Great Depression.

Following my junior year at the University of Missouri, I went home for a brief visit, at which time this family picture was taken. *Left to right:* Leonard Elroy, Father Jacob, Ella Mae, Rachel Aileen, and Mother Ella Ora. *Standing left to right:* Jacob Douglas, Harry Edward, Marion Eugene, and Garnett Atwell.

1933–1937
AFTER COLLEGE – DURING THE GREAT DEPRESSION

The Great Depression—during which I attended college, and following graduation I was issued into—was a blessing in disguise for me. Without it, I would never have had the great job variety and experiences that were mine, including, while I was in college: working in a grocery store, "hopping" tables in a cafeteria, and hauling garbage to the pigs; feeding experimental steers and swine at the college farm; one summer at the Soil Erosion Station, Bethany, Missouri; two summers teaching at Missouri State University, Maryville, Missouri; and serving as field agent for the University of Missouri for two summers, recruiting students and getting them jobs so that they could go to college.

Following graduation with an M.S. degree, I went home to the farm, where I developed a thriving business raising broilers, dressing them, and selling them roadside. Then came the New Deal! Because of my soil erosion experience, soon I had a supervisory job in the newly created Civilian Conservation Corps (the CCC camps), first in Missouri, and later in Illinois. Then, beginning at age 27, and for the next four years, I supervised more than 800 people developing the 15,000-acre Dixon Springs Project in Southern Illinois.

I was truly a product of the Great Depression! I was issued out of the College of Agriculture, University of Missouri, with B.S. (1931) and M.S. (1932) degrees. No one in my graduating class got a job, for there were no jobs to be had.

One of the insurance companies had foreclosed on several thousand acres of good Missouri land, much of which was producing lush, but ungrazed, forage. I proposed that they put cattle on these abandoned farms and harvest the forage at a profit; and I offered to manage the operation if they would merely pay for my room and board. They declined.

So, for a brief period of time, I went home to my parent's farm near Grandview, Missouri, where I raised broilers, dressed them, and sold them roadside. I soon had regular customers. In addition, I used the surplus eggs to make cakes to send to my brothers still in college. The broiler project was profitable. More importantly, it kept me occupied and prevented me from becoming despondent.

The Great Depression was unkind to my parents. They had a Studebaker car that they left in the garage, because they had no money with which to buy gasoline. We went to church in a big wagon drawn by mules. Instead of buying coal for our potbellied stoves, we burned corn as fuel.

In 1934, I Served as Technician/ Engineer for the CCC Camps in Missouri and Illinois

The Civilian Conservation Corps (CCC) was a "New Deal" program, designed to provide employment for young men doing soil erosion work. The program was under the supervision of Secretary Harold Ickes, U.S. Department of Interior.

The CCC provided an opportunity for me to capitalize on my earlier experience at the Soil Erosion Station, Bethany, Missouri. At that point and period of time, few people were experienced in terracing, gully control, and other soil conservation techniques. An engineer by the name of Miller was the superintendent of the 300-man CCC unit at Platte City, Missouri, to which I was assigned. The facilities were army style. I slept in an army tent, and the mess hall, the food, and the latrine were army style.

Unfortunately, some of the foremen were political hacks, selected because of their political connections, rather than on the basis of any soil conservation knowledge. One ex-banker and one ex-businessman were prone to getting drunk. But, I discovered that they could be handled easily by giving them a football, whereupon they would play football until they fell asleep.

Early one afternoon, I suffered the most excruciating stomach pains that I had ever endured. (Later, it was diagnosed as a perforated duodenal ulcer, although I didn't know that I had an ulcer.) Mr. Miller telephoned my parents, loaded me in the back seat of his car, and headed for the U.S. Army Hospital at Ft. Leavenworth, Kansas, a distance of about 75 miles. During most of the trip, I was unconscious.

When I regained consciousness following surgery, I was told that peritonitis had set in (this was before the days of antibiotics), and that Colonel Qualls, the surgeon, had performed a gastrectomy. Later, I learned that Colonel Qualls told my parents that I only had a five percent chance of coming through. Twenty-five years later, when the scar tissue had closed off the duodenal opening and I had surgery a second time, I learned that the surgery at Ft. Leavenworth was never performed; obviously they had sewed me up to die. The Lord was my shepherd! Obviously, too, the Lord had missions for me.

Following the so-called surgery, I was placed in a large ward in the army hospital that was occupied by a bunch of regular army men. For several days, the nurses kept me heavily sedated with morphine, for I was less bother that way. One day, I realized that I was sitting up in bed begging for morphine. I was addicted! From that day forward, I refused to let the nurses give me more morphine. Upon gaining consciousness, and not being sedated with morphine, I was thoroughly disgusted with the old army men in the ward, whose main conversation was "wine, women, and song," and if they left anything out, it was the song. Following two weeks in the ward, I was released from the army hospital at Ft. Leavenworth, Kansas.

While I was in the hospital, I received a promotion. I was transferred to LeRoy, Illinois, and put in charge of a technical group consisting of two engineers, Wayne Lowery and Leon Casidy, and a jack-of-all-trades by the first name of Pete. I soon discovered that the two Irishmen, Leon and Pete, would rather fight than work. Also, there were several able foremen, and a large contingent of CCC workers. The Illinois group was under the supervision of F. A. Fisher, who was stationed in Champaign-Urbana, Illinois, with whom I enjoyed an excellent relationship.

In LeRoy, Illinois, Wayne, Leon, Pete, and I stayed at a boarding house, where each of us had a bedroom with boardinghouse meals, and a rented room for an office.

My ulcer continued to bleed, despite the fact that I had been told that I had gastrectomy surgery, and that the ulcer had been removed. Moreover, the lady who operated the boarding house wouldn't provide an ulcer diet. Her attitude: "Eat what I give you." Also, her son came home on army leave for a few days, following which my new suitcase disappeared with him.

My bleeding duodenal ulcer worsened. As a result, I called upon one of our local foremen, Russell Washburn, a fine gentleman, to help me find another place to stay where I could get a proper diet. He suggested an elderly lady by the name of Story and her daughter, Sibyl, a school teacher, who lived in a big house. So, I went to see them. In addition to finding that they were fine Christian people, they were eager to have a man in the house for protective reasons. With a proper diet, my ulcer improved. I was very grateful, and I kept in touch with Sibyl and her mother since that time. Sibyl's mother passed away, but Sibyl continued on to age 100.

Leon and Pete had only one consuming interest—the Masonic Lodge, which they had joined. Their work was minimal. Instead, they spent much time in the library reading all about the Masons. One of my local foremen who was a Mason pressured me to permit him to submit my name for membership. I finally acceded, only to have Leon and Pete blackball me (according to the local foreman who submitted my name; who apologized profusely for the revenge of Leon and Pete). Through this incident, and many others that followed through the years, I learned of *The Penalty of Leadership*. As a result of the Masonic blackballing, I also developed a philosophy that "everything happens for the best, even though it never happens." Although the Masons are a fine organization and I have had many good friends who were ardent Masons, I could never have endured the ritual of the Masons.

The Pitchfork Incident

Prior to going on each privately-owned farm to do terracing, gully control work, or other soil conservation work, the farm owner was required to sign an agreement, requesting the work and permitting entry to the farm. On one particular farm near LeRoy, Illinois, the absentee owner had signed the contract, but his tenant threatened to kill anyone attempting to do soil conservation work on the farm. All of my staff, including the foreman of the CCC workers, were afraid of the tenant, who had a reputation of carrying out his threats (including a rumor that he had killed three people). So, the staff looked to me—perhaps as a sacrificial offering. My choices: risk being killed or be a coward. I elected to proceed. So, I rode in the cab of the first truck of the caravan of CCC workers. Upon arrival at the farm, I saw that the entrance gate was closed, but not locked, and the big, fierce-looking tenant was on a mound about 20 feet from the gate, leaning on a pitchfork. I got out of the truck, said a cheery good morning to the big, burly tenant, and opened the gate, prepared for a pitchfork to be stuck through me. But the tenant continued to lean on his pitchfork, without moving or speaking. I waved all of the trucks in and closed the gate. We completed our soil conservation work over a period of several days without incident. The Lord was my shepherd!

While I was at LeRoy, Illinois, the chief engineer of the Soil Conservation Service for the State of Illinois resigned. For a brief period of time, I was appointed to this post. However, I never actually functioned in this capacity because my superiors wanted that I assume an even greater responsibility.

The Dixon Springs Agricultural Center in Illinois

For four years, 1934–1937, I was the Project Manager of the Dixon Springs Agricultural Center, during which time the land was bought and the vast majority of the construction and development work was completed.

The Birth of the Dixon Springs Agricultural Center

In 1933, the Agricultural Adjustment Act was passed and the Land Utilization Division of the USDA and the Resettlement Administration were created which gave the University of Illinois the opening for requesting an Experiment Station in Southern Illinois. At the request of Dean H. W. Mumford, on August 22, 1933, Professor H. P. Rusk, Head of the Animal Husbandry Department, sent a proposal to Henry A. Wallace, Secretary of Agriculture. Rexford Tugwell, Assistant Secretary of Agriculture and "New Deal Brain Truster," took up the cause; but, at his suggestion, the University of Illinois request for an Experiment Station was increased from 2,000 to 16,000 acres.

About Little Egypt (Southern Illinois)

The name "Little Egypt" is of historical interest. In 1831, there was crop failure over all the land in northern and central Illinois. Southern Illinois became the source of food and feed for the rest of the state that year. The situation was likened to the Biblical story of the sons of Jacob going into Egypt for corn. From that point and period of time forward, the southern third of Illinois became known as Little Egypt.

But Little Egypt fell on hard times in the early 1930s. It became a land of sassafras, sumac, persimmons, possums, abandoned farms, and squatters.

The average yield of corn in Pope County was only 26.2 bu per acre, *provided all the nubbins were gathered.* A survey at the time showed an average annual income of only $277 per family.

In the early 1930s, Pope County corn sold at 29 cents/bu, wheat at 44 cents/bu, hay brought $3.90/ton, cattle were valued at $26.00/head, hogs at $6.40/head, and sheep at $3.80/head.

But things were not all that bad! Five gallons of corn meal could be made into about 10 gallons of moonshine liquor—a profitable outlet. *Note:* As the successor to the panel delivery Chevy, the first car assigned to me by the University of Illinois, my second mode of transportation at Dixon Springs was a bullet-riddled car which was confiscated by the government from a moonshiner who attempted to outrun the law—but didn't make it.

Poverty! A survey revealed that 138 families had an average annual income of $277.

The New Deal Came to the Rescue

In 1933, Uncle Sam was

taking the first faltering footsteps in Southern Illinois. Three managers had been "kicked upstairs." (Government employees are never fired!) Both the federal government and the University of Illinois faced a dilemma: The need for a Project Manager with soil erosion experience, able to relate to the down-trodden farmers of southern Illinois, and capable and willing to supervise more than 800 WPA and CCC camp workers. H. W. Mumford, Dean of the College of Agriculture, University of Illinois, and H. P. Rusk, Head of Animal Husbandry at the University of Illinois, thought of "that fellow Ensminger; but he's too young, only 27 years old." However, they couldn't think of anyone else out there!

The Inside Story of My Selection as Project Manager

At the time, I was employed by the Soil Conservation Service and stationed at LeRoy, Illinois, where the following message was relayed to me: "Please report to Professor H. P. Rusk's office at the University of Illinois immediately."

There, Dean Mumford, Professor Rusk, and Dr. Burlison looked me over as if they were buying a horse. Then, they *ordered* me to report to Dixon springs immediately, as Project Manager. What! I exclaimed, get me slaughtered! (I was aware that three other Project Managers had "graduated.") But, at the time I was a government employee in the Soil Conservation Service, stationed in Illinois; and the alternative to doing what I was ordered was unemployment. I had no choice! I was instructed to take over as the Project Manager at Dixon Springs. This involved the entire operation, with responsibility for supervising more than 800 people, acquiring 15,000 acres of land, and being responsible for all the construction and development work from building roads and power lines to an Administration Building. *Get this:* No one offered to accompany me to Dixon Springs: Professor Rusk merely pointed south and said: "It's 225 miles down there; the University will provide a car for you."

My chariot: A worn out Chevrolet panel delivery. As I left Rusk's office, he followed me into the hall, at which time he admonished me as follows: "Ensminger, I just have one bit of advice: It is a lot easier to tell a man to go to hell at my age than at yours."

Subsequently, I learned by the grapevine the bases of my selection as Project Manager. The powers that be reasoned as follows:

> He's only 27, but Father Time will take care of that. He has soil erosion experience; he has been supervising a lot of people, and he does it well; he is a good administrator; he is a tireless worker; he will cut government red tape, smile at those who object, and move ahead; he can relate to the poor southern Illinois farmers because he grew up in the Ozarks of Missouri and as poor as a "church mouse"; and he is able, honest, and street smart.

That evaluation was a mixture of brickbats and bouquets!

I Arrived at the Dixon Springs Station

Unaccompanied and at age 27, I introduced myself, and announced to the staff and workers: "I am your new manager."

As Project Manager in the Land Use Division, I had overall charge of, and responsibility for, all operations, including the U.S. Forest Service, the Soil Conservation Service, and the Works Progress Administration. My charge: supervise more than 800 people, buy 15,000 acres of land, and do all the con-

The office and administrative staff. I am in the second row (standing) second from the left.

Katie Buster's home and land were among those that we bought for an average of $14.04 per acre.

struction and development work—build roads, power lines, and an administration building; drill wells, develop ponds and a lake; and construct all other facilities.

Here is what I faced when I took over as Project Manager:

■ Low morale of the staff and workers.

■ My office in the Robbs' garage.

■ Disgruntled and poor farmers. A total of 42% of the families were receiving, or were certified as eligible to receive, public assistance. 75% of the homesteads had no wells. Very few homes had bathrooms. A survey revealed that 138 families had an average annual income of $277.

A. L. Robbs Owned the Whole Town

A. L. Robbs and his family moved to this location to take over the construction of a section of railroad, including three tunnels, after another contractor had defaulted. During and after the railroad construction, Mr. Robbs built the town which bears his name. At the time I arrived as Project Manager, Robbs' empire consisted of the village and considerable surrounding farmland. The town included a garage, blacksmith shop, Ford agency, farm machinery agency, insurance company, post office, lumber yard, telephone exchange, electric light plant, grain elevator, flour mill, a race horse, and a combination restaurant and barber shop (food and hair were in separate rooms, with an open door between them). The whole complex was owned and operated by A. L. Robbs, and supervised by him and his son, Buell. *Note well:* The restaurant menu frequently offered a choice of roast beef or quail—all at the same price. The toughness of the beef indicated that it came from aged steers that had fought all the way up and down the trail.

A. L. Robbs had one of the best minds that I have ever known; he was a shrewd businessman.

■ In order to get the office out of the garage as expeditiously as possible, I, personally, rented a

The tall building was A. L. Robbs' mill, where he ground corn to make corn meal for human food.

A. L. Robbs built and owned the entire town of Robbs, Illinois. *Left:* Some of the houses. The brick buildings in the distance and to the right are the garage and a multiple use building, with rooms for rent upstairs, a restaurant, and a barber shop. *Right:* A corn meal grist mill.

house for use as an office, and paid the rental until I could get the government to do so.

■ The first 93 tracts of land cost an average of $14.04 per acre. In the hills section, most of the farms were assessed at $3 to $5 per acre.

■ An unimproved, and often impassable, road led from Robbs to the highway—a distance of about six miles. It rained the night before my first scheduled trip out of Robbs to the Regional Office in Indianapolis, Indiana, so I engaged a team of mules to pull my car from Robbs to the highway.

Henry Perly Rusk was the Right Person at the Right Time to Spearhead the Development of the Dixon Springs Station

He served as Head of Animal Husbandry at the University of Illinois from 1922 to 1939, and as Dean of the College of Agriculture from 1939 to 1952. Additionally, he chaired the University of Illinois' Dixon Springs Committee. Without H. P. Rusk, there would never have been a Dixon Springs Agricultural Center.

■ H. P. Rusk and I operated on the same sound wave. Moreover, he was a profile in courage, joining me in battle whenever I needed him. We were dear friends from the time that I became Project Manager to his death.

■ Rusk was dedicated to helping the people of southern Illinois.

■ Rusk and his pipe belonged to each other. The bigger the problem and the greater the concern, the more violently he puffed.

■ Rusk was a promoter of pole type barns.

■ The stories of H. P. Rusk were legion:

One time he called his longtime secretary into his office and told her that he was going to do a certain thing in a certain way. Thereupon, Miss Smallhausen, who knew all the university regulations, cautioned her boss: "But, Professor Rusk, in the regulations, it says that this constitutes a violation."

My second office (a converted house). Note the sign in front. My first office at Dixon Springs was a desk in one corner of Robbs' garage.

A modern 5-room dwelling built for a caretaker.

Pole type barns of the type promoted by H. P. Rusk, several of which were built on the Station.

Shelter house on a 5-acre recreational area.

Horse and mule barn, and a nearby house built for the University of Illinois Superintendent.

H. P. Rusk

Thereupon, H. P. explained to his able secretary: "You are supposed to know and follow the university regulations, and I am supposed to know how to get around them."

At this point, Miss Smallhausen frowned a bit; then, both she and the Professor laughed—and Rusk did what he intended—his way.

Then, there was the time when H. P. left the building, lighted his proverbial pipe, and was sending up some big signals. As he hurried toward his car, Miss Smallhausen opened a window and called out, "Professor Rusk, Dean Mumford wants to see you, and he wants to see you right now."

In haste, Rusk poked his pipe in his pocket, because smoking in the Dean's office was forbidden. In the middle of the session, the Dean broke in: "Professor Rusk, something in this office is on fire, and I think that it is you."

Sure enough, Rusk's coat pocket was belching smoke.

Along the way, pressure was exerted on Professor Rusk to do something about his general foreman and handyman at the college farm, John Munson. The complaint was that John cursed like a sailor. Worse yet, he was foul-mouthed when parents, visiting their college children, stopped at the college farm. Finally, H. P. decided to reform old John once and for all. So, he called him into his office and reprimanded him severely. Meanwhile John looked remorseful and said nothing until H. P. had finished. Then he spoke out: "Professor Rusk, you are right, but I want you to know that I learned some of my most fancy words from you when you were a young man." That ended the session!

Dean Mumford was Killed in an Automobile Accident

Following Dean Mumford's tragic death, Dean Blair was appointed Dean for a year, thereby allowing for the traditional search and the usual college politicking. But educated jealousies and politics were especially vicious as candidates jockeyed for the deanship. Finally, H. P. got the word that he had been selected, and that the Regents would announce his appointment on a certain date. On the day that it was announced that he would be the new Dean, H. P. went to Dixon Springs to let "campus politics simmer down," as he put it.

My Last Visit with Dean Rusk

At the last meeting of the American Society of Animal Science that Dean H. P. Rusk attended, I spent a long evening with him in his hotel room in Chicago, as we relived Dixon Springs together, interrupted only by his alarm clock reminding him to take his medication. He won the battle of Dixon Springs, but he lost the battle with time.

H. P. Rusk and I Connived

My confessions follow:

■ H. P. and I connived in providing water to thirsty natives—There was a severe drought in the Dixon Springs area. Many of the local farmers were without water for either their families or their animals. So I was pleased to accommodate them by letting them haul water from the deep wells that we had drilled on the Station. All went well until Rex Tugwell got wind of it in Washington, D.C. Thereupon, Mr. Tugwell wired me in no uncertain terms, to the following effect: "Cease and desist sharing water from government wells with local people and animals."

I couldn't bring myself to see people and animals die of thirst. So, I called Professor Rusk. It was

Drilling a deep well on the Station.

agreed that Rusk would send a telegram to me requesting that I report to Urbana immediately to discuss important matters, and that I should be prepared to stay for several days. I packed my oversize briefcase with several days' work and headed north, forgetting to arrange for a guard to enforce the "no water" edict of Mr. Tugwell. Fortunately, five days later, torrential rains fell on Dixon Springs. At that time, I returned to the Station.

■ H. P. Rusk and I connived in order to circumvent the request that I truck laborers to the polls—When running for reelection, United States Congressman Claude V. Parsons was very insistent that I truck all the laborers on the Dixon Springs project to the voting booths. Here again, I couldn't bring myself to comply. So, H. P. Rusk and I evolved with "operation election day." I should go goose hunting down the Mississippi River. While hidden in a blind (pit) and shooting geese that came in to feed on the wheat field, I couldn't be reached. So, "a-hunting I did go" on election day.

When I returned to my office that night, there was a whole stack of telephone messages marked *urgent*, received at about 20 minute intervals, from Congressman Claude V. Parsons.

■ H. P. Rusk and I connived at the time of the Ohio River flood in 1937—The rampaging river flooded all the lowlands. Fortunately, our head office in Washington, D.C. gave me permission to use our tractors, trucks, and workers in rescue work. We worked around the clock, taking many people off the roof tops. When the waters receded, thousands of bushels of ear corn stored in cribs were water-soaked, mud-laden, and sprouting. As H. P. Rusk looked at some of the corn, he remarked: "If corn could have smallpox, this grain looks as if it has it."

H. P. and I decided to buy some of that corn and put it in a trench silo. Then, we designed an experiment and fed the flood-damaged corn to finishing cattle. The University never had such a profitable experiment!

I Settled a Sit-down Strike

Late one afternoon, all the workforce struck for higher wages. Upon meeting with them, I told them that I didn't set WPA wages—that they were set in Washington, D.C. So, I ended the session by saying: "Those who report for work tomorrow morning will have a job. Those who do not show will be dropped."

Fortunately, all of them reported for work the next morning. But, two weeks later, a lawyer from

One of the many houses inundated by the rampaging Ohio River flood in 1937.

Washington, D.C. arrived with a suitcase full of documents, for the express purpose of conducting hearings on the sit-down strike of which he had heard. I'll never forget the expression on that lawyer's face when I told him that I had settled the strike—and how I had settled it. Then, the lawyer went on to read to me the government rules relative to settlement of a strike, pointing a finger at me as he did so. But, a few minutes later, I saved the lawyer's life.

Red faced from fury, the lawyer remarked: "I want that you go with me to serve papers on a squatter by the name of Holly. Do you know him?"

I replied in the affirmative, and went on to explain that Mr. Holly served as our janitor in the administration building. Moreover, I warned the young lawyer that Mr. Holly was a tough old character; that being a member of a Brush Arbor Religious Sect was the only restraint that kept him from shooting more people. So, I urged the lawyer to let me get the squatter out, and not get him stirred up. I explained that I was always in my office early in the morning, at the time Mr. Holly did his janitorial chores, and that he and I were on very friendly terms. But my offer to get Mr. Holly out landed on deaf ears.

The lawyer didn't get to conduct long, drawn-out hearings on the sit-down strike; thus, he wasn't about to forego his mission of serving papers on Mr. Holly. So, off we went to the dilapidated house of the squatter! Mr. Holly greeted me warmly, but he kept a jaundiced eye on the stranger, whom I introduced as a lawyer from Washington, D.C. Without further ado, the lawyer opened his briefcase and explained that he was there to serve papers on him and get him out. Quick as a flash, Mr. Holly grabbed a loaded shotgun from back of the door and pointed it, close range, at the lawyer's heart. The lawyer turned white and speechless. "Mr. Holly," I yelled, "don't shoot him! Give me that gun!" I took hold of the barrel and pointed it toward the ceiling; then, Mr. Holly let go of the gun. I admonished the lawyer to go to the car—and he scrammed. I thanked Mr. Holly for sparing the life of my friend, handed him the gun, and departed. With the sit-down strike settled and my commitment to get the squatter out, the lawyer left for Washington, D.C.—never to return.

A Medley of Memories Follows

■ None of the stonemasons who laid the walls of the administration building had ever used a trowel before. But the building still stands!

■ Along the way, the Soil Conservation Service was transferred from the U.S. Department of the Interior to the U.S. Department of Agriculture. But old government agencies never die!

■ Reporter Garet Garret of the *Saturday Evening Post* was critical of the Dixon Springs Project. He portrayed the beautiful cabins in the wildwood, instead of the dire poverty.

■ Corn was harvested with a husking peg, a thin piece of metal 5 to 6 inches long strapped to the hand, which cost 25 to 50 cents. Today, corn pickers and picker-shellers, costing several thousand dollars, are used.

■ Spout Springs, which was the chief source of water for the Dixon Springs area before deep wells were drilled, was alleged to have sex control properties. To get a boy baby, a man was supposed to drink the water as it came from the side of the hill, either just before sunset or at sunrise, and hold his hat in the left hand and bend over toward the north; then drink deeply.

■ The natives were resentful of government red tape and the vast majority of government employees. But, I, personally, was never unwelcome on any farm or in any home in the Dixon Springs area during the four years that I was there.

■ A lot of people made contributions along the way. But Dixon Springs was Henry Perly Rusk's dream.

■ History will evaluate for posterity, as it will for each of us, my role in the development of the Dixon

The beautiful administration building, constructed with WPA labor from limestone quarried on the project.

A limestone ledge on the Station from which agricultural limestone was produced.

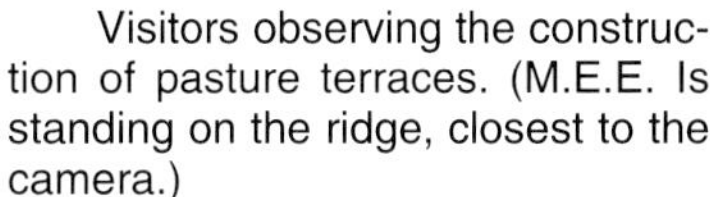

Visitors observing the construction of pasture terraces. (M.E.E. Is standing on the ridge, closest to the camera.)

Spreading agricultural limestone on pasture.

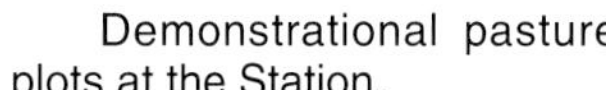

Demonstrational pasture plots at the Station.

Springs Station. At this point and period of time, suffice it to say that anyone less resolute would never have made it through those first four years, 1934-1937.

Following four golden years of fabulous experience, from 1934 to 1937, and with most of the development work completed, I decided that I should move along with my career objective—college work and writing. So, I accepted a position at the University of Massachusetts in the fall of 1937. Now, 60 years later, my autumn leaves are more fruitful and beautifully colored as a result of ushering the Dixon Springs Agricultural Center into the world. (The Dixon Springs Agricultural Center was dedicated on October 8, 1938.)

■ Robert J. Webb, the University's longtime Superintendent at the Center, made H. P.'s dreams come true.

Two quotes from letters written by Dean H. P. Rusk following the completion of the Dixon Springs Project, giving his evaluation of me. The following are excerpts from two different letters written by Dean H. P. Rusk:"

> Gene won my admiration and respect when he was Manager of Construction and Land Rehabilitation on the more than 5,000 acres that is now the Dixon Springs Experiment Station. He did an outstanding job in a very difficult situation, getting things done in spite of conflicting memos from different agencies in Washington.
>
> I was also amazed by his ability to handle all sorts of labor and to get loyal cooperation from WPA workers who, I thought, were hopeless. Some of these WPA workers drove their own teams to work and used them on the job without charge until Washington learned about the amount of donated work and cracked down.

> I had an excellent opportunity to get a different slant on Gene's general attitude and ability. He was General Manager of operations at our Dixon Springs Station when we had as many as 800 men, most of them from WPA, working on that area. He did an amazing job of handling a diffficult situation. I was impressed again and again with the smooth way he handled labor diffficulties, which won the unquestioned loyalty of his numerous assistants and foremen; and his nerve in handling negotiations with outside organizations, all the way from federal agencies down to local politicians. He had a way of cutting through red tape, smiling at those who criticized him for it, and making them like the way he got things done.

Years later, the University of Illinois published a book entitled Redeeming a Lost Heritage—The Development of the Dixon Springs Agricultural Center. *M. E. Ensminger was never contacted prior to its publication. Sadly, it was inaccurate. It mentioned M. E. Ensminger only once, to say he was the local agent for resettlement and that he attended the dedication. Both statements were inaccurate.*

It was unbelievable to Dr. E that this happened when he had put in nearly 18 hours per day, seven days per week to get the land bought, roads, water system, electricity, administration building, and houses all built in a span of four years; on a project where three previous managers had failed. He had looked on the Dixon Springs project as one of the most rewarding experiences of his life. He was extremely proud of his accomplishments there; moreover, he realized then that the greater the challenge, the more he enjoyed the success.

After Dr. E passed away, I wrote to President B. A. Nugent of the University of Illinois to apprise him of these errors. I did receive a response from him in which he said that they "intend to remedy the matter in subsequent publications when there are opportunities to do so."

I think it is important to record history as accurately as possible.

AHE

1937–1940
THE UNIVERSITY OF MASSACHUSETTS

With the development work at the Dixon Springs Agricultural Center in Illinois nearly completed, I decided to accept a staff position at the University of Massachusetts in the fall of 1937, thereby permitting me to pursue my two longtime goals: complete a Ph.D. degree and perfect my writing skills. Before leaving Dixon Springs, the federal government tried to get me to head an important government division in Washington, D.C. The enticements: I would be the youngest person ever to head up this division, and the salary would be nearly three times the salary of the post at the University of Massachusetts. However, earlier in my career, I had decided that money was secondary to filling a need and doing what I enjoyed. So, I accepted the position at the University of Massachusetts, and I followed the rule of the sulkey driver: "You never win a race by looking back." So, in the fall of 1937, I loaded my possessions in my faithful Buick and headed for Massachusetts.

This photo was taken after my marriage on one of our visits to see my brother Doug in Washington, D.C. Audrey is taking a picture of George Washington's house and Doug is next to her.

I encountered snow and treacherous roads, with the result that I became ill by the time I reached New York. I went to an M.D., who prescribed some medicine. I continued on to Ithaca, New York, where I stopped to visit my brother, Doug, and my sister-in-law, Mary. Doug was completing a Ph.D. degree in rural sociology at Cornell University. Mary was a daughter of Dr. E. L. Morgan, a noted rural sociologist at the University of Missouri. At the time, Doug and Mary had a daughter, Mary Ellen.

Doug completed his Ph.D. in 1939, after which he moved to Washington, D.C., where he served the USDA for ten years in the Bureau of Agricultural Economics. During that time I visited his family several times while I was stationed at the University of Massachusetts. It was good to have some of the family that close, because Missouri was a long trip away, and during the depression years travel was a luxury that most of us couldn't afford. Doug and Mary had five children (three girls and two boys) when Doug was hired to head the Ford Foundation work in India in 1951.

When I arrived at the University of Massachusetts, at Amherst, the ground was covered with snow. Amherst was a beautiful New England town, with a very fine city library built from local quarried stone. The University of Massachusetts was an uncrowded campus, with an enrollment of 4,500 students and a small lake in the middle of the campus that was used for ice skating in the winter. The college farm division harvested the forage on the campus for ensilage, using equipment that was drawn by the college Percherons.

I shared a 12 ft. by 20 ft. office with Professor Richard Foley, who taught courses in dairy science and nutrition. Each of us had a roll-topped desk back to back, which provided a bit of privacy.

My first place of stay, which had been arranged by Professor V. A. Rice, was an upstairs room in a beautiful New England house owned by the widow of a dentist who had passed away shortly before my arrival.

Professor Rice, the Dean of Agriculture and Chairman of the Animal Science Department, was an author of the leading animal breeding textbook of the period. In addition, he wrote feature articles for magazines, was a top teacher (some of the townspeople audited his classes), an ardent golfer (and winner of many trophies), and without a car (he never learned to drive). Professor Rice was married and had two beautiful daughters.

One evening a few years into my tenure at the U of M, Professor Rice called to say he was in deep trouble. He said that Mrs. Rice was out of town and his two daughters wanted to invite the Ensmingers for dinner. (I had married Audrey in Minnesota the previous year.) He had forgotten to ask us, but we said not to worry, we would be there in 15 minutes. So, in order to help him out we dutifully ate another dinner which was delicious.

My assignments at the university consisted of teaching 21 credit hours. I got out of one class just in time to get to my next class; so, I prepared my lectures each night. Additionally, I supervised the university's Percheron horses. Later, I added Morgans, Southdown and Hampshire sheep, and Chester White swine. I also coached the livestock and meat-judging teams which competed at the Eastern States Exposition and the Chicago International, answered letters in the animal field, represented the department in agricultural extension assignments, and wrote livestock bulletins during the summer months. I authored, and the university published, the following bulletins: *Horse Production* (1938), *Sheep and Wool* (1938), *Beef Production* (1939), and *Swine Production* (1940).

Photo taken in 1939 on the campus of the University of Massachusetts. Wayne Dinsmore (driver), Executive Secretary, Horse and Mule Association of America, Chicago, is welcomed as a program participant in a Livestock Field Day at the U of M by President Hugh Potter Baker. Dean V. A. Rice is seated beside Mr. Dinsmore. I promulgated the field day and took the picture.

The IRS Agent Cometh

Soon after my arrival in Amherst, I received a command notice from the Internal Revenue Service, ordering me to meet an Internal Revenue agent in my office at 7:00 p.m. on a specified date. Unfortunately, that same evening, and that same hour, a big meeting was scheduled in the auditorium of the building in which I officed; and the hallway leading to the auditorium also served as the entrance to my office. Being new on the campus, I didn't know any of the people streaming into the auditorium, and I certainly didn't know the IRS agent. So, I decided that the best thing to do was to remain in my office, with the office door open.

About 15 minutes after the scheduled time, the IRS agent stood at the open door to my office and asked: "Why weren't you at the front door to meet me?" In as friendly a tone as I could muster up, I explained that, being new on the campus, I wouldn't be able to recognize him in the lineup of those entering the auditorium. I thought: I'm in for some real trouble with the IRS. Anyway, I have always been a detail-type of person, so I had good records of my expenditures. So, as the agent pulled from his briefcase my IRS report and challenged item by item, I showed him my receipts. Finally, he got to the bottom line and found that I had overpaid taxes in the amount of $2.50. He groaned about the difficulties that it would cause him and the IRS to refund $2.50. Then, he sheepishly asked: "Would you be willing to sign a waiver on that $2.50?" My answer: "I suppose so." Thereupon, I signed the waiver and the *friendly* IRS Agent departed. It was a never-to-be-forgotten experience.

Feeding Garbage to Rental Horses

Soon after my arrival on the campus, Professor Rice, the department chairman, informed me that a battle was raging between the rental riding horse establishments in Boston. *The issue:* Some owners had lowered their price per hour, and were undercutting their competition by collecting and feeding garbage to their horses. My job was to meet with all the owners of rental saddle horse units in the Boston area and calm the waters. Legally, there was nothing in the world to keep owners from feeding garbage to their horses instead of traditional oats and hay. So, I arranged for a night meeting with the group. My prepared approach consisted of an educational program emphasizing the importance of proper feeding and nutrition in order to maximize performance. Moreover, for horse welfare reasons, self-respecting horsemen shouldn't feed garbage, which contains glass and other injurious objects, to horses. It worked! Very soon, no one ever heard of garbage being fed to horses in the Boston area.

The Little International Livestock Show

Prior to my arrival, the students had a *Little International*, modeled after the great Chicago International Livestock Show which was in its heyday at the time. But the U of M Little International was poorly done, imparted no pride to students, and attracted few spectators. I decided either to make it come alive or give it a decent burial. So, I trained the students in proper fitting and showing of horses, dairy cattle, beef cattle, sheep, and swine; required that they dress neatly and properly for the show; emphasized that the show would operate on schedule (not one minute late); recruited top judges for each of the several classes; and publicized the event. And the spectators came! Annually, the students vied for the honors. To my surprise, in the third year of the show, Jimmie Watson, editor of the *New England Homestead*, Springfield, Massachusetts, provided "The M. E. Ensminger Rotating Silver Trophy" to be awarded to the premier showman each year. Students vied for this high honor.

M. E. Ensminger (standing near trophy) is about to present "The M. E. Ensminger Rotating Silver Trophy" to the premier showman in the 1939 Little International at the U of M. The Ensminger Rotating Trophy was the brainchild of Jimmie Watson, editor of the *New England Homestead.*

The Indian Boy from Martha's Vineyard

Among my students at the University of Massachusetts was a full-blooded American Indian from the Wampanoag tribe on Martha's Vineyard, the fishing and vacation island off the coast of Massachusetts. They are tall, handsome, smart, Indians. Leonard Vanderhoop was known as "Van" to his fellow students and me. Van was a good student, but of few words. In response to my questions in class, whenever possible his answers were limited to "yes" or "no." The most that I ever heard him say was: "We welcomed the Pilgrims." There are only 250 Wampanoags left on Martha's Vineyard, and only 630 in the nation. Van will be mentioned later in this book.

Annual Student Trips to Fuerst Stock Farm and Madrey Farm

During my tenure at the University of Massachusetts, there were two annual field trips, made in chartered buses, to which the students always looked forward. One of them was to Fuerst Stock Farm, Pine Plains, New York, owned by Myron Fuerst, noted for fine Angus cattle and Percheron horses. In addition to parading and showing their fine animals, along with a judging contest, Mrs. Fuerst always served a bountiful and delicious luncheon.

The other annual field trip was to Madrey Farm, Brewster, New York, owned by Mrs. Max Dreyfus, famed for Percheron horses. It is noteworthy that at this period of time (1937–1940) Mrs. Dreyfus showered her love for horses on a draft breed (Percherons), rather than on light horses.

Sheep Dog Trials on the Campus

At the time of my tenure at the University of Massachusetts, sheep dog trials were a popular spectator sport.

Sheep dog trials are tests of the intelligence, talent, and ability of sheep dogs. Historically, it is of interest to note that the first sheep dog trial was held in Wales in 1873. It was won by a Scotsman with a strong-eyed dog. Today, sheep dog trials are held in England, Scotland, Canada, Australia, New Zealand, and the United States. The superiority of working Border Collies for sheep dog trials is due to their tremendous instinct to work sheep—and to work them a certain way. As a wide-run, strong-eyed dog, they can control a flock of sheep with a quiet efficiency unknown in any other breed. Without a dog, a shepherd or herder is helpless in handling a large flock or band of sheep. On the average range, a herder and one Border Collie can handle 1,000 sheep under most conditions. Where larger bands are run, or where the terrain is broken and rough, more than one dog is used by the herder in working his band.

With quiet efficiency, and without fences, a good sheep dog must have the flock under perfect control. With a good working dog in command, the shepherd has no fear that the flock will escape.

The conduct of a sheep dog trial must, of necessity, vary somewhat according to conditions that prevail, particularly the size and kind of area available. I conducted sheep dog trials on the playing field of the University of Massachusetts. Dogs were required to perform four phases of work: gathering, shedding, driving, and penning. Each dog was scored individually in each phase of work. Five sheep were used, and each dog was allowed 12 minutes.

The Bachelor's Apartment

The lady in whose home I roomed during my first year at the University of Massachusetts was very gracious. But, I found that one room was too confining for me. Also, I had tired of eating most of my meals out. So, I decided to rent a bachelor's apartment.

Elliott Barrick, a graduate of Oklahoma State University, had just arrived at the University of Massachusetts to complete a Masters Degree in the Animal Science Department. So, he and I teamed up in the bachelor's apartment. This proved to be a very happy arrangement for both of us. We prepared most of our meals. Also, we officed in the same building on the campus. So, after working in our respective offices until about 10:00 p.m. each night, on the way home, we stopped at the bowling alley and got our exercise. During the nearly two years that we shared the bachelor's apartment, there was never a cross word or disagreement between us. After completing a Ph.D. degree at Purdue University, Elliott Barrick had a distinguished career at North Carolina State University.

After Elliott Barrick left, a Harvard graduate arrived on the campus. As a *Harrvarrd* graduate, cleaning an apartment or cooking were below his dignity. Worse yet, I could cook a roast of beef, only to have the bone left by the time I was ready to eat. I never knew a person with such an expandable stomach!

Have Golf Clubs, But Did Not Play

Professor V. A. Rice, Dean of Agriculture and Chairman of Animal Science, whom I greatly admired, was an ardent golfer. He was good, too, as evidenced by the number of trophies that he had on display.

After I had been on the University of Massachusetts staff for about a year, Prof. Rice strolled into my office one day, carrying a new set of golf clubs, which he plunked down near my chair and leaned against my desk. I braced for what followed: "You have been working too hard. Here is a set of golf clubs and here is the bill."

I wasn't prepared for the triple shock administered by Prof. Rice: working too hard, a new set of golf clubs (which I hadn't bought), and the bill.

Since I had the clubs, along with the bill, I decided to take lessons from a pro. I took three lessons, then stopped. I simply couldn't get enthusiastic about clubbing a little ball, then following it around a golf course. However, after we were married, little Audrey persuaded me to do a little golfing. I spent a summer trying to like the game. Alas, it was too slow a game for me, so we decided that bowling and tennis were better for us. Audrey was a good tennis player already with two club trophies from Canada, and I had spent many an evening bowling after my work for the day.

Christmas on Beacon Hill

At Christmastime in the United States, cities, towns, and villages sparkle with bright lights and gay decorations. Shoppers fill the streets, carrying colorful packages for their families and friends. Many churches and homes set up a scene of the Christ Child in his crib, surrounded by Mary, Joseph, and the wise men, along with shepherds, animals, and angels. People send gifts and Christmas greeting cards. Church choirs practice Christmas carols, and children rehearse Christmas plays in school. Cakes, cookies, and Christmas puddings are prepared for the holiday meals. The family puts up a Christmas tree, with hangings of candy canes, Christmas ornaments, popcorn, tinsel, and lights. The home is decorated with wreaths of holly and branches of evergreen. Mistletoe is hung over doorways. Schools usually have about a two-week vacation. Christmas is a family occasion, and relatives gather and exchange gifts and share in their happiness. Many people have their Christmas dinner in the afternoon. The family dinner usually features turkey, although chicken, duck, goose, or ham may be served. As a final treat, the family may enjoy fruit cake, plum pudding, pumpkin or mince pie, along with eggnog. Churches and social groups often share food with needy persons in the community.

During my second Christmas in Massachusetts (in 1939), I experienced a traditional Christmas Eve on Boston's Beacon Hill. I learned that Bostonians did all the above things, but that Beacon Hill did much more on Christmas Eve. Beacon Hill glowed with candles in all the windows. Legend has it that the Irish who migrated to Boston continued the tradition of the motherland. People of Ireland leave a candle burning in the window to light the way for the Christ child on Christmas Eve; and lights at Christmas represent Christ as the light of the world.

On Christmas Eve, every residence on Beacon Hill had open house. Doors were open to all people (there were no strangers); and drinks (mostly punch) and Christmas goodies were served by the hosts. The streets at the foot of Beacon Hill, which were closed to traffic, were filled with people—all in a holiday mood, including little groups of Christmas carolers and bell ringers. Christmas cheer prevailed; and crime on Beacon Hill on Christmas Eve was unknown.

Maple Syrup/Sugaring Off

During my first spring in New England, I witnessed the making of maple syrup and maple sugar (the natives refer to the latter as sugaring off); and I was fascinated with the origin and history of these products.

Years before the "white man" arrived in North America, the Northeast Indians tapped the maple trees by gashing the trunks with their tomahawks. As the sap flowed from the trees, it was collected in birch bark dishes. Then, by continually adding heated rocks to a hollowed-out cooking log, the Indians evaporated the sap down to a thick dark syrup. Upon arriving in the New World, the early settlers soon learned the art from the Indians, but they were able to improve upon the system by using iron drill bits to tap the trees and copper or iron kettles to boil the sap to syrup. Today, a more modern method of collecting the sap involves a system of plastic pipelines which transports the sap from the hole tapped into the tree to the sugarhouse.

Collection of the sap commences in the spring of the year, usually between January and April, when warm days begin to follow cool nights, causing the sap of the sugar maple trees (called "sugar bushes") to flow. During the winter, some of the starch that the tree made the previous summer and stored in the roots is converted to sugar, primarily sucrose, and carried in the first sap of the spring.

Processing occurs in the sugarhouse. It is here that the sap is strained and then placed in shallow pans—evaporators—over wood, oil, or gas fires. As the sap boils, the water evaporates. When the sugar concentration reaches 66.5%, it is drawn off, filtered, and bottled as maple syrup. During the boiling and evaporating, the characteristic maple flavor and color develop. Depending on the sugar content of the sap, 30 to 50 gallons of sap are required to make one gallon of maple syrup. Maple sugar is produced by further boiling and evaporation of most of the water. One gallon of syrup yields about eight pounds of sugar. An old-fashioned treat enjoyed by those making maple sugar is called "Jack Wax"—a taffylike confection formed by pouring the hot syrup onto the snow. Often sugaring off gatherings are held at which friends sample the maple syrup and sugar.

Enough Onions to Change the Breath of an Entire Nation

Upon visiting the Connecticut River Valley for the first time, the late Will Rogers said of it: "They produce enough onions to change the breath of an entire nation."

For the most part, the acres and acres of onions were produced by farmers of Polish descent, on small farms, using horses for power.

Each spring, about the time the danger of the first hard frost had passed, and just ahead of the onion planting season, one or more draft horse auctions were held in Springfield, Massachusetts. There, Polish onion farmers would buy their horses; new horses for new farmers, and replacements for old-timers.

Most of these horses were shipped from the Midwest, where there was an increasing surplus of horse power created by the use of more and more tractors by corn and soybean farmers. Typically, horse dealers bought surplus horses following harvest; and fattened them in corrals during the winter months, where they made phenomenal gains of four to six pounds daily. Exercise was limited to that obtained naturally by running in a paddock. Such animals became fat, slick, and attractive. But heavily fed horses kept in idleness are apt to become unsound! This gave rise to the statement that "fat and hair will cover up a multitude of sins in a horse."

During my first year in Massachusetts, I attended one of these spring horse auctions. I was appalled to see so many new buyers getting "taken" with their eyes wide open. The auctioneer made the following announcement more than once: "This horse is sold at the end of the halter." To a knowledgeable horseman, this horse auction lexicon meant: "sold with no guarantee except title."

The other term: "This is a balky horse." Translated into reality, this means that the horse stands still—refuses to go. This vice was not uncommon in the draft horse and horse-and-buggy era. The causes of balking were numerous; among them, too severe punishment when overloaded, and sore shoulders. The legendary cures (none of which are recommended by the author) included: pounding on one shoe to divert the balky horse's attention; pouring sand in one ear, which was supposed to shake the idea of balking out of its head; and building a fire under it. Belatedly, some uninformed buyer learned that this horse wouldn't pull the hat off your head.

Over the years, relentless mechanization replaced the horses in the Connecticut River Valley, but sturdy Polish farmers and fields of pungent onions remain.

I Coached the Livestock Judging Team

Among my teaching assignments at the University of Massachusetts was that of coaching the livestock judging team. The team, consisting of five members, was chosen from the students enrolled in the livestock judging course, which I taught. The judging team participated in two annual intercollegiate contests: a Northeast Regional Contest at the Eastern State Exposition, Springfield, Massachusetts; and the International Livestock Show, at Chicago, Illinois. Although winning the two contests was the goal, I always felt that the two greatest lifelong benefits that I could impart to students were: making the right decision, and justifying their choices. The essential qualifications of a good livestock judge are: knowledge of the parts of an animal, a clearly defined ideal or standard of perfection, keen observation and sound judgment, honesty and courage, logical procedure in evaluating, and tact.

A judging contest consists of the independent placing of four animals of each class of livestock, followed by giving oral reasons before an expert judge.

Each year in preparation for the contest, I arranged for the students to practice, practice, practice—in both placings and reasons; similar to a football coach preparing for a bowl game. In order to have new animals to place, trips were made to the livestock farms of the area. During these travels by bus, I got to know the students well. I have vivid recollections of Burton Gregg, the son of a minister who dearly adored his parents, imitating his father preaching—even to quoting the scripture and adding the amens. Burton Gregg later had a distinguished career as a dairy cattle specialist in the New England States.

Wool—Precious Fiber Through the Ages

In the late 1930s wool was a precious fiber, as it had been through the ages.

The wool industries, like most other industries, developed as a household craft, rather than as a

Photo taken in 1938, showing sheep shearing demonstration by and for students. Standing immediately back of the students and to the far right, right to left: Ken Warner, expert sheep shearer; Claude Koch, U of M shepherd; and M. E. Ensminger.

primitive factory system. The ancient Egyptians, Babylonians, Greeks, and Hebrews did hand spinning and weaving in their homes. In Greece, flock keepers spread skins over their sheep to protect their fleeces from inclement weather. When Rome was in its glory, its wealthy and refined citizens boasted of their achievement in producing the finest quality wool in the world; sheep were given extraordinary care, and they were even blanketed so that a luster and gloss might be imparted to the wool. At frequent intervals, the fleece was parted, combed, and moistened with the rarest oils, and oftentimes with wine. The distinctive toga, a loose outer garment which was worn by officials of ancient Rome when they appeared in public in time of peace, was made from woolen fabric. All over the world, and through the ages, the efforts of flockmasters were devoted to the search for methods of improving the quality and increasing the quantity of wool produced.

Graders often check with each other by "show of hands." This consists of two or three graders examining the same fleece, then secretly and independently recording their grades in the palm of one hand, followed by opening their hands palms up.

In the late 1930s, Wooster, Massachusetts, was the wool capital of the United States, in both wool marketing and research. Moreover, wool was an important commodity, nationally and internationally. So, I decided to avail myself of this unique opportunity to do a wool study for my Ph.D. thesis, with the research done at the University of Massachusetts in cooperation with the top wool scientists at Wooster; and to complete a Ph.D. degree at the University of Minnesota, with my thesis study prior-approved by the chairman of the committee at the University of Minnesota.

The Dean of the College of Agriculture, V. A. Rice, assigned a basement room in Stockbridge Hall for my use as a research laboratory. Additionally, he provided $1,000 for student assistants. I selected student Burton Gregg, the preacher's son, and Priscilla Jacobs, a temperamental Jewish girl, as my lab assistants. Their pay: 25¢ per hour. But, there was no money for equipment or anything else! So I made a "Rube Goldberg" photomicrograph from discarded parts, with which I took hundreds and hundreds of beautiful cross section photos of wool from different body areas of sheep. I used the college Shropshire and Southdown breeds, from which I made determinations of fineness, length, density, and clean wool yield of different body areas.

On the basis of these studies, I reported that the head wool is finest, whereas the britch wool is coarsest. The britch wool is the longest, whereas the head wool is the shortest. In density, the head wool ranks at the top of the body areas, but in yield it is the lowest.

It is noteworthy that years later the U.S. Department of Agriculture recommended a similar objective method of grade determination for arbitration and legal purposes where there is a dispute as to grade.

Leave to Complete My Ph.D. Degree at University Of Minnesota

During my fourth year at the University of Massachusetts, every minute of which I enjoyed, I recognized that the time had come when I should take leave and complete a Ph.D. degree (the union card in college work). Earlier, I had decided that I would like to pursue a Ph.D. degree at the University of Minnesota, with Professor E. F. Ferrin serving as chairman of the committee; and Professor Ferrin had prior-approved my research work for a Ph.D. thesis on wool. Professor Cy Tirrell, University of New Hampshire, had indicated that he would like to take my place at the University of Massachusetts during the year that I would be at the University of Min-

Wool scouring equipment. The vat in which the one gallon crocks are found was formerly an old cheese vat. The interior of this antiquated vat was removed, a new lining installed, and steam coils run along under a raised platform.

With this arrangement, it is possible to hold the scouring and rinsing solutions at a steady and uniform temperature of 115°F.

A part of the 756 wool samples that were stored in moisture-proof containers. Each sample was labeled according to the individual sheep from which it was secured, the definite body area, and the particular wool character.

nesota, which met with the approval of Dean V. A. Rice, my immediate superior at the University of Massachusetts. So, I formally requested leave from my post at the U of M for the school year 1940–1941, which was granted. Before leaving the University of Massachusetts, I started studying French on my own, because at that time the University of Minnesota required the reading knowledge of two foreign languages for a Ph.D. degree. Additionally, I enrolled in two good statistics courses at the University of Massachusetts. Thus, upon departing for the University of Minnesota in the fall of 1940, I was off to a running start on a Ph.D. degree by completing the research for my thesis, reading French, and studying statistics.

The cross section of the wool samples were enlarged under the microscope and photographed using the equipment shown.

1940-1941

THE UNIVERSITY OF MINNESOTA: TWO FABULOUS ACCOMPLISHMENTS – A BRIDE AND A PH.D.

In early September 1940, I loaded my faithful Buick with my worldly possessions (which were few) and headed for the University of Minnesota, to complete a Ph.D. degree, within nine months. This involved completing all course work, passing the stiff requirements in reading German and French, and passing the oral examination administered by a formidable committee of five, which included two world-famed chemists, Drs. Goitner and Palmer. Additionally, I was on a teaching assistantship at the university, with responsibility for teaching the animal nutrition course, plus filling in for any of the professors who called upon me, along with addressing some of the state and national livestock meetings on the campus.

My Place Of Stay

Well in advance of my arrival on the University of Minnesota campus, I asked the Animal Science staff to arrange for my place of stay. They engaged a nice room for me at the home of Mrs. C. P. Fitch, the elderly widow of the former dean of the College of Veterinary Medicine. It was on Knapp Street, within walking distance of my office cubicle on the campus.

The C. P. Fitch house on Knapp Street, St. Paul, where I lived while pursuing a Ph.D. degree at the University of Minnesota.

Later, I learned that Mrs. Fitch had some students rooming in her big house, and that prior to my arrival the house had been looted of all the silverware. So, unbeknown to me, Mrs. Fitch and her female students had decided that, for safety reasons, they needed a man in the house! I was their decoy! Mrs. Fitch introduced me to the other roomers who, along with their friends, were coming and going constantly. But, with the heavy work load that I was carrying, I had no time for, nor interest in, girls.

On Sundays, Mrs. Fitch liked to go out to dinner. So, Sunday after Sunday, she very graciously invited me to go with her and some of her girls. Finally, I reasoned that I had to eat anyway, and that a free meal would be a welcome diversion from the low-cost meals at the university cafeteria. So, I accepted her Sunday dinner invitation. She happily handed the keys to her Buick to me. I was to be the driver. Unfortunately, she had never learned to drive until her husband died, and she was still very nervous when driving. That Sunday, she also invited a couple of her students to dinner. One of them was a winsome Canadian lass by the name of Audrey Watts. She reported that she had met Dean and Mrs. Walter Coffey of the College of Agriculture when they were vacationing at Banff, Canada, and that the Coffeys had suggested she stay with Mrs. Fitch.

I knew Dean Coffey well. His fabulous career had taken him from college shepherd at the University of Illinois, to professor at the University of Illinois, to dean at the University of Minnesota; and finally to president of the University of Minnesota.

Subsequent to that first Sunday dinner with Mrs. Fitch and her students, I was invited many times, but accepted few. I was much too busy. Besides, I noticed that all of them had boyfriends.

The Armistice Day Blizzard of 1940

On Armistice Day, I was in my cubicle on the campus studying when I heard warnings of an impending blizzard. So, I followed the admonition of the natives and fled for my room on Knapp Street, which I reached only minutes ahead of a blinding snowstorm and 90-mile-per-hour winds. But the worst was yet to come! Throughout the night, the snow and 90-mile-per-hour winds continued, leaving in their wake more than 80 Minnesota people frozen to death, many of them hunters with matches on them, but they couldn't get a fire started. Others were in stalled automobiles; some of them set out walking, but didn't make it. Thousands of turkeys perished. Some cattle froze standing up. It was the blizzard of the century. The next day I went to Sears Roebuck in downtown St. Paul, where I bought an ankle length sheepskin coat. I didn't want to freeze to death.

Chief Walter H. Peters

Chief Walter H. Peters Always Gave Half the Road

One day I was invited to accompany the Chief, along with two other staff members—Dr. Lawrence Winters, animal breeding specialist; and Dr. H. R. C. Kernkamp, veterinarian—on a field trip to a branch experiment station some distance from St. Paul-Minneapolis. The Chief was driving. Suddenly, there was the chilling sound of a siren, and a highway patrol car came to a screeching stop right behind us. The Chief stopped the car—on the right side of the road. Kerney (Dr. Kernkamp, DVM), who never met a stranger, peered through the back window and recognized the officer as a former student at the University of Minnesota, whom he knew. So, he jumped out of the car and greeted the officer like a long lost friend. Upon gaining his composure, in friendly tones the officer told the Chief that he would give him a warning ticket, and admonished him to drive on the right side of the road.

Later in the year, the Chief and Mrs. Peters were in downtown Minneapolis, with the Chief in the driver's seat, when a police officer stopped him. Upon sensing that the cop was very angry, the Chief decided to keep quiet and act very remorseful while the officer told him off. Finally, Mrs. Peters, who could contain herself no longer, spoke up: "Officer, he is as deaf as a post. He hasn't heard a word that you've said."

In telling the ridiculous story on himself, the Chief remarked—"Of course, that was the wrong thing to say." The officer became furious, thinking that he had given vent to his feelings only to have his rage bounce off the deaf ears of the driver. So, he looked straight at Mrs. Peters and spewed out: "Have him follow me down to the police station so that we can fine him."

Meeting the Language Requirement

In that day and age, for a Ph.D. degree, the University of Minnesota required that all graduate students have a *good* reading knowledge of two foreign languages. I chose French and German.

While at the University of Massachusetts, I nibbled at French on my own, without taking courses or having a tutor.

When I arrived at the University of Minnesota, I learned that the head of the Foreign Language Department at nearby Carleton College charged a fee of $25 for tutoring German, and that he guaranteed that you would pass the reading tests *provided* you complied precisely with his instructions. So, I set aside the two weeks of Christmas vacation as the time in which I would study both French and German, followed by taking the reading test in each of them. In the meantime, I scheduled my examination in both languages at the resumption of classes following the New Year.

I elected to continue the self-study of French. But, I paid the Carleton College professor $25 for his tutoring services in German. At the very first meeting with the German tutor, he asked me two questions: "How soon do you want to pass the German test, and how many tutoring lessons do you wish to take?" He gasped when I told him that I had scheduled both tests within two weeks, and that I only wanted to take four tutoring lessons in German. Right off, he emphasized that the $25 fee was for his services as my conscience, and that studying and passing the German tests was my responsibility. My four German tutoring lessons, spaced two days apart, consisted of mastering the following assignments:

Lesson No. 1. Recognizing and translating 2,000 German/English words, wherever I saw them, which the tutor had on cards (with the German on one side, and the English on the other).

Lesson No. 2. Recognizing and translating an additional 2,000 German/English words, making for a vocabulary of 4,000 German words.

Lesson No. 3. German sentence structure and grammar.

Lesson No. 4. Reading and translating German books.

I scheduled myself for 18-hour days studying French and German during the two weeks of Christmas vacation, allowing only six hours to eat and sleep. During much of the time, I was alone in the big house; Mrs. Fitch and her girls were shopping, visiting relatives and friends, or celebrating Christmas. So, I had the run of the house. In reading French and German out loud, I alternated between my room and the downstairs sitting rooms. The latter room was shared with a canary, which I am sure would have taken flight had it not been in a cage. I drilled, drilled, drilled. The more I drilled, the better I read French and German. So, with the resumption of French and German examinations following the Christmas holidays, I took the examination which I had prior-scheduled. I passed both tests. Believe me, it was a great relief not to have the language requirement hanging over my head.

My Graduate Work and Orals

At the time I was taking the required courses for the Ph.D., the College of Agriculture of the University of Minnesota boasted, without challenge, of having the greatest array of world-famed agricultural scientists of any American university. The names of Goitner (biochemist), Palmer (biochemist), Winters (geneticist), Stakeman (plant physiologist), Petersen (dairy scientist), and Hayes (agronomist) loomed large, globally. Goitner, Palmer, and Winters were members of my graduate committee, along with Professor Phillips, a noted human nutritionist, and Professor E. F. Ferrin (animal scientist), the chairman of my committee. I had the privilege of taking graduate courses taught by Goitner, Palmer, and Winters. Their courses were tough, but great.

Professor E. F. Ferrin scheduled my oral examination for the end of the school year. About midway through my orals, Drs. Goitner and Palmer sparred off at each other in a friendly disagreement relative to my answer to a certain question. They were not putting me on the grill. Rather, it was a case of two eminent scientists advancing different theories. *Note:* While Drs. Goitner and Palmer argued, I had a "breather;" so, I avoided disturbing their bantering. At the end of the orals, the committee excused me and asked that I wait out in the hall. Within a few minutes (although it seemed like hours to me), they

Professor E. F. Ferrin (right) and his former student (me) standing in front of Professor Ferrin's portrait at the time it was hung in the famed Saddle and Sirloin Gallery.

called me back, announced that I had passed, and congratulated me.

Job Offers

While at the University of Minnesota, I received attractive job offers in university administration, as dean and higher. This prompted me to seek the counsel and advice of Dr. Walter Coffey, president of the University of Minnesota, whose phenomenal career had taken him from college shepherd at the University of Illinois to college president at the University of Minnesota; and who was also the author of a textbook.

Right off, I told President Coffey that my goal was to be a writer of top animal science books. Without hesitation, he admonished me: "If you become a college dean or president, you will no longer be a specialist in animal science. It follows that college administrative work higher than chairman of animal science will mitigate against your eventual goal to be a writer of top animal science books." From that day forward, I declined consideration for positions as a college dean or president.

I Wed Thee!

Despite my full work load during the nine months at the University of Minnesota—taking graduate courses for a Ph.D. degree, passing tests in French and German, taking the Ph.D. orals, and serving as a half-time teaching assistant—I couldn't get that winsome Canadian lass in Mrs. Fitch's covey of girls out of my mind. But I disciplined myself: *I have no time for girls; besides, at age 33, my family (parents, brothers, and sisters) have grown accustomed to my helping all of them financially. Moreover, Audrey Watts has many boyfriends.*

As the completion of my degree neared, increasingly Mrs. Fitch invited just the two of us—Audrey and me—to go out to Sunday dinner. Also, the Chief and Mrs. Peters invited Audrey and me to the annual animal science dinner in their home. The ploy with Audrey—they needed her to help serve the dinner, whereas I was expected to be present. Increasingly, our comings and goings coincided. But time was running out. In another six weeks, I was scheduled to take my orals, following which I must return to the University of Massachusetts. I telephoned my mother (father had passed away) and told her that I was about to take the "leap"; and I asked mother to share the alert with my four brothers and two sisters. Their reaction: complete surprise. Audrey conveyed the message to her parents, and asked them to inform her sister and brother. Their reaction: complete surprise! I bought an engagement ring, sealing the intent.

But the obstacles to marriage were mountainous: I must first pass my orals as scheduled; both Audrey and I were down to our last dime; and World War II was underway, so a wedding in Winnipeg, Canada, Audrey's home, was impossible. Nevertheless, the wedding was scheduled for two days after my orals; Mrs. Fitch arranged for us to be married in the Saint Anthony Park Congregational Church, of which she was a member, engaged the minister, and planned a reception at her house following the wedding. The staff and fellow graduate students in the Animal Science and Home Economics departments rallied with their presence at the wedding, food for the reception, and gifts; Audrey's parents requested, and subsequently received, war-time permission to come from Canada; and President Coffey of the University of Minnesota facetiously remarked that he was practicing giving Audrey away in case her parents couldn't get permission to come for the wedding, due to war-time restrictions.

The wedding proceeded without any hitches, but because of the final exams and packing for the trip to Massachusetts, the bride and groom suffered the usual nervous anxiety. What a relief when it was over.

Audrey's father gave us a wedding gift that cost

The Congregational Church, in St. Anthony Park, St. Paul, where Audrey and I were married on June 11, 1941. Subsequently, it became the United Church of Christ.

Little Audrey—my beautiful bride, and my ever beauteous wife.

me dearly, year after year, for many years. It consisted of a small amount of oil stock that paid about $12 annually. Exerting her independence, Audrey would buy something for our home or some new clothes for herself. Thereupon, I would ask: "How much did it cost, and where did you get the money?" Inevitably, Little Audrey would reply: "I bought it with the money that I received from my oil stock!" Until this happened to me, I never knew that so much could be purchased with so little oil stock money, and that purchases could be made long after the oil well had gone dry.

Return to the University of Massachusetts

We arrived in Amherst in June 1941, when the vegetation was fully awake and beautiful, following a long, hard New England winter. My friends were anxious to meet my bride, "Little Audrey."

Remember the "Little Audrey Stories"? Throughout our entire married life, I have lovingly called Mrs. Ensminger "Little Audrey." When people raise their eyebrows, with a perfectly straight face, I swear that all the "Little Audrey Stories" stemmed from Audrey Watts Ensminger.

In Amherst, our first place of stay was the third floor apartment that I occupied soon after I arrived in Amherst in 1937. Later, we moved to a second floor apartment in the home of Dr. and Mrs. Beaumont. Dr. Beaumont was formerly head of the Agronomy Department at the university. Several friends invited us to dinner. In addition to busying herself making the apartment "homey," Audrey took riding lessons from Dick Nelson, the expert horseman at the University of Massachusetts. In the evenings, we would often golf, or play tennis on the campus courts.

I immediately resumed the 21 credit hours of teaching, which necessitated my getting out of each class fast enough to begin another.

A Summer Living in the President's House

During the summer of 1941, President and Mrs. Hugh Potter Baker of the University of Massachusetts contacted the Ensmingers. They advised us that they would be spending some time in Germany, where Mrs. Baker was born and had lived for many years. Then, they asked if Audrey and I would like to live in the president's house—rent-free, utility-free, and canned goods-free from a well-stocked basement. Our only obligation would be to care for their little Dachshund. We accepted. It was a pleasant experience despite one very great surprise. There were many clocks in each room; and they all struck at different times day and night, but they told us not to wind them. So, it was like Hayden's Last Symphony as the clocks ran down. *The story back of the clocks:* Following speaking engagements, President Baker was frequently offered a fee. He declined accepting money, but in doing so he would always add that he was very fond of old clocks. As a result, the president's house was a "house of old clocks."

I Got Job Offers

Following the completion of a Ph.D. degree, and upon my return to the University of Massachusetts, I received several job offers. Although I wasn't eligible for a sabbatical leave (meaning leave *with salary*, usually following seven years' service), when I took leave without salary to complete a Ph.D. at the University of Minnesota, I made a commitment to Dean V. A. Rice that I would return to the University of Massachusetts for a minimum of one year.

Although the University of Massachusetts was a fine institution, with an attractive campus and in a beautiful area (which Little Audrey loved), except for dairy and poultry, the livestock industry was declining. Since my eventual goal was to write a book pertaining to each class of livestock, it seemed prudent that I should relocate in an area that had all classes of farm animals. Among the jobs available in the early summer of 1941, was an inquiry from Dean E. C. Johnson, Washington State College (later WSU), Pullman, Washington, searching for a chairman for their Animal Husbandry department. I expressed interest, and submitted my credentials. Soon thereafter, Dean Johnson wrote and suggested that the Ensmingers have breakfast with WSC's President E. O. Holland at a specified time and place, in Washington, D.C. We accepted. The breakfast meeting with President Holland was very pleasant. To my surprise, Dr. Holland's primary concern was to determine whether my two-years-in-one graduate work at the University of Minnesota had left me "burned out" for the rest of my life. Apparently, he decided that it had not. So, he offered to pay my travel expenses to go to Washington State College for an interview. I accepted the invitation, subject to the blessings of Dean V. A. Rice, my immediate superior at the University of Massachusetts. Dean Rice approved, following which I telephoned Dean Johnson and arrived at a mutually convenient time for my visit.

Dean E. C. Johnson scheduled my visit on the WSC campus, including spending a great deal of time with him.

Although I was impressed with President Holland and Dean Johnson, I was shocked with what I saw and learned about the Animal Husbandry department. Without listing what I unearthed in order of importance, details follow:

■ **The previous chairman of Animal Husbandry.** Howard Hackedorn, the previous chairman of Animal Husbandry, who had passed away with a heart attack about a year earlier, was well liked by the cattlemen and sheepmen of Washington, to whom he was a "good ole boy." Following the annual conventions of the Washington Cattlemen's Association and the Washington Sheep and Wool Growers, Professor Hackedorn was reputed to need a couple of days to return to normal before returning to the campus.

■ **The two animal husbandry instructors.** The two remaining animal husbandry instructors were Jerry Sotola and Hector McDonald, neither of whom had a Ph.D. degree, and both of whom were part of the problem.

Sotola had a fine reputation as the instructor of animal nutrition, but he was bitter because the WSC administrators would not make him chairman of the Department of Animal Husbandry. So, he spent a minimum amount of time in the Animal Husbandry Department. Instead, he officiated in track meets and other events in the Athletic Department.

Hector McDonald was a thoroughly honest, high-type, mild mannered person, but a poor teacher. The students liked him personally, but they took advantage of him.

■ **The beef cattle herdsman.** John Burns, a Scotchman from the old country and a bachelor, was the beef cattle herdsman. John lived in the big house on the hill. He always provided rooms for two or three students, who usually served as his assistants. Together, John and the students hired a cook. John Burns was an expert cattle fitter and showman, and he took great interest in students. But, typical of the Scotch herdsmen of that era, he abhorred records and research.

■ **A medley of deficiencies in the Animal Husbandry Department.** The Department of Animal Husbandry had a half-time student secretary. The research allocation for the entire department was a mere $1,800 per year.

The animal husbandry student club, known as the "Lariat Club," took great pride in having a hard-drinking, rough initiation. There were no girl students in animal husbandry—it was strictly machismo; the student enrollment was down; there were no graduate students; and the public relations of the department was in shambles.

Because of lack of funds, the dirt road leading from the campus (Stadium Way) to the college farm was impassable following rains; the animal husbandry farm buildings were in need of repair; few fences would confine animals; and the quality of the animals left much to be desired.

My overall impression of the WSC Department of Animal Husbandry at the time of my interview was that it had only one direction to go—and that was up. But I was much impressed with Dean E. C. Johnson, who would be my immediate superior as the new head of the Animal Husbandry Department.

I was offered the position effective in September 1941. Paraphrasing Sir Winston Churchill, I recognized the "blood, sweat, and tears" which would be required to breathe new life into such a rundown department. So, I asked President Holland and Dean Johnson to give me a bit of time for thinking, and for returning to Massachusetts to discuss the matter with Little Audrey and with Dean V. A. Rice.

I Accepted the Washington State College Challenge

Upon my return to the University of Massachusetts, I conferred with Little Audrey and Dean V. A. Rice. Little Audrey loved New England. When considering the move to Washington, she facetiously remarked, "I married you so that I could live in New England." Yet, she was a great trooper. Her attitude then, and throughout our married life, was supportive of what I felt would be prudent professionally.

Dean V. A. Rice of the University of Massachusetts was both my immediate superior and a good friend. Moreover, he didn't have a selfish or jealous bone in his body. When I described the rundown Department of Animal Husbandry at Washington State College to him, he reacted:

You have done a great job here, and I would like that you remain here throughout your career. But you would have fun out of building up that rundown department. Remember, too, that there is little challenge in chairing and maintaining the status quo of a department that has everything.

(Years later it was my pleasure to spearhead the movement which culminated in Dean Rice being the recipient of the "Distinguished Teacher Award" of the American Society of Animal Science, which he richly deserved and greatly treasured.)

So, I submitted my formal resignation to the University of Massachusetts effective September 1, 1941; conveyed my acceptance of the position at Washington State College September 15, 1941; completed all of my assignments at the University of Massachusetts and left my records and files in good order; and Little Audrey and I bade a fond farewell to our Massachusetts friends, loaded our Buick with our possessions, and headed west. The travel across the United States from the East Coast to the West Coast was uneventful except for encountering an unseasonably early snow storm in Yellowstone Park, which necessitated that we turn back and take a different route.

1941–1962
WASHINGTON STATE UNIVERSITY LIFE WAS NEVER BORING

WSC campus, from Pioneer Hall, when we arrived in Pullman.

In 1891, the Locating Commission for the state of Washington selected Pullman as the best site for a new agricultural college. In 1909, the name was changed to Washington State College (WSC); and in 1959, the name was again changed to Washington State University (WSU). Hence, throughout my 21 years at the institution, it was referred to as WSC and WSU.

I devoted 21 prime years of my life to building the WSC Animal Science Department from one of the weakest in the nation to one of the strongest in the nation. Repeatedly, I admonished my staff that building the department could not be accomplished by sitting on a cactus and hollering for funds to precede programs. Rather, the programs must move ahead and the facilities and funds would follow. Additionally, I emphasized that such procedure is hard on staff.

My 21 years as chairman of the animal science department were much affected by the three presidents, along with their agricultural administrators, under whom I served. During my four years under the E. O. Holland/E. C. Johnson regime, I enjoyed great support from both the president and the dean. Likewise, I had the solid support of President Wilson Compton during his six years, 1945–1951.

The E. O. Holland/E. C. Johnson Years of Scholarship, 1941–1944

Audrey and I arrived in Pullman, Washington by car in September 1941, following a drive in a snowstorm across the Rockies. We moved into a little apartment, which we had engaged prior to our arrival. At the end of our first year, we bought a house with a down payment of $600, loaned by a friendly banker.

President E. O. Holland was a scholar, a fine gentleman, and a bachelor—married to the college. The Bursar, William C. Kruegel (business manager), controlled the purse strings.

Dean E. C. Johnson was in charge of the agricultural division, assisted by Leonard Young—an affa-

Audrey and I are sitting on the steps of our new house in 1942.

ble and able executive secretary, and E. V. Ellington— who doubled as vice dean and as head of the Dairy Department.

John Burns, a Scot from the old country and a bachelor, was the sole, full-time herdsman. He, along with a few part-time students, looked after the herds and flocks. John was popular with the purebred beef cattle breeders of the state and well liked by the students. He was very partial to the WSC beef cattle herd; he merely tolerated looking after the sheep and swine, and doing maintenance work.

Although the college had meager funds (they were long on titles, but short on salaries), the administrators were fine characters, and caring people. My relationship with all of the administrators was superb. Occasionally, Dr. Holland would take the Ensmingers to a movie. The president was concerned that I was driving myself too hard; so, one time he admonished me to lie down and relax for at least five minutes after lunch. Mr. Kruegel was stern and stringent with most administrators, but he could always find a few dollars for animal husbandry when I was in need.

The seven-room house we bought for $6,000. Because it was on a hill, there was a semibasement and a garage on the west side.

Our old house as it looked in May of 1984. It now seems to have a forest of trees around it. We had planted many evergreens on both the east and west sides, because it was on top of a hill, with a beautiful 180° view, but with very strong westerly winds all winter long.

E. O. Holland, the first of three WSU presidents under whom I served (1941–1944), and from whom I enjoyed great support.

Dean E. C. Johnson was a good administrator, thoroughly honest, and dependable—his word was his bond. At the time of my interview, the dean told me that he wanted that I be a mover and a shaker of the Animal Husbandry Department, which had gone to seed. So, soon after my arrival on the campus, he called me into his office and told me to be prepared for educated jealousies. But he admonished me to move ahead, and he promised his full support. (The Dean never wavered in his support.)

I learned that the student animal husbandry club, known as *The Lariat Club,* was noted for an initiation which *required* that everyone get gloriously

Dean E. C. Johnson, College of Agriculture, who never wavered in his support of me.

drunk, and that all initiates be subjected to painful body hazards. One initiate sustained a leg injury that bothered him the rest of his life. So, I abolished the Lariat Club. Later, an Animal Science Club evolved, with proper faculty supervision.

Also, I changed the name of the department from Animal Husbandry to Animal Science, thereby signaling a shift from less husbandry to more science in teaching, research, and extension in the decades to come.

Work With Horses No Fit Profession for a Lady Said Dean Lulu Holmes

In 1941 Dean Lulu Holmes, the Dean of Women, was law and order on the campus. , When I arrived on campus as chairman of the Department of Animal Husbandry, she had a letter on my desk requesting that I "ease out" Gladys Christian, the one and only girl enrollee in the department, because, said the dean: "Work with animals is not a fit profession for a lady." On my second day at WSC, with fear and trembling, I went to see the dean, fully prepared that my tenure would be the shortest in the history of WSC. I told the dean that my two sisters were addicted to horses, as were their five brothers; further, I explained that the outside of a horse is good for the inside of a person, and that people need pets and pets need people. Although the dean was unconvinced by my argument, she elected not to press the matter. What a relief!

Following graduation from WSC in 1944, with a major in Animal Science, Gladys held the following positions, in the order listed: assistant to Dr. John Metcalf, equine veterinarian; Oregon Medical School, at Eugene, engaged in environmental health; Kettering Laboratory, Cincinnati, Ohio, in cancer research. While at Kettering Laboratory, Gladys established a scholarship at WSU for (guess who?) girls majoring in Animal Science. In 1994, Gladys returned to WSU for her 50th Golden Grad Reunion, proudly wearing a large gold horseshoe pin—a gift from her old professor, Dr. E, symbolic of

Lulu Holmes, Dean of Women, WSC

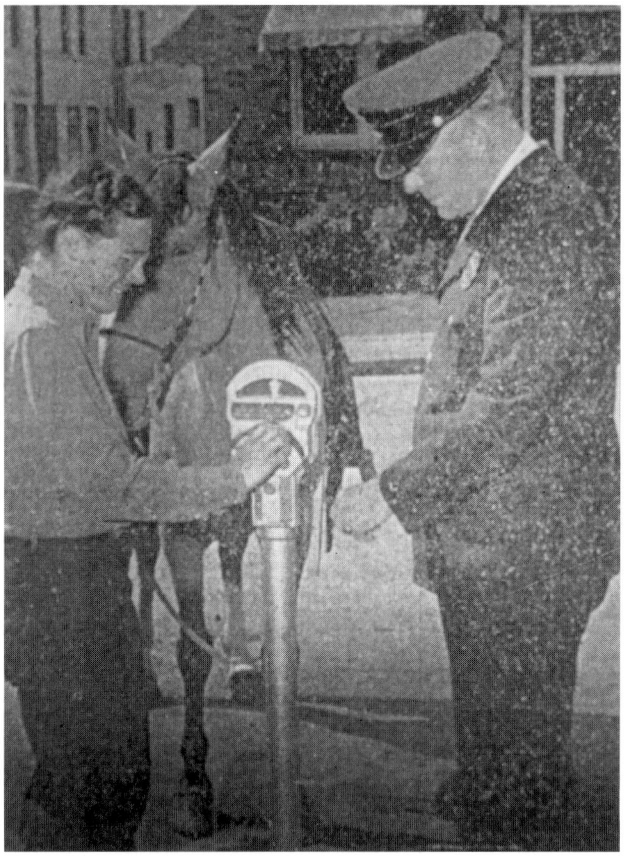

Gladys Christian inserting the first nickel in the new parking meters in Pullman, parking her horse, with the chief of police looking on. (*Pullman Herald* newspaper photo)

being the first girl to major in Animal Science at WSU. In 1995, Gladys Christian was honored as the Outstanding Alumnus of the WSU Department of Animal Sciences.

How It Used to Be

The following conditions in Animal Husbandry existed at WSC in 1941:

■ Professor Howard Hackedorn, head of Animal Husbandry, had passed away in the early summer of 1941.

■ In general, the livestock industry of the state was most critical and even bitter toward Washington State College.

■ The herds and flocks were very poor.

■ The hog herd had been infested with swine erysipelas for eight years. In the spring of 1941, an average of only four pigs per litter was raised (later, the herd average became eight pigs per litter). No animals could be sold for breeding purposes, and the purchasers of a boar pig in 1941 refused to pay for him because he was diseased and died soon after arrival on the farm.

■ The sheep were heavily infested with parasites. An autopsy of one ewe revealed an infestation of eight different kinds of parasites. Little or no sale existed for the rams.

■ With the exception of the Aberdeen-Angus herd, the cattle were greatly in need of improvement. Only one mediocre herd bull (a Shorthorn) was owned by the college. The herd bulls that had been borrowed were not too good.

■ The intercollegiate livestock judging team which competed at the Pacific International (in Portland, Oregon) had been at or near the bottom of the contest altogether too many years—lowering student morale.

■ The physical plant of the Animal Husbandry college farm—including buildings, fences, roads, etc.—was greatly run down.

■ The research program of the department was rather mediocre to say the least.

- The total annual research allocation for the entire Department of Animal Husbandry was $1,808. None of the investigations could be classified as creative research.
- No swine experiments were underway.
- Except for routine metabolism trials and the cooperative work with the USDA, no sheep experiments were being conducted.
- One pasture trial with steers (lacking somewhat in experimental design) was underway.
- No one from the department was reporting on any research work before the annual Chicago meetings of the American Society of Animal Production.
- Apparently no commercial grants for research had ever been secured.

■ There was little interest in graduate work, and only a very few students had ever taken work leading to a Masters degree in the department.

When I arrived on the campus in 1941, the road leading from Stadium Way to the beef cattle barn was appropriately known as "mud flat." When the Chinooks (warm winds) came, my daily trek to the beef cattle barn consisted of parking my 1937 Buick (which the students dubbed "the black hearse") on the side of Stadium Way, putting on my knee-high rubber boots, and wading through mud flat to, and from, the beef cattle barn. One day, an unsuspecting

A 1942 photo taken at the WSC College Farm. *Left to right:* Dick McWhorter, M. E. Ensminger, and John Burns. Dick McWhorter, a senior, wrote the gold medal essay in the nationwide Saddle and Sirloin Essay Contest in 1942. On weekends, John Burns, the beef cattle herdsman, and I built fences at the college farm.

high-ranking state official attempted to drive through mud flat. Only the bottom of his car saved him from complete extinction. The poor fellow had to be extricated by a team of the college farm Clydesdales. In the process, he remembered some of the choice words used by a teamster, which he incorporated in a letter to the WSC president. The next week, several loads of gravel were spread on mud flat.

But the mud problem wasn't limited to the road! Except when the ground was frozen, throughout the winter months the cattle in the corrals surrounding the beef cattle barn were mired belly deep. Additionally, corral fences were non-existent or in a bad state of repair. But I had two good hands and a strong back, and I knew how to pour concrete and build fences. Besides, my workweek started at 40 hours. So, John Burns, who was the beef cattle herdsman at the time, and I served as the construction and maintenance crew on weekends. We hard-surfaced corrals, and we built fences. It was a great challenge.

The winter weather in Pullman was typical. Some years there was nothing but rain. While we were there we had extremely heavy snow in 1950 and again in 1954. In 1950, we had over 80 inches!

John loved to play in the snow with Duke the Doberman Pinscher.

The 1937 Buick was buried in snow.

Our first dog, Duke, loved to stand on his house and look over the commanding view that he had.

We enjoyed getting together with family members whenever we could. But, in those days, young people did not have much money. My brother Garnet (Buck), who was in the feed division of Carnation, drove up from Burbank, California along with his wife, Theda, and son, Barry. The two boys (Barry and John) were just two years apart.

I Passed the Jidge Tippett Roundup Test

Soon after arriving on the WSC campus, Audrey and I received an invitation to the Jidge Tippett roundup. Prior to going, informed sources forewarned us as to what to expect in a traditional Tippett roundup.

The Tippett ranch was in the rugged Snake River country of Washington. Much of the ranch terrain was so rough that it could be reached only on horseback. Rumor had it that the IRS was never able to get a count on the number of cattle on both sides of the hills.

Each year, Jidge invited his neighbors and friends, along with new staff members in the WSC Animal Science Department, to participate in his roundup. It was a festive event. Further, I was forewarned that the particular delight of Jidge was to give his "roundup test" to a greenhorn. The test: ride a bronc that would likely buck him off, then castrate, dehorn, and brand several calves.

I soon discovered that the horse assigned to me fit the mold—he was a bucker. As I rode by Jidge's seven-year-old son, Doug, I asked: "Did your dad give me this horse so that I would get bucked off?" Doug grinned as he responded: "Yes." About that time, Lou Whitmore, a cattleman/neighbor of Jidge and an experienced cowboy, rode alongside me. Thereupon, I asked him: "How would you like to trade horses?" His response: "Let's do."

Ten minutes later, that bronc bucked Lou off and broke four of his ribs. I felt badly, but my fate would likely have been worse, because I was not in the saddle daily as was Lou Whitmore.

Once the cattle were in the corral, the castrating, dehorning, and branding of the calves followed. Soon Jidge gave me the second test: He handed me the knife. Fortunately, my father had taught me all these livestock basics. So, I passed this test to Jidge's satisfaction—and surprise.

Following the castrating, dehorning, and branding, Mrs. Tippett had a roundup dinner served on tablecloths spread on the range, along with strong coffee made from whole coffee beans, boiled in an iron kettle, on an open fire.

The Course Work in Animal Science Was Greatly Strengthened

In a letter dated November 16, 1944 to Alan Rogers, a prominent rancher from High Valley Ranch, Ellensburg, I reported as follows:

I am mounted on the bronc just before I traded horses with Lou Whitmore. The horse's ears are laid back—a signal of *anger.*

The teaching work in the Department of Animal Husbandry has been greatly strengthened, with new courses being offered. As an example of the effectiveness of a small part of our teaching program, WSC Animal Husbandry students have compiled the following record in the National Saddle and Sirloin Medal Essay Contest (a contest open to all undergraduates in the United States and Canada):

Year	Placing
1942	1st, 2nd, 6th, and 9th places
1943	2nd, 5th, 8th, 10th, 17th, 18th, and 19th—winner of the Silver Cup
1944	1st, 4th, 7th, 10th, 14th, and 19th

The Leonard Vanderhoop Story

I mentioned Leonard Vanderhoop in the chapter 1937–1940—The University of Massachusetts. Soon after I became Chairman of the Department of Animal Science at Washington State College (WSC) in 1941, I received a letter from Van seeking employment on my staff at WSC, stating that he had never been west of the Hudson River. I needed help for our expanding herds and flocks at the college farm; so, I told Van to come on, and that I would have a job for him.

When Van first came to WSC, he was single—and lonely. On Sunday afternoons, he would come knocking on the door of the Ensmingers' home, have a quiet visit with Audrey and me, eat a big stack of pancakes prepared by Audrey, then go on his way. The next Sunday, Van would return for much the same routine, with Audrey showing her slides if we had other visitors. One Sunday afternoon when showing her slides, somewhat apologetically Audrey said to Van: "Van, you have seen these slides before." Thereupon, Van, still a man of few words, replied, "four times."

Van was either employed or a student at WSC from 1941 to 1949. Then, from 1949 to 1957, he served as herdsman or manager of four different livestock operations in Washington and California.

In 1957, Van acquired his first McDonald's franchise for less than $1,000. Today, he owns nine McDonald's in the San Bernardino, California area.

I was very touched and pleased when, a number of years ago, Van made a special trip to Clovis, California, to see me one Sunday afternoon. While Audrey was scurrying about to prepare Sunday evening supper, Van, still a man of few words, sat on the divan in front of our fireplace. Finally, he spoke as follows:

This morning, the minister in the church that I attend handed out cards for the members of the congregation to write a thank you message to the person who had done the most for them throughout life. I said to myself, "Dr. E. I'll just drive up and tell him in person."

Other Notable Caretakers of the Herds and Flocks

Not long after I left the University of Massachusetts and went to Washington State College, Claude Koch, my great shepherd at the U of M, expressed interest in joining me at WSC as college shepherd. I lost no time in bringing this about. Along the way, I also had two very outstanding swine herdsmen; namely, S. A. Palmer and Arvid Neiberg. Arvid Neiberg emigrated from Lithuania, where he had been taken prisoner and branded during World War II.

Establishing the First College Meats Lab West of the Rockies

In the early 1940s, most of the nation's animal science departments focused their teaching, research, and extension programs on production. Meats as such were the province of meat packers, the National Livestock and Meat Board, and college home economics departments. But I established a modest meats laboratory in the WSC livestock arena, with slaughtering, processing, and refrigeration facilities; and we hired a midwestern meat specialist. We offered meats courses, and we did research work on beef, pork, and lamb carcasses. All went well until other western colleges heard about my starting a meats laboratory at WSC. I received a two-page letter from a prominent scientist telling me that I was being foolhardy and that there was absolutely no place for a meats laboratory on a college campus. But I wasn't deterred!

Approval to Offer a Ph.D. Degree

Following my preparation of endless documents and marathon college committee meetings, effective in 1942 the Department of Animal Husbandry was authorized by the faculty, the president, and the board of regents to offer the degree of Doctor of Philosophy. Thus, the State College of Washington became only one of ten institutions to offer such advanced training in the field of animal husbandry.

We Filled a Need, So the Facilities, Students, Research, and Dollars Followed Abundantly

Beginning with my arrival on the campus in 1941, improvement in both teaching and research was given high priority.

Teaching needed improvement in lectures, laboratories, facilities, and equipment. Student enrollment spiraled and we began attracting students from throughout the United States and abroad. By 1944, 23 percent of the students in the College of Agriculture were enrolled in the Animal Science Department.

Research in animal science was almost nonexistent at WSC in 1941. So, at the outset, I insisted that great teaching and great research could enhance each other. From 1941 to 1948, 54 research publications were issued by the Department of Animal Science. Hand-in-hand with increased research, staff members presented papers at scientific meetings, both in the United States and abroad.

Blueprint for the Future

At the outset (in 1941), it was obvious that it would be necessary that "we pull ourselves up by our own bootstraps" and that we improve our public relations. Our problem was to build a Department of Animal Science with a national reputation with a very modest allocation to do the job. To this end, I blueprinted a program designed to obtain eminence through excelling in three areas where we might become unique in comparison to the nation's other animal husbandry departments. Namely, through short courses, feeders' days, commodity days, shows, and judging schools; writings (books, feature articles, and a column); and gifts and grants from industry. Throughout their administrations, President E. O. Holland and Dean E. C. Johnson gave me excellent support and encouragement in building this program and the livestock industry was magnificent. As I look back, I would not have changed that blueprint in the least.

President E. O. Holland and Dean E. C. Johnson Remained My Friends and Ardent Supporters until Their Deaths

Dr. Holland retired from the presidency in 1944. In 1950, Dr. Holland was asked by the federal government to go to Austria as counselor on higher education to the military government in Vienna. A few days prior to his departure, he called me early one morning and asked if I might know of a friend who would give a sizable sum with which he could buy some rare old books while in Europe. I made a call to my good friend, W. E. Boeing, owner of Aldarra Farms (Hereford and Guernsey cattle, and Thoroughbred race horses) as well as Boeing Aircraft. I had the money two days later. Dr. Holland went happily on his dual mission of counseling the military government in Austria, and buying rare old books for the E. O. Holland Library at WSU. Although he reached Vienna, he became ill and was unable to complete his missions. He returned to a military hospital in Boston, where he passed away on May 30, 1950.

My last letter from Dr. Holland, written on February 20, 1950, three months before his death, is herewith reproduced. (In his letter, Dr. Holland refers to my letter of the 19th. This was my letter transmitting the money from Mr. Boeing and wishing Dr. Holland a pleasant journey.)

> Thank you for your letter of the 19th. I hope to see both of you before I leave Pullman. I am delighted to learn that you are now reviewing many pages of the page proof of your new book, *Animal Science*.
>
> Do not permit Mrs. Ensminger to do too much in the way of entertaining your friends. However, you should feel secure in the enormous support you have from the stockmen of the Pacific Northwest.

Likewise, Dean E. C. Johnson remained my friend long beyond his retirement.

The Historical Book Entitled E. O. Holland and the State College of Washington, 1916–1944

In this historical work, published in 1958, William M. Landeen, Professor Emeritus of History, State College of Washington, reported as follows on page 216:

> By early 1943, the situation was coming to a head. Department heads and staff members had been told so long to exercise the greatest economy in expenditures as to feel almost rebellious at another mention of the subject. From various statements coming to the president, we select

one to illustrate the point. The head of the department of animal husbandry wrote:

> "I am greatly grieved and depressed that during my nearly two years' stay at the State College of Washington, it has been necessary that I spend so much time wrestling with finances. Under the circumstances, it has been impossible for me to do the most effective work. Moreover, the operations of the Department are kept in a constant state of flux.
>
> "To me the answer is perfectly clear. The State College of Washington must maintain a Department of Animal Husbandry in keeping with the industry of the state which it serves, a state in which more than one-third of the income is derived from the sale of livestock and livestock products. Thus, the department must have, even in war years, the financial support that will ensure that it does not lose its momentum, or worse yet become hopelessly lost for the duration. Once a Department retrenches to a point where it is restrictive, once it has been denied the resources that have been its livelihood, it is injured. More important, the recovery process is long, slow and painful." (M. E. Ensminger to Dean Johnson, April 20, 1943.)
>
> To be sure, this communication dealt with the operations of but one department, but it exemplifies feelings that were general on the campus with reference to both operations and salaries.

The above statement was directed primarily to the governor and the state legislators. Both President E. O. Holland and Dean E. C. Johnson were in agreement with me. But without sufficient state appropriations to the college, they were helpless.

Dr. Wilson Compton, President of WSC from 1945–1951, who gave me great support.

The Wilson Compton Years of Growth, 1945–1951

Following World War II and the influx of veterans to college campuses, the time was ripe for the growth of all colleges, including Washington State College. At WSC, student enrollment was up, new buildings were on the drawing board, and the state and federal governments were loosening their purse strings. With the retirement of Dr. E. O. Holland, Dr. Wilson Compton was the right president for WSC at the right time. His stated goal was to transform the institution from a highly reputable (but poorly financed) college, to a well-financed, great university. Aware of the road blocks that would be strewn along the way when making such a great leap forward, at the outset of his administration Dr. Compton signed a letter of resignation, which he gave to the regents for their acceptance at their pleasure. Moreover, he predicted that resistance to change would barricade him within five years. (His projection was almost on target; he lasted six years.)

President Wilson Compton was one of three famous Compton brothers, all of whom became presidents of universities. (Dr. Karl was President of MIT; Dr. Arthur was President of Washington University, St. Louis [and a Nobel Prize winner in physics]; and Dr. Wilson Compton was President of WSC.)

Mrs. Helen Compton was a vivacious lady, with dancing brown eyes. She would host a tea at the president's home with only a moment's notice. Her idea of showing distinguished visitors the campus frequently involved a visit to the college farm.

During the Compton administration, I had great support from the president. Also, the livestock industry throughout the state was magnificent.

1946 Feeders' Day.

An Animal Science Advisory Committee

During the period 1934–1937, when I was serving as project manager in the development of the Dixon Springs Agricultural Center in Illinois, I learned that Professor H. P. Rusk, Chairman of the Animal Husbandry Department at the University of Illinois, had an advisory committee made up of the presidents of the statewide livestock organizations in Illinois. Further, I learned that he was very pleased with their assistance in two areas: as sounding boards for teaching, research, and extension programs in the department; and in obtaining the necessary public and private funds. So, I requested, and secured, administrative approval for a similar advisory committee for the WSC Animal Husbandry Department. They were a great help to me.

The Animal Husbandry Advisory Committee was made up of, among others, the presidents of the Washington Cattlemen's Association, Washington-Idaho Wheat Grower's League, Washington Wool Grower's Association, Washington Swine Breeder's Association, Inland Empire Shorthorn Breeder's Association, Northwest Hereford Breeder's Association, and Inland Empire Aberdeen-Angus Association. At the very first meeting of the advisory committee on February 5, 1945, they unanimously adopted the resolution which follows:

> Resolution to the Board of Regents, the President, the Dean of the College of Agriculture and the Head of the Department of Animal Husbandry of the State College of Washington.
>
> We, the representatives of the various livestock organizations in the state of Washington, do hereby unanimously adopt this resolution:
>
> I. We wish to express our sincere appreciation for the opportunity to become more familiar with the present and contemplated program in Animal Husbandry.
>
> II. We hereby commend the College for the recent and marked improvement in the Department of Animal Husbandry.
>
> III. We pledge our full support and active cooperation in bringing about continued and needed improvements in the Department of Animal Husbandry, and request that the following developments be given early consideration:
>
> 1. An enlargement of the herds and flocks at the college farm together with an improvement in the quality of same. This to include the ownership of outstanding sires.
> 2. The early construction of the following new and modern buildings which shall be designed and equipped to meet the needs of more sizable herds and flocks:
>   a. Sheep barn with provision of experimental lamb-feeding quarters.
>   b. Swine barn.
>   c. Steer feeding shed.
>   d. Houses at the College Farm for each of the three herdsmen.
>   e. Meats laboratory.
> 3. The purchase of a considerable acreage of additional land, making possible the practical handling of the enlarged herds and flocks.
> 4. A greatly enlarged research program designed to meet the many problems of the livestock industry of the state and embracing all classes of livestock, including cattle, sheep, and hogs.
> 5. The immediate enlargement of the teaching and research staff of two full-time men. It is recognized that the staff of most departments of the College has been greatly enlarged during the past two decades. We commend such expansion. However, no such growth in personnel has occurred in the Department of Animal Husbandry. Accordingly, it is urged that two additional qualified and competent staff members be added to that department without

delay, and that such other staff members as may be needed for the education of returning veterans be added as necessity demands.

IV. We request that the necessary annual appropriations be made available to the Department of Animal Husbandry in order that such an expanded program may be established on a sound basis and move forward uninterrupted.

V. We pledge our united and active cooperation to bringing about the above enumerated improvements in the Department of Animal Husbandry. To this end, we shall be glad to assist the College in getting the needed appropriations from the State Legislature.

Self-feeding cattle on pasture at WSC. Dr. Tony Cunha is on the left, Dr. Everett Warwick is on the right.

I Hired Stars on the Way Up

Because the salary scale at WSC at that time was low in comparison with other institutions, I had two choices when selecting new staff members: hire experienced staff members who had been mediocre (or worse) elsewhere, but who would be permanent because no one would want them; or hire young stars on the way up, realizing full well that they would secure higher salary offers and leave in a few years. With approval of the Compton administration to add two new full-time staff members, I elected the latter. So, I telephoned my good friend, Dr. Gus Bohstedt, University of Wisconsin, in whom I had great confidence. He reported that he had two outstanding young men who were completing Ph.D. degrees whom he could recommend without reservation; namely, E. J. Warwick in animal breeding, and T. J. Cunha in animal nutrition. I hired both of them. They made lasting contributions at WSC, but soon they had more remunerative offers. Dr. Warwick went to Purdue, and Dr. Cunha went to Florida.

Among the other stars on the way up whom I had the pleasure of having on the teaching-research staff at WSU were: Professor Richard Johnson, who became Head of Animal Husbandry at California Polytechnic State University; Charles Lindley, who became Dean at Mississippi State University; John Bohland, who became Dean at the University of Alberta, Edmonton; Gary Smith, who became Head of Animal Science at Texas A&M; and Walter Galgan, who became Acting Chairman of Animal Science when I left WSU.

Consultant for General Electric Company, Nucleonics Department (Atomic Energy Commission)

Now it can be told! It is generally known that the atom bomb was developed at Richland, Washington. But, among the best kept secrets was that an integral part of the development involved the effect of radiation on swine, sheep, and laboratory rats (using animals instead of people). Because of the animal studies, Dr. Parker, Dr. Kornberg, and other officials of GE/AEC, asked me to serve as a consultant, which I did for more than 20 years. Of course, the studies were highly classified, even to the point that they provided a big vault in my Pullman office for storage of documents. I, and I alone, was permitted to know the combination of the vault, which the FBI changed every six months. Not only that, the FBI wouldn't permit me to use such easily remembered combinations as birth dates, wedding anniversaries, or events on the campus. More restrictive yet, they wouldn't let me record the combination anywhere. So, the inevitable happened. One time, I forgot the combination. As a result, the GE/AEC expert locksmiths had to remove the vault from my office by hoisting it with a crane through a large upstairs window, then take it to Richland, Washington for opening. I was embarrassed to tears.

As the animal work increased, I suggested to the GE/AEC officials that the time had come when a full-time animal scientist should be stationed permanently in Richland, with me continuing on a part-time consultant basis. They agreed, and asked that I select the person, with interviews restricted as follows: "You may state the salary, and reveal that the person will be stationed at Richland, Washington—*nothing more*."

My choice for the position was Leo Bustad, a brilliant student who was just completing two degrees at WSC: a Masters Degree in my department, animal science; and a DVM degree in the College of Veterinary Medicine. Leo had also co-authored with me the animal health chapter in the first edition of my book *Animal Science*. I called Leo to my office and offered him the position in keeping with the restrictions that were given to me. I did add one further statement: "Leo, you will find the work challenging and interesting." Leo was interested, but he wanted to talk to Mrs. Bustad, as well he should. It was agreed that he would give me his decision the next day. The next morning, Leo reported to me as follows: "I have full confidence in you; so, I accept."

Dr. Leo Bustad, my longtime friend, who gave me the highest vote of confidence that I ever received.

This was the highest vote of confidence that I have ever had. Leo served with distinction with GE/AEC for 16 years, during two years of which he took leave and led his class, scholastically, in the Medical School at the University of Washington, Seattle. Subsequently, Dr. Bustad was in charge of the radiation laboratory at the University of California, Davis; then, Dean of the College of Veterinary Medicine, Washington State University. Leo's honors and accomplishments are legion: He founded the Delta Society (people need pets); and the new veterinary building at WSU is named after him.

In addition to Dr. Bustad's achievements, it is noteworthy that the working relationship between WSU and GE/AEC (and the latter's successor Battelle Northwest) gave both participants a new dimension. For example, before I left WSU, two graduate students conducted radiation experiments for their Ph.D. theses at GE/AEC, Richland; studies which could not have been done on the WSU campus.

We Regularly Had Get Togethers

Pullman was a very small town of 4,000 when we arrived in 1941 and 10,000 when we left in 1962. The size of the town seemed to parallel the number of students attending WSU. So when the students were there in the winter, the population doubled.

Even so, Pullman had no industry except the surrounding agricultural area; therefore, we had to make our own entertainment.

Audrey and I usually had a reception for all of the students in Animal Science at the beginning of the semester.

At Christmas, we tried to make sure that all animal science students who could not go home for Christmas dinner were invited to our place.

We had various parties, especially on New Year's eve, because there was no place to go in Pullman to celebrate. We planned a progressive dinner for the entire staff and grad students. We usually visited three different houses. Some of the other departments wished they could do the same thing, especially the graduate students, who were not usually invited to faculty events.

The William Edward Boeing Story

The Wright Brothers developed and flew the first airplane, but William E. Boeing envisioned its potential and pioneered in both airplane manufacture and commercial airlines. Because of Mr. Boeing's lifelong interest in farming and animals, I got to know him, along with the history of airplanes and air transport, as few people did.

The W. E. Boeing home at Aldarra Farms, near Fall City, Washington. Mr. Boeing founded Aldarra Farms in 1942.

About The Wright Brothers under Whom Mr. Boeing Took Flying Lessons

The first sustained flights ever accomplished by man in a powered flying machine were made by Orville and Wilbur Wright, December 17, 1903. The machine used on that historic day was invented and manufactured by the Wright Brothers. It weighed 750 pounds, had a 12-horsepower motor, and flew at a top speed of 40 miles per hour.

Early History of William E. Boeing

William E. Boeing was born in Michigan, October 1, 1881; schooled in Switzerland and at Yale, then moved to the state of Washington in 1903. His first business ventures in Washington were in timber.

In 1916, Mr. Boeing founded the Boeing Airplane Company (manufacturing); and in 1929, he founded United Air Lines (commercial flying). Along the way, Mr. Boeing took flying lessons under the Wright Brothers. In the early days, the sales of airplanes were few and far between. So, to keep the manufacturing company going, Mr. Boeing made furniture in one end of the factory.

In the 1930s, the federal "trustbusters" ruled that Mr. Boeing's ownership of both Boeing Airplane Company (manufacturing) and United Air Lines (commercial flying) constituted a monopoly. So, they decreed that he must divest himself of one of the companies. Thereupon, Mr. Boeing sold all of his stock in United Air Lines, but he was bitter until his death at what he considered to be an unjust ruling.

Founding of Aldarra Farms

In 1942, Mr. Boeing founded Aldarra Farms near Fall City, Washington, on which he and Mrs. Boeing built a beautiful home. On this farm, he developed outstanding herds of Hereford and Guernsey cattle. Also, he owned and raced Thoroughbred horses, which were stabled and handled by professional trainers at different locations across the country. Dutch Abbott, who had been a longtime and faithful employee in Mr. Boeing's timber interests, served as the first manager of Aldarra Farms; and he was succeeded by his son, Dave. Don R. Drew, who headed up the Seattle office, ably served as Mr. Boeing's chief executive. (The Don

Aldarra Farms barns. On this farm, Mr. Boeing had superior herds of Hereford and Guernsey cattle. As Chairman of the WSC Department of Animal Science, I served as Mr. Boeing's consultant without salary.

Drews, the Bob Hopes of Palm Springs and Hollywood, and the Jack O'Neals of Fresno [Fresno County rancher, after whom the O'Neal Dam was named] vacationed together.)

I Served as Mr. Boeing's Consultant at Aldarra Farms

Soon after establishing Aldarra Farms in 1942, Mr. Boeing contacted me, following which he sought my counsel and advice for the next 15 years. Because I looked upon assisting Mr. Boeing as part of my job as Chairman of the Animal Science Department at WSC, I didn't feel that it would be ethical for me, personally, to benefit from my association with him. So, I declined with grateful thanks Mr. Boeing's offers to pay me a consultant fee, to finance an eastern Washington wheat farm for me at the early part of World War II (which, due to wartime price for wheat, would have been free and clear in three years), and to finance the publication of my books. Also, throughout our 15-year association, he was "Mr. Boeing" to me, never "Bill" as he repeatedly requested.

The Taconite, Mr. Boeing's private yacht, which he anchored in Canadian waters.

The Mr. Boeing that I Knew

Few people were privileged to know the warm, friendly Mr. Boeing that I knew. He was rather distant to his employees and associates. Among my treasured remembrances of Mr. Boeing are the following.

Deputy Sheriff Bill Boeing, Jr.

Bill Boeing, Jr., Mr. Boeing's only child, talked the county sheriff into making him a deputy. So, he bought a motorcycle and roared throughout the county, proudly displaying his deputy sheriff's badge. Mr. Boeing confided in me that he feared that his son would be killed in a motorcycle accident, or shot by robbers. I calmed Mr. Boeing by reminding him that the genetics of Bill Jr. were good, and that the motorcycle/deputy sheriff stage would pass with the teenage stage.

The Taconite Ore and Taconite Yacht.

Taconite is a low grade iron ore. So, I was curious as to why Mr. Boeing named his private yacht after such a product. He told me that he, personally, had large holdings of taconite in north-central United States, and that someday science would evolve with a way in which to process taconite profitably. Mr. Boeing had great confidence in science. Subsequently, scientists did discover ways in which to process taconite profitably, and a multimillion dollar taconite plant was built in the heart of the taconite area.

Mr. Boeing kept his private yacht, the Taconite, anchored in Canadian waters. During World War II, he offered to lend the Taconite to the Canadian Government, for use in the war. They declined because of a law which made it illegal for them to accept gifts from private individuals, prompted by an earlier gift of a private island which they accepted, following which they were embarrassed by its use for smuggling purposes.

Thereupon, Mr. Boeing offered the use of the Taconite to the U.S. Government, and they accepted. But Mr. Boeing was greatly disappointed that the Taconite was merely used for luxury purposes by admirals; the Navy explained that it couldn't be used for other purposes because of its wooden hull.

Phil Johnson and His Daughter, Esther

Along the way, Mr. Boeing told me that Phil Johnson, President of Boeing Aircraft, wanted to meet me because his daughter, Esther, was very interested in animals. Before we had an opportunity to meet, Mr. Johnson suffered a heart attack and died. Esther—a petite, attractive, smart young lady—arrived on the WSC campus a few days later. She came into my office with a well-prepared schedule of 22 credit hours for the first semester. Upon my commenting about 22 credit hours being a much heavier than normal workload, Esther let me know that this was a closed subject. Said she:

> It is necessary that I be very busy in order not to relive a recent sadness.

I got the message! Esther was a top student and a great student leader. Following graduation, she married a Montana rancher and mothered a big family. For 50 years, Esther has kept in touch with her old Professor.

This was taken at WHR. I am on the left and Frank Ritchie, Yakima, WA, a good cattleman friend, is on the right.

Bull Buying With Mr. Boeing

In the 1940s, Wyoming Hereford Ranch (WHR), Cheyenne, Wyoming, owned by Quaker Oats Company and managed by Bob Lazear, was the top Hereford establishment in America. So, upon my recommendation, Mr. Boeing latched onto their linebreeding program, buying bulls and heifers in their annual sales.

At that time, Mr. Boeing always used a Boeing plane, fully equipped with the latest gadgets that technology could devise, piloted by two experts. But, Mr. Boeing was in command. I recall times when the weather was bad—there was either fog, a snowstorm, or low visibility—whereupon the pilots would remind Mr. Boeing that the plane was fully equipped to fly in such weather. Mr. Boeing would calmly remark: "Remember the careless pilots aren't living."

When buying Hereford bulls or females, usually Mr. Boeing would fly from Seattle, pick me up at the Pullman airport, then fly to our destination.

When we arrived, the first thing we did was to look over the bulls and heifers. In one of WHR's great sales, I selected a Hereford bull for which Mr. Boeing paid $50,000, following which he turned to me and said: Now select and buy a bull for the college; and I'll pay for it. The bull that I selected only cost $25,000!

Mr. Boeing also gave WSC Hilltop Stables two famous thoroughbred stallions, Porter's Mite and Piccolo.

WSC Conferred an Honorary Doctor of Laws Upon William Edward Boeing

I spearheaded the movement which culminated in WSC conferring the Doctor of Laws, *honoris causa*, upon Mr. Boeing on October 17, 1947. In the brochure that was printed for the occasion, the opening paragraph in President Wilson Compton's address of conferment tells it all—

> Few American names are more widely known over the world than the name "Boeing." Wherever there is aviation, the name of Boeing is known and honored.

They Never Forgot!

In the November, 1979, issue of *WSU Hilltopics*, Dave Abbott, who was WSU Alumni President at that time, and who succeeded his father as manager of Aldarra Farms, made the following statement, 17 years after my departure from WSU:

> Mr. Boeing frequently asked Dr. M. E. Ensminger, Chairman of Animal Science at WSC from 1941 to Mr. Boeing's death in 1956, for advice.

Mr. Boeing Bequeathed His Animal Library to Me

Mr. Boeing died September 28, 1956, at age 74. Before his passing, he told Mrs. Boeing that he wanted that I have his animal library. Many of the books are expensively leather-bound; and several of the volumes are collector's items. Thus, the library of

Conferring an Honorary Doctor of Laws degree upon Mr. Boeing on October 17, 1947. *Left to right:* Bill Boeing, Jr., Mr. W. E. Boeing, and Mrs. Bertha Boeing.

my longtime and dear friend, William Edward Boeing, now enhances the Agriservices Foundation conference room, and afterwards it will go to the Ensminger room at Iowa State University.

All About Horses

The WSC Hilltop Stables story, which started in 1945, and which is never ending after over 50 years, is presented contiguously for reasons of comprehension and readability.

Although WSC Hilltop Stables first took form with the purchase of the land in 1945, as I record this history over 50 years later it brought on a bad case of nostalgia, and tears filled my eyes as I lived again the trauma at the birth of WSC Hilltop Stables.

One horseman in Washington stood out! George Newell came to my office at WSC and introduced himself as an insurance broker from the Seattle area. He told how he had heard that Guernsey cattle breeders had an association, and that they had a field representative. So, he reasoned, the Thoroughbred breeders of Washington should organize and hire a field representative. Before Mr. Newell left my office, I blueprinted for him both the Washington Horse Breeders Association (WHBA) and WSC Hilltop Stables; and I recommended Ed Heinemann as their first field secretary. My longtime friend, Col. Bill Koester, general manager of the California Thoroughbred Breeders Association, and I participated in the first organizational meeting of the WHBA.

Later, Ed Heinemann and others revealed George Newell's characterization of me. George said:

> If I were stranded on a remote island and surrounded by a group of hungry cannibals, and if through sign language I received a message to the effect that I could have the help of just one person whose name I must write down, I would scribble out the name: Dr. M. E. Ensminger.

Yes, I was there! Not only did I serve as "nursemaid" at the birth of the Washington Horse Breeders Association, but I hand-picked and recommended

The new sheep barn at WSC in 1960.

Ed Heinemann as the first field secretary; and I had Ralph Vacca, Heinemann's successor, as a student.

But the formation of the Washington Thoroughbred Breeders Association was simple and easy compared to the agony of establishing a light horse facility and program at WSC. When I mentioned securing part of the gift funds from racing, I was told by the WSC agricultural administrators that "racing money is tainted money, and unacceptable." Besides, they didn't see any need for a light horse establishment at WSC.

Finally, I got the WSC agricultural administrators to agree not to *oppose* the project provided I made it clear to President Wilson Compton that they were not giving it their blessings; that I would acquire the land, facilities, horses, and future operational funds, entirely from gifts and grants, without one penny coming from WSC appropriated funds; and that they considered racing money "tainted" and unacceptable.

The next Sunday, President and Mrs. Wilson Compton and the Ensmingers were invited to a dinner by a Pullman area ranch family. The Comptons picked up the Ensmingers. En route to the ranch, I informed Dr. Compton of my desire to develop a light horse establishment, and I repeated, word for word, the three stipulations of the Deans and Directors—that they wouldn't oppose, but neither would they approve; that the entire facility, including future operation and maintenance, must come from gift funds; and that they considered racing money "tainted and unacceptable." The president not only approved, but he was enthusiastic. Also, he added "The only kind of tainted money that I know about is the kind 'tain't got." (I never enjoyed a Sunday dinner so much!)

The very next week, I had sufficient gift funds committed, so I bought the 54.9 acres on which to establish WSC Hilltop Stables. However, at this point, Guy Brislawn, WSC Business Officer, called me on the telephone and upbraided me for 20 minutes for buying the choicest housing area in Pullman—just for horses. He added: "You have done a great disservice to both the city of Pullman and Washington State College." After Guy Brislawn "ran down", I responded by saying: "You have made your views known. But I have already bought the land, and it is in escrow."

I kept the pledge! During my stay at WSC, the marvelous horsemen of Washington, Longacres Race Track, and the Washington Racing Commission provided every penny of the funds for WSC Hilltop Stables.

Ushering in WSC Hilltop Stables and a horse program was almost the *coup de grace* for me, but get this: The life of an innovator is never easy! My autumn leaves are more beautiful for having persisted and overcome. Details follow:

History of WSC Hilltop Stables as Recorded by Gene Stark, WSC Horse Specialist

Excerpts from a 49-page report, prepared by Gene Stark, WSC Horse Specialist, covering the *History of WSC Hilltop Stables* through 1958, follows.

The successful development of a plant, with the size, scope and objectives of WSC Hilltop Stables, can come about only through the guidance of a person, or persons, who can foresee a need and a place for such a program for future generations. This sort of guidance and planning must stem from a source, dedicated to serving an industry as well as the immediate institution. This diligent and untiring effort was, and still is, furnished by Dr. M. E. Ensminger, Chairman of the Department of Animal Science, State College of Washington, Pullman, Washington.

Dr. Ensminger accepted the post as Department Head in 1941, and since that time he has never ceased in his efforts to build a balanced and full-scale Department of Animal Science. During the ensuing years of World War II, Dr. Ensminger's dream of a light horse establishment and horse program, for the State College of Washington, began to take shape, and by 1945 this dream became transferred to paper, and actual planning began.

The early promotional campaign, by Dr. Ensminger, though beset by a countless number of reversals, soon "caught fire," and by 1946 his program merited the support of the Washington State Horse Racing Commission, the Washington Horse Breeders Association, and numerous horse enthusiasts in industry and agriculture. Through his efforts, Dr. Ensminger arranged for gifts and grants from the Racing Commission, with which the original 30-acre tract was purchased. Soon thereafter, he arranged for private gifts of two adjacent tracts of land, now known as Murray Meadows and Linden Meadows.

Fortunately, Dr. Wilson Compton, who was then President of the State College of Washington, was very receptive to the idea of founding a light horse establishment and most helpful in bringing it about.

A lasting tribute to Dr. Ensminger is assured by thousands of horse lovers throughout the Northwest and the entire nation, and, perhaps most of all, from the hundreds of us who have

Hilltop Stables were presented to Washington State College in a ceremony held in 1946. Among those present were *(left to right)* Joe Knott, A. E. Penney, Ed Heinemann, unidentified man, Dr. Harry Deegan, Morrie Alhadeff, Wayne Dinsmore, George Newell, Frank Brewster, Dr. Wilson Compton, Wayne Sutton, Oscar Levitch, Frank Granger, J. K. Macomber and Dr. M. E. Ensminger.

had the privilege to train under his guidance, in the light horse program and with the facilities provided by WSC Hilltop Stables.

WSC HILLTOP STABLES, THE PHYSICAL PLANT

WSC Hilltop Stables, which in its heyday was recognized as the finest light horse establishment at any college in America, was first blueprinted in 1945.

The original 20.12 acres, then known as Hilltop Stables, and formerly owned by Mr. Wyman Cox, were purchased from Mrs. Ruth Jeffers in June 1946, for the sum of $14,000. When the area became the property of the State College of Washington, the original name was retained, and the prefix WSC was added.

Dr. Ensminger, personally, took up the option on a 10.84-acre tract adjoining to the west of Hilltop Stables, November 11, 1946, with the purchase price fixed at $10,000. The money for the purchase of both of these first two tracts was provided by the Washington Horse Racing Commission.

Dr. Ensminger took options on the adjoining Hathaway and Bartram tract, and in August 1947, interested Mr. L. T. Murray, of Ellensburg and Tacoma, in donating $14,500 for the purchase of the Hathaway property. This new addition, consisting of 10.44 acres to the north of the original Hilltop Stables tract, was then named Murray Meadows. In November of 1948, Mr. Harry Linden, Spokane, Washington, donated $9,000 for the purchase of the Bartram tract, which is now known as Linden Meadows.

Buildings on the original 30-acre tract, at this time, consisted of a main barn with indoor ring, a stallion barn, a quarantine barn, a house, and garage.

During 1950, the isolation barn and the house on Murray Meadows were remodeled. The house provides quarters for the animal husbandry farm foreman and his family. The isolation barn was designated as "receiving quarters" for new animals being added to the college herd.

The box-stall barns, just north of the broodmare barn (known as the "main barn"), were constructed in 1951 by Wayne Moore, WSC farm foreman, and his crew.

The combination grandstand-stables was constructed in 1952 by Mr. Moore and crew. The grandstand seats 1,000–1,200 people. There are

WSC Hilltop Stables in its glory days. The main buildings left to right: stallion barn, grandstand and show-ring, and the main barn.

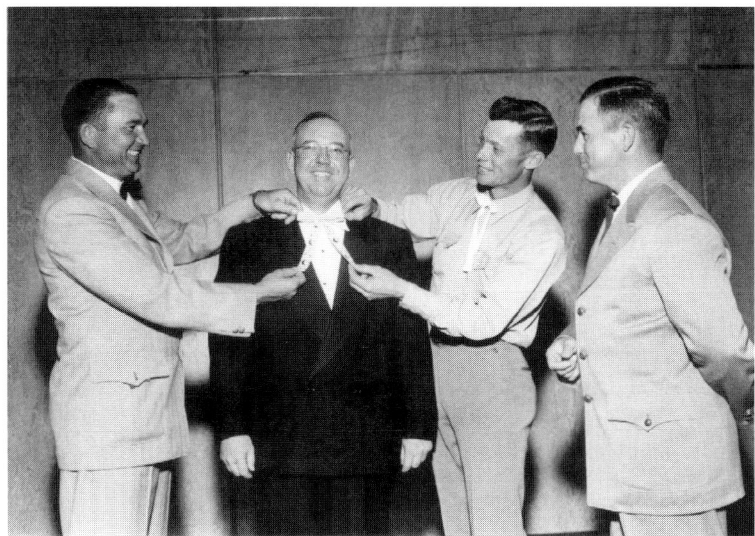

Under the able direction of Ed Heinemann, executive secretary, Washington Horse Breeders Association, Eli Patnode, Thoroughbred breeder (left) and Gene Stark (WSC Horseman, 3rd from the left), outfit Dr. E with a suitable bow tie during the 1954 WSC Horse Show and Judging School.

twelve roomy box stalls underneath the grandstand to accommodate extra horses and to provide isolation for visiting broodmares during the breeding season. There are also two washrooms located underneath the grandstand.

In addition to the buildings, WSC Hilltop Stables consists of a large showring, a smaller warm-up ring, four stallion paddocks, three small paddocks, and eight fenced pastures. Most of the fences are of sawed cedar posts, and bolted-on 2- by 6-in. panels.

Years of Building During the Compton Administration (1945–1951)

With the great support of President Wilson Compton and the horse industry of Washington, along with the quiescence of Knott, Buchanan, and Swenson, we built one of the nation's top light horse establishments and programs.

However, in 1956, the college took a six-acre parcel from Linden Meadows, for housing for married students. This tract was bought with gift funds provided by Harry Linden, an Arabian breeder, especially for WSC Hilltop Stables. The administration made no attempt to buy a like amount of land for horses at a greater distance from the campus. As a result, many potential donors lost faith in WSC. Even to this day, more than 40 years following the first pirating, WSU has never replaced the land which the donors provided for a horse establishment.

Charles Kyd, WSC Extension Livestock Specialist (left) and Eli Patnode, Thoroughbred breeder, get an honest start in a donkey race, a special event in the 1954 WSC Horse Show and Judging School.

I Cannot Fade Away from WSU Hilltop Stables

In 1987, in a memorandum dated March 19 (25 years after my leaving WSU) at the request of Washington legislators, horsemen, and WSU concerned staff, I prepared a memorandum, along with exhibits, giving pertinent background information relative to WSU Hilltop Stables. A copy of this memo follows.

> Paraphrasing General Douglas MacArthur, "Old professors never die—they just fade away." But, I haven't been able to fade away, even though I have been gone from Washington for 25 years. Perhaps this was inevitable because WSU, the livestock industry of Washington, and I became part of each other during the 21 years that I served as Chairman of the Animal Science Department (1941 to 1962). Anyway, the horsemen of Washington and the concerned staff at

WSU have shared with me their recent problems in retaining the horse program at WSU; and they have asked for my suggestions and help.

Even though I am miles away, my heart will always remain in Washington. Nothing would please me more than to be of assistance to all of you. My comments and suggestions follow.

History of WSU Hilltop Stables

You will be interested in the early history of WSU Hilltop Stables. This was recorded by Gene Stark, WSU Horse Specialist, pertinent parts of which are herewith reproduced in Exhibit A. **Note well:** *Exhibit A* covers the history through 1958 only. Subsequently, the program grew and grew; for example, more than 600 horses were entered in the 1962 horse show.

On March 18, 1987, Dean J. L. Ozbun telephoned the *Exhibit B* report to me, in answer to my request. **Note well:** A total of 54.9 acres were initially acquired. Currently, approximately 25.84 acres are available for horses and approximately 29.06 acres are being used for college housing.

The Value of Equines to our Best Products—Our Boys and Girls

During these troubled times, the human values to accrue from an equine program at WSU merit emphasis.

Through association with their good equine friends and stout companions, boys and girls develop courage, work habits, care habits, judgment, rhythm, balance, and grace—all very important traits for a successful and satisfying life.

Let me cite one actual story: A judge in Connecticut was hearing protests of those who wanted to zone horses out of a suburb area, on the basis that horses made for flies, dust, and odors. After hearing, over and over, the reasons for zoning horses out, finally the judge remarked as follows:

You folks have convinced me that horses do make for flies, dust, and odors. But, let me remind you that I have never had in this court a juvenile delinquent that owned a horse, because caring for horses occupies the time of youngsters, and gives them an animated object on which to shower their love and affection.

As the above sank in, the protesters filed out much like the musicians in Haydn's Farewell Symphony, in the finale of which they blew out the candles and stole out one-by-one.

Keep Faith with Your Donors

Even though I raised the money and purchased the land without any strings attached, a college, or any other charitable organization, will lose if they do not keep faith with the donors. The donors of WSU Hilltop Stables had reason to expect that they were perpetuating a light horse program for posterity. May I add that one of the Trustees of Agriservices Foundation, which I direct, has given liberally to the educational institutions of Texas, where he resides. But he always attaches the following stipulation:

Should there come a time when the donee does not use the gift for the intended purpose, it will revert to the donor.

Our Land Grant Colleges Are the Envy of the World

Since leaving WSU in 1962, I have worked in 69 countries of the world. Our Land Grant Colleges—with their teaching, research, and extension—are the envy of the world. We should count our blessings, and provide adequate financial support for these institutions.

The Solution

I have the highest esteem for President Samuel H. Smith and Dean J. L. Ozbun of Washington State University. They are providing able and enlightened leadership for WSU, but they need funds.

It is my understanding that you are giving consideration to providing *new money* from the state legislature for the WSU equine program as follows:

1. $50,000 for the current year of 1987.
2. $150,000 per year annually beginning in 1988.

The above seem to be very reasonable and modest figures. I feel very strongly that these funds should be administered by the Dean of the WSU College of Agriculture and Home Economics, and in the Department of Animal Sciences; in the same organizational pattern as equine programs in other Land Grant Colleges from coast-to-coast. That's where the equine program was initiated at WSU, and that's where it belongs.

Should the land that was initially acquired for WSU Hilltop Stables ever be sold, I suggest that the funds obtained therefrom be ear-marked for the WSU equine program with the interest on the principal used therefor. Likewise, on land that was initially purchased for WSU Hilltop Stables but presently used for other purposes, I suggest that a sum representing the *current appraised value* of that land be established as an equine fund, with the accrued interest on the principal used to perpetuate the horse program.

Again and again, I emphasize that the above suggestions are submitted in a helpful spirit.

The WSC "Student Flood Relief" Story

On February 26, 1948, a flash flood broke through the dikes of Pullman, Washington, inundating or damaging most of the 130 trailer homes occupied by the 304 GIs and their families.

After spending an average of two to five years in the service of their country, these GIs were eager for an education. To them, the fact that they were married and there were no houses in Pullman was merely another obstacle, but their recent experiences had taught them how to overcome. They bought, borrowed or rented trailers and brought them in—many of them on borrowed wheels. They were dead earnest in their desire to learn, and they were good students. Many of them had families, and the visit of the stork to "Trailer City" was a frequent occurrence. In fact, proud parents with twin babies only a few days old at the time of the flood occupied one of the trailers.

Everything went along fine until the rains descended and the floods came. Finally, at five o'clock in the morning of February 26th, 1948, the pressure from the raging Palouse River was too great. Improvised dikes made of mud and sandbags could no longer hold the waters back. The evacuation of Trailer City was orderly but hasty. There were no casualties. Most of the GIs and their families merely took out the clothes that they had on their backs, and some of these were ruined in the rescue work which followed. In the more fortunate cases, the water and silt merely covered the trailer floor. But others were more tragic. Some trailers were torn from their bases. Still others were upset, and all the material possessions of the owners were lost. In total value, in terms of dollars and cents, the loss may not have been great, but it was all they had—clothes, radios, guns, books, diapers, canned foods, dishes, and cooking utensils.

True to tradition, the Red Cross arrived; and it did a marvelous job. But more help was needed.

Historically, stockmen have always taken care of their neighbors in distress. So, they were merely running true to form when, at the time of the March cattle sales in Spokane, Washington, I mobilized them to contribute to a *WSC Student Relief Fund*. Lindsey Staley, Staley Hereford Ranch, led the way by very generously offering to contribute the sale receipts from one of his choice Hereford heifers. Two Angus breeders—Oxbow Ranch, Prairie City, Oregon; and Lawrence Mellergard, Ellensburg, Washington—followed suit and contributed the receipts from the sale of heifers.

But many other stockmen insisted that they be given an opportunity to participate in this humanitarian need. Thus, prior to selling the heifers in each of the auctions, Col. H. B. Sager, the auctioneer, along with the ring men, took voluntary contributions from any who desired to assist in the cause. From the sale of the three gift heifers plus voluntary contributions, along with donations following the sale, nearly $5,000 was raised for the WSC Student Relief Fund.

On March 9, 1948, I sent a news release to the livestock magazines, telling about the WSC Student Relief Fund, and listing the donors. On that same date, I sent the money, along with a complete list of donors and the amount contributed by each one, to President Wilson Compton. Further, I made the following two suggestions to President Compton: that he write a letter of appreciation to each of the donors, and that a committee be appointed for the distribution of the flood relief funds, with Lindsey Staley, Hereford breeder, a member of this committee.

Brochure Entitled WSC Animal Husbandry Herds and Flocks

In 1948, we published a 38-page illustrated booklet, proudly extolling our herds and flocks. Pertinent excerpts and information from this brochure follow:

> Animal agriculture is essential to a well-nourished and happy people. If we could look in the family refrigerator, we would find a lot of animals represented—beef and dairy cattle, pigs, sheep, and poultry. Behind the livestock, we would see vast expanses of pasture and range land, feed grains, and such by-product feeds as cull peas, pea straw, meat meal, beet by-products, and cull potatoes—all being utilized as animal feeds. Back of the feeds are the soil resources, spring rains, and the energy of the sun. With calloused hands, the farmer and rancher combine these to produce a tasty platter of meat for the table, cream for the peaches, butter for the biscuits, cheese for the macaroni, and lightness for the cake—all derived from the land via animals. But back of present-day successful animal production has gone the modern agricultural training of the youth of America and years of scientific research—investigations in animal breeding, feeding, physiology, disease and parasite control, management, and the improvement of the quality of meat, milk, and eggs—studies which have extended from the farms and ranches to the nation's kitchens.

Among the animals pictured in the brochure were:

- *Eileenmere 701*, an Angus bull which I selected from the J. Garret Tolan herd, Pleasant Plains, Illinois, and for which I paid $3,500. The first two calves of his get repaid the purchase price.
- *Killearn Norseman 73rd*, a Shorthorn bull that I purchased at the Claude Gallinger sale on May 4, 1948, for $4,500.
- *WHR Regality 1st*, purchased by W. E. Boeing, Aldarra Farms, Seattle, Washington, for $20,000 from Wyoming Hereford Ranch, Cheyenne, Wyoming.
- *Renk's Beau Geste*, first prize Hampshire ram lamb at the 1946 International Livestock Exposition, Chicago, purchased from William F. Renk and Sons.
- *A Chester White barrow*, Grand Champion over all breeds at the 1947 Grand National Livestock Exposition, San Francisco.
- *A Chester White barrow*, Grand Champion over all breeds at the 1948 Pacific International Livestock Exposition, Portland.
- The thoroughbred stallions, *Porter's Mite* (holder of the world's record for 6½ furlongs) and *Piccolo* (twice victorious over the mighty Seabiscuit), gifts to WSU Hilltop Stables from Mr. W. E. Boeing.
- *Muallim*, an Arabian stallion, on loan to WSU from the U.S. Department of Agriculture.
- *Pictures of experimental animals:* riboflavin deficient swine, a vitamin A deficient lamb, and experimental steers.

Administrative Request that I Delete the Animal Health Chapters from All of My Books

In 1949, prior to the publication of my first book, some members of the administration called me to Director Knott's office, and requested that I delete from the manuscripts of my books all the chapters on "Animal Health, Disease Prevention, and Parasite Control." I declined on the basis that an author should determine what he writes in his own books; and that such matters are not properly a college decision. Subsequently, the *Journal of the American Veterinary Medical Association* accorded wonderful reviews of my books. So, beginning with the first editions, each of my livestock books has carried an important chapter on animal health, disease prevention, and parasite control, which has been beneficial to students, stockmen, veterinarians, and others interested in animal health.

I Enjoyed the Contacts with the Livestock Producers of the State

Neal Tourtelotte was a successful businessman. His hobby was a swine operation. He and his wife, Janet, were dear friends, so when he asked me to help him conduct a field day at his farm, I was pleased to do so.

I was interviewed by the press at Neal Tourtelotte's swine field day.

Left to right: Janet Tourtelotte, Audrey, and Neal serving a barbecue lunch at his swine field day.

The Stockmen Camped on the Capitol Steps

During my 21 years as Chairman of Animal Science, WSU had great public support from the livestock industry of Washington. On one occasion when addressing the faculty, President Compton alluded to this support as follows:

> When I need help in the State Legislature, all I have to do is to tell Dr. Ensminger, and the stockmen of Washington will be camping on the capitol steps the next morning.

The great support from the stockmen of Washington came as a result of my serving them. In 1942, when custom cattle feeding was practically unheard of in Washington (and even nationally) Alan Rogers, a prominent Washington rancher, telephoned me one Friday, saying that he had an opportunity to secure a lucrative contract for custom feeding a large number of cattle for one of the national meat packers. So, he needed a sample contract. When I asked "how soon," he responded "next Monday." I stayed up all night Friday night, and worked through that weekend, sending Western Union telegrams and making telephone calls throughout the United States. On Monday, I delivered a proposed custom cattle feeding contract to Alan Rogers, which both he and the meat packer signed. The rest of the story: Later, Alan Rogers became a regent of Washington State University.

Salary of Janet Martson

In 1951, following his resignation as President of WSC, Dr. Compton, with whom I had a most pleasant relationship, shared with me some of his best kept secrets; among them, the following:

Janet Martson, my longtime head secretary (for 12 years) was recognized as one of the very best on the campus. Also, she was dedicated; for example, without telling me, she would rent a typewriter and take it to her home over the weekend when she felt that it was important to speed certain work on its way. So, each year, I recommended a well-merited salary increase for Janet Martson, which was approved. As a result, she became the highest paid secretary in the WSC College of Agriculture. The rest of the story as told to me by President Wilson Compton after his resignation follows:

> In one of my sessions with some of the administrators, they were unhappy. "Why are you allowing Ensminger to pay his head secretary the highest salary of any head secretary in the College of Agriculture, including the director's office?" To this, I (Compton) replied: "If, and when, any of you do as much good for WSC as Dr. Ensminger, I shall approve a comparable salary for your head secretaries." Then, Dr. Compton added, "That shut them up. They never again raised that question."

Unfortunately, Janet developed multiple sclerosis and spent about 30 years unable to walk. I kept in touch with her all that time, and from time to time sent her various things. Her attitude was always upbeat. When she died in 1997, the family asked me to conduct the service. Trustee Norm Purviance and I flew to Spokane to do as they wished. Shortly thereafter, her daughter, Pattie, along with her husband Garry Collins, flew down to visit us and thank us for the kindness. We only wished we could have done more.

Garry and Pattie Collins came to Agriservices headquarters for a visit. Pattie is a daughter of my longtime, great, and faithful secretary, Janet Martson. This shows the group at Harris Ranch Restaurant. *Left to right:* Norman Purviance, Pattie Collins, Garry Collins, Marilyn Purviance, and Audrey. Dr. E is seated.

In 1952, We Were Number One In Both Teaching and Research

1952, the WSC agricultural administrators asked that Dr. Knoblaugh, U.S. Department of Agriculture, give an independent ranking in each teaching and research of all departments in the College of Agriculture. *The WSC Department of Animal Science ranked No. 1 in both teaching and research.*

This was the one and only time that such a ranking was ever made at WSC during the 21 years that I served as Chairman of Animal Science.

Johne's Disease In WSC Beef Cattle

In the spring of 1952, Dr. Frank Bracken, DVM, the college veterinarian assigned to the health of the Animal Science herds and flocks, reported to me that tests showed an infection of Johne's disease in our beef cattle herd. At that time, little was known about this disease. So, I scurried to my animal disease reference library, from which I learned the following facts about it:

> This is a chronic, incurable, infectious disease seen chiefly in cattle. The disease is very widespread, having been observed in practically every country where cattle are raised on a large scale. It is one of the most difficult diseases to eradicate from a herd.
>
> The disease seems to involve exposure with no evidence of infection for 6 to 18 months. At the end of this time, the animal loses flesh and displays intermittent diarrhea and constipation, the former becoming more prevalent. Affected animals may retain a good appetite and normal temperature. The feces are watery but contain no blood and have a normal odor. The disease is almost always fatal, but with the animal living from a month to two years.
>
> The disease is caused by the ingestion of a bacterium, *Mycobacterium paratuberculosis*. Inasmuch as this organism is acid-fast (that is, it retains certain dyes during a staining procedure), it resembles tuberculosis.
>
> Effective prevention is accomplished by keeping the herd away from infected animals. If it is necessary to introduce new animals into a herd, they should be purchased from reputable breeders; and the owner should be questioned regarding the history of his herd.
>
> It must be borne in mind that apparently healthy animals can spread the disease. Testing at regular intervals of 3 to 6 months with "Johnin," removing reactors, disinfecting quarters, and removing newborn animals from their dams immediately after birth, without allowing them to nurse, and raising them away from mature animals should be practiced in infected herds. In using the Johnin test, however, it should be realized that it is not entirely accurate as a diagnostic agent. Some affected animals fail to react to the test.
>
> No satisfactory treatment for Johne's disease has been found.

Throughout the next year, Dave Foster, our dedicated beef cattle herdsman, along with his student assistants, caught all calves at birth in the cradle of their arms, without letting them touch the bedding in the maternity stall, and fed them previously collected and stored colostrum along with a milk replacer. At the end of one year, the concerned staff of the WSC College of Veterinary Medicine declared the beef cattle herd Johne's free.

My Family

During the Compton years, our two children were born, John Jacob on July 11, 1946; and Janet Aileen on June 28, 1949

Because of my heavy workload and travels, I felt that I neglected my family. However, Audrey understood the pressures that were thrust upon me and never wavered in her support.

One of Audrey's favorite stories gives evidence that John saw little of me. One time, when John was age two, Audrey and John were at the Pullman airport awaiting my arrival. Soon, John was roaming around the airport calling every man "Daddy." Nevertheless, Audrey and I loved our John, on whom we doted without spoiling.

Additionally, John had two nearby playmates, David Manus and Jeannie Stumbo. One Saturday, when John was age 7, he had a friend as his guest for lunch. The conversation between them was about what they were going to be when they grew up. When John's turn came, he said, "I want to be short and fat, and have an ulcer just like my dad."

That's ambition!

Pullman was a great place to raise a child. At the age of seven, John fed a lamb to show in the local fair. He did a good job, but didn't win a ribbon. He

November, 1946. John Jacob at 6 months of age being held by his mother. I am holding onto the collar of our Doberman, Duke.

John feeding his lamb to show at the fair.

spent more time hugging the lamb than he did showing it.

As he grew up, we realized that John was a very good student. He graduated from Clovis High School fourth in his class, as a member of the California Scholarship Federation. He was accepted to, and graduated from, the University of California, Berkeley. After a year on a scholarship at the University of British Columbia, he went on to Hastings Law School. He had some unique experiences along the way, but he ended up working in the publishing of law journals. He inherited the love of writing from me.

I always had a large garden for vegetables, bordered by beautiful iris. One year, I obtained some manure that had become a nuisance at the college. It was spread on the vegetable garden and plowed under. The next year, the garden produced giant-sized vegetables like this potato, which weighed 4 lb and 5 oz.

One year we hired John to weed the vegetable garden. He would do two rows, then sit with his arms around his two cocker spaniels—Sandy on one side and Blackie on the other.

John Liked the Sugar at the Student Union Building

John and his friend, David, frequented the Student Union Building until we learned that they liked the packets of free sugar in the coffee shop. Thereupon, Audrey explained that the sugar was for paying customers to use in their coffee.

John Liked to Browse through the Books at the Student Book Store

John loved books. But, to our chagrin, we learned that he was going to the student bookstore for the purpose of reading through all of their interesting books. Thereupon, Audrey thanked the lady in charge of the books for her understanding and explained to John that the bookstore books were for sale, and not a reading library. Subsequently, when Audrey would run into the bookstore lady at some social event, she would say that she helped raise John.

John Liked to Dig through the Garbage

One day, John and his little friend David were heads down and feet up in the dumpster at the Student Union Building. A campus police officer happened along and asked them what they were doing. They proudly held up some of the treasures that they had found—old notebooks, old briefcases, and other similar items discarded by students. Instead of reprimanding them, the smart police officer diverted their attention. He wrote an automobile license number on a piece of paper and told John and David to be on the lookout for a car with that particular license number. Then, he asked the boys where they lived, and took them home in his "paddy wagon." Imagine Audrey's concern to see them arrive in a police car!

John Loved His Pets

He had a parakeet, which he named Billy Bird. When Billy Bird was 6 years old, he died, and I conducted a first class funeral, with John crying his heart out.

Sandy and Blackie, both Cocker Spaniels, were John's favorite dogs. In my book, *The Complete Book of Dogs*, my eulogy to Sandy is headed "Our Sandy Is Gone," and my eulogy to Blackie is headed, "My Next Reincarnation." Both eulogies follow.

Our "Sandy" is Gone

Out of consideration, the sad news had been withheld from Mrs. Ensminger and our twelve-year-old son, John. Johnny and Sandy had grown up together; they had been pals for ten years. When I arrived at my office, a telephone call awaited me; the word—Sandy was dead. After I collected myself, I proceeded with the difficult and unpleasant task of informing the rest of the family, personally. All of us wept bitterly.

It wasn't as if Sandy had lived to a ripe old age and died of natural causes; he had been run over by a car. We had always feared this sort of thing because Sandy—gentleman that he was—never realized that anything would ever harm him; he trusted people and machines implicitly. But at least there was the consolation that it wasn't a hit-and-run affair. The lady had not left him at the side of the road; instead, she wrapped the body in a blanket, placed it in her car, and delivered it to our home. She was kind and apologetic. Instead of bitterness, I felt sorry for her. But I choked up and couldn't speak. I managed, or hoped I did, a faint "thank you—I understand."

Then I gently gathered Sandy's cold body in my arms and walked to our garden. Under a beautiful tree, which will ever be his living monument, we buried Sandy. A friend offered to help, but the assignment was much too sentimental to entrust to others; it was a family affair. In the quiet of the evening, by the light of the moon, we dug a grave of adequate size and depth. John made sure that Sandy would be comfortable therein—that he was in a restfullike sleeping position. As I closed the grave, Mrs. Ensminger and John walked slowly to the house, arms around each other and weeping. The job was completed; unashamedly, I removed my hat, bowed my head, and said a little prayer:

"Oh Lord, I hope that I may be as good a man as Sandy was a dog; he was quiet, patient, considerate, loyal, and a gentleman in the canine world. And, Lord, if there be a dog heaven, may it have a garden with carrots in it, for Sandy loved to dig and eat them. Also, may Sandy be watched over by angels that love animals. Amen."

Our son, John Jacob, born in 1946, loved his pets. Here he is shown with his two Cocker Spaniels, Sandy and Blackie.

My Next Reincarnation

He was one of the most unforgettable characters I've ever known. In love, he could outdo Mark Anthony; in climbing, he could put *Jack and the Beanstalk* to shame; and in pirating, he could make Long John Silver look like a rank amateur.

His love affairs were frequent and ardent—but all quite proper for him. To be near the one being wooed, he would forego sleep and food for days at a time; once he was gone so long that the local police listed him as a "missing person." As an escape artist, he used a high fence for his ladder. He borrowed carrots (he didn't steal them; he just wasn't particular about whose garden they came from); he dug them himself, and then dined on them in a spot of his liking.

When old age crept upon him and infirmity struck, he met it with dignity and courage befitting his breeding and station in life. He lived in a specially built, insulated house, surrounded by his own private patio and garden of violets; he relished eggnogs, provided they were spoon-fed; and he loved to be held. He didn't want to die; and understandably so, for he was in heaven already. But the end finally came to Blackie, our dog, as it must come to each of us.

If there be such a thing as reincarnation—Oh! Lord—I hope that I may return to earth as Blackie. And, Lord, if this should come to pass, please restrain me lest I should bite a few select people.

Life's Darkest Hour

In July of 1949, Audrey and I endured life's darkest hour.

Our Janet Aileen, born June 28, 1949, died five days later, without my getting to hold and love her. Audrey was both bereaved and ill. So, I alone arranged, and was present for, a private Christian graveside service and burial in the Pullman, Washington cemetery. A dozen red roses were there, which I was told had been arranged by Helen Compton, wife of the WSC president. In 1984, Audrey and I designed and constructed a large and attractive Italian marble memorial fountain at the Peoples Church, Fresno, California, where we are members.

Audrey and I were pleased to have our son John, and his wife Jane, accompany us to China from June 18 to July 11, 1984. Upon our return to the United States, John and Jane stayed for the dedication of the fountain.

Left to right: John Jacob Ensminger, Jane Ensminger (wife of John), Dr. E, Audrey, and Pastor G. L. Johnson, at the dedication of the fountain at the People's Church on Sunday, July 15, 1984.

Beautiful memorial fountain in memory of Janet Aileen Ensminger at the Peoples Church, Fresno. Note the three angels and the jets in the fountain.

The beautiful Italian marble fountain, with three jets, was designed by Audrey and constructed under my supervision. We wrote, and had engraved on a metal marker, the following memorial statement:

In Memory of
Janet Aileen Ensminger
and all the other little
angels who live in the hearts of
those they left behind.
Dr. and Mrs. M. E. Ensminger

The French Years

During the years 1952–1962, Dr. C. Clement French became president, Dr. Joe Knott, followed by Dr. Louis Madsen, were Deans of Agriculture, Dr. Mark Buchanan and Dr. Stan Swenson were assistant deans.

Dr. C. Clement French

The accomplishments in the Department of Animal Science that are chronicled in this chapter did not come from my ability alone. It

Dr. Mark Buchanan

was a team effort. I had many hard-working and loyal staff members, including secretaries, herdsmen, and professors.

But there were some interesting times!

The Bing Crosby Story

Bing Crosby was my friend. In 1952, he graduated from the International Stockmen's School that I conducted at Washington State College. I had his twin sons, Phil and Dennis, as students in 1954; and Phil returned in 1957. The story of the Bing Crosby that I knew follows.

Harry Lillis "Bing" Crosby 1904–1977

Harry Lillis Crosby was born May 2, 1904, in Tacoma, Washington. He grew up in Spokane; and he attended Gonzaga University. The Crosby Library on the Gonzaga campus is named after him. He starred in many movies, including "Going My Way," playing the inspirational Father O'Malley, for which he won the Oscar for Best Actor in 1944. He also starred in "White Christmas" and "Bells of St. Mary's." In addition to his fabulous movies and melodious voice, Bing Crosby is remembered for his golfing and for his bantering with Bob Hope.

Some of Bing's philosophy which was reported in the *National Enquirer*, October 18, 1977, and which I heard him express, follows: "I would break off relationships with my children completely if they decided to live with someone before getting married," he said, making no bones about his disapproval of such loose lifestyles. His reasons: "Premarital sex destroys the concept of the family. I think a family concept is very important—a good solid family means a good community, and a good community means a good nation."

Commenting on the role that television plays in influencing people, Bing continued: "There is a dangerous element creeping into TV today. It's starting to get a little bawdy, risque, and salacious, and that should be restricted."

Bing as an Enrollee in the International Ag-Tech School

Bing Crosby was an enrollee in the 1952 International Stockmen's School which I conducted annually at WSC. At that time, he owned a large cattle ranch near Elko, Nevada. Bing attended classes just like all the other enrollees in the School. He showed a preference for the front row, and he made notes of the lectures in his clip notebook. Bing was distinct and different from most of the other enrollees because of his piercing blue eyes, being very photogenic, his ever-present pipe, and never being caught without his toupee or hat on when a picture was being taken.

Phil and Dennis Crosby as Students at WSC

Bing Crosby and Dixie Lee Crosby, Bing's first wife, had four sons—Gary, Phillip, Dennis, and Lindsay. In 1948, Dixie discovered that she had cancer. She died in 1952.

In 1954–1955, I had Phil and Dennis Crosby as students majoring in animal science at WSC. When they enrolled, Bing gave me a phone number which would reach him quickly, day or night, "without going through the palace guard," as he put it. Further, he requested that I call him if Phil and Dennis got into trouble, or in case of emergency.

Because their name was Crosby instead of Smith, they were constantly in the limelight, even when the fender on their car was merely scratched. Perhaps the most difficult task that Bing and I tried to overcome (without too much success) was getting them to an 8 o'clock class. Bing felt that their sleeping-in habit stemmed from the Catholic boarding schools that they attended, where they were herded throughout their scheduled day; beginning with a wake-up call, a buzzer to start and end each class, meal times by the bell, and a curfew at night. In an effort to overcome their sleeping in, Mrs. Ensminger telephoned a wake-up call to them each morning.

One Saturday morning, Phil called Mrs. Ensminger and asked if she would chaperone their Sunday dinner at the fraternity, as they were having unexpected female guests for dinner, and their

The Crosbys snowballing on the WSC campus in the winter of 1954-1955. *Left to right:* Phillip, Bing, Lindsay, and Dennis. Phil and Denny were my students in animal science.

house mother was away. She accepted, for which Phil was most grateful.

One Saturday, I scheduled a field trip for my horse science class to the famed Harry Linden Arabian Horse Farm, with the caravan of cars to assemble in front of the animal science offices for departure promptly at 7:30 a.m. All 40 students were present and ready to go except Dennis. So, I led the caravan up by the fraternity house to pick up Dennis. The student who responded to my ringing the doorbell reported that Dennis was sleeping-in on the top floor dorm. So, I asked him to wake him up and tell him that Dr. Ensminger wanted to see him right away. Within a few minutes, Dennis appeared in his robe and met me in the parlor. I asked him to dress promptly and join the rest of the students. Initially, he refused to do so. In my no-nonsense, mule-skinner voice, I said: "Dennis you will go; so get dressed, and come quickly." Dennis sheepishly said "yes sir," and scampered upstairs. Within minutes, he appeared fully dressed and ready to go. I even made him go without breakfast. Later, I told Bing about this incident. His response: "That was the right thing to do."

Except for sleeping in and Dennis' one incident, Phil and Dennis were well mannered and cooperative.

Along the way, Phil and Dennis moved out of the fraternity house and into an apartment. On a Friday morning soon thereafter, the dean of men telephoned me and reported that, suspicioned if not real, Phil and Dennis were operating a disreputable apartment; hence, I must ask that they move out immediately. Thereupon, I decided to push the panic button as Bing had requested.

So, on Friday morning, I dialed the number that Bing had given to me. Within seconds, Bing was on the line. I briefed him on the problem. He asked where I would be the next morning (Saturday morning). I told him that I would be in my office. His comment: "I'll meet you in your office tomorrow morning. Don't tell Phil and Dennis that I'm coming. I want to surprise them."

Bing travelled all Friday night, partly on commercial airlines, and partly by private plane, but he was in my office at 10 o'clock the next morning. Together, we decided that the best solution to the problem was to move Phil and Dennis back to the fraternity house. Bing expressed the desire that he handle the matter alone, following which he would meet Audrey and me at our home at 3:00 that afternoon.

Promptly at 3:00 p.m., Bing arrived at the Ensminger home. He reported that Phil and Dennis were back in the fraternity house, apologized for the boys, and thanked us profusely for taking such a personal interest in them. As always, Bing was warm and friendly.

The Bing Crosby Letters

In beautiful script, Bing wrote many letters to Phil and Dennis. They were masterpieces! Without fail, he sent a blind copy of each of these letters to me. When I left WSU, I very carefully noted these letters, labeled the box, and stored them in the archives of the E. O. Holland Library for posterity. Later, I could have wept, when I learned that someone had destroyed all of these letters.

Phil Crosby Returned in 1957

Following the 1954-1955 school year, both Phil and Dennis dropped out of school. In 1957, Bing contacted me relative to their desire to return. Phil did return but Dennis did not. Copies of two letters that I received from Bing follow; one dated January 12, 1957, and the other dated April 8, 1957. When writing to me, Bing's letters were typed, but when writing to the boys, Bing personalized the letters by writing them in longhand.

January 12, 1957
From: Bing Crosby
Hollywood

You were very kind to send me all the material relative to the imminent application of the twins for re-admission into Washington State. I must confess I was somewhat dubious about the possibility of their being eligible for re-entrance and I am much pleased that Philip is acceptable and that Denny has a chance.

Denny has applied for admission into Santa Monica City College in the hope that he can make up the quarter's work, and when I learn some more about his move, I will be back in touch with you.

Philip called me this morning from New York. He's just arrived from Germany, and he'll be home here in a couple days and I'll go over the material with him and then have him get in touch with you. He certainly should have plenty of time to get up to Pullman for registration on February 8th.

Many thanks, Gene. With kindest best wishes to you and your family.

April 8, 1957
From: Bing Crosby
Hollywood

Thank you so much for your note of March 29th. I have been in touch with Phil, and from our conversations, I was somewhat apprehensive of the situation. I'm going to talk to him on the phone again tonight. He's currently in Hollywood and I'm in Georgia, but I feel that I'll be able to get the facts and some indication of the seriousness of his intentions in this manner.

With regard to his living quarters, I was very firm at the start that he live in the fraternity house, which he tried to do for a few weeks, but he said it was impossible to study there—the dormitory was cold and drafty, and the food bad, and the company not too agreeable. He averred that the two boys he was going to take the apartment with were hard workers, back from the service, and seriously desirous of achieving some progress at the college, and he thought the atmosphere would be good. I was inclined, in view of these representations, to go along with his wishes. I hope it doesn't prove a bad move.

In any case, Gene, thanks very much for your information. I'll be after him.

All good personal wishes

Bing's Letter Relative to the Ensmingers' Book on China

In 1972, Audrey and I went to China. At the invitation of the People's Republic of China, I gave a lecture before the Chinese Academy of Agricultural and Forestry Sciences, the first time that an American agriculturalist had been invited to lecture before this distinguished group in 25 years. Following my lecture, Audrey and I were given permission to travel extensively in China to collect material, and take pictures, for a book, entitled *China—the impossible dream*, which came off press in 1973. Bing Crosby was among our friends to whom we sent a copy of this book. A copy of Bing's letter follows:

> Thank you for sending me the book *China—the impossible dream.*
>
> China has always been a tremendously interesting country to me—as it must be to everybody who has an interest in the future, because China is going to be a considerable part of that future.
>
> Very best wishes to you and Audrey.

Bing the Golfer

Bing lived and died a golfer. Pebble Beach was his pride and joy. In its glory days, it was very difficult to gain acceptance to play there.

Along the way, Charles Lambur, a friend of mine since college days and a noted mining engineer, and Father Martin, a Catholic priest, both ardent golfers in New York, were turned down in their request to play at Pebble Beach. Thereupon, they telephoned me and asked if I would intercede with Bing on their behalf. I agreed to do so, but I emphasized that I wasn't optimistic about the outcome. I telephoned Bing and briefed him about my two friends. His response: "Tell them to come on. I'll take care of them."

They went—and played at Pebble Beach. Bing gave them the red carpet treatment. He even assigned his private cottage at Pebble Beach to them.

Bing was an ardent golfer until his death. At age 74, following an exhausting three-week concert tour in England, the crooner went to Spain. There, on October 14, 1977, "Der Bingle" died as he had lived—singing, laughing, and playing golf. As Bing and Madrid's La Moraleja golf club's pro, Valentin Barrios, passed the eighth tee, Bing spotted some bricklayers nearby; so, he stopped, smiled at them, and sang a Spanish song. When Bing and Valentin arrived at the final hole, Bing sank the putt and did a little victory dance. Moments later, as he started to leave the golf course, he died.

My Treasured Friend Bing

From the time Bing attended the International Stockmen's School in 1952, followed by my having

Phil and Dennis as students, until his death in 1977, he was my friend. One time, he and his pal Phil Harris were at the Patterson-Rademacher fight in Seattle, at which I had a ringside seat, because the challenger (Pete Rademacher) was a former student of mine at WSU. Bing spotted me, whereupon he raced around the ring and gave me a big bear hug.

Each Christmas from 1952 until his death in 1977—a span of 25 years—Bing sent a personalized card to me, sometimes accompanied by a personalized gift, with his name inscribed thereon—among them, a cigarette lighter and a bill clip.

In a letter dated October 25, 1977, eleven days after Bing's death in Spain, I wrote to Mrs. Kathryn Crosby as follows:

> Bing was a friend of mine, dating to the time when I had Phil and Dennis as students at Washington State University. Since I have not had the pleasure of meeting you, I am enclosing my biographical sketch.
>
> I was greatly saddened to learn of the passing of Bing, whom I greatly admired.
>
> I share with you the following consolation, which is so apropos to Bing:
>
> To live again in the hearts of those
> we leave behind is not to die.

In response, I received a card, the front of which read:

> Thank you for caring.
> Kathryn Crosby and Family

On the inside of the card was Bing's favorite poem:

> It's been a joy, I can't deny
> Though some may think
> I took things lightly.
> But man and boy
> I looked on High and never failed
> To thank Him nightly.
>
> When I look back, I can't forget
> The friends I've met
> And the things they've done.
> I thank them all.
> It's been great fun.
> As for me, I have no doubt
> That's what life is all about.

When the book entitled, *My Life with Bing*, by Kathryn Crosby, came off press, I complimented Kathryn Crosby for recording the story of Bing for posterity. Thereupon, I received an autographed copy of the book, along with the following letter from Kathryn Crosby:

> I was so delighted to hear from you and I am pleased that you were interested in my book. It is always a joy to hear from people who have been closely associated with Bing. As Phil and Denny's teacher, you must have been much in Bing's thoughts.
>
> I loved the picture of Lindsay and you with the Hereford bull and I hope that we can meet in person one day.

[In the mural that was done for the Ensminger room in Kildee Hall, Iowa State University, Bing Crosby is featured in the center panel. AHE]

The 1953 Steers for Know-How Cattle Feeding Laboratory

The Animal Science Department desperately needed a cattle feeding laboratory, but the college did not have the necessary funds. So, I decided to overcome the situation by calling upon the marvelous cattle industry, along with other friends, for gifts and grants.

First, I had to secure the approval of the WSC administrators to go the grant route just as I had done earlier in buying the land and developing WSU Hilltop Stables. To this end, I evolved with a "Fact Sheet Relative to Steers for Know-How Project," on which I secured administrative approval. The name "Steers for Know-How" expressed the proposed basic procedure: I proposed to call upon the cattlemen of Washington to donate steers which would be sold at public auction with the proceeds used to build the cattle feeding laboratory for research—for know-how. Additionally, I proposed to secure gift lumber, cash, and free construction labor—all farmers and ranchers of that era were excellent carpenters:

Presentation of the Program

With missionary zeal, I delivered three illustrated speaking engagements daily (usually following breakfast, lunch, and dinner), for an entire month, all over the state, at which time I summarized the current animal science program, presented some new and pertinent findings of research, and told of the plans and needs for the proposed new cattle feeding laboratory. While in each county, I contacted lumbermen and manufacturers of other needed construction materials for gifts, and I contacted individuals and companies for cash donations.

I started in the Okanogan area, in the heart of the range cattle industry. During the first week, the commitment of steers and lumber was so great that I called my friend, Sherm Markley, WSC buildings and grounds superintendent, and asked that he immediately prepare the site for the new cattle feeding laboratory for which delivery of lumber would be started the following week.

Gift Steers

I asked each county to organize its own gift steer campaign, establish quotas, secure healthy steers weighing 425 to 475 pounds, and assemble, and truck all steers to Hutsell's Auction Yards, Moses Lake, Washington, so as to arrive there before noon on November 23, 1953.

The Auction Sale

The most unusual sale ever was held November 24, 1953, beginning at 1:00 p.m., with 450 gift steers sold. The unique features of the sale follow:

- It was a "model feeder calf sale," with Charlie Kyd, WSC extension livestock specialist, assisted by some of the best cattlemen in the state, grouping the steers according to weight, grade, and breed; and selecting and ranking the three top steers.
- Each of the three counties doing the best job of meeting or exceeding its quota was awarded one of the three top steers, with the ranking of the award steers and the ranking of the counties coinciding. Each of the three top individual solicitors of steers received a Lord Elgin watch, courtesy of the Sears-Roebuck Foundation.
- Upon arrival at the auction yard, all steers were vaccinated, *gratis*.
- The Grant County Cattlemen's Association provided the feed, *gratis*, for the steers while they were in the auction yard.
- Bill Hutsell served as the auctioneer and provided the use of the auction yard. *Gratis*.
- The sale was a tremendous success.

Other Donations

In addition to the money derived from the Steers for Know-How Auction, donations of lumber and cash were received; among the cash donations was $10 from a maintenance worker on the campus.

Construction of the Cattle Feeding Laboratory

My initial program, which the WSC administrators approved, called for the farmers and ranchers constructing the cattle feeding laboratory free of charge. All farmers and ranchers of that era took pride in being good carpenters. Besides, it was their project. They had provided the money and materials, and constructing it together would make for comradeship. However, when construction started, the labor unions descended upon us. I argued that the cattle feeding laboratory was not on the campus proper, and that it was a simple farm building. Thus, it should be constructed in much the same manner as any farmer or rancher would—that is, with farm labor. Besides, the farmers and ranchers were constructing the building free of charge. But the WSC administrators acceded to the union. The only good thing was that the college provided the necessary funds to pay the union labor, but they lost many cattlemen friends.

Cattle Feeding Laboratory Dedicated April 25, 1955

Dedication of WSC's new "Steers for Know-How" cattle feeding laboratory was featured at the

Steers for Know-How cattle feeding laboratory, a state-of-the-art gift from 1,275 donors.

college's annual Beef Cattle Day, April 25. The program opened with the inspection of the new building, one of the most modern cattle research facilities in America. A plaque bearing the names of each of the 1,275 donors was unveiled. The campus maintenance man who donated $10 proudly pointed to his name on the plaque.

The new laboratory, built with funds from the sale of steers donated for the purpose by members of the State Cattlemen's Association, along with lumber and cash donations, was presented to WSC by William Fancher, Tonasket, association president; and Otto Wagner, cattleman and lumberman of Winthrop.

Alan Rogers, Ellensburg, President of the WSC Regents, and WSC President C. Clement French accepted the laboratory for the college.

The all-day program featured the latest research on various phases of cattle production at WSC and elsewhere in the nation. Research reports included studies on the causes of kidney stones; irrigated pastures for fattening steers; production testing of beef cattle; feeding hormones, antibiotics and animal fats; new developments in feeding beef cattle; and fitting cattle operations to feed production.

Guest speakers were: Dr. A. L. Neumann, Urbana, Ill., head of the beef cattle division of the University of Illinois; and Dr. R. M. Bethke, St. Louis, Vice and Research Director of the Ralston Purina company.

WSC scientists who appeared on the program included Drs. Wendall Ham, Walter Galgan, and Irwin A. Dyer, all of the animal husbandry research staff at Pullman, and Dr. Wilton Heinemann, associate animal husbandryman, located at WSC's Irrigation Experiment Station near Prosser. Dr. M. E. Ensminger, Chairman, WSC Department of Animal Science, presided over the day's program.

Time Out for an Ensminger Family Reunion

In the summer of 1954, the Ensminger clan gathered for a family reunion at the home of mother Ensminger, at Grandview, Missouri.

The seven Ensminger brothers and sisters were very close. All of them married, and there was never a divorce among them. Mother and Dad must have done many things right!

This shows the seven Ensminger children with mother Ensminger. Father passed away in 1941. *Front row, left to right:* Rachel Aileen, mother (Ella) Ensminger, and Ella Mae. *Back row, left to right:* Marion Eugene, Garnett Atwell, Harry Edward, Jacob Douglas, and Leonard Elroy.

The W. H. "Bill" Stuart, Jr., Story

One of the perks of being a college professor is working with so many interesting and bright students. Bill Stuart, Jr. is a former student of mine of whom I am very proud. He is deeply religious, a fine family man, a great public servant, a natural leader, a trustee of Agriservices Foundation, and my friend. I could go on and on with superlatives about Bill; but suffice it to say that he is a truly great person, and a great person to know. He would make a great President of the United States!

In the fall of 1954, Bill traveled all the way from Florida to the state of Washington to enroll in the WSC Animal Science Department. I have often wondered whether my moving and shaking in the Animal Science Department at that time attracted him, or this was the farthest that Bill could get away from home—from Florida to Washington state. Bill graduated from WSU with a B.S. degree in animal science in 1959; and from Wharton School of Finance and Commerce, University of Pennsylvania, with an M.B.A. degree in corporate finance in 1965. In 1961, Bill married the former Nancy Sell of Seattle, Washington, whom he met while attending WSC. Bill and Nancy have two daughters, Kennedy and Crosland.

Student President

During his junior year at Washington State College, Bill wanted to run for president of the student body. But the dean of men, along with a number of others, had discouraged him, primarily because he was a member of a fraternity (Acacia); and, at that time, the independents (non-fraternity students) were in power and had the votes. So, Bill came to see me. I told Bill that he should run for student president and that he would win. I admonished him to write down, then discuss, the student issues of the day, and address every student group on the campus—from firemen to waitresses. He campaigned hard and well; and won by a landslide.

Bill made a great student president. He really worked at it, even to the point that he consumed too much coffee and too many cokes as he participated in endless meetings, and neglected a proper diet. He very wisely carried a lighter course load than usual during his senior student body president year, and planned to return for an extra semester the following year in order to complete his course work for graduation.

All went well as scheduled. Bill returned to WSU for the extra semester to complete his course work. But, at midterm, the dean of men called me and reported that Bill was not attending classes, and that he was flunking out of school. I was shocked! This just couldn't be true because Bill was a good student. It was midmorning. I immediately called the Acacia fraternity and asked for Bill. I was told that he was in the dorm sleeping. I asked that he be called to the phone. Without asking Bill why or what, I told him that I wanted to meet him in the parlor of the Acacia house, and that I would be on my way just as soon as I hung up the phone.

Upon my arrival at the Acacia house, I was ushered into the spacious parlor where Bill was waiting for me, dressed only in his robe. Only Bill and I were in the room. I told Bill of my call from the dean of men, informing me that he wasn't attending class, and that he was flunking out of school. Then I asked: "What is the problem, Bill." His reply: "I don't feel good, Dr. E."

I asked: "Have you told your parents?" (I had met Bill's wonderful parents on an earlier speaking engagement in Florida.) The reply, which I expected: "No, I don't want to bother them."

At this point, I spotted a telephone right there in the parlor. So, I said: "Bill, I feel that I should get on that telephone over there and call your father, right now and in your presence. But I won't do so unless you approve." Bill squirmed and shrugged his shoulders, following which he uttered a reluctant: "Okay. If you say so, Dr. E."

Bill gave me his father's office telephone number, and I had the good fortune of reaching him right off. I briefed Mr. Stuart relative to Bill Jr. having a health problem, as a result of which he wasn't up to going to his classes and was flunking out of school. Without hesitation, Mr. Stuart asked that I put Bill Jr. on a plane to Baltimore the following Monday morning, and stated that he would meet him at Johns Hopkins Hospital.

The Johns Hopkins examination revealed that Bill had a thyroid deficiency that was easily corrected. Bill went to his home in Florida to await the opening of the new semester. He returned to WSU for the second semester, and graduated with honors.

Bill Never Forgot

In his keynote address at the 1988 International Stockmen's School in Houston, Texas, Bill paid me the tribute which follows:

> It is a privilege and a pleasure to be with you this morning to keynote this International Stockman's School. More years ago than I care to admit, I sat at the feet of Dr. M. E. Ensminger, "Dr. E" as he is affectionately known to all, and I consider it an honor to be pressed into service by my mentor.
>
> Dr. E has been an inspiration to me for the past 34 years. He is a clear thinker with an eye on the future; he's an articulate speaker with a prolific pen, and a man blessed with an energy that has the potential to exhaust most people to repentance.
>
> You know there are three types of people in the world. Those who watch things happen, those who wonder what happened, and those who make things happen. Our Dr. E has been making things happen—for agriculture and education—for over half a century.

1955, Problems and Practices of American Cattlemen

In 1955, Alan Rogers—chairman of the research committee of the American National Cattlemen's Association; owner of Walking T Ranch, Ellensburg, Washington; and a regent of Washington State College—elected to secure from the cattlemen of America the necessary information through which to "pin-point" the problems of the nation's beef cattle industry, and to chart the industry's future in research, promotion, and education. Mr. Rogers and his research committee had concluded that in no other manner could they expect to get their fair share of research funds; that they must first show what and where their problems were, then ask for help in solving them. They decided to accomplish these objectives through a nationwide survey of the American cattle industry.

Initially, Alan Rogers had a commitment from the U.S. Department of Agriculture to do this study. But, this fell through. Thereupon, Regent Rogers asked that I assume responsibility for this huge task of conducting such a nationwide survey, summarize the questionnaires, and publish the results. Since he was a regent at WSC there was but one answer: "Yes, I'll do it." To help me in this mountainous task, I mobilized the assistance of the following WSC staff members: Dr. M. W. Galgan, Mr. Roy Smith, Mrs. Ruth Crowe, and Mrs. Jean Lucas in the Department of Animal Science; Dr. W. L. Slocum, Chairman, Department of Rural Sociology; Mr. J. McCorkill, research consultant, who processed the data on the IBM; Mr. J. G. Darroch, station statistician; Mr. Steve Allured, college artist; Mr. Charles Kyd, extension livestock specialist; Dean E. C. Stone and Dr. J. Dunlap, College of Veterinary Medicine; and Dr. Owen Brough, Department of Agricultural Economics.

At the outset, we obtained gift and grant funds from cattlemen and agribusinesses with which to defray part of the cost of the study; constructed the questionnaire, following which we did a trial run; obtained the membership lists and scientifically sampled the more than 60,000 members of the 24 state associations; and prepared the follow-up letters, and set up an organization for handling the personal follow-up in each state.

A whopping 81 percent of the nation's sampled cattlemen responded to the questionnaire. Two states—Nebraska and New York—turned in 100 percent responses. In Nebraska, the executive secretary of the Cattlemen's Association drove 450 miles to obtain the last questionnaire. Upon receipt of the questionnaires, they were edited and summarized expeditiously on an IBM machine operating around the clock and over the weekend, following which I wrote the two bulletins: *Problems and Practices of American Cattlemen*, Bulletin 562, December 1955, 90 pages; and *Problems and Practices of Washington Cattlemen*, Bulletin 567, May 1956, 64 pages. Both bulletins were published by Washington State College. Several thousand copies of Bulletin 562 went out.

As a result of this grass-roots survey—the first major scientific one of its kind conducted by a livestock industry in the United States—the cattlemen of America were in the position of saying "we know," rather than "we think," when discussing their problems and needs. Thereafter, they could tell scientists what their problems were, and they could more intelligently request needed legislative appropriations—on both state and national levels. Dr. Leslie Johnson, who was Head of the Department of Animal Husbandry at Iowa State University at that time, stated that he referred to the bulletin *Problems and Practices of American Cattlemen* more often than any other publication.

Mr. Rogers was extolled by the cattlemen of America for doing the impossible, and his image as a WSC regent soared to Paul Bunyan size—a campus building was named after him.

Charles R. Kyd Told It like It Was

The late Charles R. Kyd was a truly great livestock specialist. I often said of him: "If I had my choice of any livestock specialist in America to serve as the extension livestock specialist with whom I worked, I would choose Charlie Kyd." This evaluation takes on greater significance when it is realized that, administratively, Charlie was responsible to the director of the WSC Agricultural Extension Service, and not to me. He was knowledgeable and practical relative to livestock, and a superb PR person. Charlie was blunt and honest, and the stockmen of Washington trusted and loved him.

Mother of the Year

In 1956, some of our family's friends in Missouri contacted Ella Mae and urged that the family submit Ella Ensminger's name for Missouri's Mother of the Year.

Ella Mae called me and asked if I would put together the necessary letters and documentation to be submited. I was only too happy to do so. It was a delightful surprise when we learned that Mother Ensminger had been chosen.

The state of Missouri has established a Missouri Mother of the Year State Park on the highway between Columbia and Jefferson City. They invited the families to put a tribute to honor their Mothers of the Year.

In May 1989, the remaining children gathered to see the bronze placque and stone wall which they had erected in the park for Mother Ensminger.

The 1956 Missouri Mother of the Year presentation to Mrs. Ella Ensminger of Hickman Mills.

HONOR AS AN EMBLEM

MISSOURI MOTHER OF THE YEAR IS HUMBLE AT CEREMONY.

Mrs. Ella Ensminger of Hickman Mills Says She Accepts Award as Representative of All Mothers.

[PICTURE ON PAGE 3.]

With a gracious smile, Mrs. Ella Ensminger of Hickman Mills, a mother of seven children, yesterday received a scroll designating her as the Missouri Mother of the Year

"I accept this as an emblem for all mothers—here and everywhere," she said, asking that all the mothers in the audience rise and share in the honor to motherhood.

A good many of the more than 150 persons attending the ceremony in the Hickman Mills Community Christian church rose while their husbands and children watched proudly.

Widow of a Farmer.

Mrs. Ensminger, 70-year-old widow of a farmer, Jacob Ensminger, has reared six nieces and nephews in addition to her seven children. She has 16 grandchildren and a great-grandchild.

The scroll was presented to her by Mrs. George W. Diemer, Warrensburg, chairman of the state committee of the American Mother Committee, Inc. Mrs. Ensminger automatically becomes a candidate in the contest to select the American Mother of the Year.

Lewis Shultz, president of the Hickman Mills Lion's club, which submitted her name for the honor, said it was fitting that the presentation be held at the church where Mrs. Ensminger "nurtured her children."

The event was described by Dr. Robert M. Myers, a Kansas City physician who was minister at the church about 25 years

Many Home Tasks.

Through her years as a farm wife she has canned fruits and vegetables, baked bread, cured meat, churned butter and cared for chickens and the garden.

Five of Mrs. Ensminger's seven children attended the program. They were Harry Edward Ensminger, Grandview, owner of a general contracting company; Garnett Atwood Ensminger, Burbank, Calif., vice-president of feed sales of the Albers Mill company; Dr. Marion Eugene Ensminger, chairman, animal husbandry department of Washington State college, Pullman, Wash.; Mrs. Rachel Aileen Ensminger Bennett, Grandview, and Mrs. Ella Mae Ensminger Ervin, jr., Hickman Mills.

Two sons were unable to attend. They were Dr. Douglas Ensminger, a representative in New Delhi, India, of the Ford Foundation, and Dr. Leonard Elroy Ensminger, an associate soil chemist and an associate professor of soils at the Alabama Polytechnical Institute, Auburn, Ala.

Newspaper article on Ella Ensminger being named Missouri Mother of the Year in 1956.

1989. *Left to right:* Leonard, Ella Mae, Aileen, Gene. Missouri Mother of the Year State Park.

We Take a Trip to California

In July of 1958 we took John on a trip to California to see Disneyland. He was 12 years old. Of course, we managed many stops along the way to visit stockmen friends. Among the friends that we stopped to visit were Otto and Evangeline Battles of Congdon & Battles Aberdeen Angus which originated in Iowa. We became acquainted when they had a farm at Yakima, Washington, with some of their Black Angus cattle. We would drive over for a weekend and there would be long discussions about cattle in front of the fireplace.

Later, they acquired a ranch at Los Olivos in California where they retired with a few of their Angus cattle.

Congdon & Battles were the top breeders of Angus cattle for many years. Myron Fuerst, one of Agriservices Foundation's trustees, attended their dispersion sale and bought several individuals.

John Ensminger, Evangeline Battles, Dr. E, and Otto Battles stand in front of the Battles' Spanish style hacienda.

An Interesting Trip

Roger Jessup, who had a large dairy in southern California, also had a large cattle ranch in Okanogan, Washington. He was a generous man on whom I could depend to help raise funds for a worthy cause. In 1961, Roger scheduled a banquet for 200 of his friends and neighbors, at which he proposed to honor three outstanding stockmen (one each from Colorado, California, and Oregon). I accepted a speaking engagement at this banquet, at Mr. Jessup's urging. Later, Dean Hazlet of the WSU Graduate School initiated the procedure of having the chairman hood doctorate candidates at commencement. The WSU commencement and the 6:00 p.m. banquet in Okanogan were the same day. I felt that I should do the hooding honors, out of esteem for James Nofziger whom we all loved, and as indicative of my endorsement of Dean Hazlet's idea. I telephoned Roger that I would come, but I had to charter, and personally pay for, a private plane and pilot to get there. In my mind there was no other choice.

So, immediately following the hooding of Dr. Nofziger that afternoon, Mrs. Ensminger and I sneaked out of the commencement exercises and raced to the airport to board our private plane. We arrived just in time for the banquet, following which I addressed the group. Then, we flew back to Pullman that night.

I Began Writing Books

As I have previously indicated, upon my assuming the chair of the Animal Husbandry Department at WSC in 1941, I blueprinted a course for the department that included writing articles and books.

The Ensminger family in my study in the Ensminger home. This was taken by the college photographer when the first edition of my book *The Stockman's Handbook* came off press.

I discovered that a number of years earlier, the Agricultural College of the University of Wisconsin was in the same predicament—without funds. So, they decided to excel in writing books; among them, was the classic *Feeds and Feeding* by W. A. Henry (later *Feeds and Feeding* by Morrison), the first edition of which was published in 1898. So, during the latter part of the 1800s and the early part of the 1900s, the College of Agriculture, University of Wisconsin, built a great reputation based primarily on good books. I merely emulated them. But, in addition to books, I added columns, feature articles, and student participation in a national essay contest.

Over and above the usual and expected research publications and Stockmen's Short Course handbooks, during the 21 years of my chairmanship at WSU, I authored the following:

■ Six widely used textbooks, now in several languages and used all over the world.

■ A monthly column that was carried in 13 magazines with nationwide circulation.

■ A chapter in a German book entitled *Handbook of Animal Breeding* (3 Vols.) by three European authors—Dr. John Hammond, England; Dr. Ivar Johansson, Sweden; and Dr. Fritz Haring, Germany.

■ Feature articles which, in total, appeared in 136 magazines with nationwide circulation.

■ The U.S. Department of Agriculture bulletin No. 2127 entitled *Light Horses*, of which more than 1,000,000 copies were printed.

I authored this bulletin at the request of the USDA; and I did it free-of-charge because it was needed for 4-H Club members and FFA students, as well as for the nation's rapidly growing light horse industry.

Additionally, as training in writing, I required that all the seniors in animal science enter the annual nationwide essay contest sponsored by the Saddle and Sirloin Club of Chicago. During the first three years of competition in this great contest, WSC students compiled the following enviable record:

Year	Placings
1942	1st, 2nd, 6th, and 9th places
1943	2nd, 5th, 8th, 10th, 17th, 18th, and 19th places and winner of silver cup for school with best record
1944	1st, 4th, 7th, 10th, 14th, and 19th

Voting on Chairmen

The practice of voting on chairmen or other people in executive positions is not always a good idea. Voting on managers often results in a popularity contest and poor production—there are days when top ranch foremen wouldn't win the majority vote of the cowboys.

When the voting on chairmen at Washington State University was instituted, Professor John Carver, Chairman of Poultry Science, and I decided that we would administer our respective departments as we had done before the voting procedure, fully aware that we could get voted out at the time of our first unpopular decision.

Ask people on the street, or on the farms or ranches, in Washington who is chairman of the WSU Sociology, History, or English Departments, and more than likely they cannot tell you; moreover, they couldn't care less. The reason: These departments are not involved in public relations and in serving an industry over the state. Not so with Animal Science! When I was hired by President E. O. Holland and Dean E. C. Johnson, they made the following statement:

> The post of Head of the WSC Animal Husbandry Department is the most difficult position in the College of Agriculture because you must keep ahead of the stockmen of the state." (It was a much larger group than the poultry or dairy producers.)

During my 21 years at WSU, I kept ahead of the livestock industry of Washington with whom I had a wonderful rapport.

In 1960, I Was the Recipient of the American Society of Animal Science Distinguished Teacher Award

It was a great boost to my morale! History will evaluate my works, as it will all those with whom I was associated, and determine whether our respective footprints shall live on in the sands of time, or be obliterated by the next passerby.

Some supporting letters for the ASAS Distinguished Teacher Award follow. What wonderful friends I had!

September 14, 1959
From: Howard Doane, President
Doane Agricultural Service
St. Louis, MO

I consider it an honor to support the nomination of Dr. M.E. Ensminger, Chairman of the Department of Animal Science of the College of Agriculture, Washington State University, Pullman, Washington, for the Distinguished Teacher Award.

My work during the last fifty years has given me an unusual opportunity for visiting and working with members of the faculties of most of our agricultural colleges. Out of this broad and fruitful experience, I came to know Dr. Ensminger as a good administrator, a fine organizer, but most of all as an inspiring teacher and fashioner of men. Over the years I have seen him grow into one of, if not the, strongest man at any of our agricultural colleges in the field of animal sciences.

One of my early contacts with him came while attending the annual Stockmen's Short Courses that he so ably organizes and directs. He begins planning for the new course immediately after the last one has concluded. Even though it is a multi-ring operation, it moves with precision and dispatch. The one who appears to have the least to do during the week-long session is Dr. Ensminger. Evidence of his ability to organize material and direct both instructors and listeners is abundantly demonstrated.

I consider the Short Course the outstanding educational activity in its class. It enlists a large number of instructors and lecturers and hundreds of participants who pay a substantial attendance fee. The handbook resulting from the course is exceedingly well done.

His students give evidence of thorough training and display keen understanding of the field.

Dr. Ensminger's relationship with students goes far beyond a casual office conference with a student during registration. His wise guidance is sought in both academic and personal matters by many students. He has also aided groups in the creation of clubs, societies and fraternities that widened their horizons. His counseling which starts with freshmen continues throughout the campus years and then follows the graduate into his chosen work where knotty problems are best solved by an older head. He fills one of those niches held by few college professors of an enduring friend and aid to students, both while on campus and later in life.

Another area in which Dr. Ensminger has achieved beyond the usual relates to his willingness and ability to raise funds to accomplish worthy objectives not attainable within the normal university budget. His campaigns, conferences and suggestions have resulted in grants to his university of more than one-and-a-half-million dollars. His ability to perceive a need, and then enlist individuals and corporations in financing that need, is a rare talent. It has greatly enlarged the scope of his work and advanced research and extension at Washington State University far beyond their usual limitations.

Dr. Ensminger has coached judging teams, inspired and led many outstanding research projects and through publications, lectures and demonstrations enhanced the content and breadth of instruction in the animal sciences.

His authorship of six informative books is a task that would challenge the entire energies of most men. These books are widely read and used for both classroom and reference work.

I can think of no possible candidate that your committee may consider who does so many things so outstandingly well as Dr. M. E. Ensminger.

I feel it is a great privilege to offer this tribute to a man who richly deserves any honor your committee can bestow upon him.

September 17, 1959
From: W. A. Coon
Western Area Vice President
Armour & Company

I have had the privilege of knowing and working with Dr. Ensminger since his association with Washington State College. I want to say without any reservations that Dr. Ensminger has done more for animal agriculture in the State of Washington than any other single individual.

In addition to his development of students through the many student-conducted activities, followed by placement of these individuals in good positions through the West, Dr. Ensminger has been outstanding in his adult education events. The participation of established livestock operators in the Stockmen's Short Course proves that successful farmers have turned to Dr. Ensminger for assistance.

Dr. Ensminger gives unselfishly of his time; in fact, his whole life is wrapped up in the betterment of livestock, and in the betterment of people. He is a gentleman and a scholar. He has pulled animal agriculture at Washington State University and in the State of Washington up to its present height by his bootstraps.

September 23, 1959
From: Cecil Hagen
Managing Editor
Pacific Northwest Farm Quad
Spokane, WA

As managing editor of the Washington, Oregon, Idaho and Utah Farmers, I believe I am in a good sideline position to evaluate the stature and contributions of staff members of the land grant colleges in the four states we cover. It is my responsibility as an editor to judge them objectively as reliable and practical sources of much of the technical information we pass along to our total of 193,000 subscribers.

We have, and have had, some fine animal husbandry specialists in our region since I joined the staff in 1943, but among them Dr. Ensminger is outstanding. I always have been amazed by his seemingly inexhaustible source of energy. His capacity for work is almost unbelievable.

His standing as a scientist is best exemplified to me by his record of attracting donated funds for financing animal husbandry research projects at Washington State University. I doubt that WSU ever has had a more capable "money getter." True, that involves personality as well as promotional ability, but to me it is convincing evidence of the respect and confidence that leaders in the meat packing and other industries have for him as an individual and a scientist.

Back in 1953, Dr. Ensminger thought up a "Steers for Know-How" promotion for getting cattlemen of the state to finance a new laboratory building. He put that campaign over by motivating Washington Cattlemen's Association leaders to help him out. They, like industry sources that donate money to his department, wouldn't have done it unless they held him in high regard as a department head.

Even more convincing testimony of his stature in the livestock industry is the Cattlemen's Short Course which he instituted at Washington State University 10 years ago. It, as far as we are concerned, is a 100 percent Ensminger show, in that he saw the need for it and built it up to its present standing. The success formula Dr. Ensminger has used is a simple one: Get together a visiting faculty of the best livestock authorities in the country to augment your own staff and cattlemen will attend. And they do, by the hundreds each winter. Dr. Ensminger's reputation goes far in attracting nationally known livestock specialists as faculty members and top livestock producers as students. Moreover, the "students" come not just from the state of Washington but from points all over the west.

One final observation. Without question, Dr. Ensminger gets more publicity than any other livestock specialist in our region. We publish his monthly column, "The Livestock Guide," and quite a number of his miscellaneous articles. I can imagine that envy might prompt some individuals to tag him as a "publicity hound." Not once can I recall of his ever having asked me, or one of our staff members, for publicity. Instead, we look upon him as the ablest exponent we know of creating his own news stories. When he breaks into print it is in connection with some event, promotion or idea that is so newsworthy in its own right that we, as editors, can't in fairness turn it down! Higher praise we, as editors, can't give a news source.

September 26, 1959
From: Hector McDonald
Rancher
Crossfield, Alberta, Canada

I had the good fortune of serving in the Department of Animal Science, Washington State University, as a member of the teaching and research staff under Dr. M. E. Ensminger's chairmanship during the first few years of his tenure at that Institution. In accepting the chairmanship of the department, he was confronted with the tremendous challenge of building a strong department of Animal Science from a start with a very meager budget and much too limited facilities.

Several return trips to the Campus for the purpose of attending Beef Cattle, Swine Days, and The Stockmen's Short Course, impressed me with the fantastic expansion and improvement of the Washington State University Animal Science teaching and research facilities, as well as the broadened sphere of influence of that Institution in Animal Agriculture. Dr. Ensminger deserves full credit for the progress of the Department of Animal Science, which he envisioned at the beginning of his chairmanship at W.S.U.

Many stockmen are fully aware of the almost unsurmountable task, both on and off the campus, that confronted Dr. Ensminger in raising sufficient funds to make progress in his Department possible. The sincerity of Dr. Ensminger, along with his outstanding ability to translate research into "The Layman's Language" and show how the results of research may be applied in useful practice, succeeded in inducing the Industry to place at his disposal one-and-a-half-million dollars in grants. State and Federal appropriations for teaching and research also increased several fold under Dr. Ensminger's leadership.

The name *Ensminger* is well and very favorably known across Canada. His outstanding teaching skills and mastery of his subject were much in evidence in three entirely different addresses I heard him give to widely diversified audiences in Alberta. These lectures were given on repeated trips to this province, in response to respective invitations from the Western Stock Growers Association, the Agricultural Institute of Canada, and the Alberta Light Horse Association.

Numerous key ranchers from Alberta and British Columbia, as well as district agriculturalists from these two Provinces, have attended the W.S.U. Short Course.

Former students of Dr. Ensminger in Canada range from Ph.D.'s to Short Course enrollees. These persons represent a wide diversification of employment and include cattle buyers for U.S. Packing Companies who maintain buyers in Calgary, College Professors in Animal Science, Professional Agriculturalists in various commercial enterprises, District Agriculturalists, Field Editors for Canadian agriculture publications, and ranchers.

The views expressed in this letter are shared by many Western Canadian students and stockmen, who are strongly of the opinion that Dr. M. E. Ensminger would be a most worthy recipient of the Distinguished Teacher Award of the American Society of Animal Science.

The Penalty of Leadership

With the widespread recognition of the department, the demands on my time increased. I was called upon to preside at Spokane, Washington's big annual Farm Forum, speak at meetings throughout America and abroad, chair breed association congresses, conduct state and national surveys, appear on TV programs, and give magazine interviews. I even had a Hampshire boar pig and an Angus bull named after me.

Meanwhile, Back at Home

When the land around us became prime building territory, we acquired neighbors. Dr. Louis and Frankie Manus and their three children were our dearest friends. Their youngest son, David, and our son, John, were very good pals. They regularly played together for hours.

When we acquired a Doberman Pinscher, I was the expert animal scientist, so naturally it fell to me to

Dr. Louis and Frankie Manus, 1956.

Bathing Duke the Doberman, 1946.

I am sitting in the back garden. Audrey was responsible for the flowers. We built the fireplace in one day. The stone came from a quarry a short distance from Pullman. I spread the mortar and Audrey lifted the stones. I can assure you that we were barely able to move for a few days afterwards.

bathe him. He didn't especially appreciate it. He was a little too big for John, so eventually we replaced him with two Cocker Spaniels, first Sandy, and two years later, Blackie. They had grown up together from the time they were puppies, so they were inseparable.

I loved to garden, so in order to help the war effort, I put out enough vegetables to feed several families. In addition, one summer we were asked to raise chickens and turkeys. We started out with the turkeys in the pasture on the north side, and chickens in the converted garage. It was quite an experience. They always say that knowledge comes from experience, and experience comes from mistakes. We didn't try it a second year.

The Watts family: E. W. and Bernard (standing). Audrey's sister Frances, Helen Watts, and Audrey (sitting).

Audrey's family was living in Vancouver, Canada, so we made at least one trip each year to see them.

When the second world war ended, we were urged to fix accommodations for the influx of GIs waiting to take advantage of a college education under the GI bill. We converted our semi-basement into an apartment. In 1946, Zilla and Charles Paeth occupied it until they graduated. They were a delightful couple to have. After they departed, we needed the basement for the book writing.

In 1957, I had a speaking engagement for the Western Canadian Stock Growers Association in Calgary. After the meetings, Hector and Ollie McDonald, who were now living on a farm close to Calgary, accompanied us to Banff and Lake Louise, where we spent several days just visiting, hiking around the lake, and dining in elegance.

One year the Boeing's begged us to see their boat, Taconite, berthed at Vancouver. So we did. It was indeed luxurious. *Left to right:* Dr. E, John, Frances on the ladder, Helen and Ernest Watts.

Zilla and Charles Paeth with Duke, 1946.

John and I are standing with the McDonald family next to their farm house.

Audrey in front of the chateau.

The Stockmen's Short Course and Livestock Days

The Stockmen's Short Courses and Livestock Days were one of the three programs that I charted in 1941. The purpose of the events: to present to stockmen an interpretation and application of the latest in animal research.

The Stockmen's Short Course was the "flagship" of the events. It was always held in early December,

John and I hiking around Lake Louise.

and an enrollment fee was charged in order to defray the cost of operation. Eventually, I built up a sizable reserve fund, following which I slept more comfortably should a snowstorm or icy roads cause poor attendance.

The requisites for a successful school, to which I rigidly adhered in conducting each of 20 Stockmen's Short Courses at WSU (and 24 more similar events after I left WSU) follow: it must be helpful, so it must cover the problems and issues of the day; the people with the greatest expertise in the world must be invited to make the presentations as guest professors; there must be a proper mix of guest professors—one-third to consist of each academics, farmers/ranchers, and agribusiness representatives; the papers must be published in handbooks in advance of the Short Course (for the enrollees, for sale, and for libraries), without deviating from the rule: no paper, no lecture; it must be organized to perfection; it must operate on time—not one minute late, for which I used an old-fashioned country school bell; all enrollees completing the School must receive a signed graduation certificate; and all guest professors and enrollees must fill out a questionnaire for future guidance in making the Short Courses better and better. Among the guest professors at WSU were: Sir John Hammond of England, F. B. Morrison of Cornell University (author of *Feeds and Feeding*), and Howard Doane of St. Louis—innovator and founder of the oldest and largest farm management service in America.

Soon, the Stockmen's School became a prestige event, and I had a waiting list of those who wanted to serve as guest professors. It attracted enrollees from throughout the United States, Canada, and Mexico. Guillermo Osuna, a large and successful

F. B. Morrison, Cornell University and author of *Feeds & Feeding,* who lectured in four WSU Stockmen's Schools.

Mexican cattle rancher and his cousin Juan Antonio Saenz, Jr., flew their private plane from Mexico to Pullman, Washington. (Later, Mr. Osuna became a charter trustee of Agriservices Foundation.) The enrollees treasured the signed certificates, which they framed and hung in their offices. Forty years after being an enrollee in the Short Course, the obituary of a prominent stockman of Washington read: "...and he graduated from Dr. Ensminger's Stockmen's Short Course."

Statistics Relative to the December 10–15, 1961 Stockmen's Short Course

This was the last Short Course that I directed at WSU. Pertinent statistics relative to this event follow:

■ 126 guest professors (from New York to Hawaii, and from Northern Canada to Texas) and 235 lecture and laboratory periods.

■ 420 paid enrollees from nine states, two Canadian provinces, and Mexico.

■ 712 in attendance at the student-stockman banquet (the largest banquet ever held on the campus). Dan Thornton, Governor of Colorado, a colorful cattleman and golf crony of presidents, was the

Sir John Hammond of England lectured in two WSU Stockmen's Schools, in 1960 and 1962. He is on my right in this photo that includes the whole Animal Science Department—faculty, graduate students, and herdsmen.

banquet speaker. Governor Thornton lauded the Short Course as "outstanding in America."

■ 1,500 people exposed to the Short Course for one or more lectures during the week, including students, non-registered visitors, and others.

■ 750 additional people in 13 civic and scientific organizations of Spokane, Colfax, and Pullman, Washington, and also Moscow, Idaho before whom guest professors appeared.

■ Impact throughout the United States, Canada, and Mexico through news releases, radio and TV, reports of enrollees before local farm and civic organizations, magazine articles taken from the handbooks, and libraries (each head of animal husbandry is being provided with the three handbooks for this purpose; plus the Library of Congress, the Cambridge, England library, and many others).

There is no doubt in my mind that I thoroughly enjoyed planning and conducting the Stockmen's Schools. They gave to the stockmen the latest developments, and vice versa the stockmen gave the staff their problems and concerns. It was a two-way street.

Some of the Accolades

I herewith share with my readers excerpts from some of the accolades that were received from guest professors and enrollees following the 1961 School.

Part of the 712 people in attendance at the banquet at the close of the December 10-15, 1961, International Stockmen's School, at which Dan Thornton, cattleman-Governor of Colorado, was the banquet speaker. To that date, this was the largest banquet ever held on the campus. (Courtesy, WSU, Pullman, WA)

December 13, 1961
From: L. R. Wells, Manager
Armour and Company
Spokane, Washington

Thank you very much for the hospitality and very fine breakfast at your home this morning. This was a very enjoyable event for me and I really appreciate being included.

The Short Course leaves me tremendously impressed with the vigor and good management incorporated into this successful event.

December 14, 1961
From: John K. Westberg, Sales Manager
Feed Ingredients Dept.
Int'l. Minerals & Chemicals Corp.

Gene, I want to thank you, again, for all that you did for me while I was in Pullman this week. I appreciated it very much.

As usual, you have done a grand job. That was certainly the best meeting yet. You should be given a lot of credit by the men at the college and by agriculture in the State of Washington for what you have done in your program at Pullman.

December 15, 1961
From: J. H. Miller, D.V.M., Secretary
Washington State Meat Packers Assn.

I want to compliment you on an excellent program and know that you have put many hours at work in making it the success that it is.

I notice that you had some talks on meats and when you are ready to program next year's stockman's course, please let me know and I will give the program publicity to the Meat Packers Association.

December 18, 1961
From: Richard H. Johnson, Ph.D.
Western Technical Service Representative
Dawe's Laboratories, Inc.
Chicago, IL

I would certainly like to thank you, particularly, for the many hours and the effort which you obviously put into the planning and execution of the entire course. May I also wish you every success on future Short Courses, and send along my best personal regards and wishes for the holiday season.

December 18, 1961
From: Judd Morrow, Director
Southwest Agricultural Institute
San Antonio, Texas

Just a brief note to tell you how much Don Wideman and I appreciated the opportunity to appear on the program of your Stockman's Short Course. The program and its execution was very impressive and, I felt, highly successful. You are to be commended in your forward looking attitude in the development of this type of activity for the betterment of the livestock and ranching industry in the west.

December 18, 1961
From: Charles Riemcke
Yakima, Washington

For the past eight years it has been in my mind that I should attend your "Stockmen's Short Course". This year that took precedence in my planning, and I believe it was the most productive week of the year.

In some respects the week proved to be something of a shocker, and when I summarize my experience I find I must say that I learned primarily that there is at least twice as much I don't know as I had previously imagined.

Two years from now I will plan to return, and hope that I'll be able to arrange for one other employee to attend also.

You are to be complimented for assembling such excellent and provocative instructors and the work of your staff in presenting them and in coordinating all the varied activities was certainly praiseworthy.

Thank you again for a wonderful week. Please convey my thanks and best wishes for the season to all of your staff.

December 19, 1961
From: W. M. Beeson
Purdue University
Lafayette, Indiana

It was a real experience to have an opportunity to participate in the Stockmen's Short Course. I have attended many conferences and meetings, but I have never seen one that was more precisely carried out and more earnest interest on the part of the participants. You and your staff are to be congratulated on a lot of forethought and preparation to run a conference of this type. I am sure it is of real benefit to the livestock feeders throughout the northwest region and Canada.

December 19, 1961
From: Ferry Carpenter
Pure Bred Hereford Cattle
Hayden, Colorado

I want to thank you for a most interesting and educational week.

You are to be congratulated for setting the pace for Live Stock improvement by conducting a course that combines a combination of under and post graduate work, for students, operators, and teachers.

Your management and courtesy was faultless. The results will outlive us all.

December 19, 1961
From: Lyle Liggett
Director of Public Relations
American National Cattlemen's Assn.
Denver, Colorado

I wanted to tell you how much I was impressed with the Short Course.....and how that impression grows in retrospect!

You put on something so unique that it is hard to classify. But I certainly can attribute its success to the hard work that you and your staff have devoted to it for, obviously, many months. Although it may have been apparent to you, I was not aware of a single hitch......and I'm a real critic of organization and such-like things........

Incidentally, I shall tote the handbook on agricultural public relations with me to Washington, D.C. Jan. 4-5 when Secretary Freeman has called the first meeting of his special advisory committee on PR. Several of us on the PR short course are members of same and know that the handbook will be helpful in establishing a firm, practical program of coordinated endeavor.

December 19, 1961
Dan Thornton, Governor
Englewood, Colorado

I have never had a more enjoyable experience than participating in your great event at the college in Pullman. You are truly a wizard when it comes to organizing and putting on a successful event.

One of the highlights of my trip was your breakfast the morning following the banquet. Also a pleasure I shall not forget was having as my luncheon partner on Tuesday, the very lovely lady, Audrey.

Again, my thanks for all of your courtesies and congratulations on a superb event. Remember, I told you Jessie and I would be in Palm Springs and to let us know if you are on your way through or contemplating coming our way. You can reach us at Thunderbird Country Club in Palm Springs.

December 21, 1961
From: Victor B. Beat, D.V.M.
Nutrition Consultant
Vitamineral Products Co.

We thank you for having given me the opportunity of serving as instructor for the Stockmen's Short Course. Also wish to thank you and Mrs. Ensminger for the delicious breakfast you served to us on Wednesday morning. I certainly enjoyed it along with the other hospitality you and your staff have shown me during my stay in Pullman.

Attending the Short Course was quite an education to me, since I was able to visit with other instructors and students and learn of the many problems which they have.

Status of the WSU Department of Animal Science in 1941

In 1941, the WSC Department of Animal Husbandry had three staff members, none of whom had a Ph.D. degree; a one-half time student secretary; a research allocation of $1,800 per year, and no grant funds; 30 student majors; offered only B. S. and M. S. degrees; a dirt road leading to the college farm, which became impassable following rains; and few fences that would hold animals.

Additional facts pertaining to the status of the Department of Animal Husbandry in 1941 are presented in the book entitled *E. O. Holland and the State College of Washington* (1958), page 403, by Dr. H. M. Landeen, a highly respected historian, an excerpt from which follows:

> For example, as late as 1941, the department of animal husbandry had not recovered from the effects of the depression years. The hog herd was infected with swine erysipelas, the sheep with parasites, and, with the exception of the Aberdeen Angus herd, the cattle were of inferior quality. The physical plant of the department was greatly run down. Its intercollegiate livestock judging teams, which had made fine records for the college in the 1920s, now placed near the bottom, consistently. Its livestock exhibits at the various local and interstate fairs, which had once been its pride, had been greatly curtailed. Worse still, the research program of the department was mediocre, and there was little or no interest in graduate work. As late as 1943, the Washington Cattlemen's Association deplored the department's inefficiency, demanded a better program, and insisted that the department should not be forced to sell its livestock for the upkeep of the division. Some newspapers in the state were asking the question: "Is agriculture a side issue at the State College?" and were answering it in the affirmative. It was to take years of arduous effort on the part of the new head of the department, Dr. M. E. Ensminger, to restore what had been lost during the depression era.

The Status in 1962

The record of accomplishment from 1941 to 1962 speaks for itself. Even with limited state and federal support we accomplished the following in the WSU Department of Animal Science:

■ Secured 2.5 million dollars in gifts and grants (which was big money at that time).

■ Built up the Animal Science enrollment to where, on the average and year after year, it is one of the largest in the College of Agriculture. Also, the students in Animal Science came from several states and from other countries. In 1952, the only year that the WSC administrators asked the USDA Federal Examiner to give an independent ranking of the teaching in the departments, Animal Science ranked first.

■ Developed the research program from one of minor importance to where the federal examiner rated it number one in the WSC College of Agriculture in 1952, the only year that a comparative rating was requested by the WSC administrators. (Animal Science also ranked first in teaching.)

Also, it is noteworthy that the Animal Science Department is faring well in obtaining research gifts and grants from industries and foundations, where such gifts are made on the basis of merit and expected results. For example, a committee of eminent scientists reviews the numerous requests of Swift and Company, from whom the WSU Animal Science Department received $100,000 for one project; which is the largest allocation that Swift and Company has ever given to one research project in the United States. (I, personally, paid every penny of my travel expenses to Chicago to meet with the officials of Swift and Company, travel which culminated in a $100,000 grant for research. The department had little in the way of travel funds.)

■ Built up an internationally known program of short courses, feeders' days, shows, etc. that attracts enrollees from several states and from foreign countries. Each year, approximately 7,500 people participate in these events.

In December, 1961, the Stockmen's Short Course attracted 420 *paid enrollees* from nine states, Canada, and Mexico; and 712 attended the annual Short Course banquet, which, to date, was the largest banquet ever held on the WSU campus.

The May, 1961, 14th annual WSU Horse Show and Judging School attracted 614 horses from eight states and Canada, 807 Judging School enrollees, and 5,575 spectators.

■ Developed a graduate program from one student and a masters degree basis to 10–15 students and granting of a doctorate degree in animal science.

■ Placed our graduates in responsible positions from coast to coast.

■ Built up the physical plant and the herds and flocks—which serve as student laboratory material, and which provide the basis for the research program—to where everyone may take pride in them. Among these developments, it is noteworthy that WSU's beef cattle, sheep, and swine were winning in the nation's major livestock expositions; that WSU Hilltop Stables, which is recognized as the finest establishment of its kind at any college in America, was provided, and is maintained, entirely through gifts; and that approximately half of the square feet of Animal Science building space available for herds, flocks, and laboratories at the Animal Science farm has been provided through gifts.

■ Developed what is recognized as one of the finest college-stockmen relationships that exists in any state. As evidence of this statement, the new "Steers for Know-How" Cattle Feeding Laboratory—a gift from 1,275 cattlemen and related agribusinesses—could be cited.

■ Authored the following: Six widely used books by M. E. Ensminger; namely *Animal Science, Beef Cattle Science, Sheep and Goat Science, Swine Science, Horses and Horsemanship,* and *The Stockman's Handbook*; two monthly columns—*The Stockman's Guide* and *Horses! Horses! Horses!* and numerous feature articles for the livestock magazines.

Grand Champion steer at the Grand National Livestock Exposition, San Francisco, in 1958. *Left to right:* Dr. C. C. O'Mary, WSC beef cattle specialist; Dr. E; Miss Carol Ramsey, 1958 Livestock Queen, Grand National Livestock Exposition; Miss Patricia Duffy, Miss Grand National for 1958; and Bill Bennett, Jr., WSC' beef cattle herdsman, who fitted and showed the champ.

1962
TIME TO MOVE ALONG TO A DIFFERENT LIFE

It was an extremely difficult decision to leave Washington State University, but there were compelling reasons to do so. It was not easy to part from our many friends that we had made in the livestock field in the state of Washington. It was heart wrenching to abandon the loyal staff in the Department of Animal Science. They were like family to us.

In September 1960, in preparation for our retirement, Audrey and I had bought 79 acres of choice property and a beautiful house on a golf course at Santa Rosa, California. In 1962, we decided that the Santa Rosa air service wasn't good enough to accommodate our anticipated travels; so in August, 1962, we purchased 10 acres near Clovis, California. Later, we acquired an adjacent 10 acres. In October, 1964, we sold the Santa Rosa property—financially, we did very well because of the upswing in real estate prices.

In a letter dated July 9, 1962, I submitted my formal resignation to President C. Clement French; and he accepted it in a letter dated July 10, 1962. Copies of these two letters follow.

July 9, 1962
From: M. E. Ensminger
Department of Animal Science
Washington State University

Please accept this as my resignation from the staff of Washington State University effective September 1, 1962, with accrued annual leave taken thereafter.

Also, I wish to express my sincere appreciation for the opportunities that I have had and to thank all those who have been helpful.

I shall be entering private consultant work, with headquarters at Clovis, California.

July 10, 1962
From: C. Clement French, President
Washington State University

I have your letter of July 9, 1962, presenting your resignation from the staff of Washington State University, effective on September 1, 1962.

I have discussed this with you fully and can well understand your desire, after 21 years, to undertake the challenge of the new opportunity which your private consultant plans will offer you. Therefore, I accept your resignation as presented.

In doing so, may I express to you my sincere appreciation for the many and varied contributions you have made to the development of the Department of Animal Science and to its program in the university and in the state. Your imaginative and driving enthusiasm has been the primary factor in this development, and I know it will be missed by many.

I wish you and Audrey much happiness and the fullest possible success in the new work you are undertaking. My associations with you during these ten years have been interesting and stimulating, and I hope that, even though you will be in California, our paths will cross frequently. If I can be of any assistance to you in the years ahead, I know you will not hesitate to call on me.

Following my resignation, President C. Clement French appointed Dr. Galgan "Acting Chairman," effective September 1, 1962. Galgan had served as my right hand man for many years; so, he was the logical choice. Walt was mild mannered, thoroughly honest, and a fine character.

I Announce My Resignation

The WSU News Service announced my resignation and new work in a July 16, 1962, news release; and I made a similar announcement in my syndicated column, "The Stockman's Guide" of July, 1962.

In a memorandum dated July 17, 1962, I thanked the livestock industry of Washington.

Dean E. C. Johnson Remained My Staunch Friend

Dean and Mrs. Johnson were in Tacoma, Washington, visiting their daughter and son-in-law, at the time announcement of my resignation hit the press. On August 28, 1962, Dean Johnson penned the following message to me:

Dear Folks: The enclosed clipping is from the Sunday *Tacoma News Tribune*. Though of course we have read all the news in the *Pullman Herald* relating to the same subject. So together with the interesting and most helpful information you gave us in advance, we feel well informed.

What a pity that WSU should lose two such men as you. Dr. Ensminger and Dean Stone of Vet Medicine at the same time. Howsoever worthy the successor may be, it will take a year or more for each one to have his feet firmly on the ground. But as for you Mrs. E., I am sure that your husband and I, and many friends will say "she is irreplaceable." Again, our very best wishes for you in your new location and the opportunities there and elsewhere.

What Great Friends I Had!

Along the way, I received feelers for other positions. Herewith are copies of six letters that were written in my behalf.

January 11, 1961
From: E. C. Johnson, Dean Emeritus
College of Agriculture
Washington State University

To: Dr. Arnold D. Rhodes
Chairman Committee to recommend a Dean of Agriculture
College of Agriculture
University of Massachusetts

Your letter of January 6 asking for my evaluation of Dr. M. E. Ensminger, Head of the Department of Animal Science at Washington State University, as a candidate for the Deanship of the College of Agriculture at your Institution, arrived just as I returned from the hospital and I have been unable to give it attention until today.

As you undoubtedly know, Dr. Ensminger came to us from your university after four years of able service, with the highest recommendations from your former President Baker and others. He came to us at a difficult time in our Animal Husbandry Department, and within a short time he more than justified the excellent recommendations from your Institution. He has built here a Department of Animal Science outstanding in research, in teaching and in public relations. He really is a master in all these fields.

Dr. Ensminger has cooperated very effectively with the Extension Service and the agricultural, industrial and commercial interests of our state and region.

Dr. Ensminger is just the type of man to carry the banner high for agriculture both within the University, throughout the State, and, if called upon, in relation to the Legislature.

Since I was Director of the Washington Agricultural Experiment Stations for twenty-seven years I had opportunity to observe intimately the work of the agricultural scientists here, both in planning projects, securing support and in getting results. Among these I would place Ensminger right at the top, and believe he would be immensely effective and happy in serving as his own Director of your Agricultural Experiment Station.

From the foregoing you will note that on all counts I endorse Dr. Ensminger for your position.

It should be added, I think that Dr. Ensminger has abundant initiative and broad vision. He is a tireless worker. He is a man of high ideals and fine character, and further, he is blessed with a well educated cultured wife, who is of great assistance to him in all his work.

It is a pleasure to recommend Dr. Ensminger to you.

May 8, 1961
From: B. R. Bertramson, Chairman
Department of Agronomy
Washington State University

To: Dr. Ralph A. Young, Professor
Department of Soils
North Dakota State University
Fargo, North Dakota

Bob Hausenbuiller has shown us your inquiry to him of April 28 relative to candidates for the presidency at North Dakota State University. I should like to call to your attention, Dr. M. E. Ensminger, who is Chairman of the Animal Science Department at Washington State University. He is a man of extensive administrative experience and certainly is well-known in agricultural circles. He has published several outstanding books in animal science that are used across the country and in foreign countries as well.

Dr. Ensminger has a very impressive record of accomplishment for himself and for the Department of Animal Science here at Washington State University. He is an effective and vigorous administrator. He works very hard at public relations and has a way of handling it that gets results. Some years ago, he conducted a campaign to get a special cattle feeding laboratory established here, costing close to $100,000. He initiated a vigorous campaign for contributions and in a few months, he had all the funds for building this laboratory.

Each year he handles a cattleman's short course which brings people from all over the U.S. and Canada and some from foreign countries as well. This covers all of the various aspects

My loyal friend, Dr. Rodney Bertramson, Chairman of Agronomy (later, Dean of Agriculture) outlined my accomplishments at a luncheon of Department Chairmen on August 3, 1962. (Since coming to Clovis, Rod has been a loyal friend to my family and me. I will always remember his warm and wonderful letters.)

of the beef industry from the standpoint of production and management. It is a good example of what can be accomplished with his talents.

His wife is a capable writer and scientist in her own right. Together they make a wonderful team. They are a very fine religious family. I count it an honor to consider them as my friends and I would recommend that your committee give his name as a candidate serious consideration. If there is further information you would like from me, I would be glad to have you contact me.

September 16, 1961
From: Wilson Compton (former WSU President)

To: Dean H. B. James
North Carolina State College
Raleigh, North Carolina

I have just had word from Dr. M. E. Ensminger of Washington State University that he has been in correspondence with you concerning the chairmanship of your Department of Animal Husbandry.

Although I have been away from Washington State for some years I have kept in rather close touch. I would of course not like to see Dr. Ensminger leave Washington State. But he has the capacity to build and administer a much broader program in the agricultural sciences than he now has at Washington State. I assume that he is seeking larger and perhaps more "worlds" to conquer and I am confident that he can conquer them.

If I were the President of North Carolina State, I would let no grass grow under my feet in getting in touch with Dr. Ensminger for the kind of position which evidently is under consideration. Ensminger is an outstanding teacher. He also has a superior research talent. But he has more than that. He has an unusual capacity to encourage research interest on the part of his associates. He has had valuable administrative experience in a department at Washington State which combined the various aspects of teaching, research and extension. While I was the President of Washington State University, I regarded its Department of Animal Sciences as the top division of the Institute of Agricultural Sciences from the standpoint of its professional program and its public relations.

With respect to the latter, Ensminger has an outstanding talent. He commanded and held the respect of the livestock and related industries. He justified increasing support through public funds and he had phenomenal success in securing private support for various research and other undertakings of his department. Also he was an excellent lecturer and public speaker.

I hold Dr. Ensminger in high regard both professionally and as an individual. I might add that Mrs. Ensminger is a distinct asset in her own right. If your "opening" is open I would commend your consideration of Dr. Ensminger.

April 5, 1962
From: H. A. Kornberg, Manager
Biology Laboratory
General Electric Company
Richland, Washington

To: The Honorable Orville L. Freeman
U.S. Secretary of Agriculture
Washington, D.C.

Last week, when I was on the Washington State University campus for the purpose of participating in administering two doctorate examinations in Animal Science, Dr. M. E. Ensminger apprised me of his interest in obtaining an appointment in the U.S. Department of Agriculture. The purpose of this is to recommend him to your favorable consideration.

I have known Dr. Ensminger since 1947, when he helped us establish our large animal research program. In the ensuing fifteen years, he has served as a consultant to the Company's Atomic Products Division, contributing importantly to our research productivity and to improved public relations between Northwest agriculture and Hanford Operations.

Further, his association with us has made possible a closer liaison with the University, again to the general benefit of Hanford and its scientific staff, particularly members of this laboratory whose educations have been extended as a result.

A measure of his progress in bringing industry and the University closer together is evidenced by the fact that when Dr. Ensminger joined the University, there was only $1,800 per year available for Animal Science research. As Chairman of the Department, however, he has progressively increased research funds, with industry having contributed $2,000,000 to them during his tenure.

However, these are but small parts of Dr. Ensminger's distinguished career as one of the Nation's top flight agriculturists. Although we would miss his presence in the Northwest, the greater benefit that would accrue to the Nation by his occupying a post in your Department causes unreserved support of his interest in doing so.

The Fabulous Offer from the University of Kentucky

I received a telephone call from the president of the University of Kentucky, at Lexington, inviting me to come to Lexington to meet with him and offering to pay my travel expenses. I accepted his invitation—and went. It was a delightful visit, followed by a luncheon at the president's home. The president made a most attractive offer. If I would teach just one seminar each semester, the university would pay me a salary, provide all the offices and secretarial help that I wanted, and let me be free to do as much writing and consulting as I wished. It was a fabulous offer! Because I hesitated, the president requested that, prior to reaching a decision, I think it over, then return for a second visit accompanied by Mrs. Ensminger. Audrey and I did just that. Although it was very difficult to turn down this University of Kentucky offer, Audrey and I decided to go on our own.

Left to right: Dr. E, and Mr. and Mrs. Ira Drymon, who were old friends and parents of the president's wife.

The News and Editorials

The news reports and editorials relative to my leaving WSU and my new work were very generous, for which I am both grateful and humble. A few of the many reports and editorials are herewith reproduced.

THE SPOKESMAN - REVIEW
July 17, 1962
Ensminger to Leave WSU Post

A teacher with a national reputation will leave the college classrooms Sept. 1.

M. E. Ensminger, chairman of the Department of Animal Science, Washington State University, said he will open a private consultant business outside Fresno, Calif., called Agriservices.

During Ensminger's "more than overnight stay" at WSU, he blue-printed a program designed to make WSU unique in comparison with other animal husbandry departments.

His program featured (1) short courses and commodity days, (2) writings in books, magazines, and newspapers, and (3) gifts and grants from industry. A federal examiner rated the WSU research program No. 1 in the only year that a comparative rating was given.

Although proud of his relationship with stockmen, Dr. Ensminger said he frequently "baited" them, just to make sure of their reactions. A colleague described it: "He kicks them on the shins, and they kick him right back again."

Dr. Ensminger also will continue with his writing of books and syndicated columns on agricultural subjects. He plans to write a non-fiction book, if the duties of operating "Dr. E.'s School of Horse Science" do not interfere.

THE FRESNO BEE
July 22, 1962
WSU Official Will Become Consultant

Dr. M. E. Ensminger, chairman of the animal science department at Washington State University since 1941, will open a consulting service September 1st in Clovis following his resignation from the university staff.

The United Press International quoted Dr. Ensminger as saying the new business will be called Agriservices and will offer consulting services to farmers and farm related businesses. He said he plans to gather a staff of specialists to be on call for any job in the field of agriculture.

Beginning next year he also will conduct two-week summer classes in horsemanship and animal care in the east, midwest and California, he said.

During Ensminger's tenure as chairman, the WSU department of animal science obtained $2.5 million in grants and developed a program of short courses which attracted farmers from throughout the west.

Ensminger also is author of a syndicated column and six published books.

THE WASHINGTON HORSE
August 1962
Industry Suffers Loss

Elsewhere in this issue is reported the resignation of Dr. M. E. Ensminger who for 21 years headed the Animal Science department at W.S.U. Announcement of his leaving jolted the entire livestock industry of the Northwest where he has so creditably and ably labored to bring International renown to his department and the institution it was part of. Almost single handedly this dedicated educator and scientist pulled up an ailing department—literally by its bootstraps to the point that it became the number one research program at W.S.U. according to the federal examiner several years back. Through Dr. Ensminger, the college secured two and a half million in gifts and grants for research, building and scholarship programs. He also led the way in establishment of Hilltop Stables, the great stockmen's short course program, and a superb undergraduate and graduate educational program.

We say here and now that W.S.U. administrators will look far and wide but they will never find a department chairman as dedicated to the service of the livestock industry as was Dr. Ensminger.

This man was never a follower—always a leader, and never content to look backward or rest on his laurels which included being selected in national competition for the "Distinguished Professor Award" by the National Society of Animal Production in 1960.

If but half of the W.S.U. administrators and its staff were as dedicated, industrious and sincere in their efforts as Dr. Ensminger has been throughout his 21-year term of service, then we would have the world's number one institution of higher learning.

Our loss in Washington is California's gain. Dr. E and his family will be at home near Fresno, California after September 1st.

STOCKLAND MARKET NEWS & VIEWS
August 2, 1962
Gene Ensminger Resigns Post

The Space Age has even reached the announcement of retirement of a top livestock educator at Washington State University.

M. E. "Gene" Ensminger, chairman of WSU animal science department, announced his retirement from that position by this Space Age method:

"Effective September 1 I'll have a new launching pad! At that time the Ensminger family—wife Audrey, son John, and I—will take up residence in Clovis (Box 473), Calif., with our residence-office just a quarter mile east of the Fresno city limits."

Dr. Ensminger is going to be sorely missed by livestock people everywhere. His influence knew no state boundaries. He accepted leadership of the department in 1941 and under his far-reaching influence WSU became well known in animal science.

A prolific author (six books, syndicated column, and many articles), "Gene" Ensminger leaves behind him a record of accomplishment that establishes him as an all-time great in his field.

In his new work he will be a private consultant on agriculture business, a public relations representative to and for farmers and stockmen.

He will continue with his writing of books and columns and even plans to write a nonfiction book!

To his many friends he ended the announcement with: "I'm not saying goodbye; merely, so long! With this I wish to express my heartfelt thanks to all those who assisted with the WSU program and became a part of me."

I Got Letters

I loved the many letters that I received, excerpts of a part of the letters are herewith reproduced:

From: Mrs. Virginia Lewis
Spokane, WA

My first reaction when I read the paper during my lunch hour today was "He can't do this!!!!! What about the horse show?" The next was and is a sincere and heartfelt wish for success and happiness for you and Mrs. Ensminger in the new venture.

The Pullman Horse show, with its associations and friendships made and continued there each spring has become one of the most enjoyable weekends of the year, and for those weekends I wish once more to thank you. The show just won't be the same without you at the helm.

After having the experience of working with you and seeing what you can accomplish, I am sure the new venture won't dare not succeed.

July 17, 1962
From: H. E. Goldsworthy
Rosalia, Washington

It came as a bit of a shock to us to learn that you are leaving Pullman. It is going to take some doing for us to adjust to the thought of the place without you.

You leave a fine monument to your intelligence, industry and devotion. The State, the University and your friends will miss you.

May your usual success attend you in your new field is our wish and expectation.

July 18, 1962
From: W. A. Coon, Vice President
Armour and Company
San Mateo, California

Thank you for giving me advance notice of the fact that you are going to locate in California. I also read a notice about it in the Spokane paper.

I have a great deal of respect for persons who believe in their convictions as strongly as you do, and who have that burning desire to keep going forward. I know that you will be successful. I will consider it a privilege to have you visit me whenever you are in San Francisco. Perhaps after you have moved, the Ensmingers and the Coons can get together on occasion for some friendly visits.

July 18, 1962
From: R.S. Dubigk, D.V.M., Consultant
Port Angeles Washington

Notice of your resignation was in this morning's paper. I and many, many, many others were stunned at this announcement. To me, it is the end of an era. You probably cannot recall, but I was a senior at the Department of Animal Science when you first came to Washington State University. As time and events progressed, you proved to all that your department was without a peer in any of the Land Grant Colleges. Congratulations, Dr. Gene, on a job well done, and our best wishes for your success in your new adventures.

Your counsel, guidance and presence will be sorely missed.

July 23, 1962
From: James G. Fletcher
The Prudential Insurance Company of America

I'm nearly shocked to tears over your resignation. Future Animal Science students and livestock men of the State, will never have the opportunity to excel under your leadership. It's a crime.

Without reservation, I wish you unlimited success in your new venture.

July 26, 1962
From: J. C. Miller, Head
Animal Science Department
Oregon State University
Corvallis, Oregon

I have just read with interest and surprise your open letter to your friends concerning your resignation and venture into private enterprise. This comes as a surprise to me, and I must admit I have mixed emotions. First, I regret seeing you leave academic circles, and secondly, I envy you having the courage to embark on an entirely new venture after many years of fruitful service in academic circles.

I extend my congratulations and best wishes to you and your family on this new venture, and trust it will bring rewards in the form of satisfaction, good health, and enough economic rewards to make it interesting and worth your while.

July 26, 1962
From: W. B. Young, Dean & Director
College of Agriculture
The University Of Connecticut
Storrs, Connecticut

I am somewhat shocked and surprised to learn that you are leaving formal education and research work connected with Land-Grant Colleges and the U. S. Department of Agriculture. On the other hand, I appreciate the fact that you are not giving up your work entirely in your professional field as an animal scientist and agricultural educator. Your new business "Agriservices" should provide you with an excellent opportunity to serve more people on a wider base than heretofore.

I congratulate you on your interest, foresight, judgment, devotion to the field, and your fortitude in taking on this new challenge.

August 7, 1962
From: Corwin King
Prior Land Company, Inc.
Yakima, Washington

I am sorry to learn that you are leaving our area. I want you to know that, as one stockman, I feel your presence, your advice, your guidance will be sorely missed by all of us.

Furthermore, I want to thank you for the splendid cooperation and help you gave me the three years I was president of the Washington Wool Growers Association. I also want you to know that the time that I served on the advisory board of the Animal Science Department of Washington State University was a terrific experience for me.

Please accept my best wishes for your outstanding success in your coming new ventures.

August 7, 1962
From: Bob Kull (formerly with WSU news bureau)
Yakima, Washington

Well, WSU won't be the same. It was with some surprise and a flashback of several dozen memories that I read of your new venture—our first acquaintance, you and Charley Kyd indoctrinating me into the ways of the State's livestock industry, our intense promotion efforts on WSC livestock events, later meeting at State Cattlemens' meetings, pictures of Bing Crosby at the Short Course for the national AP wire, and the short course.

Gene, I've always admired your directness, your tenacity, your organizational ability. You have ambitious plans, but I am sure that you will make them work out. Sincere regards for a constructive and pleasant future for both you and Mrs. Ensminger.

August 21, 1962
From: A. M. Bledsoe
Vice Admiral, USN (ret.)
Seattle, Washington

I'm sorry to hear through Stew that you will be leaving us before long. He seems to think that you will go to California.

Your many friends feel that this will be a real loss to Pullman and to us personally.

I have heard fine reports from the Science Fair. I am proud of the Judges I was able to assemble for that work.

As soon as you get settled please let me know and also call me if you pass through Seattle en route to your new destination and always remember that you have a friend in Seattle.

August 30, 1962
From: M. W. Durham, M.D.
WSU Regent
Spokane, Washington

Please accept my sincere best wishes for your success in your new venture. I know that with your great energy, background and ability, you will do extremely well.

I want to thank you for all your personal favors, and hope that our paths will cross in the future as they have in the past. I do get to California frequently and will certainly call if I am anywhere near.

At the time of my departure, Dr. Walter Galgan, who was on my staff, served as acting chairman of the department. Subsequently, the departments of Animal Science, Dairy Science, and Poultry Science were combined into one department of Animal Science of which Dr. Galgan continued to serve as acting chairman until Dr. Timothy Blosser became chairman. Nothing could have pleased me more than the selection of Walt Galgan and Tim Blosser as my successors.

When the news broke, we did not realize how many wonderful friends were genuinely sorry to see us leave. We enjoyed many farewell parties and the staff had a wonderful party for us at the horseman's house at Hilltop Stables.

Dr. Walter and Ina Galgan were two of the world's nicest people. They came from Canada to WSU. They were completely honest and devoid of college politics. They entertained just as much as we did. Their hospitality was a definite plus for the Department of Animal Science.

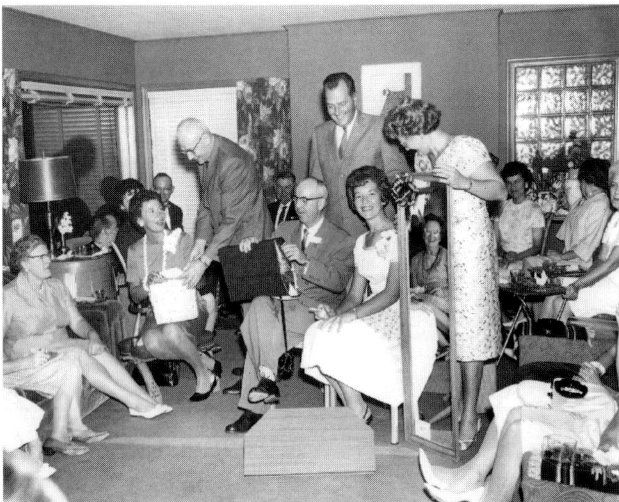

The Animal Science Department's farewell party for the Ensmingers and for Janet Martson, my longtime secretary, who had also decided to leave the Department of Animal Science.

Left to right: Audrey; Jeanette Patterson, secretary in the Animal Science Department for three years; Dr. E; and Janet Martson, my able and loyal secretary for 12 years.

The Beef Cattle Research Center

The unbelievable happened on September 20, 1983. I received a conference call from President W. Glenn Terrell and Regent Jack Cole of Washington State University. Dr. Terrell did most of the talking. Said he:

> During my administration, again and again I see, and become aware of, the many great and enduring things that you did for Washington State University during the 21 years that you served as Chairman of Animal Science. So, we want to honor you by naming our new and modern *Beef Cattle Research Center* after you.

I was shocked, surprised, and pleased—all at the same time. When I recovered my equilibrium, I thanked President Terrell and Regent Cole—inadequately, for I was in a state of shock.

Imagine a building at Washington State University being named after me 22 years following my departure from the University! Imagine being remembered 22 years later!

Soon after WSU announced that *The Ensminger Beef Cattle Research Center* would be dedicated on May 10, 1984, at which time I would be present and make an address, the Washington Cattlemen's Association invited me to address their annual banquet that evening, in nearby Colfax, Washington. I accepted. So, I made a second major address on May 10. My subject: "The Livestock Industry: Past, Present and Future." Although I had been away from the state of Washington for 22 years, I enjoyed reminiscing with a host of my old cattlemen friends and former students, and getting acquainted with many young cattlemen.

> **October 14, 1983**
> **From: Glenn Terrell, President**
> **Washington State University**
> **Pullman, Washington**
>
> I thought you might like to have a copy of the minutes from the meeting of September 16, 1983, when the naming of the Cattle Barn in your honor was announced. This follows.
>
> *Naming of the Cattle Barn.* President Terrell reported that, on the recommendation of the appropriate faculty members and administrators in the College of Agriculture and Home Economics, it was with great pleasure that he announced the naming of a subunit, the Animal Sciences Beef Cattle Center, a very strong facility for research and teaching, for Dr. M. E. "Gene" Ensminger who had been Chair of the Department of Animal Sciences from 1941-1962. Dean Ozbun said it was indeed a pleasure for him to recommend that this facility be named in honor of Dr. Ensminger, for his textbook on livestock production had been a key one for him as a student. He added that another textbook Dr. and Mrs. Ensminger had written was a vital one for him to use in preparing for his visit to China in 1978.
>
> Jack Cole said he certainly wanted to thank the central administration for approving the honor being bestowed upon Gene and Audrey Ensminger. He said that he and his wife had been friends with them since 1942, and that, having known Dr. Ensminger, knowing how he feels

Jack and Maxine Cole in front with me standing in back. They were warm friends of the Ensmingers. Jack was an astute farmer with a large acreage southwest of Spokane.

Dedication of The Ensminger Beef Cattle Research Center May 10, 1984—22 years following Dr. E's departure from WSU. Dr. E and Audrey with WSU President Glenn Terrell (center) May 10, 1984.

about WSU, knowing of the scholarship at WSU to which he contributes every year, knowing of the books he has written in several languages, and knowing of his worldwide reputation, he believed this was a most appropriate recognition for Dr. Ensminger. He added that he would certainly want to be involved when the building was being dedicated. Dr. Terrell said that he would be making the major address at that dedication.

We shall be looking forward to a dedication date later this year. I am asking the Office of University Relations to work with you in setting a convenient date. It will be my pleasure to host you while you are on the campus.

Dr. E and Audrey with WSU Provost Al Yates (who later became President of Colorado State University).

November 1, 1983
From: J. L. Ozbun, Dean
College Of Agriculture and Home Economics
Washington State University
Pullman, Washington

This is to express my pleasure relative to the recent decision to name our Beef Cattle Center in your honor. This is well deserved recognition for the many contributions that you made to WSU, the Department of Animal Sciences, and to animal science at the national and international level.

As I indicated to the Board of Regents when proposing that the Beef Cattle Center be named the Ensminger Beef Cattle Center, I have not had the privilege of meeting you personally. However, I have known of you since my days as an undergraduate student at North Dakota State where we used your textbook. More recently

The Ensminger Beef Cattle Research Center.

during a tour of China, we used the book that you and Mrs. Ensminger prepared on the agriculture of China and most recently I corresponded with you in connection with my new responsibilities at WSU. Thus, I am enthusiastically looking forward to the dedication of our Ensminger Beef Cattle Center and the opportunity to meet you in person.

A few excerpts from the talk I gave at the dedication are included here.

For future generations of students and stockmen, I trust that the M. E. Ensminger Beef Cattle Center will ever and ever serve as a beacon to the triumph of dedication, work, and accomplishment.

Through the years, many people have helped mold me, and usher me into the 21st century. For more than 40 years, Mrs. Ensminger has done most of the work for which I take the credit; an arrangement which I wouldn't change for anything in the world. During my chairmanship at WSU, I received great support from many people—some of whom have passed on to their rewards. In particular, I wish to pay tribute to (1) the late Dean E. C. Johnson, and (2) three distinguished persons who are present today: Jack Cole, a dedicated three-term regent of WSU; Rod Bertramson, former Chairman of Agronomy and Dean of Agriculture; and Sherm Markley of the buildings and grounds department.

No Chairman of Animal Science, before or since, ever had such great support as I received from the livestock industry of the state.

Through the years, we had many great staff members at WSU; among them, Dr. E. J. Warwick, Dr. T. J. Cunha, Dr. Charles Lindley, Dr. Stewart Fowler, Dr. Walt Galgan, John Burns, Claude Koch, Dave Foster, Bill Bennett, Arvid Neibergs, and many others. Today, I want to pay special tribute to an unsung hero among the staff—my longtime, dedicated and faithful head secretary, Janet Martson, now stricken with multiple sclerosis, and in a rest home in Moscow, Idaho. The dedication of my book, *The Complete Encyclopedia of Horses*, reads as follows: "to Janet Martson—my longtime secretary who made me look good professionally."

But universities are for students! I loved teaching. I was a demanding teacher. I expected students to perform to their full potential; a statement to which Ron Baker readily agrees when he tells how I got after him for making one lone B, when all the rest of his grades were straight A during his entire four years in college. But, Ron may fail to give my reason for getting after him for making the one B; he was capable of making an A in that course, too.

Dr. E giving his response, appropriately entitled, "I Was A Maverick."

Dr. E at the entrance sign bearing his name.

I found teaching very rewarding. I am pleased to have many of my former students in the audience today; among them, Leonard Vanderhoop, whom I had as a student 45 years ago, at the University of Massachusetts. Today, he's a successful businessman in Southern California.

My graduate students were something else! Late one night, a downtown restaurant was being held up. The cops had surrounded the building, but couldn't flush the robber. "Lone Ranger," Don Miller, one of my grad students, came to the rescue. He poked his straight stemmed pipe through the door and yelled, "Come out; I've got you." And out walked the robber, with his hands high over his head.

May 12, 1984
The Pullman Herald
University honors noted animal scientist

Dr. M. Eugene Ensminger was lionized here Thursday as the man who has had more influence than any other on animal sciences—an influence that will last for decades.

He was honored at the annual Washington State University Beef Research Information Day, and the university's beef center was dedicated and named the Ensminger Beef Cattle Research Center.

The program participants in the dedication of The Ensminger Beef Cattle Research Center May 10, 1984. Dr. Leo Bustad, Dean Emeritus, College of Veterinary Medicine, is shown giving Dr. E a copy of his address. Dr. James L. Ozbun, Dean, College of Agriculture (left) and Audrey Ensminger cheer and smile.

Participants in the dedication. *Left to right:* Dr. James Carlson, Chair, Department of Animal Sciences; R. Dan Leary, President, Board of Regents, who presented the dedication plaque to Dr. E; Dr. James L. Ozbun, Dean, College of Agriculture; Audrey Ensminger; Dr. E; and Jack Cole, rancher and three-term Regent of WSU.

Metamorphosis from Beef Cattle Barn to Stately Masterpiece

Yesterday's beef cattle barn, today's alumni center, is rich in early American history and WSU's land-grant heritage.

In 1922, Rudolph Weaver, WSC's first architect, designed the building. In 1982, Architecture Professor Henry Matthews referred to it as a "superb example of barn construction of the early part of the century, and as belonging to a carpentry tradition that can be traced to medieval times."

Today, this classic structure, combined with modern styling and enhancements, enables WSU to boast of one of the finest architectural masterpieces in the nation. The architects utilized restoration and conversion techniques to retain the original

The beef cattle barn as it was when I was Chairman of the Animal Science Department.

Metamorphosis from beef cattle barn to stately masterpiece.

design and the building's distinctive character. Today, the Alumni Center is the legendary symbol of Washington State University's proud history, and dreams of the future.

But preceding the metamorphosis from historic and beautiful beef cattle barn to elegant Alumni Center, I had to do battle with, and save, the building from destruction. First, they wanted to demolish it to make way for a new plant science building, Thereafter, their eyes were glued to the prime site, completely oblivious to the beauty and potential of the existing structure.

So, in 1986, I was delighted to learn that the WSU beef cattle barn would be transformed into the WSU Alumni Center.

When I received word that a "message or name" could be engraved in the tile floor for posterity (as a fund raiser), I decided to honor my six faithful Beef Cattle Herdsmen, and all of my colleagues, students, and stockmen, by recording the following message:

M E ENSMINGERS
AnSc 1941-1962

SALUTE 6 GREAT
BEEF HERDSMEN

JOHN BURNS
1929-1944 &

DUNCAN BREITHAUPT
1945-1947 &

REED BENEDICT
1947 &

FRANK ROACH
1947-1950 &

DAVID FOSTER
1950-1957 &

BILL BENNETT
1957-1963 &

ALL
COLLEAGUES &

STUDENTS &
STOCKMEN

KEEP ON
KEEPING ON MEE

CONSULTANTS-AGRISERVICES AND THE AMERICAN SOCIETY OF AGRICULTURAL CONSULTANTS

When we moved to Clovis, California, we rented a house in which we could live for six months as we built our house on the 20 acres on Sierra Avenue we had purchased from Murt Sullivan. Murt had a small cattle feeding operation on the 20 acres, and he was familiar with my name because of the livestock journals he read. Murt's main business was building houses. He offered to build our house with us paying only for the building supplies—an offer we couldn't refuse.

North side of the foundation headquarters, as it was in the early days.

The final view of the front driveway, after we had sold additional frontage to the city of Clovis, so that they could widen Sierra Avenue.

Aerial view of the foundation headquarters, taken in July, 1995. The 1.97-acre area is enclosed by a 6-foot board fence painted beige, with white stone pillars. The main complex, embracing 11,400 square feet under one roof, is on the north end of the premises. The warehouse, consisting of 2,400 square feet, plus a double garage and a storage building, is on the south end of the complex.

I am leaving our house to go to a meeting.

We were ever conscious of the fact that people who came from other countries to visit us should take home with them a lasting impression of warm American hospitality in a pleasant environment. Therefore, we always gave a dinner party in their honor, and we showed them through our office complex and the gardens surrounding them. Here are some of the pictures of our gardens.

The front driveway from the west.

Another area in the back.

The front driveway from the east.

Audrey and I in the center back garden.

An area in the back garden.

Fountain area on the west side of the pool room.

You can tell by the preceding pictures that we had a wonderful gardener. Greg Rivera was his name, and he and Audrey planned it all. What one did not think up, the other did. I was the forgotten man with the pocketbook.

Greg on the left, and Audrey on the right.

Because I was so terribly busy and travel was not as quick and easy as it is today, I was not able to return to Missouri to see Mother and the rest of the family as often as I would have liked. However, whenever there was a meeting close by, I always took the opportunity to see them.

Mother Ensminger and me in 1971.

1972. *Left to right:* Gene, Doug, Mother Ensminger, Harry, and Ella Mae.

As a Consultant, I Had an Interesting List of Companies and Individuals Who Were My Clients

One of the most interesting clients I had as a consultant was Dr. Ugo Galassi of Milan and Aimonetta, Italy. One day, he called me from New York and said he would like to meet with me in Los Angeles at the Beverly Hills Hotel , where he would be staying. We agreed to meet at 2:00 p.m. on a Saturday afternoon, poolside. That was a first for me.

Audrey and I drove down for the appointed meeting. He was lounging beside the pool; and there were a lot of people sunbathing and swimming.

I found that Dr. Galassi was in charge of worldwide sales for Olivetti (office equipment—especially calculators). He had a large farm just north of Milan, close to Alexandra. I could tell that he was a very capable man. His farm enterprise included growing grapes, making wine, growing feed, and feeding double-muscled cattle. He also had a wooded area, which he rented for hunting wild birds and other animals.

Each year I spent about five days with him going over everything.

Also, he was an avid art collector. Sometimes we could tie a trip to Italy along with another trip we were making.

In Aimonetta, the courtyard is surrounded by two-story buildings that house the owners and the workers at one end, and the animals at the other end. The courtyard is gated and locked at night.

The Galassis in their Milan apartment. *Left to right:* Mrs. Glassi, Dr. E, Dr. Galassi's interpreter, and Dr. Galassi.

The Italy That I Saw

Italy is uncommonly rich in the greatest raw material of all—human character. We are beneficiaries of Italy's great cultural past, but the Italians are the direct heirs. They live in an art lover's paradise. There's hardly a town in Italy that cannot boast at least one priceless work of art. As I stood in the Church of Santa Maria delle Grazie, in Milan, and looked at the world-renowned painting of The Last Supper, I bowed in silent respect to Leonardo da Vinci, the genius who painted it, and in thanksgiving to Italy for its impact on all the art, science, and religion of the world.

I saw narrow, winding roads teeming with fast, little cars and big trucks. There are no speed limits in the country. On the highways, my host cruised along at 105 to 110 miles per hour. One night in Milan, following a late dinner, my two friends, each in his Ferrari, staged an impromptu matched race across Milan—a city of more than a million, with me a silent (scared stiff) passenger in one of the cars. They are a nation of "hot rodders" and the older jockeys are less timid and more expert in producing thrills than the teenagers. Drivers are very courteous—they always give half the road, but sometimes they aren't particular which half. Next time over, I'm going to invite all my friends to take out insurance on me. As evidence that it could be a good investment, by actual statistics, one out of every two automobiles insured in Italy crashes into something.

Italy's Agriculture

In spite of the growth of industrialization, agriculture remains the most important Italian economic activity, and farming engages more than one-third of the population. Italian farmers supply the greater part of the country's food requirements and contribute about one-quarter of its exports.

Their farming is variable in method and tenure. It runs the gamut from industrialized farming on a large scale, with sophisticated agricultural machinery, to primitive methods where the hoe and the sickle are the chief tools. In the main, the farming that I saw was very intensive, both on small holdings and large commercial estates.

Food

I found one for Ripley! Typical Italian food does not contain garlic. I was told that I could travel from one end of the country to the other and never smell it.

Bread and pasta, both made from wheat, are the staple foods. Pasta, which is the alpha and omega of their diet, comes in an amazing variety of sizes and shapes—spaghetti (tubular), ravioli (rectangular), pizza (pie), fettuccine (ribbon-like), lasagna (flat), farfalle (butterflies), conchiglie (shells), ziti (big elbows), and a host of others.

Italian truffles (an edible subterranean fruiting body of fungi) are the most scrumptious in the world. Specially trained dogs are used to sniff out their earthen hiding places and to root them up.

No discussion of Italian food would be complete without mention of their "espresso" coffee, which is brewed in Rube Goldberg contraptions that make use of forced, compressed steam. By our standards, it's strong and bitter. I'm an old "coffee hound," but, admittedly, that espresso coffee almost cured me of the caffeine habit.

The American Society of Agricultural Consultants (ASAC)

During my 25-year college career, I never did consultant work for pay within the state in which I served. I always felt that it was my duty to serve the livestock industry of the state, along with my teaching and research responsibilities at the institution. Nevertheless, in 1962, I was a veteran in the consulting field. Among my clients was General Electric Company, Nucleonics Department (Atomic Energy Commission), for whom I had served as a consultant for 17 years. Also, while I was in college work, I trained many students who, subsequently, were highly successful in consultant work.

For my consultant work, I chose the name Consultants-Agriservices. Also, for launching my work, I prepared a flyer with my picture, facts about my training and experience, a list of the areas of my expertise, and the following statement:

> **LET'S TALK DOLLARS AND SENSE**
>
> Remember that the question is "how" rather than "whether" the agricultural production needs of the future will be met. It's a matter of who's there first with the most and the best. Business, science and technology will join together to up the ounce to the pound, the pint to the bushel, and the dozen to the gross.
>
> What would it be worth to you to have a consultant with a lifetime of know-how and experience in agriculture to help you chart the course of your business for the years ahead? What would it be worth to you to lower production costs, improve prices, spread and reduce risks, create new and assured markets, and/or apply modern business concepts to your farm, ranch or agribusiness?
>
> Thousands of engineers can design bridges, and calculate strains and stresses, but the engineering consultant is the one who can tell you whether the bridge should be built at all, where it should be built, and when. Likewise, hundreds of agriculturalists can formulate rations and plan crop rotations, but the agricultural consultant is the man who can tell you whether the business should be launched at all, where it should be launched, and when; and how to operate it successfully. The consultant is the person who is regularly called upon to display one of the most valuable of all commodities—judgment.

Right off, I was booked full in my consultant work. During my first year, I tripled the salary that I received during my last year at Washington State University. But I was shocked by the following two incidents, which underscored the need for a code of ethics for agricultural consultants.

I recommended the use of a certain commercial product to one of my clients. Soon thereafter, I received a telephone call from the Midwestern manufacturer of the product, telling of the sizable commission due me and asking where to send the check. I declined.

A very successful industrialist-rancher engaged my services as his consultant. Very soon, I discovered that many of his practices were illegal, which I called to his attention and asked that he rectify. His response: "I've always done it this way, so I don't plan to change." I promptly resigned as his consultant, and gave up a handsome fee.

For 25 years, I was a member of a highly respected profession—a college professor. So, upon launching Consultants-Agriservices in 1962, I wanted that it be highly respected. This desire prompted the formation of the American Society of Agricultural Consultants.

Organizational/Charter Meeting of Agricultural Consultants

On June 1, 1963, I sent out a news release inviting all full-time agricultural consultants throughout the United States and Canada to participate in an organizational meeting in Fresno, California on December 9 and 10, 1963. Also, I invited three distinguished agriculturalists outside the agricultural field to address and advise the group, namely: Charles E. Bell, Jr., USDA, Washington, DC; Dean Lloyd C. Dowler, California State University–Fresno; and Jack T. Pickett, Editor, *California Farmer*, San Francisco, California. Additionally, well in advance of the meeting, I detailed a full two-day program; and I appointed the following committees and admonished them to do their homework ahead of the meeting and be off to a running start when they arrived at the meeting: Constitution and By-Laws Committee, Membership Committee, Code of Ethics Committee, and Grievance Committee.

On December 9 and 10, 1963, 30 agricultural consultants from 14 states met at the Hacienda Motel, Fresno, California.

Excerpts from my opening address before the group on the morning of December 9, 1963, follow:

> The word "consultant" is derived from the 16th century Latin term *consultum*, meaning to take council together, deliberate, confer, consider, to plan, devise, contrive, to ask advice, seek counsel from, to have recourse for instruction or professional advice. Thus, it is a very old term; but in agriculture the concept and look are new.
>
> Consultants long have been an integral part of the noble professions of medicine and engineering, and they have contributed richly to each. Also, many of the most distinguished professors of our better colleges and universities serve as part-time consultants; thereby making it possible for these institutions to retain these outstanding people, and enhancing their value as teachers and researchers. Although we have always had a sprinkling of agricultural consultants, the real impetus for, and growth of, the profession is of rather recent origin; it came hand in hand with the transition of American agriculture—with the development of larger farms, ranches, and allied enterprises, with the rapid developments in agricultural research, and with the myriad of agribusinesses that have sprung up and enlarged everywhere. There is every indication that this transition in agriculture will continue; indeed, that more and more agricultural consultants will be needed.

Jack Pickett, Editor, *California Farmer*, the banquet speaker, opened his address as follows: "I find myself in the unusual position of being asked to make a speech on a subject about which I know very little. I accepted the challenge as I was intrigued by Dr. Ensminger, whom I consider a very unusual man."

During the two-day meeting, the fledgling organization accomplished what many predicted would be impossible—thereby proving their qualification to serve as consultants. In addition to discussing, freely and openly, their problems and organizational needs, they banded together as the American Society of Agricultural Consultants (ASAC); prepared and accepted a Constitution and By-Laws, a Membership Committee Report, an Ethics Committee Report, and a Grievance Committee Report; elected the following officers: President, M. E. Ensminger, Clovis, California; Vice President, Tillman Bubenzer, Noblesville Indiana; and Secretary-Treasurer, Gordon Shillingburg, Scottsdale, Arizona; and selected the following chairmen of standing committees: Membership, Dr. James Nofziger; Constitution and By-Laws, Marcellus Palmer; Code of Ethics, Dr. Spencer H. Morrison; and Grievance, Dr. J. D. Aughtry.

First Annual Meeting of the ASAC

The American Society of Agricultural Consultants (ASAC) met at the Denver Hilton, Denver, Colorado, September 11 and 12, 1964. It was the society's first annual meeting; the organizational-charter meeting having been held in Fresno, California, nine months earlier. Forty-five members from 14 states, Washington, DC, and Canada assembled for the historic two-day session. As the society's first President, I presided with "parental pride" and congratulated the society on its accomplishments during the first year, particularly the setting up (and adoption) of constitution and by-laws, membership requirements, code of ethics, and grievance procedure; the publication of two proceedings ('63 and '64); a paid-up membership of 65 from throughout the United States and Canada; and a cash balance of $599.38, plus an inventory of proceedings valued at $1,196.00. I also admonished the society ever to "keep in mind their noble objectives, invite for membership all those who qualify and comply, and maintain high standards." I concluded my formal report by saying: "This Society has given point, purpose, stature, and a new look to the profession in which we are engaged."

I also advised the nominating committee that under no circumstances would I succeed myself as President of the Society, and recommended that the society rotate all elected officers.

December 30, 1969, Luncheon Meeting of California Consultants

Several of the newer agricultural consultants in California expressed interest in getting together for the purposes of meeting other agricultural consultants, exchanging ideas, and developing an on-call working relationship in some cases. So, Audrey and I invited all California consultants to our home/office for a luncheon on Tuesday, December 30, 1969. Twenty consultants came.

Address to Western Section

I was invited to address the Western Section of the ASAC on May 9, 1981. For that speech I chose the title, "A Pilgrim and a Stranger." I opened my address with the following story: "Squanto, a Narraganset Indian, was the first agricultural consultant in America. He showed the struggling Plymouth Pilgrims how to cultivate corn in the rocky Massachusetts soil; he insisted that each hill be fertilized with three herring heads, pointed inward like the spokes of a wheel."

Then, I pondered: "Squanto worked with the Pilgrims; they were upright, deeply religious people, who came to this country seeking freedom. The following excerpts are taken from my May 9, 1981 address:

> Today, you are working as consultants in a sick society—circumstances that require great moral fortitude. As evidence of our sick society, if any evidence is needed, I direct your attention to the following current events:
>
> - President Ronald Reagan was shot by a would-be assassin on March 30, 1981.
> - When the school principal announced that the president had been shot, some seventh- and eighth-graders at the Academy Central School in Tulsa, Oklahoma cheered.
> - *The Washington Post* published and won the Pulitzer Prize on a story about "Jimmy," the addict who never existed; then forfeited the award.
> - Thirty percent of American households—34 million families—were touched by crime in 1980.
> - At the Calder Race Course in Florida in the early morning of March 29, someone went down the row of stables and stuck a knife in the necks of six horses who had their heads poked out of stall doors.
> - In two different California cities, bodies in funeral homes have been bothered, disfigured, and/or robbed.

25 Years of ASAC

In my judgment, the ASAC peaked at its 25th anniversary meeting, October 9–12, 1988, at the Minneapolis Marriott City Center Hotel, Minneapolis, Minnesota. With real regret, I could not be present in person, but I was there in spirit.

The inside front cover of the program carried my picture along with the following two quotes:

> Agricultural consultant services will be as honorable as those of us in it make it. More and more agribusinesses, and farm and ranch owners, will need and seek the services of consultants, just as has long been the practice in medicine and engineering, and other fields. Both agricultural clients and consultants merit the protection of high standards and ethics, with which both will prosper. Consultants must be above reproach, and they must have the moral courage to tell clients things which the clients may not wish to hear.

> The society's professional influence over the past 25 years, long recognized by U.S. agribusiness clients, has now reached out to encircle the globe, a development that was made possible as membership growth set new records year after year.

I sent 175 autographed copies of *China—the impossible dream*, as gifts to each person in attendance.

At the banquet, John Airy, a past president of the ASAC presented the following citation:

M. E. ENSMINGER CITATION
(Dr. Ensminger was the first President of the American Society of Agricultural Consultants)
PRESENTED AT THE ANNUAL MEETING
OF THE AMERICAN SOCIETY OF
AGRICULTURAL CONSULTANTS,
MINNEAPOLIS, MINNESOTA,
OCTOBER 11, 1988
by
John Airy
Consultant of Agriculture
1916 - 68th Street, Des Moines, Iowa 50322

Dr. M. E. Ensminger has been characterized as an innovator who makes his dreams come true. Throughout his long career, *he has made a difference.*

Some Accolades

I never inhale; nevertheless, I appreciated the following accolades:

From: Bill Helming, President
The Helming Group
Shawnee Mission, Kansas

I want that you know that you have many, many friends, including myself, who very much appreciate the major contribution that you have made not only to ASAC, but to agriculture throughout the world.

From: W. T. (Dub) Berry
The Helming Group
Shawnee Mission, Kansas

It must make you quite proud to have founded the Society by calling the first meeting and guiding it in its early years, plus seeing its growth in size and influence.

From: John D. Baker & Associates
Bethesda, Maryland

We are fortunate to have such an organization as ASAC and are indebted to you for your foresight and energy in founding it.

From: Walter W. Mininger
formerly Bank of America
Burlingame, California

Your name came up often during the ceremonies and a number of past presidents and long-time members named you as their mentor.

On February 24, 1995, we hosted a dinner for the American Society of Agricultural Consultants who were in Fresno for a meeting.

Of the many things that I did, I would be hard pressed to say which facet I enjoyed the most—consultant work, writing books, conducting Ag-Tech schools, teaching, or the foreign work on our trips around the world. I loved everything I did. It was never work to me.

When a professor, I always taught the beginning animal science course because I wanted the students to have a strong background of the field. Even after I left college work, I would conduct special seminars for students at the nearby colleges.

Dr. Randall Perry, Beef Cattle Science, California State University, Fresno, regularly called me each year, and brought his classes to Agriservices Foundation either for dessert or for lunch, and to have me give an hour's lecture.

Professor David De Silva, Animal Science Coordinator, College of the Sequoias, Visalia, also brought his classes for some extracurricular experiences. I was always happy to accommodate any of the students who wanted to hear my story.

ABOUT AGRISERVICES FOUNDATION

The Ensmingers, Audrey and I, were synonymous with Agriservices Foundation, to which we happily dedicated our lives without stipend, in humanitarian work around the world.

Written records are made by mortals like me. But indelible records in the sands of time are written by works, and evaluated by others with the passing of time. So, as each of us must, I am willing to let history evaluate and record in the sands of time the contributions of Agriservices Foundation in a troubled world.

History of Agriservices Foundation

It is important that the history of Agriservices Foundation be preserved for posterity because the unique programs of the foundation have had an enormous impact on the era.

Also, it is logical that I should write the history of Agriservices Foundation because, paraphrasing Sir Winston Churchill, it represents my "blood, sweat, and joy." I conceived of the idea, gave it birth, and guided it through its first faltering steps. I was a part of the history of Agriservices Foundation, and it became a part of me; we were inseparable.

Agriservices Foundation is a nonprofit foundation, incorporated November 12, 1964, in the State of California, for the following purposes (as stated in the Articles of Incorporation):

> To foster and support programs of education, research and development which will contribute toward wider and more effective application of science and technology to the practice of agriculture, for the benefit of mankind.

Agriservices Foundation has a proud and proven record of achievement, dating back to 1964, when it assumed responsibility for carrying forward The International Stockmens' School, which I had started more than 20 years earlier at Washington State University. Under the sponsorship of the foundation, I directed the school for another 30 years (the schools abroad were not conducted annually.) Thus, I directed the school for a total of more than 50 years. Under my leadership, it was recognized as the oldest, most complete, best-known, and most prestigious school of its kind in the world. Also, I conducted 21 Horse Science Schools in cooperation with colleges from coast to coast. Today, Agriservices Foundation continues to serve U.S. and world agriculture in a unique way, and to render a multitude of services throughout the world. We conducted schools/seminars in 69 countries. Also, we waive all the royalties on the foreign editions of our 21 books in order to help the people. So, our books are in several languages and used all over the world. The whole world is our classroom. The main thrust of the Foundation is in self-help programs in the area of world food, hunger, and malnutrition—the major global issue in the decades to come.

The program of the foundation is conducted as a dedicated service, without financial remuneration

We had many friends who contributed both money and service to help us along the way. Jerry Calvin, Manager, Jostens, Visalia was one of those. He contributed richly in publishing our brochures, etc. We were extremely grateful for his much needed help.Here I am pictured with Jerry and his wife Linda at the foundation's headquarters in 1994.

to those in charge. I direct the program, happily give of my time without stipend; and the trustees do not even accord themselves travel expenses to the annual meeting. Thus, there is low overhead; funds obtained from gifts, grants, and wills go for the intended purpose.

My guiding philosophy in establishing the Foundation and in directing the program for 30 years, follows:

> We need to offer hope and help to all humankind. We need to apply and share our science and know-how. We need to hear and heed the hungry and malnourished as they cry out, "Give us this day, our daily bread." We need to do all these things—and more—so that each of us and the whole world will have a brighter tomorrow; so that our dreams will come true, faster and more abundantly.

1973. Mr. Tatsuo Soya, Chairman of the Board, National Pork Producers Council, Tokyo, Japan, who led a delegation to Agriservices Foundation headquarters.

Agriculturalists from around the world beat a path to (or wrote) Agriservices Foundation. The foundation had the dubious honor of the highest postal charge of any firm in Clovis, California; and hosted 1,500 to 2,000 people for meals each year.

In 1969 we hosted a group from Germany. Among the group were Mr. And Mrs. Konrad Jacob and their son, Dieter Jacob, who was doing graduate work at University of California, Davis. Mr. Jacob was president of a co-op, President of Hessian Farmer's Union, and President of German Agriculture Society. Others in the visiting group included Mr. K. Ruschka, Director of Central Milk Marketing Co-op; Mr. Fisher, Director of Livestock Marketing Co-op of Hurhessen and Dr. J. K. Damm, FAO Rome in charge of pig development for all developing countries. We gave them the usual tours and a dinner party in their honor.

It would be impossible to document all of the foreign visitors we hosted, so I am covering mainly those for whom we have photos.

In the summer of 1978, we received a call from the state department, requesting that we host a group of 28 high-level visitors from the People's Republic of China. They wanted us to plan a five-day tour, and to find a way of paying all of their expenses. This was a trifle over our budget.

I immediately started to plan the tour. Because of the very considerable expense involved for transportation, hotel, and food for 28 people, the Ensmingers mobilized others to assist with the cost. Approximately one-half of the cost was borne jointly by USDA Foreign Agriculture Service and the Department of Food and Agriculture, State of California; and the Ensmingers and their friends financed the rest. Also, the Ensmingers hosted the Chinese delegates for a 7:00 p.m. gala dinner on Saturday evening, September 2, with invited guests; a total of 105 people came for dinner. Trustee and Mrs. Wesley Sawyer also hosted them for a luncheon.

During the tour, Mr. Ho Kang, Deputy Minister of Agriculture, People's Republic of China, who was one of the delegates, asked if I would arrange for slides depicting U.S. agriculture—production, processing, and marketing. I sent out 1,500 letters,

1976. *Left to right:* Dr. Konoplev, Dr. Balakshin, Audrey, John, Dr. Prahov, and me. These Russian scientists lectured at the International Stockmen's School in San Antonio, Texas. I invited them to come to Clovis before the school, where we gave them the usual tours and a dinner party in their honor.

1976. I was an expert witness at a trial in New York city involving horses, so we contacted the Chinese Ambassador to the United Nations, Huang Hua and his wife Lillian. They were delighted to come to the Plaza for dinner with us, where we had an enjoyable evening. *Left to right:* Huang Hua, Dr. E, and Lillian. In our trips to China, we managed to see the Huang Huas every time. They invited us to to various restaurants, and in 1997, to their home.

1984. A group of Japanese swine men. I am in the center of the back row, with Karl Sera second from right.

1978. David Landa and his family visited the foundation from Australia. I worked with David on several consulting projects. He is a skilled attorney, who has since held some important government positions.

which resulted in the following visual aids, all of which were sent to Mr. Ho Kang in China: 3,514 slides of agriculture production, all properly captioned; 3 cassette tapes; 2 films; a new and modern Kodak carousel projector (with a built-in selector adapter) for either 220 or 110 volts. When plugged into an outlet, it automatically selects the correct voltage. Eastman Kodak provided the projector without cost, and the Ensmingers paid the $365 to ship it via air to China.

The entire program of the foundation is centered around the life work of the Ensmingers. The trustees of Agriservices Foundation are all friends of the Ensmingers. The International Schools, the worldwide study-tours, and the books are dependent upon their talents, enthusiasm, and support.

1983. Jacques Decouer, a college graduate from France, wrote to me and asked me to help him get a job working on a ranch so he could get some experience—sort of like a one-year internship. I found him a top ranch, which had holdings in both New Mexico and Texas. When he finished, he came out to Clovis to thank me. He told me that he had originally written about 40 letters to people in the U.S. with the same request, and he had received just the one reply from me.

Left to right: Jesus Martinez, from Mexico, Dr. E, and John Stewart-Smith, Calgary, Canada (formerly from Africa).

This shows the Ensmingers with four of the Chinese delegates. Mr. Ho Kang is to my left. Subsequent to the visit, Mr. Ho Kang became Minister of Agriculture for China.

1984. Kevin Yang, our excellent guide in Inner Mongolia, called from Portland, Oregon where he was doing graduate work and said that he wanted to see us. Yang Zhijian arrived by bus and we took him to the Harris Ranch where this photo was taken. We could never forget Kevin, because he loved to entertain us at the dinners with Mongolian folk songs. He was a real professional.

1986. Bing Huang, son of our good friends, Foreign Minister of China, Huang Hua and his wife Lilian, came for a visit. He had finished his university work in the U.S. and was returning to China. We took him to the usual points of interest and had a gala dinner for him.

1988. *Left to right:* Dr. E, Christine Berger and her mother from France, and Li Sheng, from Chengdu, China. Christine had graduated from the same university as Jacques Decouer and was interested in horses. I was able to make arrangements for six months with the Pollard horse ranch, where they raised and trained race horses; and six months with the Harris Ranch Horse Division, Coalinga. Li Sheng was a visiting professor at Fresno State University, which I had arranged.

1988. We received a call from Brian Young, the South African agricultural attaché in Los Angeles. Of course, we invited him to come to the foundation for a visit. Soon, we became good friends as he stopped quite often when traveling through the valley. Brian Young is on the left.

1988. One day, in January, I received an urgent call from Eta Trabing, a superior Spanish interpreter that we had used for many Stockmen's Schools. She had three nephews from Argentina on her hands, and they wanted some ranching experience. The three Quinn brothers were here for three weeks because it was their summer break in Argentina. After many calls, I found the perfect place, just southeast of Fresno on Jack and Sandra Shannon's ranch. They arrived in Fresno by bus all dressed in suits with ties, and their manners were impeccable. After two weeks on the ranch, we hosted a dinner party for them.

1989. On our seven trips to China, we always had excellent interpreters. An Lin Ge, who was an instructor at the Beijing University, was our guide in 1972. Some of her children had come to the U.S. for graduate work, which brought her here to see them. We were delighted to have her and her husband visit us. Of course, we took them to the Harris Ranch, as we did most guests. They are shown at the feedlot.

1997. Barney and Connie Quinn were in this country for graduate work and they came for lunch and a visit. It was great to renew our friendship.

1990: The Honorable H. J. Coetsee, Minister of Justice, Republic of South Africa, along with six of his staff visited the foundation. This photo was taken at a luncheon in his honor. I am making him an Honorary American Cowboy, with a miniature western saddle.

1990. Duan Liancheng came to the foundation for a meeting. He was in charge of English publications for all of China. When we were in China in 1984, Duan and Mary Liancheng invited us to their home, which was a rare privilege.

1991. Mr. Huang Hua, ambassador/foreign minister, made 20 major U.S. addresses in 18 days, from New York west. A few days before the end of the speaking engagements, he and Mrs. Huang telephoned the Ensmingers and invited them to come see them their last morning in the U.S. So, we were their guests in their suite of rooms at the Biltmore Hotel, Los Angeles, California. Audrey is wearing a jade necklace that was given to her by the Huang Huas.

1992. I was invited to visit the Animal Science Department at Colorado State University. This shows me with Al Yates, the university president. I knew him first as chancellor at Washington State University, when the Beef Cattle Center was named after me. In college work, it is a small world because many people have moved from one university to another, either as students, or later as faculty members. Al Yates is considered a top administrator.

1992. We enjoyed the warm support of some of the Fresno city officials. Mayor Karen Humphrey was interested in foreign liaison because Fresno had a sister city in Russia.

1992. Dr. Thomas Sutherland was held hostage in Lebanon from 1985 to 1991. In 1980, while on the staff of Colorado State University, Tom was the recipient of the Ensminger/Interstate Publishers NACTA Distinguished Teacher Award. Mayor Karen Humphrey presents the key to the city of Fresno to Tom.

1992. At the same dinner party, I made Tom an honorary American cowboy. Trustee David McGlothlin (on the right) was a student of Tom's at Colorado State University.

1996. We hosted an off-press party for Tom and Jean Sutherland when their book *At Your Own Risk*, telling their story of Tom's 5½ years as a hostage, came off press.

1992. This was a dinner in honor of Hiram Drache (extreme right). He is an excellent author of several historical agricultural books. More importantly, he is an excellent speaker with a good story to tell, and I used him frequently at the International Stockmen's Schools. He lives in Fargo, North Dakota.

1995. It was our pleasure to welcome back old friends Reggie and Carol Gomes. Reggie had grown up in Clovis, graduated from Fresno State University, and did graduate work at Washington State University, where I first met him. He proceeded through a college career, mostly in the Midwest, where he became Dean of Agriculture at the University of Illinois. In 1993, he returned to California to take the prestigious position of Vice President of Agriculture for the University of California, Berkeley. At the dinner table he is at the end on the right side, and Bishop Schofield, Episcopal Cathedral, is at the end on the left side.

1995. Dr. Robert Osland's life touched mine several times. I knew his father, who was on the staff at Colorado State University. His father left college work to go with various livestock enterprises, eventually moving to the Staley Hereford Ranch close to Pullman, Washington. Bob got a Ph.D. in Dairy and eventually wound up on the staff at California State University, Fresno (which is not far from us in Clovis). He was on the staff for several years, then took a foreign assignment in Saudi Arabia. This dinner party was in honor of Bob and his Russian wife, Lilia, shown at right, with Dr. E standing behind her.

1995. It was always a real treat, and it happened quite often, when former students came up to me and introduced themselves. I always remembered them. We were in Mexico City en route to Cuba, when Bill Johnson of Louisiana came up and said hello.

1998. Helen Zharkikh, Dr. E's excellent interpreter for both the 1993 and 1996 Ukraine Ag-Tech Schools, drove from San Francisco to see Dr. E because she knew that he was gravely ill. She was in the U.S. visiting relatives. We really appreciated her thoughtfulness.

1997. Dr. Albert Beach, Pushkin Station, St. Petersburg, Russia, whom we had visited in 1996 when we took the Ag-Tech School faculty to Pushkin Research Station, visited us in Clovis in June of 1997. He also was an ISS lecturer in San Antonio, 1978.

1998. Through more than 35 years in Clovis, we have enjoyed a close working relationship with city officials. Perhaps the longest one being with the longtime mayor of Clovis, John Armstrong. I don't know how we could ever thank them enough for their help. This shows Mayor Armstrong with Audrey at a dinner party she had for Drs. Garcia and Ribas from Cuba.

Where and How the Short Course Concept Began

It all began soon after I went to Washington State University as Chairman of the Department of Animal Science in 1941, a position which I held for 21 years. First, it took the form of a series of Feeders Days, Cattle Days, Sheep Days, and Swine Days. Then, a Stockman's School and a Horse Judging School and Show followed. The primary purpose of these events was: Better to serve the farmers and ranchers of Washington through making available to them an interpretation and application of the latest in science and technology. My guiding philosophy was that the programs must evolve first, and that the funds and facilities would follow as a result of industry support. Admittedly, this philosophy is hard on staff; and it is contrary to the traditional way of not starting a program until the money, personnel, and facilities are in place.

The Short Course at WSU Did Not Survive

When I left WSU in 1962, the Stockmen's School was well established and the staff members that I left behind were well acquainted with it. So, it was logical that they should carry the program forward, which they wanted to do.

In continuing the school, the WSU staff decided on two changes: to conduct it by committee action and to operate it in a more relaxed atmosphere. The relaxed atmosphere, with no bell serving as the conscience of enrollees and staff, resulted in the enrollees getting late and cutting classes. The first year that it was tried, coffee breaks stretched out to 15 minutes instead of 10; and the lunch became 1 hour and 15 minutes instead of 1 hour. The second year, the enrollees got to class even later, or not at all. And the short course was dead!

Agriservices Foundation Was Formed

The Articles of Incorporation of Agriservices Foundation were filed November 10, 1964, and approved November 2, 1964; and the by-laws of Agriservices Foundation were adopted November 16, 1964.

Guidelines for Trustees of Agriservices Foundation

Among the many things that need to be done in order that the Foundation may meet its objectives, and to which each Trustee should direct his/her efforts, are the following:

- Provide a global perspective
- Increase scientific and cultural exchange between countries
- Get out the results of research and technology
- Get out the facts
- Guide the agricultural transition
- Control pollution
- Encourage enrollment in the Schools and in the study-tours abroad
- Serve as talent scouts
- Get chairs established
- Help when and where needed

Original Trustees and Officers

The original trustees and officers of Agriservices Foundation were:

Trustees
Mr. Don Doris
Dr. M. E. Ensminger
Mr. Clair Pollard

Officers
Dr. M. E. Ensminger, President
Mr. Clair Pollard, Vice-President
Mrs. A. Ensminger, Secretary-Treasurer

At their first meeting, the original three trustees agreed to invite the following persons to serve as trustees (all of whom subsequently accepted):

Mr. A. S. Bledsoe
Mr. Edward A. Heinemann
Mr. Charles Kyd
Dr. H. E. Robinson
Mr. Charles McKinnon
Mr. Guillermo Osuna
Mr. Guillermo Finan

The trustees of Agriservices Foundation voted to pay me a salary. But, as president of Agriservices Foundation and director of the various programs, I have happily served without stipend.

In the fall of 1964, it was decided to bring the following programs under the umbrella of Agriservices Foundation:

- Horse Science Schools (including the Farrier Science Course)
- The International Stockmen's Schools
- The publication of livestock handbooks
- The study-tours abroad
- Such other needed programs as meet the dedicated purposes of the foundation

Present Officers and Trustees of Agriservices Foundation

The distinguished trustees of Agriservices Foundation give cheerfully and freely of their time. They are a dedicated group, and great people to know. The officers and trustees in 1982 were:

Ensminger, Dr. M. E., President
Clovis, CA

Ensminger, Audrey H., Secretary/Treasurer
Clovis, CA

Farr, William D. And Judy
Greeley, CO

Finan, Guillermo And Nellie
Eagle Pass, TX
also: Muzquiz, Coahuila, Mexico

Fowler, Dr. Stewart H. And Nona
Miltown, FL

Fuerst, Myron M. And Carol
Rhinebeck, NY

Herman, Dr. Harry A. And Lucille
Columbia, MO

Matthiessen, R. Henry
Hume, VA

McGlothlin, David and Sandy
Coalinga, CA

Merthan, Claudia
Elizabeth CO

Osuna, Guillermo
Del Rio, TX
also: Muzquiz, Coahuila, Mexico

Purviance, Norman and Marilyn
Clovis, CA

Rainey, Calvin and Connie
Tucson, AZ

Sedgwick, Cabot
Nogales, AZ

Solomon, Arthur and Wilma
Humboldt, KS

Stuart, W. H. Jr. and Nancy
Bartow, FL

Taysom, Dr. Elvin D. and Myrtle
Tempe, AZ

Terrill, Dr. Clair E. and Zola
Silver Springs, MD

Vanderhoop, Leonard and Barbara
Glendora, CA

Walton, Dr. Robert and Janice
DeForest, WI

Young, Elwin and Susan
Mesa, WA

From time to time we tried to visit all of the trustees. There were a few times when circumstances made it impossible. We did, however, have a great rapport with all of them. The trustees were like family, and whenever I had a problem, I felt free to call them for advice. They were always most helpful.

We included the local ones in our dinner parties.

1979. Trustees at the head table for the banquet during the International Stockmen's School in San Antonio, Texas. *Left to right:* Bill Farr, Myron Fuerst, Henry Matthiessen, Cabot Sedgwick, Clair Pollard, Wes Sawyer, Robby Robinson, Bill Finan, Dr. E, Tom O'Connor, George Lee Hoffman, Harry Herman, Syd Kurth, and Guillermo Osuna.

1976. Lunch with Dr. and Mrs. Robinson. Robbie was an Agriservices trustee as well as Research Director for Swift and Co. Because I could not go, Robbie and Frances helped Audrey on the trip to Cuba in 1978.

1978. I guess they call this a tailgate luncheon. We were taking Robbie and Frances Robinson as well as trustee Clair and Gladys Pollard up the mountain to see the Grant Grove trees. The General Grant tree is the nation's Christmas tree.

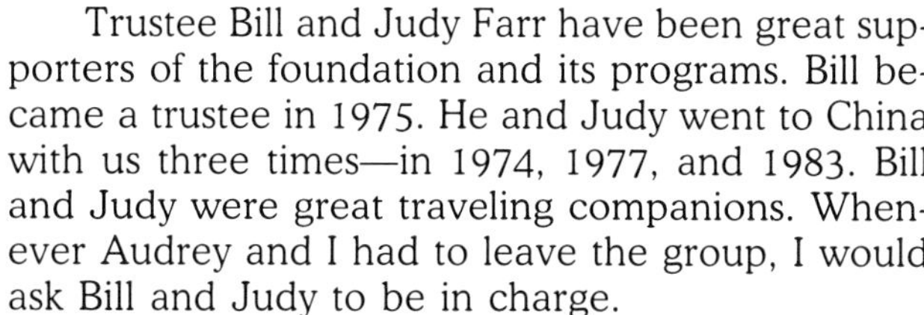

Trustee Bill and Judy Farr have been great supporters of the foundation and its programs. Bill became a trustee in 1975. He and Judy went to China with us three times—in 1974, 1977, and 1983. Bill and Judy were great traveling companions. Whenever Audrey and I had to leave the group, I would ask Bill and Judy to be in charge.

Trustee Cabot Sedgwick has a cattle ranch at Nogales, Arizona. He spent most of his career in foreign service around the world. Because of that, he was very interested in the foreign work that the Ensmingers did. He was a good sounding board, which I liked to use when I felt the need.

Myron Fuerst was a tried and true friend of mine for almost 60 years. When I was in Massachusetts, I would take a group of students to his farm to help with various events. The students loved to get a day off from classes with a bountiful lunch served at noon.

Myron was about three weeks older than I was, and he never let me forget that I shouldn't challenge my senior!

Clair and Gladys Pollard supported the Agriservices Foundation in many different ways. They came to all of our dinner parties; they would take our guests on sightseeing tours of the area; they sponsored the all-time greats for the schools; and—to keep our gardens blooming—they would send us a load of manure and have their hired man come with a spreader.

Trustee Dr. Elvin Taysom was a graduate student of mine at Washington State University. After graduation, I recommended him to Arizona State University, Tempe, where he taught in the Animal Science Department until his retirement. In 1963, when it

1979. Trustee Thomas O'Connor (left) of Texas and Jan Bonsma from South Africa. Thomas O'Connor and his family sponsored several of the foreign professors as well as helping in other areas, for the International Stockmen's Schools.

1983. Bill and Judy Farr in Chengdu, China.

1976. Cabot Sedgwick and Dr. E at the foundation headquarters in Clovis.

The Farr's ultramodern feedlot.

The Ensmingers with Gladys and Clair Pollard. We always celebrated Gladys' birthday with a luncheon and a cake at the foundation.

1996. Valentine's Day photo showing a dinner part in honor of Myron and Carol Fuerst.

1981. *Left to right:* Peter Gacarra from Kenya Africa, who had enrolled in the International Stockmen's School; Dr. and Mrs. Cas Maree, trustee and I.S.S. professor; trustee David McGlothlin, Horse Division, Harris Ranch; and Dr. E. Dr. Cas Maree is head of the Animal Science Department at the University of Pretoria. Peter Gacarra has several farms in Kenya, raising mostly sheep.

1975. Elvin is hanging the sign for the dairy bar that we had for coffee breaks, along with coffee and doughnuts.

came time to start the International Stockmen's Schools, Elvin was of tremendous help. As we often had to improvise, he was superb! He kept everything running smoothly. Without his super personality and his devotion to me and to the program, the schools would not have been so successful. In addition, he seemed to thoroughly enjoy what he did.

In 1992, he accompanied me to Russia to set up the school for 1993. If we had not made that trip, there would not have been any school. Elvin, you have my undying gratitude.

Trustee Norman and Marilyn Purviance have been so very considerate through the years and have helped the foundation in countless ways. Norm was an executive with J.C. Penney for most of his career,

1991. At dinner with Myrtle and Elvin Taysom.

At the time of the International Stockmen's School, Agriservices Foundation honored the stockmen who had made a measurable difference. We called them the "All-Time Greats." In 1983 the honorees were, *left to right:* Bazy Tankersly, a trustee and breeder of Arabian horses; Henry Bethusden, a successful sheepman; Gladys Pollard; Clair Pollard; Bill Farr, a cattleman and trustee; and Robert Walton, President of American Breeders Service and also a trustee.

1990. Jim Tappan of Chandler, Arizona has been a good friend for many years. We took countless visitors to see his extremely successful dairy, but it was a long time before I could persuade him to become a trustee of Agriservices Foundation. Finally, he capitulated. *Left to right:* Vicky Tappan, Audrey, Dr. E, Jim, and Dr. G. A. Bogdanov from Kiev, Ukraine.

Trustee David McGlothlin is a loyal supporter of our program. As he is in charge of the horse division at Harris Ranch, we were able to take innumerable visitors to see their facilities and to eat at the popular Harris Ranch Restaurant. *Left to right:* Donald Palmisano, M.D. of Louisiana, David, and Dr. E.

1998. We were privileged to attend a beautiful wedding when their son Paul Purviance married Wendy. The service was held in the garden of the Elderberry House and the reception was in the restaurant, one of the finest in California, and possibly in the west.

and Marilyn was a superb R.N. They helped us host literally hundreds of visitors. When we had large groups arriving by air, they would meet every plane and reverse the procedure when the guest left. They often assisted in setting up the tables for the dinner parties, and afterwards they always stayed to put everything away and get the offices and rooms ready for business the next morning. They are a great blessing to us.

1988. We drove up the mountain to the Elderberry House in Oakhurst for lunch on a Sunday. *Left to right:* Dr. E, his sister Aileen Bennett of Oklahoma, Marilyn and Norm Purviance.

We enjoyed many trips to Mexico to be with our two Mexican trustees, Bill Finan and Guillermo Osuna, and their wives, Nellie Finan and Doris Osuna. Even though their ranches were 100 miles apart, we usually visited both of them on the same trip. Travel was always in their small planes. We were fortunate to attend most of their children's weddings, which were gala affairs.

I loved to sit and talk about cattle with Bill Finan at his ranch.

1987. This picture of me with Bill and Nellie Finan was taken on the occasion of Sergio and Fernandes Osuna's wedding.

1989. Guillermo is interpreting into Spanish the plaque that Dr. E presented to the Finans on the occasion of Bill receiving the highest honor bestowed by the President of Mexico—the Presidential Merit Award to a Cattleman. The Finans were also celebrating 50 years of ranching.

1991. The beautiful wedding of Monica Finan and Luis Lauro in Piedras Negras.

1991. Audrey and Dr. E are at Monica Finan's wedding.

1979. Guillermo and I survey the Osuna's cattle.

1979. I loved to hunt wild turkey on Guillermo's ranch.

1987. The beautiful bride, Fernandes, and her new husband, Sergio. They had the same eight-violin group playing at the dinner as Guillermo and Doris had at their wedding 25 years previously.

1987. This was taken at Fernandes Osuna's wedding. Audrey and I are seated. Guillermo and Doris Osuna are standing.

1989. We traveled to Del Rio with trustee Leonard Vanderhoop and his wife Barbara to attend the Finans reception and lunch celebrating their 50 years of ranching. Guillermo drove us over his ranch. We stopped to see the flume they made to catch what little rain they get. It funnels the water into a large round tank (behind us)—a very ingenious idea.

1982. Trustee Wes and Maida Sawyer of Diamond "S" Ranch in Waterford, California entertained many groups who visited their dairy and walnut ranch. The tables were set on the lawn in their beautiful garden. We had brought with us a group of trustees and friends who had come for the off-press party of Dr. E's book *Feeds & Nutrition.*

Art and Wilma Solomon visited the Ensmingers from Kansas several times and Art made two foreign trips with us. We always enjoyed being with them and hearing about the mules that Art was training.

1991. Guillermo Osuna, Jr. and his bride Patricia, stopped to see the Ensmingers on returning from their South Pacific honeymoon. We presented them with a gold trimmed ropes and bows tray at a dinner party we hosted in their honor.

1991. Trustee Leonard and Barbara Vanderhoop (center) sponsored a luncheon for a group of eight Russians who had come to set up some schools in the U.S.S.R. Before the plans could be completed the U.S.S.R. was no more. But we did go on to plan three schools in Russia and Ukraine and some of the group shown were involved. There is more about the Vanderhoop's philanthropy in the "Awards" chapter about the dedication of the Ensminger Room and the mural at Iowa State University.

1991. We were invited to Leonard's 70th birthday. Barbara loves to give Len surprise parties. I presented to him a golfing rabbit because of his love for the game.

1992. At Iowa State University where we were preparing for the upcoming school in Russia. *Left to right:* Dr. Gerald E. Klonglan, trustee Arthur Solomon, Audrey, Dr. E., trustee Dr. Robert Walton, Janice Walton, and President Martin Jischke.

We always enjoyed a visit to trustee Elwin Young's place in Pasco, Washington. They are modern day German Baptists. It is like turning back the clock to a gentler and quieter time. Butch (Elwin) and Susan are the perfect couple, and the much loved parents of two boys and three girls, and their offspring.

We attended church with them, and witnessed baptism in the river. Also, we attended two of their daughters' weddings. An invitation was a command performance.

Elwin and Susan Young, along with their preschool children, first came to the International Stockmen's School in Phoenix. Elvin said later that he had an idea at that school which saved $10,000 and he couldn't afford not to come for the next eleven years

When he had to sell his dairy because of the encroaching city of Modesto, he moved his operation to the state of Washington.

1996. Dr. Robert Walton (left) and Dr. James Oldfield (my co-author of the second edition of *Feeds & Nutrition*) are enjoying their malts and hamburgers at McDonald's in Moscow, Russia.

1994. We attended the wedding of Janet Young to Ken Blocher. *Left to right:* Elwin Young is performing the service, Mary (whose back is to the camera), and Janet (Ken is standing beside her).

1995. A group from Iowa State University came to visit the foundation. Our local trustees were all there for the dinner in ISU's honor. *Left to right:* Dr. Scanes, Assistant Dean of Agriculture, ISU, trustees Waymon Watts, Norm Purviance, Dave McGlothlin, and Dr. E.

1996. We attended the wedding of Mary Young to Sidney Bauman. This is a photo of Audrey and Dr. E with Mary and Sidney.

Fund-Raising

Agriservices Foundation never had a fund-raising campaign as such. As a result, we have operated "lean and mean." Despite the handicap of lack of funds, no other American foundation has accomplished so much with so little, and has such a fine reputation, nationally and internationally. This has been possible because the Ensmingers have largely assumed the burden of keeping the flagship of the foundation (the headquarters of the foundation at Clovis, California, and the program emanating there from) going by providing the facilities and most of the operating funds.

100% of the Gifts to Agriservices Foundation Go for the Intended Purpose

How many charitably-supported organizations can say that? Since the foundation was formed in 1964, the Ensmingers have happily given half of their time to directing the program of the foundation. Likewise, they contribute the headquarters of the foundation and an automobile; and they pay their own travel expenses. In the last few years, they have made large contributions to the foundation each year.

With Discontinuing of the International Stockmen's School and Study-Tours Abroad, We Lost Funds Therefrom

For many years, the primary sources of funds for operation of the foundation were the approximately 10% derived from the enrollment fees of the International Stockmen's School, and the charges made for the foundation-sponsored study tours abroad. Additionally, there were few, but much appreciated, "Chairs" provided for the International Stockmen's School. But for the most part, the foundation generated its own operating funds. This, along with the free services of the Ensmingers and free office headquarters, made for a "least-cost foundation." So, since 1981, the foundation flagship has received precious little financial support, with the result that the burden of keeping it afloat has largely fallen on the Ensmingers.

Lee and Claudia Hoffman's Offer of $150,000

The "Committee to Perpetuate Agriservices Foundation" held a meeting in the foundation offices on April 20–21, 1979.

Those present were: Mr. S. P. Kurth, chairman of the committee, Mr. LeRoy Hoffman, Mr. Myron M. Fuerst, Mr. Calvin S. Rainey, Mr. Clair Pollard, Mr. Wesley N. Sawyer, and Dr. M. E. Ensminger. Also, we were pleased to have the presence of the following ladies: Gladys Pollard, Claudia Hoffman, Maida Sawyer, and Audrey Ensminger.

The program started with a 7:00 p.m. gala dinner at the foundation headquarters on Friday evening, April 20, with invited guests.

The next morning, LeRoy Hoffman led off. He reported on the meeting in Clovis last spring at which time he and Myron Fuerst were given the responsibility of raising $1 million to $10 million. He stated that he does not know enough people who can contribute this kind of support. Hoffman voiced the opinion that Dr. Ensminger is the only person whom he knows who could raise the necessary funds. Fuerst concurred in the latter thinking.

Then, LeRoy and his wife Claudia, electrified the meeting with the following offer: If a suitable future director can be found, Claudia and I will guarantee a salary for him of up to $50,000 per year for three years.

Cabot Sedgwick moved that the trustees give the Hoffmans a singular vote of appreciation for their generous offer to guarantee up to $50,000 per year for three years for an assistant director. Cal Rainey seconded the motion and the motion carried.

Following the generous offer of Lee and Claudia Hoffman, we started a search for an assistant director, with the intent that Dr. E would train him, then pass along the torch to him. But able and willing people for this assignment are scarce and hard to come by. Before the search was completed, Lee Hoffman developed lung cancer and passed away on November 26, 1980; without Agriservices Foundation being able to implement the Hoffman offer of $150,000.

Nothing ever came of the generous George Lee Hoffman offer, due to his untimely death! But I shall ever be grateful to LeRoy and Claudia Hoffman for this vote of high confidence.

A History of Agriservices Foundation, 1962–1982

In 1982, I wrote and copyrighted *A History of*

Agriservices Foundation, 1962–1982. I covered, in depth, the formation of the foundation; the Horse Science Schools held from 1963 to 1972; the evolution of the Beef Cattle/Stud Manager's School; the addition of dairy and sheep; and the final name change to the International Stockmen's School; the study-tours abroad; and the handbooks published for the schools.

The International Stockmen's Schools were always held in early January, because most stockmen were not as busy at that time of year. It was held in Phoenix, Arizona for about 10 years, then transferred to San Antonio, Texas to take advantage of larger facilities in the convention center. Across the street was the very excellent Hilton Palacio Del Rio, which became a second home to us.

There was an annual trustee's party, sponsored for many years by Elanco, the agricultural division of Eli Lilly. Mr. James Lay, of Elanco in Fresno, was in charge of this event. The trustees, who paid their own travel to the school, received only a ticket to the ISS banquet, plus the Elanco dinner party. We all looked forward to our times together.

1995. Jim & Merri Lay are now retired and living in Sun City West, Arizona. They are heavily involved in charitable work. This photo was taken at a Christmas time dinner party that they hosted for the Ensmingers and the Ensmingers' adopted Russian daughter and granddaughter, Elena and Kate Polouchkina, who now live in Ames, Iowa.

Before Dr. E passed away, he had made plans for the dedication of the mural in the Ensminger Room at Iowa State University in November of 1998. Also, he had planned for a meeting of the trustees. So, we met, as this picture shows. Elvin Taysom took the photo. It was a bittersweet time.

I asked each one to say a few words and we had the election of officers. I guess those of us who knew Dr. E well, will always miss his dynamic presence. Left to right: G. Osuna, R. Walton, E. Young, N. Purviance, A. Ensminger, B. Farr, L. Vanderhoop, B. Finan, A. Solomon, and, behind the camera, Elvin. AHE

1963–1972
TWENTY-ONE HORSE SCIENCE (FARRIER) SCHOOLS

Following World War II, interest in light horses mushroomed, but few well-trained horsemen were around. Most of the great horsemen of the draft era had either retired or passed on, and colleges and the U.S. Department of Agriculture couldn't drop their horse programs fast enough.

I was one of the few animal scientists with interest in and knowledge of light horses. In 1946, I established horse facilities and a program at Washington State College, known as WSC Hilltop Stables. In 1956, at the request of the U.S. Department of Agriculture, I authored a light horse bulletin, known as *Light Horses*, Farmers' Bulletin No. 2127, which came off press in 1958. (This bulletin, of which more than 1 million copies were printed the first 3 years, was written free of charge, because its primary purpose was for 4-H Club members.)

Upon leaving WSU in 1962, pressures were brought to bear for me to fill a void that neither colleges nor the U.S. Department of Agriculture were qualified for, nor interested in filling—the training of horse lovers in the art and science of horses, horsemanship, and horseshoeing. I responded by starting the Horse Science School in 1963, with three schools held that year—one school in each California, Missouri, and Pennsylvania. These schools were continued annually through 1972, with a total of 21 schools held from coast to coast. We trained hundreds of equestrians; and we trained 500 farriers (horseshoers).

Staff of the fifth annual Horse Science School (1967), at Agricultural and Technical College (A&TC), Cobleskill, New York. *Front row left to right:* Walter J. Clark, Chairman, Animal Husbandry Department, A&TC; Frances Reker, Director, Frances Reker School of Horsemanship, Rockford, MN; Audrey H. Ensminger; and Dr. E, Director of the Horse Science Schools. *Back row left to right:* Prof. Robert W. Miller, Horse Specialist, Montana State University, Bozeman; Jack Brainard, Diamond B. Ranch, Rochester, MN; Dr. James C. Dollahon, Dean, College of Agriculture, Wisconsin State University, River Falls; Dr. Robert F. Behlow, D.V.M., Prof. and Extension Veterinarian, North Carolina State University, Raleigh; Dr. S. W. Sabin, Extension Equine Specialist, Cornell University, Ithaca, NY; Dr. Robert R Smalley, Professor, A&TC; and Donald Canfield, Farrier, Murfreesboro, TN.

All Horse Science Schools were conducted in cooperation with colleges and universities. Again and again, we emphasized that the Agriservices Foundation schools were designed to enhance the programs of the colleges and universities, and *not* to compete with them. In this spirit, I am happy to report that each of the 21 Horse Science Schools was held in cooperation with a college or university, and that all of them carried college credit for those who were eligible and interested.

In 1967, Agriservices Foundation conducted two Horse Science Schools; one at Wisconsin State University, River Falls, and the other at A&TC, Cobleskill, NY.

Distinguished Equine Awards

Distinguished Equine Awards were made at the Horse Science Schools for the purpose of publicly recognizing those who had contributed richly to the nation's light horse industry. Each award carried with it a handsome plaque and a citation. Recipients were recommended by previous award winners and leaders in the horse industry, and selected by the trustees of Agriservices Foundation.

A list of the recipients of the Distinguished Equine Award follows:

Colonel Fred William Koester
Fullerton, California, in 1963

A colonel in the U.S. Army Remount Service; Commanding Officer of the famed Kellogg Ranch; General Manager of the California Thoroughbred Breeders Association; and developer of the lip tattoo method of identifying horses.

Mrs. Claud H. Drew
Columbia, Missouri, in 1963

Noted horse breeder, exhibitor, horse show manager, horse show judge, and instructor of horsemanship.

Brigadier General Wayne O. Kester, DVM
in 1963

Equine veterinarian, official, contestant, writer, and director of research; and leader of the Morris Animal Foundation and the American Association of Equine Practitioners.

George A. Pope, Jr.

George A. Pope, Jr.
El Peco Ranch, Madera, California, in 1964

He distinguished himself as a polo player; as a breeder/racer of Thoroughbreds, including the 1962 Kentucky Derby winner, *Decidedly*; as a board member of the California Thoroughbred Association; and as a member of the Jockey Club.

Lawrence B. Sheppard

Lawrence B. Sheppard
Hanover Shoe Farm, Hanover, Pennsylvania, in 1964

Famed Standardbred breeder, who produced the fastest trotters and pacers in America; top driver; and esteemed leader of harness racing and of the United States Trotting Association.

Charles J. Cronan

Charles J. (June) Cronan
Secretary, American Saddle Breeders Assn., Louisville, Kentucky, in 1965

A lawyer by training, a horseman by choice; the dean of light horse breed registry secretaries; a director of United States Pony Clubs, and of the American Horse Shows Association.

Colonel Floyd C. Sager, DVM
Claiborne Farm, Paris, Kentucky, in 1966

From 1917 to 1948, he served in the U.S. Army Veterinary Corps, where he was decorated by two grateful nations—the United States and France. In 1948, he became resident veterinarian of famed Claiborne Farm, Paris, Kentucky.

Col. Floyd C. Sager,

Humphrey S. Finney
Versailles, Kentucky, in 1967

He distinguished himself in practically all phases of the horse industry, from caretaker to businessman. He carved a wide niche as a stud manager, Field Secretary of the Maryland Horse Breeders Association, Editor of *The Maryland Horse*, President of Fasig-Tipton Co., and President of the Thoroughbred Club of America.

Humphrey S. Finney

Professor L. V. (Cy) Tirrell
Department of Animal Science, University of New Hampshire, Durham, New Hampshire, in 1967

Teacher and immortal in the horse world, whose contributions to the horse industry, and impact on students and horsemen, will live on and on.

Professor L. V. Tirrell

Edward A. Heinemann
Executive Secretary, Washington Horse Breeders Association, Seattle, Washington, in 1968

The dean of executive secretaries of state horse breeders associations. He pioneered in 4-H horse pro-

Edward A. Heinemann

grams, Thoroughbred sales, and *The Washington Horse Magazine*.

Ed H. Honnen
Quincy Farms, Denver, Colorado, in 1968

Quarter Horse breeder, and President, American Quarter Horse Association. Ed Honnen caused horse registries to support and extol equine research and education with pride.

Ed H. Honnen

Professor Byron H. Good
Department of Animal Husbandry, Michigan State University, East Lansing, Michigan, in 1969

He greatly pursued the light horse industry as a teacher at Michigan State University, as horse show judge throughout America, as an advisor of Kellogg Arabians, Cal Poly, Pomona, California, and as an inspector of Arabian horses in Poland and Spain.

Prof. Byron H. Good

Leslie Combs II
Spendthrift Farms, Lexington, Kentucky, in 1969

Master breeder, super salesman, and without a peer as an equine syndicator. He perfected and popularized the art of syndicating stallions. Mr. Combs was a member of the Jockey Club and an honorary life member of the Thoroughbred Club of America.

Leslie Combs II

Leslie L. Boomhower
Executive Secretary, Pony of the Americas Club, Mason City, Iowa, in 1970

Leslie Boomhower, a successful lawyer and an ardent horseman, set about developing a breed of ponies suitable for children who had outgrown the Shetland Pony, but who were not ready for a horse. To fill this need, he created the Pony of the Americas. From 1954 to 1961, Mr. Boomhower served the registry without stipend. From 1961 to 1970, he served as Executive Secretary of the Pony of the Americas Club.

Leslie L. Boomhower

Dr. William R. McGee, DVM
Hagyard-Davidson-McGee, Lexington, Kentucky, in 1970

Dr. McGee completed the veterinary degree at Washington State University, following which he entered equine practice in Lexington, Kentucky. He served as President of the American Association of Equine Practitioners, President of the Thoroughbred Club of America, and as a director and Treasurer of the Grayson Foundation.

Dr. William R. McGee, DVM

George B. Hatley
Executive Secretary, Appaloosa Horse Club, Moscow, Idaho, in 1971

During the formative years of the Appaloosa breed, George Hatley served as executive secretary without stipend. The growth of the breed will ever remain as a living tribute to George B. Hatley, architect of the Appaloosa breed.

George B. Hatley

Marion Flint
Square Top Three Quarter Horses, Midland, Texas, in 1971

Mr. Flint is "Mr. Cutting Horse." He is a noted Quarter Horse breeder, and the longtime President of the National Cutting Horse Association. Under Mr. Flint's leadership, Cutting Horse events were transformed from a mere exhibition to a major sport; and a permanent home for the National Cutting Horse Association was established in Fort Worth, Texas.

Marion Flint

Stanley Dancer
Stanley Dancer Stables, Egyptian Acres, New Egypt, New Jersey, in 1972

Stanley Dancer made the mountainous leap from 4-H Club boy to superstar of harness racing, and became a legend in his time. On his way up, he never lost his love for the soil and the basic human values that he acquired down on the farm.

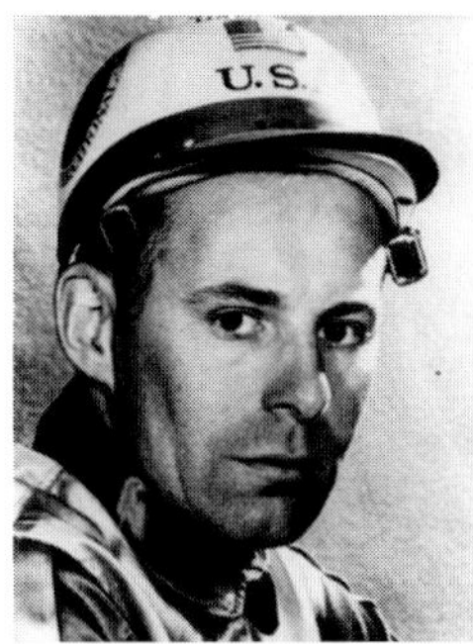

Stanley Dancer

John Eric Longden
Arcadia, California, in 1972

Johnny Longden overcame boyhood poverty on the Canadian prairies and became a front-running jockey, trainer, and humanitarian. He was instrumental in founding the Jockey Guild. In 1943, Johnny Longden won the Triple Crown on *Count Fleet*. For three years—1938, 1947, and 1948—he was the National Riding Champion. In 1956, he broke Sir Gordon Richards' record with his 4,871st victory.

John Eric Longden

I am presenting a plaque to one of our 1971 honorees, George B. Hatley, who worked without stipend to preserve the Appaloosa breed.

Summary of the Horse Science Schools

The Horse Science School was discontinued in 1972, and the Farrier Science Course was discontinued in 1975. They had served their purpose well—that of training many horsemen and 500 horseshoers during an era when good equine schools were few. In the meantime, a number of horse schools and horseshoeing schools had sprung up across the country. Then, too, we recognized the need to expand the International Stockmen's School, in which there was a horse division.

A class in western riding. Dwight Stewart (center) is the instructor.

A class in jumping.

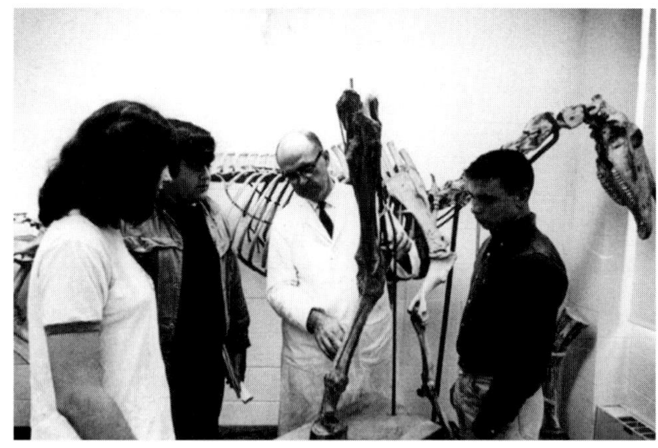

A class in equine anatomy.

Horse Science School luncheon at Wisconsin State University, River Falls, WI, in 1965. I am seated behind the podium, with Rex Ellsworth, noted Thoroughbred breeder and speaker at the luncheon, seated to my right.

This shows the farrier stations. Each farrier had a forge, an anvil, and other horseshoeing tools.

The Horse Science Schools Live On

I received the following communication on September 27, 1989:

From: Bertram Ellis

My wife & I were wondering if your schools are still in existence and if so where in Calif.

Our daughter Virginia Ellis Stanley was in your school at Sam Houston U. years ago and now is an accomplished dressage instructor here who represents Jeff Moore.

I responded to Mr. Ellis in a letter dated October 3, 1989, a copy of which follows:

Thank you for your communication of September 27, reminding me that your daughter, Virginia Ellis Stanley, was an enrollee in the Horse Science School that was held at Sam Houston State University, asking if the schools are still being held, and telling me that Virginia is now an accomplished dressage instructor. Hearing from you brought back pleasant memories!

The school at Sam Houston State University, in 1971, was one of 21 great Horse Science Schools that Agriservices Foundation sponsored, and I conducted, from coast-to-coast. In those schools, we trained many of those who went on to become the great horsemen of America—your daughter among them. We also trained 500 farriers. Incidentally, the present Chairman of the International Stockmen's Educational Foundation, T. Michael O'Connor, Victoria, Texas, was a 15-year-old enrollee in the same 1971 Horse Science School at Sam Houston State University in which Virginia was an enrollee. Like your daughter, T. Michael O'Connor is a person of very considerable stature and accomplishment today.

Now to the status of the schools! After conducting 21 successful Horse Science Schools, the trustees of Agriservices Foundation and I decided that there was urgent need to increase our foreign work in the area of world food, hunger and malnutrition, as well as to continue the International Stockmen's School which I had started at Washington State University in the early 1940s. So, we discontinued the Horse Science Schools. Besides, we had trained many good horse specialists in those Horse Science Schools; for example, Dr. Sam Sabin, the longtime horse specialist at Cornell University, was a 3-time enrollee in the Horse Science School.

In 1967, when the school was held at the State University at Cobleskill, NY, Prof. Cy Tirrell was given the Distinguished Equine Award. Cy had been a longtime friend of mine since the years I spent at the University of Massachusets, and Cy was at the University of New Hampshire.

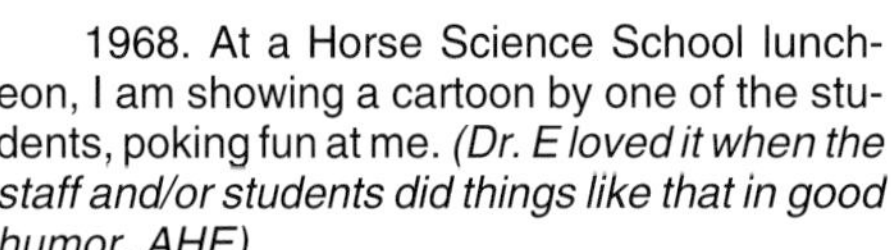

1968. At a Horse Science School luncheon, I am showing a cartoon by one of the students, poking fun at me. *(Dr. E loved it when the staff and/or students did things like that in good humor. AHE)*

In 1976, Johnny Longden came for lunch and a visit (*left to right:* Robert Vann, Johnny Longden, Dr. E). Johnny and his wife, Hazel, liked to reminisce with Audrey about growing up in Winnipeg, Canada. Johnny told how he spent time riding bareback with some of the Indians on a nearby reservation. We honored Johnny for his illustrious career as a jockey at the 1972 Horse Science School.

In 1972 one of the Horse Science Schools was held at Horseman's Park, Stardust Hotel, Las Vegas, Nevada. It was in cooperation with the University of Nevada. As seen in the photo, middle background, they had plenty of stalls and two show rings, one with bleachers. The school drew a big crowd.

1964–1981
TWENTY-FOUR MORE SUCCESSFUL INTERNATIONAL SCHOOLS

When my stockmen friends contacted me wondering how they could keep abreast of developments in the livestock industry with the stockmen's school at Washington State University no longer available, my arm twisted easily.

I reviewed the simple format that I had used at WSU:

- Keep in mind the following simple test when selecting topics, preparing papers, and delivering lectures—is it helpful and does it address the most important issues or problems of the day?
- Have a selection of topics from which the enrollees may choose each hour—6 to 12 topics each hour.
- Secure the best guest professors in the world to make the presentations; with about one-third each coming from colleges and USDA, agribusinesses, and farmers or ranchers. All guest professors to be invited by, and under the control of, the director of the school (a divided responsibility won't work). The director can and should have a lot of sounding boards, but he must not rely on committee action. Actually, he must operate as a benevolent dictator.
- Have three concentrated days of classes and one day for a farm/country/agribusiness tour. It seems to be just the right amount of time.
- Provide a variety of visual aids; with a capable troubleshooter in charge.
- Operate absolutely on time.
- The subject matter should be changed from year to year, but the same format applies to all schools whenever and wherever held.

As a result of a careful study at that time, I concluded that the most desirable place and time for such a school was in Phoenix, Arizona during the first full week in January. The first two schools were held at the Sands Motor Hotel, but the facilities were not adequate. The third year's school was held at the Phoenix Ramada Inn, after which I engaged all of their facilities for the first full week in January for a 10-year period.

In keeping with Agriservices Foundation policy, we always tried very hard to conduct the International Stockmen's School either "in cooperation with" or "cosponsored by" a college or university in the state in which it was held, preferably with the

The Ramada Inn, Phoenix, Arizona, with 400 rooms, fine food, and spacious grounds, was the home of the International Stockmen's School for 11 years, the first full week in January beginning in 1965, and continuing annually until the enrollment outgrew the facilities.

Audrey and I taking telephone calls during the 1964 International Stockmen's School at the Sands Motor Hotel, Phoenix, AZ.

Introducing the banquet speaker, Mr. A. S. Bledsoe—owner-operator of The Flying B Ranch, Ellensburg, WA, one of my former students of whom I am very proud and a trustee of Agriservices Foundation—at the 1965 International Stockmen's School, in Phoenix. Mr. Bledsoe addressed enrollees from 29 states, Canada, and Mexico. Clair Pollard, a trustee of Agriservices Foundation, is shown seated on the right.

The 1972 International Stockmen's School banquet in Phoenix. Dr. Doug Ensminger, my brother, who directed the Ford Foundation program for all of India for 19 years, is the banquet speaker. Mrs. Bonsma is on his right.

Three trustees and an enrollee at the 1972 International Stockmen's School, Ramada Inn, Phoenix, Arizona. *Left to right:* Dr. H. E. Robinson, Corporate Vice President, Research and Development, Swift & Co., Chicago; Mr. Guillermo Osuna, Infante Ranch, Muzquiz, Coahuila, Mexico; Mr. Bill Finan, Hacienda Valle, Columbia, Muzquiz, Coahuila, Mexico; and an enrollee in the school.

Left to right: Diego Redo, Jr., Cananea Sonora, Mexico; Richard J. O'Neill, Rancho Mission Viejo, San Juan Capistrano, California; Charles Redd, Redd Ranches, La Sal, Utah; Bill Verdugo, Clovis, California; Jeff Green, Feedlot Manager, J. G. Boswell Co., Litchfield Park, Arizona; Jack Wilkinson, Jr., Midland Texas; Lee Hoffman, Eureka, South Dakota; Nelson Gammon, Field Representative, Casa Grande Cotton Oil Mill, Casa Grande, Arizona; Leslie Johnson, Head, Department of Animal Science, Iowa State University, Ames, Iowa; Powhatan Carter, Jr., Ft. Sumner, New Mexico; and Edward J. Czarnetzky, Vice President, Miner Institute, Chazy, New York.

Prof. Jan Bonsma, South Africa, guest professor in the 1972 International Stockmen's School in Phoenix.

Guillermo Osuna(right) and John Hodges(left) at the 1972 International Stockmen's School banquet.

"Little Audrey" and me at the 1969 International Stockmen's School banquet in Phoenix.

1973. International Stockmen's School registration desk in the Ramada Inn. Besides registration, we sold meal tickets because we ate both breakfast and lunch together, as well as the banquet ticket. In addition, we sold both the handbooks and my books.

land grant institution. But this wasn't always easy because throughout the 1950s, 1960s, and 1970s most land grant universities were bloated with state and federal appropriations and therefore didn't feel they needed to participate in activities such as the International Stockmen's School.

From 1964 to 1980, the Sponsorship of the School Was a Mixed Bag

In 1964 and 1965, the Foundation went it alone. From 1966 through 1972, the school was held "in cooperation" with Arizona State University, Tempe.

The 1978 and 1980 Schools, both of which were held in Arizona (1978 in Phoenix; 1980 in Tucson), were under the joint sponsorship of Agriservices Foundation and the University of Arizona, at Tucson. We greatly enjoyed working with Dr. R. W. Rice, who was then Chairman of Animal Science; and the enrollees benefited from the joint sponsorship. But we had outgrown the facilities in both Phoenix and Tucson.

Several of our trustees, especially Trustees Guillermo Osuna and Bill Finan, suggested that we move the School to San Antonio, a charming city with adequate facilities in the old Hemisphere Expo-

Coffee break at the 1972 International Stockmen's School at The Ramada Inn, Phoenix. *Note:* This was outdoors, on the Ramada Inn patio, the first full week in January.

1973. This shows me ringing the bell at the end of the coffee break.

sition complex. So, Trustee and Mrs. Bill Finan, Trustee and Mrs. Guillermo Osuna, and Audrey and I decided to check out the San Antonio facilities. We received a warm and friendly welcome in San Antonio.

Despite holding the school in Texas, California State University, Fresno continued to offer college credit to those who were interested and met the requirements.

The Texas Schools Were Fabulously Successful

San Antonio proved to be the right choice. The facilities were good, and the enrollment was excellent. We began to attract more and larger groups from agriculture businesses. Albers Milling Company, the feed division of Carnation, Inc., sent two or three the first year, and from then on the group got larger each year. The word that came back to us was "we don't know what you are doing at the school, but those who return are more enthusiastic, knowledgeable, and sometimes completely changed. We had to start rotating them because they all want to go back as often as we can send them. Thanks!"

Cas Maree from South Africa is lecturing in one of the Fiesta rooms at the San Antonio Convention Center.

The Hilton Palacio Del Rio, San Antonio, Texas, home of The International Stockmen's School from 1971-1981. It is located on the unique River Walk, across the street from the San Antonio Convention Center and the Tower of the Americas revolving restaurant. *Note:* The 1980 School was held at the Marriott Hotel, Tucson, Arizona.

With some of the ranches it was the same story. Also, we were delighted that in 1979 we had over six students from one of the Indian reservations.

As a complete surprise, the trustees of Agriservices Foundation dedicated the 1980 International Stockmen's School Banquet to me. Following

I am showing a group of native American attendees how I ring the bell.

For the first time in 30 years, two Chinese scientists/professors from the Chinese Academy of Agricultural and Forestry Sciences appeared on a U.S. program January 8–11, 1979, when Dr. Cheng Pi-Liu (above) and Dr. Liu Chin-Hsu (below) lectured in the January 8-11, 1979 International Stockmen's School, in San Antonio.

Preceding the 1979 International Stockmen's School in San Antonio, Texas, Prof. Cheng Pi-Liu and Prof. Liu Chin-Hsu, came to the Agriservices Foundation/Ensminger Home, Clovis, California. During their visit, the Ensmingers hosted a dinner in their honor. This shows the guests as they passed through the buffet line, and before seating.

The travel of Professors Cheng and Liu was sponsored by Mr. Robert O. Anderson, Chairman of the Board, Atlantic Richfield. He was also our banquet speaker in the 1974 School in San Antonio. The title of his address: "Cattle in the Global Perspective."

Prof. Jan Bonsma, Head, Department of Animal Science, The University of Pretoria, Pretoria, South Africa, appeared on five International Stockmen's School programs—in 1968, 1972, 1975, 1979, and 1981. This photo shows Prof. and Mrs. (Cila) Bonsma at the 1979 School in San Antonio, Texas.

A memorable dinner party in San Antonio, Texas, in a Chinese restaurant, hosted by Prof. Cheng Pi-Liu and Prof. Liu Chin-Hsu, from China, in 1979. *Left to right:* Prof. Liu, Prof. Cheng, Audrey Ensminger, Elvin Taysom, Frances Johnson (Mrs. E's sister), Russell Johnson, and Dr. E.

This shows Dr. Weber receiving a plaque from Clair Pollard and being inducted into the Agriservices Foundation All-Time Great Gallery in 1979. Dr. Weber's distinguished career was at Kansas State University. *Left to right:* Dr. E, Gladys Pollard, Clair Pollard, and Dr. A. D. "Dad" Weber.

This shows Cal Rainey receiving a plaque from Clair Pollard and being inducted into the Agriservices Foundation All-Time Great Gallery in 1979. Mr. Rainey served racing long and well, and in many capacities, including exercise boy, jockey, trainer, patrol judge, steward, and Executive Director of The Jockey Club. *Left to right:* Dr. E, Gladys Pollard, Trustee Clair Pollard, and Calvin Stuart Rainey. (Cal Rainey also became a valued trustee of Agriservices Foundation.)

My brothers, sisters, and sisters-in-law, *left to right: Seated:* Aileen Bennett and Ella Mae Ervin. *Middle:* Audrey Ensminger, Isabel Ensminger, Mary Ensminger, Myrtle Ensminger, and Theda Ensminger. *Back Row:* Dr. Leonard Ensminger, Dr. Douglas Ensminger, Dr. M. E. Ensminger, and Mr. Garnett Ensminger.

My brothers and sisters, *left to right: Seated:* Aileen Bennett and Ella Mae Ervin. *Standing:* Dr. Leonard Ensminger, Dr. Douglas Ensminger, Dr. M. E. Ensminger, and Mr. Garnett Ensminger.

the dinner, Trustee George Lee Hoffman took over as master of ceremonies; and my brothers and sisters paraded in, one by one, including my sister-in-law, Myrtle, widow of brother Harry. Each of them enhanced the banquet with brief and appropriate remarks. Then, the trustees presented a plaque to me with the following inscription:

1980
Agriservices Foundation
Salutes
All-Time Great
DR. M. E. ENSMINGER
Who
Dedicated His Entire Life To
The Livestock Industry
For Him, Work Is Fun
And Fun Is Work
He Is A Maverick
Who Makes
His Dreams Come True

From time to time the trustees used to ask permission to be on the ISS banquet program. I never knew what to expect. One year John Hodges, who was on the ISS staff several times, asked permission to make a presentation. It turned out to be a wooden plaque advertising the "Bell Tavern." Where they found it is still a mystery.

In 1979 Claudia Hoffman presented me with a little poem that I framed and kept in my office. The students and staff used to tease me about my penchant for ringing a bell to keep everything on time, but I always considered it a compliment.

Now, 'tis the time, the poet said, to speak of many things,
But not for us, a dialogue on cabbages and kings,
Our subjects are not royalty and vegetables to grow
But two very special people we're so fortunate to know.
Let's raise a toast to Audrey and of course, to Dr. E,
Without whose dedication, the Stockman's School would never be.
We thank them for their years of work to make our School so great.
Our plaudits should go on-and-on, but the hour is growing late.
One last thought we leave with you, to ponder in your leisure,
A memory of Stockman's School, we hope will surely please—ure!
Ask not for whom the bell tolls! Dwell not in the starting gate,
When you're five minutes early, you're already one minute late!

Following the passing of Trustee Charles Kyd in 1980, I paid tribute to him in a talk entitled, "Empty saddle in the old corral," using the prop shown above. Mrs. Kyd (Beverly) is pictured with me.

At the banquet of the 1981 International Stockmen's School in San Antonio, I presented a special plaque to Dr. Elvin Taysom (right) in appreciation for his many years of service as Assistant Director of The International Stockmen's School. Dr. Taysom is a former student of mine and a trustee of Agriservices Foundation. No one has administered so much TLC (tender loving care) to Audrey and me, and over so many years, as has Dr. Elvin Taysom.

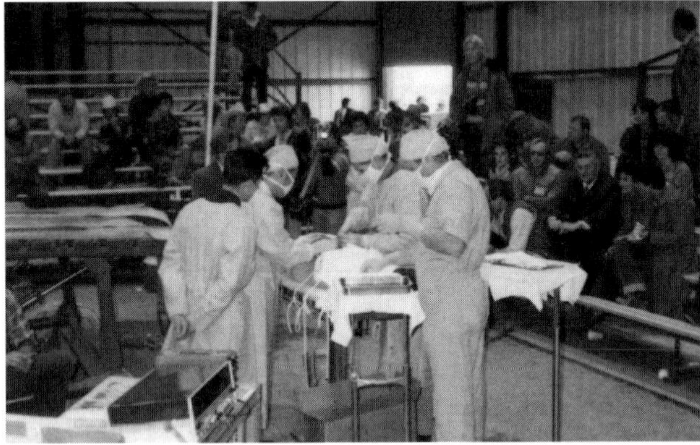

This shows the surgeons working on the animal that was anesthetized only by acupuncture.

Before the surgery, I am meeting with the press.

At the 1980 ISS in Tucson, I had arranged for three scientists to come from Wuhan, China, in order to give a demonstration of acupuncture anesthesia during surgery.

This generated a lot of interest from the press, both print and television. CBS filmed it and showed footage on their 11:00 p.m. nightly newscast. It generated considerable interest and gave the school more publicity than we ever expected.

The Demands on My Time for Foreign Work Increased

Year after year, the demands on my time for foreign work became heavier and heavier. But I couldn't increase my workload. So, something had to give. The trustees and I agreed that I should continue with the seminars and schools abroad, and transfer the San Antonio School. *The reasoning*: Foreign work is more difficult to transfer.

So the following announcement appeared on the front cover of the January 12-15, 1981 International Stockmen's School program:

> I have an announcement!
>
> At age 72, I must pull up the reins a bit. So, I shall ring down the curtain at the end of the January 12-15, 1981 International Stockmen's School. It will be the last School that I shall direct.

Following the above announcement, five different groups expressed genuine interest in carrying the International Stockmen's School forward.

Traditionally, when held in the United States, the International Stockmen's School closes with the playing of the Star Spangled Banner, with the flags of all the countries having one or more enrollees or staff on display; and with a representative of each country standing under each flag, as shown in this 1980 photo.

The 1979 International Stockmen's School banquet. The banquets usually averaged over 500 guests with a head table of approximately 40. I liked to have all the trustees and their wives at the head table, along with all foreign professors and their wives. There were letters of the alphabet left to right along the table. At the end of the program, I announced that if the students would find the letter with which their last name started, they would receive their certificate.

Guest Professors from Around the World

Prof. Jan Bonsma, South Africa. 1968, 1972, 1975, 1979, and 1981 schools.

Dr. Dryfed Lewis, England. 1970 school.

Dr. Peter D. Rossdale, D.V.M., England. 1971, 1979, and 1981 schools.

Dr. John Hodges, England. 1970, 1972, 1973, 1974, 1980, and 1981 schools.

Dr. H. C. Adler, D.V.M., Denmark. 1971 school.

Dr. G. Eric Lamming, England. 1973 school.

Dr. David Hyde, D.V.M., Ireland. 1970 school.

Mr. David W. Best, Australia. 1971 school.

Dr. Edouard J. M. Pouret, D.V.M., France. 1973 school.

Guest Professors from Around the World

Dr. T. R. Preston, England and Cuba.
1973 school.

Mr. Ian de la Rue, Rhodesia.
1975 school.

Dr. O. A. Balakshin, U.S.S.R.
1976 school.

Dr. Samuel Amir, Israel.
1974 and 1981 schools.

Prof., Dr. Hans-Jorgen Hansen,
Sweden. 1975 school.

Dr. L. P. Prahov, U.S.S.R.
1976 school.

Dr. Rex M. Butterfield, D.V.M.,
Australia. 1974, 1975, 1976,
and 1981 schools.

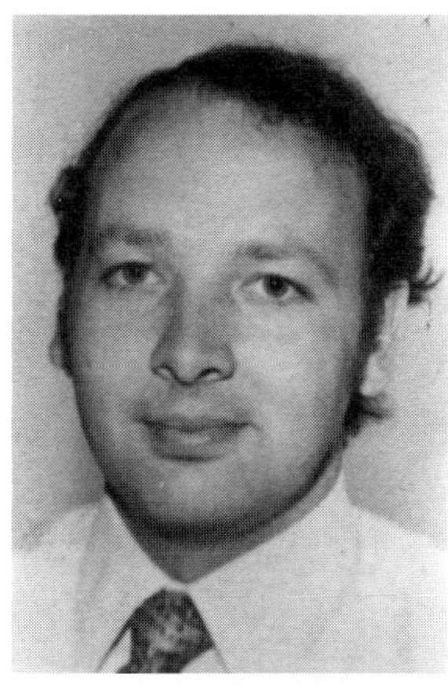

Dr. Sydney Ricketts, D.V.M., England.
1975 school.

Dr. I. S. McFarlane, South Africa.
1976 school.

Guest Professors from Around the World

Dr. H. Kraussiich, Germany. 1976 school.

Dr. Eugene G. Konoplev, U.S.S.R. 1977 school.

Dr. Casper Maree, D.V.M., South Africa. 1971, 1977, and 1979 schools.

Dr. D. F. Wishart, England. 1976 school.

Dr. Leo B. Jeffcott, D.V.M., England. 1977 school.

Dr. Walter G. Whittlestone, New Zealand. 1977 school.

Prof., Dr. G. A. Bogdanov, U.S.S.R. 1977 school.

Prof., Dr. Jorgen, Langholz, Germany. 1977 school.

Prof., Dr. Albert Beach, U.S.S.R. 1978 school.

Guest Professors from Around the World

Prof., Dr. Eduard M. Pern, U.S.S.R.
1978 school.

Dr. Maria Stolzman, Poland.
1978 school.

Prof. Liu Chin-Hsu, China.
1979 school.

Dr. Miriam Ribas, Cuba.
1978 school.

Dr. Koos Van Marle, South Africa.
1978 school.

Allan Savory, Rhodesia.
1979 school.

Hendrik Schoeman, South Africa.
1978 school.

Prof. Cheng Pi-Liu, China.
1979 school.

Dr. Chen Ci-Lin, D.V.M., China.
1980 school.

Guest Professors from Around the World

Dr. Peng Hong-Ze, D.V.M., China. 1980 school.

Dr. David L. Frape, England. 1981 school.

Dr. Michael Osborne, M.R.C.V.S., Ireland. 1981 school.

Dr. Sun Yong-Cai, D.V.M., China. 1980 school.

Dr. Ron Kilgour, New Zealand. 1981 school.

Mr. Karl H. G. Sera, Japan. 1981 school.

Dr. Stan D. Parsons, South Africa. 1980 school.

Dr. Masayoshi Kirisawa, D.V.M., Japan. 1981 school.

DR. E – THE AUTHOR

> Wherefore, come one, O young husbandman.
> Learn the culture proper to each kind.

Admonitions relative to animal care like that above by Virgil—the great Roman poet—have been given by writers to the keepers of herds and flocks ever since the domestication of animals 11,000 years ago.

With the whole world as my classroom, I have made Virgil's admonition come alive again in an era of biotechnology, pollution control, greenhouse effect, animal welfare, sustainable agriculture, endangered species, and unshared bread.

We need to usher an endangered planet, endangered people and animals, and endangered agriculture into the 21st century—and beyond.

I Trained to Be an Author

In addition to whatever natural talent that I may possess, I trained to be an author.

I grew up in a poor rural area of Missouri, where "I backed the hill up." But, when I was age 15, my parents moved to a farm south of Kansas City, where I enrolled in Raymore High School. There, I came under the tutelage of Marietta Davis, a truly great English teacher. She, as none other, encouraged me to write, and inspired me to become a writer.

While in high school, I entered several national essay contests, and won a few of them. To this day, I proudly display a set of the *World Book Encylopedia* that I won in one of these contests.

At the University of Missouri, I majored in animal science and minored in English and journalism. Along the way, I served as the editor of the *College Farmer*, the College of Agriculture's student magazine.

After I finished the Dixon Springs project, I went to the University of Massachusetts as an instructor in the Animal Science Department. There were two primary reasons why I did not start writing textbooks at that time: I didn't feel that I had enough background, especially in different geographical regions of the United States, and I would have starved to death, because it takes 10 to 15 years for a textbook to get established.

Two of My First Books Were Turned Down by Four Major Publishing Houses

At Washington State University, the manuscript for my book, *Animal Science*, evolved out of my lectures in the beginning animal science course. Traditionally, the general animal science books repeated laboriously everything pertaining to breeding, feeding, marketing, and meats for each class of livestock—beef cattle, dairy cattle, sheep, swine, and horses. I broke with tradition. I innovated. I decided to eliminate the laborious repetition by presenting the general principles in breeding, feeding, marketing, and meats, applicable to all classes of livestock, in an introductory section, then zero in on the differences under sections devoted to each species.

My first book was *Animal Science*. I submitted the manuscript to four major publishing houses—John Wiley, McGraw-Hill, MacMillan, and Prentice Hall. All four turned the book down, but all four added:

> We like your writing, Dr. Ensminger, but not the innovations. If you will change the manuscript to conform to the traditional, we would be interested in publishing it.

My answer to each of the four publishing houses was the same: "I feel that I am right." It wasn't long before they all followed along.

I decided to contact Russell L. Guin, Interstate Publishers, Danville, Illinois, an innovator, but a little known publisher. As the principal and football coach at Westville High School, maverick Guin started night football in 1928.

Mr. Guin and I met in Omaha. During our visit, I felt that I was being looked over much like a horse trader buying a horse. Finally, Mr. Guin said:

> Ensminger, I am going to select authors with

1981. Mr. Guin and Dr. E in front of Interstate Printers & Publishers.

> care, then let them tell me what to include in their books. I am not going to tell them.

When *Animal Science* came off press, I started working on another book. During the next half century, Interstate Publishers published a total of 10 of my books; and never once did Mr. Guin tell me what to put in a book.

My Writings

My major works consist of the following.

Books

I am the author or coauthor of 21 widely used books, which are in several languages and used all over the world. It is estimated that 90% of the agricultural students in the colleges and high schools of America use one or more of my books, and that 90%

Dr. E, left, having dinner with the Russell L. Guins in their home at Danville, IL in 1985. Audrey took the picture. As the principal and football coach at Westville High School in Illinois, Mr. Guin founded night football in America in 1928. Subsequently, he bought Interstate Publishers, following which he published 10 of my books over a span of 50 years.

of the stockmen of America use one or more of my books and/or read one or more of my columns. Also, three of my books are on records for the blind. In the interest of scientific exchange, and in order to help the people, I waive all royalties on foreign editions of my books.

My books are in several languages. The whole world is my classroom. It is estimated that, directly or indirectly, my books touch the lives of one billion people daily, monthly, and yearly. It's an awesome responsibility!

Two Syndicated Columns

My columns were the longest continuous running monthly agricultural columns in America. In 1956, I initiated *The Stockman's Guide*; and in 1962, I initiated *Horses, Horses, Horses!* These columns appeared in several magazines throughout the United States and abroad.

Journal Articles, Feature Articles, Bulletins, and Circulars

I have written more than 500 journal articles, feature articles, bulletins, and circulars, which have been published throughout the world.

U.S. Department of Agriculture Horse Bulletins

Beginning in 1958, at the request of the U.S. Department of Agriculture, I wrote three horse bulletins. Since these were primarily for 4-H Club members and FFA students, I wrote them without stipend. Millions of copies of these bulletins have been published and distributed. In 1958, when I started writing these bulletins, the USDA gave me the following restriction: I could not use the term "sex character," but the terms "masculinity" and "femininity" would be acceptable.

China—the Impossible Dream

The Ensmingers not only made history, but we were a part of it when we first visited China in 1972. Our book, *China—the impossible dream,* is recognized as the most exciting and accurate portrayal—ever—in pictures and words, of the Old China. In recognition of this fact, the University of Michigan, at Ann Arbor, requested that the original documents and records which we collected in 1972, out of which the book evolved, be preserved for scholars and posterity in their National Archives on Sino American Relations, Center for Chinese Studies. Mrs. Ensminger and I were pleased and honored to comply. Also, it is noteworthy that *China—the impossible dream* brought accolades from President Richard Nixon, Secretary of State Henry Kissinger, Secretary of Agriculture Earl Butz, and Bing Crosby.

Writing Is a Lost Art

The decline in writing and education is pointed up by the following:

- In a 1980 study, the Rockefeller Foundation reported: "As many as 20% of today's high school seniors are illiterate." Subsequently, the situation has worsened.

- In a government study released in December 1986, involving fourth, eighth, and eleventh graders, it was reported that "most American students cannot write well enough to make themselves understood, and that only a fraction demonstrate the writing skills necessary to succeed."

- In its December 29, 1986 issue, *Forbes Magazine* appeared on the newsstands as "Forbs Magazine," a deliberate misspelling of their own name in order to point up the sorry state of education.

- On March 24, 1989, Lee Iacocca, Chrysler Chairman, reported that so many Chrysler assembly line workers couldn't read the words "Bad Hood Fit" on the button that they were supposed to push when they detected an ill-fitting hood that the company had to replace the words with a graphic depiction.

- In April 1989, a young man of the Ensmingers' acquaintance, in the 11th grade, couldn't pass the California auto driver's test because he couldn't read the questions.

- In August, 1990, the 400 representatives from the peaks of American business, academia, and government, of the Aspen Institute lamented the decline of American education, competitiveness, and moral fiber. "With one rationale or another, we seem to be in a position of justifying retreat," said former Federal Reserve Board Chairman Paul Volcker.

- *The Kiplinger Washington Letter,* September 7, 1990, said of the work force: "Many are underqualified for even the most menial tasks."

- In December 1993, the Wingspread Group on Higher Education reported: "Too many colleges fail to educate students, fail to teach values, worry too much about research, and aren't worth the tuition they charge."

- On June 17, 1994, *The Fresno Bee,* William Raspberry, columnist, reported that the U.S. Secretary of Education, Richard Riley, revealed the following bad news: "Only one senior in six can write a passable persuasive essay, and less than 2% can render persuasive essays that are sufficiently developed and detailed to be considered good writing."

Despite the current dismal status of American education, I see the following rays of hope:

- France is holding to high standards. Recently, I placed two graduates of the leading agricultural college of France on visiting scholarships in the United States. These two outstanding students met the following college requirements in France: Each week, 34 hours of classes, 40 to 50 hours of homework, 4 hours of writing tests, and 3 one-hour oral tests. These French students were educated! Today, they have good jobs in France, and they are highly successful.

- On June 2, 1994, Stanford University professors voted overwhelmingly to restore the "failing grade" that they had done away with 20 years ago.

- On November 11, 1994, Newt Ginrich, the incoming Speaker of the House, said: "Every child in America should be required to do at least two hours of homework at night or they're being cheated for the rest of their lives in their ability to compete with the Germans, the Japanese, and the Chinese."

What it Takes to Be an Author

I shall leave it to history to evaluate my writing, as each of us must relative to our works—whatever they may be. But, as a result of writing about a million words each year, for 60 years, I can tell you what it takes to be a writer. These are requisites that I emphasize to all budding authors, for their awareness, and for the understanding of their relatives and friends. Based on my experience, here is what it takes to be an author:

- ***Superior training; a scholar***—This calls for thoroughness of training, along with expertise and versatility in many areas.
- ***Positive imaging***—In addition to positive thinking, I invoke an equally powerful force—positive imaging. Stated simply, positive imaging is merely a matter of this: believe and succeed to make your dreams come true.
- ***A higher power from above***—I am never alone in my lexicon garden. Each night, I start my writings with a silent prayer.
- ***Enjoyment***—I have never felt that I worked a day in my life, for work is fun and fun is work. When I don't feel well, I go into my study and write until I feel better.
- ***Giving it your all; long hours***—No clock watcher was ever a successful author! Thomas Edison said: "There is no substitute for hard work."
- ***Honing skills***—Great writings are preceded by practicing, practicing, practicing; and writing, writing, writing.

Dr. E in his office.

Audrey in her office

- ***The will to work, and the heart to win***—The world is full of authors who are "fixin' to write" but never do. Just as a racehorse must have the will to train and the heart to win, an author must have the will to work and the heart to win.
- ***Concentration***—A writer must shut out the world and concentrate. Winston Churchill and Ernest Hemingway wrote at night, so that was good enough for me.
- ***Making his own security***—A writer must possess enough confidence in his ability to produce works that will provide his security, without a public trough or subsidy.
- ***Ingenuity and the courage to innovate***—Successful authors are nonconformists; they're mavericks. When I climb the golden ladder, my cup will runneth over if I will have merited the epitaph: "He was a maverick who made his dreams come true."
- ***Judgment***—In Missouri, this trait is called "gumption" or "horse sense"; being able to separate the wheat from the chaff.
- ***Never "inhale"***—No matter how flattering the compliments, an author must never come to believe them.
- ***A perfectionist***—A writer on technical subjects leads or misleads many people; hence, he should be a perfectionist.
- ***Patience, persistence, and biding your time; a publisher***—An author must be patient and persistent. Benjamin Disraeli, former prime minister of Great Britain, put it this way: "Everything comes if a man will only wait."

Audrey checking a reference in the library in 1970.

At my desk writing in 1972.

At my desk in 1980 still writing.

■ ***Enthusiasm***—I have never known a successful writer who wasn't enthusiastic about his writings. Neither have I ever known a great teacher or a great lecturer who wasn't enthusiastic.

■ ***Need, quality, and service come first; the dollars follow***—In all our books, as well as in our other activities, our guiding rule is that need, quality, and service come first.

■ ***An understanding spouse, relatives, and friends***—It is very necessary that an author have an understanding and helpful spouse, because two can accomplish more than one.

■ ***Adequate facilities and a pleasant environment***—Our facilities were not always the way they are today—nearly 14,000 square feet under roof, a big library, a large meeting room, 80 steel filing cabinets of reference materials, and a warehouse. Our first filing cabinets were wooden orange crates covered with brown paper. Indeed, facilities need not be elaborate. But, technical writings are facilitated by a good library, and the kind of environment is reflected in an author's writings.

■ ***Library research***—Good library research calls for a special technique, some characteristics of which are: possessing a sixth sense—knowing what to use and what not to use; reviewing a great mass of material, then zeroing in on what is pertinent; quoting from research publications when it strengthens the story being told; and determining the most authoritative source of information.

■ ***Efficiency***—We must be efficient, for we have bills to pay.

■ ***A superior, dedicated and loyal staff***—I have always freely acknowledged that an author cannot evolve with first class books if he does not have first class secretaries.

Of equal importance to the co-authors and secretaries in our operation are the clerks, the artist, the housekeeper, and the gardener. Each enhances the other, and all have contributed richly to me as an author.

■ ***Marketing expertise***—Where an author does his own publishing, he must develop marketing expertise. Otherwise, he will end up paying interest on a warehouse full of books that are out-of-date. Book stores are no longer the only outlet for technical books. Instead, direct mail, catalogs, data banks, etc. must be mobilized.

Fortunately, the books we published on our own were eventually transferred to Interstate Publishers and CRC Press.

The three authors of *Feeds & Nutrition* seated in Dr. E's library. *Left to right:* Dr. James E. Oldfield, Dr. E, and Dr. Wilton W. Heinemann.

When the first edition of *Feeds & Nutrition* came off press, Dr. Jim Oldfield (left), one of my coauthors, attended the off-press party.

When my co-author and former student, Dr. Wilton Heinemann, and Lois heard that I was gravely ill, they made a special trip from Yakima, WA to see me on May 18, 1998. It touched me deeply.

Our staff in 1974. We added a couple of writers to help us.

Our secretaries in 1970.

1988. Richard and Marjory Johnson. Richard and Marjory were at Pullman with me doing graduate work. Richard eventually became head of Animal Science at California Polytechnical University, San Luis Obispo. Although he was busy, he would always do the artwork that I needed for my books. I never had to explain how to do them. He is an excellent artist and he knew the proportions as well as knowing animal behavior. It was trouble free.

I am at my desk with some of my staff in 1986. *Clockwise are:* Greg Bitney, artist; Robert Vann, executive secretary; and Dr. Rick Parker. They were having fun on my birthday. They knew how much I liked coffee, so they bought me a giant cup. Greg is pouring the coffee.

My faithful secretary, Joan Wright, who worked for us for over 28 years. She is one of the world's fastest typists.

Randy and Susan Rapp with David and Betsy in between them. Randy has been our typesetter for over ten years. He is the only reason we were able to keep on keeping on. It is delightful to work with an individual who is clever as well as diligent. Susan is equally good. She has helped both in the typesetting and the proof reading of the books. We were fortunate to find such a talented couple.

A trip to Kings Canyon National Park. *Left to right:* Mollee Thomas, Vernie, Susan Rapp and Randy.

1998. We had a Valentine's Day party to thank our staff for their loyal support.

May 12, 1991. Luncheon in the new Interstate Publishers headquarters in Danville, Illinois, hosted by Vernie and Mollee Thomas. *Clockwise around the table:* Mollee Thomas, Dr. E, Audrey, Vernie Thomas, Kathy Hofmann, and Robert Hofmann (Interstate's attorney).

Left to right: Dr. E, Vernie Thomas, Dr. Jasper Lee.

1994. Vernie Thomas of Interstate Publishers and I are holding *The Stockman's Handbook*. It is considered their best seller.

Vernie Thomas, President, Interstate Publishers, Danville, Illinois, and Dr. Jasper S. Lee, Interstate's editorial consultant and Chair of the Agricultural Advisory Committee, were guests of honor at a gala dinner at the foundation headquarters on June 17, 1994. Seated counter-clockwise are: Mr. Thomas, and Mr. Jerry Calvin, Manager, Jostens Printing Co., Visalia. Dr. E is standing between and to the back of Messrs. Thomas and Calvin. Mrs. Calvin is seated to the left of the table and nearest the camera. Dr. Lee is seated to the left at the far end of the table.

Harvey M. Kane *(left),* Life Science Editor, CRC Press, Boca Raton, FL; and Dr. E. CRC Press is the publisher of the Ensmingers' two human nutrition books. Photo taken at a gala dinner hosted by the Ensmingers in honor of Mr. Kane on April 22, 1994.

This *Fresno Bee* (Dec. 28, 1980) photo accompanied an article entitled: "Million words a year, no time off, help make Ensminger's work fun."

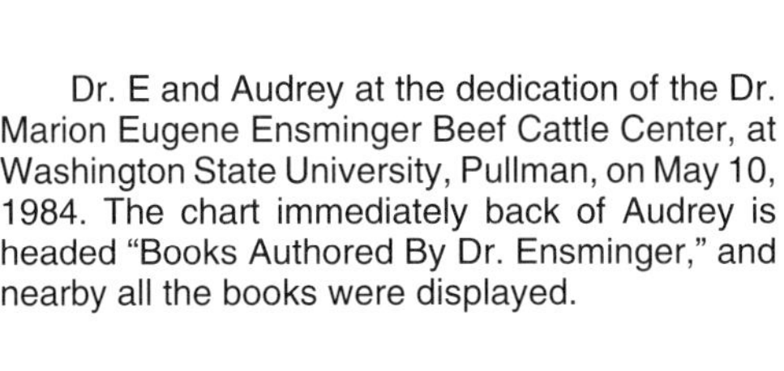

Dr. E and Audrey at the dedication of the Dr. Marion Eugene Ensminger Beef Cattle Center, at Washington State University, Pullman, on May 10, 1984. The chart immediately back of Audrey is headed "Books Authored By Dr. Ensminger," and nearby all the books were displayed.

Characteristics of Good Writing

Good writings of all authors have certain characteristics in common; among them, the following:

■ ***They are understandable***—A good writer should write for a college professor, but so that a hobo would, quickly and easily, know what he is saying and get the point.

■ ***They must be helpful***—In judging the usability of an article, *Reader's Digest* asks this simple question: "Is it helpful?" That's a good criterion for each section of a technical book.

■ ***They come alive***—Good writings make events of 2,000 years ago come alive and real. They possess vigor and energy that jumps at the reader.

■ ***They make for pleasurable reading***—People read good writings and enjoy them. I do not consider my books to be acceptable unless folks other than students and stockmen find them pleasurable.

■ ***They don't sensationalize***—For works to endure and do good, I believe with all my heart that an author must avoid like the plague the modern trend to sensationalize (sex, crime, dope).

■ ***They will be missed***—Will my silence be felt? Will my pen be missed when I can no longer push it? Will my books live on in the hearts of those I leave behind?

My Rewards from 21 Books

The enjoyment and rewards from writing are so great that I would write even if there were no royalties and I found it necessary to earn my bread-and-butter through some other means. Among the rewards:

■ ***The whole world is my classroom***—My books are now in several languages and used all over the world; and my two monthly syndicated columns, which ran for 25 years, were the longest continuous running agricultural columns in America.

■ ***The books are having a major impact on world food, hunger, and malnutrition***—These are the greatest issues of the decades to come. Remember that a hungry man knows no god, no country, and no boundary. Neither will he respect any treaty nor keep the peace. He is impelled only by his hunger and the right to survive. There can be no peace on an empty stomach.

Book Storage Problems

Through the years, we started putting some of the handbooks into ministorage places. Audrey would rent a couple of units at one place, but when she needed to store more there would be no room left, so she was forced to seek out another storage facility. Finally she ended up going to six different ones.

We were about to publish the first edition of *Feeds & Nutrition* and planned to print 5,000 copies of the complete volume and 5,000 of the condensed. But we knew we were in trouble because we had nowhere to put them. We decided to build a plain cement 2,400 sq ft block building in back of our house. We knew that it would not be used as storage forever. So Audrey drew up a house plan and our draftsman drew up blueprints. Because our farm was being developed for housing, we added some Mexican beams, a Mexican fireplace and a stone walled courtyard, then we landscaped it. We called it the prettiest warehouse in Clovis.

1987. The original warehouse shell.

The prettiest warehouse in Clovis.

Inside the books were stacked to the rafters. We added 5,000 copies of *Feeds & Nutrition Encyclopedia Complete* and 5,000 copies of the condensed version.

The Global Impact of My Books

My books are in many languages and used all over the world; among the foreign editions are Spanish, Japanese, German, Russian, Chinese, Korean, and Persian. I waive all royalties on foreign editions in order to help the people. The global impact of my books is evidenced by the following:

In China

China translated and published *Animal Science*, with my permission, long before there was any relationship between China and the United States. As a result, I was the first American to give an invitational lecture before the China Academy of Agricultural Science after the revolution. Mrs. Ensminger and I traveled to China in October, 1972. The academy invited animal scientists from all over China to my lecture. Everything was great; and I never lectured before a more appreciative audience. Following my lecture, the Ensmingers were permitted to travel anywhere they wished in China. This marked the beginning of a long and pleasant relationship between the Ensmingers/Agriservices Foundation and the People's Republic of China, some major events of which are briefed as follows:

■ **China—the impossible dream**—The Ensmingers authored and published the book, *China—the impossible dream*, which came off press in 1973.

■ **I have friends all over China**—Foreign work between scientists is based on mutual confidence, respect, and esteem. This is fiercely true of countries that have been shut off from each other, such as China and the former U.S.S.R.

■ **Other Chinese editions of Ensminger books**—After diplomatic relations between China nad the U.S. Were resumed, China translated and published my book *Feeds & Nutrition* and the two-volume work, *Foods & Nutrition Encyclopedia*, of which Mrs. E is the senior author. The phenomenal story relative to the *Encyclopedia*: China assigned 71 translators to the task, and published 10,000 sets in 5 volumes, all of which sold out in 4 months' time.

■ **In Australia**—In 1970, when Audrey and I visited King Ranch (Australia), Frank Badman, manager of King Ranch's show and sale Santa Gertrudis cattle, greeted me by exclaiming; "You saved my life!" Then, he explained that, prior to being offered the beef cattle job at King Ranch (Australia), his training and experience had been entirely with sheep. So, he went to the library where he learned of a book called *Beef Cattle Science* by M. E. Ensminger, following which he obtained a copy of it at the bookstore. He went on to say that he studied and followed *Beef Cattle Science* as his "bible." Today, Frank Badman is recognized as an expert cattleman.

■ **In the former U.S.S.R.**—My book, *Feeds & Nutrition Digest*, was the first major agricultural book to be translated into Russian since the 1940s. Dr. G. A. Bogdanov, Kiev, Ukraine, has spearheaded the translation, ably aided by Elena Polouchkina.

■ **In the United States**—Jack Maddox, a Nebraska cattleman, from whom I recently requested a picture for the new edition of *Beef Cattle Science*, and to whom I introduced myself by saying that "maybe you have used one of my books," responded by saying: "Is there anyone who hasn't?"

■ **In South Africa**—Director General Van der Merwe, Republic of South Africa, alluded to both the Ensminger books and schools in the following letter dated October 6, 1989.

> Once in a life time, if one is lucky, a unique personality will cross one's path. This is how I feel about Dr M E Ensminger and his wife Audrey.
>
> Way back in 1974 when I was professor of Animal Science at the University of Stellenbosch I had the good fortune to play host for two days to the Ensmingers and their touring party from the U.S.A. That proved to be an unforgettable experience and the beginning of many years of fruitful contact.
>
> Through his books Dr Ensminger has of course been known to us before the above-men-

tioned visit. However, for the Department of Animal Sciences at the University of Stellenbosch that visit opened up wonderfully new perspectives with the exchange of views, with the infective enthusiasm, with the meticulous attention to detail, with the old-world charm and with the vast array of publications that we came to appreciate as characteristics of the Ensmingers.

Dr Ensminger and I share much common ground in the fields of animal nutrition and horsemanship. However, since I have joined the Department of Agriculture in the central government in a managerial position, I have become ever so much more appreciative of the Ensmingers' wide-ranging contributions to the science of nutrition as well as to the ways in which science could be applied for the well-being of the populations of many countries on all continents.

In the development of The International Stockmen's School and through seminars held in many countries the Ensmingers have blazed a new trail in the extension of livestock and nutrition knowledge and in global cooperation in the fight against ignorance, hunger and malnutrition, for their wonderful example of what can be done by people with a vision, for the style in which they conduct their affairs, we salute Dr M. E. and Audrey Ensminger and wish them all the best for many more healthful and fruitful years.

Iowa State University Is Making My Dreams Come True

I searched, interviewed, and tried out aspiring writers, but none fit the "writer's mold" that I perceived. Now, Iowa State University, able and enthusiastic, is making my dreams come true. I felt it was in the best interest that I conduct a writer's school. It was held June 12–16, 1997 at the foundation headquarters in Clovis.

In preparation for the school, Audrey put all of my syndicated columns into new binders, and collected all of my writings together on the library shelves. It was quite a display of my lifetime's work!

Display of my writings at the writer's school.

June 13, 1997, the first of two Gala Dinners that the Foundation/Ensmingers hosted in honor of the Iowa State University book writers and school directors group. *On the right of the table, from nearest the camera are:* David G. Topel, Dean and Director, College of Agriculture, ISU; Foundation Trustee David McGlothlin, able horseman at famed Harris Ranch, Coalinga, CA; Corny Gallagher, V.P. Agribusiness, Bank of America; Mrs. E standing. *On the left of the table:* Harry Armstrong, highly respected City of Clovis council member for more than 20 years (and mayor at intervals); Vernie Thomas, President, Interstate Publishers, Inc., Danville, IL, leading publisher of the Ensmingers' 22 books; Ben Dunn, a dear friend of the foundation/Ensmingers; and Dr. E standing.

June 13, 1997, the Ensmingers conducted a school for those at Iowa State University who will carry forward the revisions of the 22 Ensminger books, *en masse*, as well as the ag-tech schools. *On the right of the table from nearest to the camera are:* Audrey Ensminger, standing; Trustee Dr. Elvin Taysom; Trustee Norman Purviance and his wife Marilyn. *On the left of the table:* Dr. E, standing; David G. Topel, Dean and Director, College of Agriculture, ISU; Dennis marple, Head, Department of Animal Science, ISU; Douglas Kenealy, Distinguished Teaching Professor, Department of Animal Science, ISU.

June 14, 1997 at the special school for writers and school directors. *Seated front row, left to right:* Dean Topel, ISU; Dr. E; Mrs. E; and Agriservices Trustee Dr. Elvin Taysom. Note that the Ensmingers are proudly holding special plaques that the Iowa State University group presented to them. *Standing, left to right:* Vernie Thomas, President, Interstate Publishers; Colin Scanes, Exec. Associate Dean and Exec. Associate Director, ISU; Dennis marple, Head, Animal Science, ISU; Dr. George Brant, ISU; Dr. Douglas Kenealy, ISU; Dr. Mark S. Honeyman, ISU; Dr. Donald C. Beitz, ISU; Dr. Brad R. Skaar, ISU; Dr. Howard D. Tyler, IUS; and Dr. Daniel G. Marrical, ISU (all from the Department of Animal Science).

June 15, 1997. Gala Dinner for the ISU writer's school group.

1994. Dr. E and Audrey standing in front of a display, at the Agriservices Foundation Headquarters, of the current editions of their 21 books.

1966
A GLOBAL PERSPECTIVE – THE USSR AND EUROPE WE SAW

The foundation-sponsored study-tours are an educational experience—not tourism. They are well-planned, in-depth, agriculturally oriented study groups, with all prior arrangements made by us, instead of a travel agency. We feel that when folks give of their time and money for travel, they want to see and do the most of the best. Hence, we arrange to visit the top farms, ranches, agribusinesses, trade associations, universities and experiment stations in each country; and to meet and talk with the top stockmen and agriculturalists, college staff members, agribusiness representatives, ministry of agriculture officials, and our agricultural attachés of these countries. Also, there is sightseeing and shopping along the way.

Within three weeks following the return from each study-tour abroad, I have always issued a detailed journal based on the extensive notes taken during the travels. These travel journals contain the names and addresses of everyone accompanying the Ensmingers; a master host list, consisting of a daily record of the place and date of travels, the names and the addresses of people contacted, and the services rendered or help given by people; and what I saw or did each day—everything from talks to tanks.

As a result of these detailed journals, I can tell you where we had lunch on a given day, including the names and addresses of the guests. The kaleidoscope, statistics, events, and people herein are those that existed at the time of the travels. Copies of each journal are given to those accompanying the Ensmingers abroad; to the President of the United States, Secretary of State, Secretary of Agriculture, C.I.A., F.B.I.; and to the counterpart government officials of the country visited. *Both the United States officials and the officials of the countries visited receive the same report.* A high United States C.I.A. official once remarked as follows to me: "When we want an accurate picture of each country, we read your journal."

Because of space limitations, only the highlights of the study-tours are herein reported.

Why Study-Tours Abroad?

In recognition that we can learn much from other nations by exchanging ideas and observing, and that meeting and knowing our counterparts makes for better understanding between peoples and nations, the Ensmingers decided that they would host/lead groups abroad. Further, we resolved: that our travels should be study-tours—made for scientific and cultural exchange purposes, rather than tourism as such; that our groups would be agriculturally oriented, and that we would make an in-depth study of the agriculture in each of the countries visited; that we would see what is good and beautiful in each country—that we would not go to see what is ugly or to criticize; and that we would not be concerned with the politics or religion of the countries visited.

Advance Planning Pays Off

Many months ahead of our departure, I contacted agricultural attachés, ministers of agriculture, scientists, stockmen, and agribusiness representatives in each of the countries that we wished to visit; advising them of the things that we wanted to see and do. Additionally, I sent to them copies of a special 68-page report entitled, "The Livestock Industry of the United States." As a result, the list of people who hosted us abroad reads like a *Who's Who in Western and Eastern European Agriculture.*

The Soviet Union We Saw

In September 1966, we took our first group to Eastern and Western Europe. We had been asked by the People to People Foundation to lead a group. We decided to put a news release in some of the livestock magazines that the tour would emphasize horses. We had no idea how many people would be interested. To our amazement, we ended up with a total of 82 travelers.

"Neither of us has horns!" These five expressive

words, uttered by the manager of a large collective farm in the USSR, reflect the thinking of the agriculturalists of the Soviet Union. Also, I'm convinced that this statement represents the innermost feelings of the rank and file of the Russian people. Time and again, we were told—

> We don't want war. We lost 20 million people in World War II; that's more than the entire population of Canada.

I Saw Friendly People in the USSR

Everywhere we went, the Russian people were friendly. When it comes to tour guides, we could take a page out of the book of Intourist, the Soviet government tourist agency. Galena, Alice, Lucy, and Irene, in Moscow, and Yuri Sitnov and Yuri Borschenko, in Pyatigorsk, were friendly, efficient, well informed, and skillful in their use of the English language; and they looked after our every need, from sending breakfast up to the rooms of those who were ill with the flu to repairing suitcases.

Moscow

Upon our arrival in Moscow, we were loaded in busses and taken to the Ukraine Hotel, a 1,000 room structure which was built in the early 1950s.

In Moscow, we visited the Kremlin and Red Square. Red Square is the place where they have their great parades. We saw the imposing structure on which the top officials of the USSR stand to review these parades.

We also visited the National Academy and the *Exhibition of USSR Economic Achievements*. The latter is a 574 acre area devoted to exhibits, in permanent buildings. It reminds one of a World's Fair, except that this one is housed in permanent buildings, and operates the year-round. We were taken through the premises on what they call a "rail car," which consists of several little cars hitched behind a motor vehicle. First, we were taken in a glass-domed building in which they showed movies portraying the life and scenic landscapes throughout the USSR

Next, we saw the building in which they house their "space exhibits," portraying their very considerable and well-known achievements in this field. It was most interesting.

After seeing the movie and the space exhibits, we went to the area where they had the horses on exhibit, including some Standardbreds of Hanover Shoe Farm breeding, in Pennsylvania. The chief caretaker of these Standardbreds was a woman.

Pyatigorsk

After seeing the Moscow area we flew to Pyatigorsk, about 1,000 miles to the south of Moscow, to see Soviet agriculture and livestock. Pyatigorsk is the city of spas, or mineral springs—the famous health resort area of the Soviet Union. Its mineral waters are reputed to have curative properties for those afflicted with rheumatism, certain types of heart ailments, and respiratory diseases (exclusive of tuberculosis). The workers of the USSR are sent there for treatment, at a very low cost, or in some cases free of charge. Here they drink of and bathe in these waters. Also, it is noteworthy that 70% of the city of Pyatigorsk was destroyed during World War II, in 1942, just 24 years prior to our visit; and that Gorbachev's first important political assignment was in Pyatigorsk.

I Met Mr. Yuri Borschenko

After checking into the two hotels, I remained in the lobby of the Pyatigorsk Hotel to discuss our schedule with Max Paternotte and Yuri Sitnov, the representative of Intourist (the USSR travel agency), who spoke with an Oxford accent. I asked Yuri where he planned to take us in the Pyatigorsk area. He responded by saying that we would visit the park, the museum, and one government-owned stud farm. "No collective farm!" I exclaimed. "None," came the crisp reply. Thereupon, I erupted, "Yuri, if I have to work at it all night, we are going to visit a collective farm." Who is the head man in this area? I want to see him. Go call him and tell him that Dr. Ensminger wants to see him." Yuri shrugged his shoulders—no one calls the head man. I persisted, "What's his name?" "His name is Borschenko," said Yuri. I goaded Yuri: "Go call Mr. Borschenko and tell him that Dr. Ensminger insists on seeing him."

Yuri left the hotel lobby, either to call Mr. Borschenko or the police, I didn't know which. But he didn't want to call in my presence; obviously, he didn't want me to hear the conversation. In about 15 minutes (it seemed like hours to me as I stood there alone in that hotel lobby), Yuri returned and announced that Mr. Borschenko would see me. "Where is he, and how do we get there—do you have a car, or can we call a cab?" I asked. "He's in an office building across the city; we can travel there in one of the buses that brought us from the airport," said Yuri. So, I grabbed my briefcase, Yuri and I boarded the bus, and Yuri told the bus driver where to go. We pulled up in front of an office building, and Yuri and I proceeded to Mr. Borschenko's office.

I found Mr. Borschenko to be a fine looking man who could speak perfect English. He impressed me as the kind of person whom I would expect to be the president of a corporation in the United States. He knew all about me and our group. After exchanging greetings, I said, "Mr. Borschenko, I have 82 distinguished Americans with me. Both you and I would like that they return home with a good impression of your country. But that isn't going to be if you don't let us see what we came to see."

Mr. Borschenko looked right back at me as he said, "Dr. Ensminger, it shall be. What do you want?"

I told Mr. Borschenko that we wanted to see a collective farm, a state farm, and the livestock of the area; and to visit with their agricultural leaders. Mr. Borschenko promised to join us for breakfast the next morning, to accompany us throughout our stay in the Pyatigorsk area, and to let us see anything that we wished to see.

Mr. Borschenko kept his promise. He came to breakfast the next morning and stayed with us as we visited collective farms and state farms, saw good livestock; and met Russian agricultural leaders; all of which he prearranged. At each stop, we were accorded the red carpet treatment, enhanced by bountiful and delicious food and flowers for all the ladies. Our delegates even took pictures in the airport—a well known "no-no" in the USSR. I offered to stop the picture taking, but Mr. Borschenko admonished: "Let them alone, Dr. Ensminger, they're having fun. The other Russian guides stood on the sidelines as they remarked, "Mr. Borschenko doesn't have to ask anyone."

We Were Guests of the International Club of Pyatigorsk

The club president, affable Mr. P. A. Afanasiev, a gentleman in his early 30s, met us in the best U.S. Chamber of Commerce fashion (and I mean this in a complimentary manner) as we alighted from our busses. He waved a greeting to everyone, asked that the delegates follow, and took me by the arm and escorted me to the auditorium. There, an estimated 150 English-speaking Russians stood and cheered as we filed in. President Afanasiev took me up on the platform, on which there was a table decorated with the Soviet and American flags, side by each. He made an appropriate welcoming speech, conferred upon me honorary membership in the club, and pinned the club insignia on me. Following my response, their people and ours went to the adjoining club and ballroom where we visited and danced together.

We Visited Stud Farm No. 169

Mr. Yuri Borschenko and Mr. Yuri Stinov accompanied us out to Stud Farm No. 169. The manager of the stud farm was Mr. Peter Strahov. He impressed us as very able. He's a college-trained man with years of experience.

At the stud farm, they showed us representatives of two breeds of horses; namely, Arabians and Akhal-Teke.

The buildings were of durable concrete, with tile roofs, and seemed to be very adequate. After the exhibition of individual horses, we were taken to a ring nearby where they had 10 of their riders put on a jumping exhibition. It was very well done.

Next, we went to a large alfalfa pasture, where we inspected the 100 mares, approximately equally divided into two bands—one Arabian, and another Akhal-Teke. They were in unfenced areas, herded by cowboys on horses. One interesting aspect of the visit was the very gentle nature of these horses—one could walk up to them in the little groups in which they were held for us to inspect.

This Arabian carried Polish breeding and was scheduled to be shipped to England.

Gala Dinner

At the gala dinner in Pyatigorsk, our second evening in the city, we had as our guests all of our guides, and the managers and specialists (veterinarians, agronomists, horsemen, etc.) from the nearby stud farm and collective farm. We visited, as only stockmen can, and our people danced with their people. I shall never forget our big Californian, John Wheeler (6 ft 4 in.) dancing with the short (5 ft 2 in.) Mrs. Peter Strahov, the wife of the manager of the horse farm that we visited earlier in the day. Even her husband, who couldn't speak any more English than I could Russian, got a chuckle out of it; he smiled as he held up his hands symbolic of "the tall and the short of it."

Visit to Proletarskaia Wolla, a Collective Farm

I shall always be grateful to Messrs. Borschenko and Lutchenco for the visit to the collective farm. Although our visit was on short notice and without prearrangement, both of them met the situation like true champions.

Following our briefing session, the manager took us to an adjacent room, near the auditorium, where they served different drinks, canned fruits, pickles, and the best homemade bread I think I've ever eaten (they even sent a loaf with us). Also, he gave a bouquet of flowers to Mrs. Ensminger, who was ill and had remained in the hotel that day.

All of us were delighted to get to see a collective farm, and we are most grateful to Mr. Borschenko for having brought this about.

On the way to the Pyatigorsk airport, Mr. Borschenko asked if it would meet with my approval were he to recommend to the proper persons in Moscow that they translate my books, and stated that he would like to bring a group of their stockmen to this country—if our State Department would approve. I encouraged both ideas.

Mrs. E is holding the large bouquet of flowers sent by the manager of the collective farm.

Mr. Borschenko and I became good friends. Soon after our return to the United States, I received, via airmail, a hand-carved, gold inlaid cane from him; and I sent a gold pen and pencil set to him.

The Hungary We Saw

We flew from Moscow to Budapest. At the airport, we were met by our two efficient Ibusz guides, Eva Kertesz and Edith Tenke. They soon had us on our busses, followed by checking in at the Hotel Szababaag. We spent the rest of the day seeing Budapest, including the Magyar Mezogazdasagi museum; and the Galopp-Palya Race Course, where we saw Thoroughbred and Hungarian Halfbred horses. That evening, we had a gala dinner at the Gundel Restaurant, with invited guests.

We boarded two busses accompanied by our two Hungarian guides. Eva Kertesz was in the lead bus seated beside me, and Edith Tenke was in the second bus seated beside Audrey. Our first stop was at Stud Farm Diospuszta, where they breed horses for racing and steeple chasing—primarily Thoroughbreds, although there were a few Arabians. We visited the nearby Tata Riding School, following which we boarded our busses and headed for the Hungarian-Austrian border, enroute to Vienna.

Seconds before reaching the border, which was closed by huge railroad-type gates and guarded by Russian soldiers, Eva Kertesz, the Hungarian guide who was seated beside me, shoved an envelope in my hand and commanded: "Take this across the border for me; they will search me, but they won't search you." The bus came to a screeching halt; so, there was no time to think. I reacted quickly and silently: If I refuse to smuggle the envelope across the border, Eva Kertesz may be shot. If I am searched, they will turn me loose. So, I quickly put the envelope in my inside coat pocket. The patrol officers came aboard the bus and collected all our visas before we got off the busses. Then, we were asked to get off the busses and wait in a designated building. In the meantime, they checked our visas, baggage, and the busses—they looked under the busses and under the hoods.

After a delay of nearly an hour, the guards told us that we could board our busses and travel on. The

Left to right: Dr. E; Eva Kertesz, our Hungarian guide; and Mr. Thomas Flandorffer, Hungarian horseman. Photo taken during our visit to the stud farm near Diospuszta, Hungary, the leading stud farm in Hungary at the time.

gates opened and we drove across the border, relieved that we were no longer behind the Iron Curtain. Thereupon, I gave Eva the mysterious envelope. She thanked me, without making any explanation. A little more than an hour later, we arrived at our hotel in Vienna. There, Eva Kertesz and Edith Tenke bade us farewell and departed with our thanks for a job well done.

The Austria We Saw

Liberator or unknown thief? Music, the universal language—understood by all and uniting all! Lipizzan horses flying through the air! Beautiful countryside! Easygoing people—more interested in waltzes than in politics! That's a recap of the Austria that we saw.

In Vienna, we passed by the war memorial officially christened "The Monument to the Red Army," now dubbed by some Viennese as "The Monument to the Unknown Thief." According to the terms of the Austrian-Soviet Treaty, the effigy can never be destroyed; nor are the easygoing, smiling Viennese likely to do so. But no treaty can deter them from, philosophically and without rancor, asking themselves the question—monument to what, liberator or unknown thief?

Austria is a small country, not quite half the size of the state of Washington, with a population of more than 7 million people. It's well-endowed and increasingly prosperous. Its people are predominately German speaking (99%) and Catholic (about 90%).

Vienna

Vienna, the capital city of Austria, lies at the point where the Danube carves its way between the Alps and an out-crop of the Carpathians. It's one of the most important and delightful cities of Europe.

Historically, Vienna goes back to Roman times. For the better part of a thousand years, it was the seat of the Hapsburg dynasty and capital of the Holy Roman Empire.

Vienna has long been famous for its food—and now I can add, justly so. On our first evening in the city, we dined at the Restaurant Kerzenstuberl, the same place that Jacqueline Kennedy dined during her visit to Austria. Our guests for the evening came from the American Embassy, the Austrian Ministry of Agriculture, the University of Agriculture, and the Spanish Riding School.

Today, the city has all the charm and elegance of its great past, plus a fresh, modern vitality and confidence in the future. There's music everywhere—operas, concerts and special performances; and, among the points of interest, are the homes of the great composers Mozart, Haydn, Gluck, Schubert, Beethoven, Brahms, Wagner, and Strauss. Above all, Vienna is a city of relaxation—the Danube, the Vienna Woods, the old style coffeehouses with red plush seats, and the Spanish Riding School—all conspire to refresh both body and spirit. To echo Goethe's words, Vienna is the conversation between mankind, art and nature—Europe in miniature.

Lipizzan Horses and the Spanish Riding School

One of the highlights of our entire seven-nation trip was a performance of the Lipizzaners at the Spanish Riding School, in a hall completed in 1735, adjoining the Hofburg, former palace of the Hapsburg emperors; acknowledged to be the most beautiful riding hall in the world. Here we saw white Lipizzan stallions literally fly through the air with perfectly-seated stirrupless riders. The horses were decorated in gold trappings and the riders were smartly dressed in old-time Napoleonic military uniforms.

Toward the close of World War II, the Spanish Riding School and the Lipizzan breed were threatened with extinction by both the German and Russian armies. In desperation, the school heads appealed to excavalryman George S. Patton, whose tanks were dashing across Austria in the spring of 1945. After observing a special exhibition of the historic white horses, the horse-fancier general agreed to preserve and protect the entire herd as part of European culture. To this end, the Spanish Riding School and its horses were moved, temporarily, near Salzburg, thereby preserving them for posterity.

Salzburg

"The Sound of Music" is everywhere in Salzburg. We saw St. Gerge's Riding School, the location of many of the scenes for the movie by that name, starring Julie Andrews; and it's every bit as pretty as the picture. But music abounds everywhere in Salzburg; its most sublime utterances being the works of Mozart (1756-1791), who was born there. Indeed, in Mozart, Salzburg can boast of one of the immortal contributions to the world's heritage of music; a child prodigy, who, at age four, played minuets and composed little pieces, and, at age six, played for most of the sovereigns of Germany.

George and Claudia Hoffmann.

George Hoffmann, a South Dakota rancher, had the starring roles of Don Alfonso in "Cosi Fan Tutte," and as Don Pasquale in "Don Pasquale." In a city where music critics know music, and where glowing reviews are hard to come by, George Hoffmann wrote a success story that few achieve.

Horse fountain in Salzburg, where the royal horses were bathed.

Left to right: Claudia Hoffmann, Dr. E, George Lee Hoffmann, and Audrey. The Hoffmanns were our guests for dinner in Salzburg, Austria. For two seasons, George Lee was the opera star of stars in Austria. Claudia was an enrollee in the Horse Science School in 1965, and both Claudia and George Lee were enrollees in the International Stockmen's School in Phoenix, in 1966. Subsequently, both George Lee and Claudia served as trustees of Agriservices Foundation.

Pinzgauer Cattle

We visited the 6,800-acre farm owned by Herr Hans Eder, near Salzburg, where we saw Pinzgauer cattle.

I was much impressed with these cattle, which we were told, originated in the central Alpine area of Austria. They're dual-purpose type, and mottled red-brown and white in color. The cows are large and roomy; several of them that we saw weighed 1,400 to 1,500 lb. Apparently, they're great milkers, too. They impressed me as the kind of cows that would wean off very heavy calves. The breed literature says of Pinzgauer cattle: "This breed is famous for its healthy constitution and outstanding milk and meat production."

The France We Saw

It's a potpourri! That's the French word for medley or mixture. But what a wonderful mixture. Make mine France—please.

To many, France stands for lightness and gaiety, and the French people are frivolous, and fond of dancing and light wines. Despite some opinions to the contrary, in crisis after crisis the nation has proved that underneath the fun-loving exterior there is a remarkable depth and stability.

To stockmen, France gave the world Rambouillet sheep, Percheron horses, and Charolais cattle;

and to horsemen, French-bred Thoroughbreds are rough competition.

Despite all that has been said, and will be said—about France, its people, or its political leaders—the France that I saw embodies the spirit back of the Statue of Liberty, which the French people presented to the American people in 1885, as a means of symbolizing the historic friendship between the two republics.

The Rambouillet Sheep Story

Approximately 50% of all the sheep of the United States carry some Rambouillet breeding; hence, we have good reason to be interested in them.

During the reign of Louis XVI, France was producing only a small portion of the wool that was used in its factories. In an attempt to build up the nation's flocks, Louis XVI asked, as a personal favor of the King of Spain, that he be allowed to purchase some of the famous Spanish Merinos. His request was granted, and in 1786 a total of 366 head of choice large Spanish Merinos were taken to France and put on the King's estate at Rambouillet, about 40 miles west of Paris. Other flocks were subsequently established in France and Germany, and later breeding stock from these were fused with those coming from Rambouillet. Out of these selections emerged the Rambouillet breed of sheep. From the beginning, the Rambouillet strain was selected and developed for greater size than the average Spanish Merino.

Mr. D. C. Collins, of Hartford, Connecticut, first brought Rambouillet sheep to the United States in 1840, importing fourteen ewes and two rams from the Royal Flock at Rambouillet, France. Other importations followed, and the breed rapidly increased in favor.

The Percheron Horse Story

The Percheron breed, like all other draft horses, has been the victim of mechanization, both in its native land, France, and in the United States. Nevertheless, the breed is of interest from a historical standpoint, and because they were once the most widely distributed of all draft horses in the United States.

The Percheron horse originated in northwestern France in the ancient district of La Perche, an area about one-fifteenth the size of the state of Iowa. The native stock was primarily of Flemish extraction upon which there was a subsequent and rather liberal infusion of Arab blood.

On the farm near Nevers, France, where Charolais cattle originated. *Left to right:* le Comte Roger de Boville, Charolais originator; Dr. E; and Madame Lise Vastel, our superb French guide/interpreter.

American importations of Percherons began about 1840, but it was not until the early 1850s that any great numbers came over.

The Charolais Cattle Story

The Charolais breed originated in France. Today, these large, white or cream-colored cattle, with a pink skin, are the fastest growing breed in America; the American International Charolais Association registered 31,114 head in 1965, which ranked the breed fifth in annual registrations.

As is true of so many breeds, the origin of the Charolais is somewhat clouded in obscurity. However, among Frenchmen, credit for originating the breed is generally accorded a farm near Nevers, France, presently owned by Monsieur le Comte Roger de Bouille. On October 8, 1966, it was my pleasure to be on this farm, to see the good herd of

Charolais thereon, and to visit with the owner. The barn and the castle on this farm were built in the 14th century, so we were told; and Joan of Arc slept in this barn after one of her last victories. The cattle plaques (trophies) on the sides of this barn date back to 1850. This establishment has been family-owned for 140 years, and the present owner told me that he has made provision to carry the herd forward.

Horse Races at Longchamp

We went to the races at Longchamp. The chief attraction was the great race known as the "arc de Triomphe" (the French say Prix de L'Arc de Triomphe).

This is the Kentucky Derby of Europe. The big race was their fourth race on the program.

The race is run on a grass turf. Judging from the workmen on the field, it appeared that the grass was a good 4 to 6 in. high.

In France, the races are run in the opposite direction to what we do in the United States; that is, they are run clockwise, whereas we run them counterclockwise.

They do not have a tote board like we do in the United States. As a result, it is not possible to know what the odds are, and what the winners pay. Also, I was surprised to note the number of people standing in the infield, where they also had parimutuel windows.

Longchamp race course. Dr. E on left nearest camera.

We Went to Chantilly, Where They Train and Race Thoroughbreds

They train 2,400 horses here, for flat, or running races. Chantilly is under a non-profit foundation, as are the three race tracks that they own. They get 10 percent of the racing revenue of the three tracks, and they charge for the keep and training of horses. The association was set up in 1830. Their objective: to encourage the breeding of better horses.

They train on the grass, on sand, and in the forest. They believe that change of tracks and scenery prevents boredom.

Grosbois and French Trotters

This is where they train French Trotters; a harness horse breed, similar to our Standardbreds, but perhaps a bit smaller.

The castle, according to the plaque at the entrance, is known as—Chateau Historque Grosbois.

The Germany We Saw

An uneasy feeling came over me as I looked at the Berlin Wall, a symbol of a divided Berlin and a divided Germany. It's an ugly sort of thing, and the thought and spirit back of it are even uglier. The wall, built in 1961, is approximately 6½ feet wide and up to 9 feet high. Some of it was made from the fronts of buildings, with the window openings filled with brick and stone; other parts were built from the ground up, often with barbed wire and cut glass on top.

To most stockmen, fences or walls are primarily for the purpose of keeping something in; and the Berlin Wall is no exception. It was constructed to keep East Germans in. Their concern was that the best and the youngest were escaping. We were told that two million East Germans (from East Berlin and East Germany) escaped to West Germany prior to the construction of the wall.

East Germany

We entered East Germany, the German Democratic Republic (GDR), at "Checkpoint Charley," one of seven checkpoints along the wall. We were processed (visas checked; looked at; buses checked inside and outside) by a steely-eyed guard, and a pleasant, but little-smiling woman—both in uniform!

Even a mirrored apparatus was wheeled under the buses to see underneath them. And, of course, our West German guides were left behind.

We saw where the last battle of World War II was fought, just inside the East Berlin sector. We passed "Hitler's Bunker," where Hitler killed himself on April 30, 1945. The bunker, which is now marked only by the mound that protrudes above, once extended six floors below. It was large enough to house a company of soldiers. The whereabouts of Hitler's self-inflicted, charred remains is not known, for they never want a monument to arise.

West Germany

Our visitations in West Germany were arranged by my longtime friend, Dr. Fritz Haring, Gottingen University, the Federal Republic of Germany, for whom I guest-authored a portion of a book a number of years ago; and we were led by Messrs. Messerschmidt, Wedekind, Holtz and Hartwig, all most knowledgeable and very gracious.

Nicknames

The Germans are very fond of nicknames, and all names have a meaning. For example, the Kaiser Wilhelm Church in West Berlin, is known as "Lipstick and Compact," presumably indicative of the shapes of the old and the new. Kongress Halle, the huge convention center in West Berlin, has been dubbed the "Pregnant Oyster." This building, which evolved out of a competition between architects in 1957, won by a Massachusetts architect, was constructed at a cost of $5,000,000.

An Indomitable Spirit Cannot Be Walled In

The Germany that I saw appears to be a reasonably prosperous one, particularly in West Germany; and the German people are hard-working. Their agriculturalists are outstanding. We can take a page out of their book when it comes to production testing horses, rotating and fertilizing pastures, and feeding out bulls instead of steers. The people are possessed of an indomitable spirit—that spirit which refused to be crushed by two disastrous World Wars into which their leaders threw them; that spirit which endured the Berlin Airlift; and that never-say-die spirit which will survive the Berlin Wall and live on.

State stud farm near Celle, where we saw their Hanoverian horses.

The State Stud Farm

Dr. Walter Hartwig, Secretary, Hanoverian Breeders Association, the association that registers Hanoverian horses, served as our host and leader for a visit to the State Stud Farm, near Celle. On this establishment, which was founded in 1735, they have been breeding horses continuously for 132 years.

In addition to exhibiting stallions of the Hanoverian breed, the officials at the State Stud Farm also showed us 11 stallions of the Trakehner

The Royal Coach.

At the State Stud Farm, Celle. *Standing in front:* Dr. E (left), and Mr. Heinz Messerschmidt, Director of the Foreign Bureau of German Animal Production and Director of the German Society of Animal Production.

breed. Additionally, there were four East Prussian stallions and an Arabian.

The last performance was that of the King's Coach, or Royal Coach, drawn by four magnificent black, or dark brown, Hanoverian horses. This is the same coach that the Kaiser used many times, and in which he was frequently pictured during the days of the German Empire.

Artificial Insemination Center

We visited the Artificial Insemination Center, ZBN, near Hannover. This AI Center is operated in conjunction with their College of Veterinary Medicine, with Dr. G. Rath, DVM, in charge.

The bulls at this center are of the Black-and-White breed. They are of the same lineage as our Holstein-Friesian cattle in this country. However, they have selected them for more meatiness than we have, with the result that they produce pretty good carcasses as well as good milk yields. We were also told that 99 percent of the cattle in the Hanover area are of the Black-and-White breed.

Farm of Henrich Engelke

It was our pleasure to visit the good German farm owned and operated by Mr. Henrich Engelke. Judging from the home in which Mr. Engelke lives, and the premises in general, I concluded that he is one of the most prosperous German farmers.

The Ireland We Saw

Ireland, the Emerald Isle, is the fairest spot under heaven to millions of loyal Irish, whether they still live there or have found homes across the sea.

Ireland holds undisputed claim to the world's best-known national color: emerald green, best-known patron saint: Saint Patrick, and best-known national flower: the shamrock.

> There was a dear little plant that grows in our isle
> Twas Saint Patrick himself sure that set it;
> And the sun on his labors with pleasure
> did smile,
> And the dew from his eye often wet it.
> It shines through the bog, through the marsh
> and the mireland,
> And he called it the dear little shamrock of
> Ireland.

The people of Ireland are courtly, warm-hearted, gay, witty, and brimming with humor, laughter and outlandish superstitions, and masters of the "blarney" in a delightful way.

The Republic of Ireland that I saw constitutes 83% of the island and embraces 27,136 square miles—an area half the size of the state of Wisconsin.

The Potato Famine

Ireland suffered a national famine in 1846. The potato crop, which was as indispensable to Ireland as rice is to China, failed as a result of the blight, which at that time was an unknown disease. The famine persisted in 1847, and became even more general and devastating. Also, typhus struck. Vast numbers died and hordes of people emigrated to escape death by starvation and pestilence.

Economics

Agriculture is, and always has been, the most important industry in Ireland. Ireland is also a tourist Mecca. The Republic of Ireland, with only 2.9 million people, has 15 to 16 million visitors each year.

Horses

Of course, Ireland is famous for fine horses. An Irish taxi driver may not be able to name the last four U.S. presidents or the capital city of California, but he can tell you all about the Irish Sweepstakes; chances are he even has a ticket in his wallet. By acts passed by the Irish Parliament in 1930, and further legislation of 1933 and 1940, hospitals are authorized to operate sweepstakes for the benefit of the sick poor. Today, over 400 hospitals and similar institutions benefit under the terms of these acts, and the medical schools of Eire have a long and distinguished history. A group of U.S. doctors on tour of Irish Teaching Hospitals had this to say: "The great traditions of teaching, which are exemplified so admirably in clinical teaching in Eire, are qualities any country would be proud to claim for its own." Back of it all are fine horses, millions of ticket holders, and the luck of a draw which is fair for all.

National Stud Farm

The National Stud was established by special legislation in 1945. The principal purpose of the Stud, which is managed by the Irish National Stud Co. Ltd., is the breeding of Thoroughbreds. The services of high-class stallions are made available at reasonable fees to small breeders in Ireland. Also, from time to time, courses are conducted for stud grooms and stud managers.

The National Stud is ably managed by Mr. David D. Hyde, M.R.C.V.L., a graduate of Dublin in veterinary medicine. At the time of our visit, 44 people were employed on the establishment. Although the National Stud Farm is government-sponsored, I understand that it is self-supporting.

Adjacent to and operated by the Stud Farm are beautiful Japanese Gardens, which are open to the public.

Ireland's Best Kept Secret

Many years ago, a president of Ireland wanted the Emerald Isle to be noted for something unique in addition to horses. So, he conceived of the idea that noted writers and artists, worthy of being invited by the government of Ireland, live in Ireland without paying any taxes whatsoever. Some of my Irish friends tried to persuade me to move to Ireland. Subsequently, each year when I struggle to meet the increasing appetite of the IRS, I have fonder and fonder dreams of what a tax-free life on the Emerald Isle would have been like.

At the Irish National Stud, Tuley House, Co. Kildare, Ireland. *Left to right:* Our guide, Dr. E, and Dr. David Hyde, DVM, General Manager, Irish National Stud.

The England We Saw

England, despite its differences, was the closest thing to home that I saw abroad. Without doubt, the chief reason was that I didn't encounter any language barrier, except for some cockney English. Although reserved, I found the English friendly and unfailingly courteous. Also, England is one of the few remaining countries in which royalty is respected, and this within itself breeds tradition and dignity. London has magnificence, and the English countryside is charming. And, of course, there are places of historic and cultural interest from one end of the "tight little isle" to the other.

Contrary to the opinion of Americans, the Queen isn't just a nice, pleasant figurehead. Rather, she is the symbol of national unity. The man on the street regards Her Majesty with a curious combination of awe, reverence, and simple affection. She can splice rope in a Girl Guides camp, sample a pudding at a fair, chat with miners, or go to the races—all without lowering her exalted position or her immense personal dignity. She is the knot that ties together the Commonwealth of Nations.

To stockmen, England is the cradle of the breeds—the nation that gave birth to more breeds of livestock than any other, and it's the home of the world's first breed registry.

London

London, with 8,172,600 people living cheek-to-cheek, is the grandmother of capitals. The London that I saw never sleeps. It's an exciting city—a royal city. There's the Changing of the Guard at Buckingham Palace, 900-year-old Westminster Abbey, Big Ben, the House of Parliament, St. Paul's Cathedral, and the grim old Tower with its fabulous Crown Jewels. There's always something going on in London—a famous sports event, a new play, or a royal procession.

London is a city of palaces and kings and queens, of pageantry and color, of famous streets filled with shops, restaurants and night clubs. Here are playwrights, painters, and craftsmen carrying on every kind of trade to which man can turn his hand.

Climate

Don't you believe the travel posters! On the average, the weather is pretty awful—although we were fortunate. The dampness of England is enough to give chronic rheumatism to a cigar store Indian. We didn't freeze in England, despite the scarcity of that 20th-century device—the central heating unit. But we barely escaped such fate, primarily because we were there in October.

British Agriculture

Even though only about 5% (compared to our 6.8%) of the United Kingdom's labor force lives on farms, it produces about half its food needs, the rest being imported.

The Golden Purebred Era in England

The first emphasis on ancestry occurred in human genealogies, where it is older than recorded history itself. But human pedigrees were emphasized for social purposes, in order to determine the inheritance of property or of rank in a caste system of society, rather than because of any belief in the inheritance of physical and mental qualities. Human genealogies often recorded only the male or female line of descent, as in the early chapters of Genesis, in Icelandic sagas, or in Maori legend.

More than a thousand years ago, the Arabs memorized the genealogies of their horses, tracing the pedigrees in the female line. We have little detailed knowledge of how these pedigrees were used, or if they were used at all, as guides in a breeding program.

The use of pedigrees in the modern manner had its beginning in England late in the 18th century, and the general formation of breed registry societies began around the middle of the 19th century. Soon the improvement that Bakewell and his followers had made in their breeding stock came to be known in other lands. Agriculture was on the move, and the golden age of stockbreeding was at hand. Animals possessing common characteristics were no longer to be confined to a small area and restricted to a few breeders. The number of animal generations in the pedigree increased until no man could remember with certainty all the foundation animals back in the pedigree.

To supply this knowledge and to prevent unscrupulous traders from exporting grades or common stock as purebreds, herdbooks were formed. The first herdbook, known as "An Introduction to the General Stud Book," for the Thoroughbred horse, appeared in 1791.

During this era, the breeding of superior animals engaged the interest of many persons of wealth and high position, even of royalty itself. Despite some reticence on the part of these early breeders to furnish pedigrees, for fear that they would give away valuable trade secrets, Britain spawned more new breeds and breed registries of livestock than any other country in the world.

The "Battle of the Breeds" Shifted to America

As the lot of the American colonist improved, there was a desire to secure blooded stock. Fortunately, our stockmen could draw on the improved animals already developed in Britain. Thus, it is not surprising to find that many of the present established breeds of America originated in Great Britain.

Vern Herefords

On October 17, one busload of us went to Herefordshire to attend the dispersal sale of the world famous Vern Herefords, by the estate of the late Captain R. S. de Quincey. I had known Captain de Quincey.

I traveled to Herefordshire and this historic sale with mixed emotions; for I was both seeing the birthplace of the Hereford breed, and paying homage to one of the immortals in the Hereford world and witnessing the passing of an era—the dispersal of the greatest Hereford herd in Herefordshire.

Herefordshire has a rolling to hilly topography and climatic conditions that are favorable to superior grazing—factors which account for the rustling habits of present-day Herefords.

There had never been a sale to match this one in the breed's homeland. It was Britain's Hereford sale of the century. An estimated 7,000 people were in the stands. Buyers from all over the world paid an average of $4,716 for 136 head. The top price of $44,100 was paid for Vern Scorpio, 11-month-old son of Vern Nobel—highest price ever paid for a Hereford in Great Britain.

Prior to the cattle auction, the 326-acre farm, known as The Vern, was sold (also at auction) to Dr. John N. Phillips, of Ireland, for $365,000, or about $1,120 per acre.

Newmarket: the Heart of British Racing

We visited Newmarket, a country town, but the heart of British Racing ever since the fun-loving Charles II (1630-85) established the sport there over 300 years ago.

Today, Newmarket is the very heart of British racing. It's the most important racing center in the country, if not in the world, in terms of money, number of horses, exports, and prestige.

Newmarket is strictly a horse town, and justly proud of it. Sixty percent of the population of 10,100 is employed, directly or indirectly, with the horse industry. It's the home of the Jockey Club, two race courses, Tattersalls—the world-famous bloodstock sales, the National Equine Research Station, the National Stud, and it's surrounded by some 40 of the top Thoroughbred breeding establishments of the world.

This shows some of the horses in training at Newmarket.

The Jockey Club

The Jockey Club is the guardian of Newmarket. The club began by leasing a site for a coffee house in 1771, about 20 years after its inauguration. Then, on the expiration of its lease in 1821, it bought the land. Since then, the club has acquired holdings of over 4,300 acres, of which 2,200 acres are devoted to racing—the remaining acreage being farm lands, woods, and tenanted studs.

Racecourses; Training Grounds; Nearby Studs

Newmarket is the only center in Britain with two race courses: the *July Course*, which is used during the summer only, and the *Rowley Mile Course* (named after King Charles II himself, whose nickname was taken from his favorite mount, Old Rowley), which is used during the spring and again in the autumn. One of these races, the Newmarket Town Plate—started in 1666, and won four times by King Charles II, who rode in races, is open to women riders. Also, such world famous races as the 2,000 Guineas, 1,000 Guineas, Cesarewitch, Cambridgeshire and Champion Stakes are run on this course.

Both the *July Course* and the *Rowley Mile Course* are on turf or grass; there are no dirt tracks in England.

At the time of our visit, Col. Gray reported that there were a record number 2,000 race horses in training at Newmarket, divided among 39 racing stables.

Except during dry or frosty weather (limekilns are used in dry weather; and for frosty weather there are tanbark or sand gallops), the gallops (in England, when used as a noun, the word "gallop" refers to the training ground) are on turf. These gallops stretch, like the wings of a butterfly, east and west of the town. But 2,000 racehorses are not permitted to gallop madly over them at will. Each day, pathways to be used for exercise are designated by bits of fir stuck in the ground so as to demarcate a lane wide enough to accommodate a set of horses; and each pathway is used only one year in three. We saw horses being galloped (breezed) on Warren Hill, which we were told was first used for training in 1605.

In the town of Newmarket, horses are accorded

the same absolute right-of-way privilege that pedestrians have in California. When strings of horses cross a busy road as they go to and from gallops, the head lad handles traffic control; he brings cars to a halt until his string crosses a highway, then waves them on.

Following the tour of Newmarket, we went to the clubhouse, where we were luncheon guests of Major T. P. Philipp, President, Thoroughbred Breeders Association of England. There we also met Mr. R. Fellows, agent of the Jockey Club; Mr. David Hedges, the greatest racing reporter in England; and many other notables.

The National Equine Research Station

This national institution, which was established in Newmarket in 1947, has become a Mecca for equine veterinarians from all over the world because of its research into the cause and cure of equine diseases. The famous Gladys Yule Surgical Unit was opened by the Queen in 1961, and in 1962 an adjoining laboratory, known as the Forensic Unit, was set up to examine specimens taken from racehorses suspected of having been doped.

The National Stud

The National Stud was under construction at Newmarket, at a cost of over $840,000.

It is expected that the National Stud will give added impetus to racing in England and attract more visitors to Newmarket. Also, it is the hope of many of the English that it will help to keep more outstanding English horses at home for stud duty.

A Toast

I must confide that I had a very personal reason for going to England. I wanted to learn what makes Mrs. Ensminger—whose name is Audrey Helen, and whom I affectionately call "little Audrey"—tick. Since she is of pure English stock (both of her parents came from England and settled in Canada), I have long wondered what accounts for her charm, boundless energy, intelligence, ability, and good looks. And besides, a twenty-fifth wedding anniversary was an appropriate time to ferret out this mystery.

I discovered that, to varying degrees, these same traits are embodied in all the English people. Genetically, they're homozygous for them; hence, "little Audrey" comes by them quite naturally. And so, as I bring to a close my story telling of the Western and Eastern Europe that we saw on the eight-nation magic carpet trip, I do so with a toast: "This is my best, to my best—"Little Audrey."

1968
THE SOUTH AMERICA AND MEXICO WE SAW

Mrs. Ensminger and I led a delegation of 20 people to Brazil, Argentina, Chile, Peru, Ecuador, Colombia, and Mexico, departing from Los Angeles on August 30, 1968, and returning to Los Angeles on Sunday, September 22, 1968. The highlights of the study-tour follow.

The Brazil We Saw

On August 31, we flew on Braniff Airlines from Miami, Florida to Rio de Janeiro, Brazil. Following a 7:30 a.m. continental breakfast, the group assembled on the second floor of the Hotel Gloria where Dr. Daniel W. Cassard did a masterful job briefing us on Brazil. Dr. Cassard is an old friend of mine who has been stationed in Brazil for the past two years. He speaks Portuguese fluently. In addition to giving us an insight into the agriculture and industry of Brazil, Dr. Cassard told of the people. Obviously, he is very fond of the Brazilian people; and all of us felt that he is a wonderful U.S. representative to have in Brazil.

We were luncheon guests of the jockey club.

In Rio de Janeiro We Visited the Equine Veterinary Clinic, Operated by the Jockey Club Brasileiro

In addition to seeing their very adequate facilities, we inspected a horse suspected of having equine infectious anemia (swamp fever). According to their rules, such an animal must be isolated, examined by a veterinarian twice daily, then destroyed if equine infectious anemia is confirmed. Also, we were shown a yearling colt suffering from rickets. In this case, they explained that the rickets was due to a calcium deficiency. Also, they stated that rickets due to calcium deficiency is rather common among children throughout Brazil.

We Went to the Horse Races

We were luncheon and racing guests of the Jockey Club Brasileiro of which Dr. Eduardo de Paula Machada is president. He has held this position for 10 years; and his father was president of the club before him. Sr. Joaquim Ruting, manager of the club, escorted us to our tables, which were located in a very choice area of the grandstand. The floor was carpeted, and the tables were decorated with flowers. The food was both delicious and bountiful, and there must have been seven different goblets for the different wines that they served. We stayed through five races. Their fifth race was the main event. On this particular day, all races were on the turf. However, they have two tracks on dirt, which we were informed are used much more frequently than the turf. They have running races only; there are no harness races at this track.

The racetrack is in a beautiful setting, with mountains to the west and the north, and the city of Brazil to the northeast and east. They use a tote board, and there is pari-mutuel betting, much as there is in the United States. The horses race counterclockwise. The race crowd was gay and colorful. They whoop it up much as they do in the United States, as they cheer for their favorites. We never saw so many binoculars in use.

Gala Dinner With Invited Guests at Restaurante Charrascaria Gaucha

At the door to the restaurant, we were met by the manager, Mr. Farias. He escorted us through the restaurant, then by a counter where each of us was given a small sample of the beef and pork that had been prepared for our dinner. Next, we went to our private dining room. The food was wonderful. I was particularly impressed with the fact that after our meat had gotten cold, they came around and removed it from the plate and replaced it with large servings of warm meat, even though some of us protested that this was not necessary.

Sightseeing in and near Rio de Janeiro

We traveled in our private bus and visited the following places: Dona Marda Mountain, Christ Mountain, Cascatinha Taunay Water Falls, Copacabana Beach, and H. Stern Jewelry Manufacturer.

We Flew to Sao Paulo, Brazil

Upon our arrival in Sao Paulo, we boarded our private bus and traveled to Campinas where we visited Coudelaria de Campinas, the army horse breeding farm. It is operated very much on the pattern of the former U.S. Remount Service, which the U.S. Army had up until the close of World War II. Col. Uzada is the ranking officer in charge of this horse breeding farm. In telling us about the establishment, he was assisted by Sgt. Sidney Pereira. The Colonel couldn't speak English, but Sgt. Pereira could. So, we got along very well.

On this horse breeding farm, they have a total of 185 horses, and there are 70 men in charge of them. The farm embraces 988 acres. They have two breeds of horses, Thoroughbreds and Arabians. The Thoroughbreds predominate. A few of the Thoroughbred mares (a total of 10) were brought over from England. We were told that weanling foals sell at about $3,000 a head. Also, we were shown one three-year-old Thoroughbred colt that is priced at $7,000. Their Arabian stallion was the fattest stallion

State Stud at Campinas, Sao Paulo, Brazil.

that I have ever seen. They feed the horses alfalfa hay, oats, and skimmed milk. Also, they have a sizeable vegetable garden for horses only.

I was impressed with the horse breeding farm. It is well-operated and the horsemen in charge are knowledgeable.

The Argentina We Saw

On Tuesday evening, September 3, we arrived at the airport in Buenos Aires, following which we checked in at the Hotel Claridge.

The next day, while some of our group went on a sightseeing tour of Buenos Aires, and others went shopping, I visited the head offices (in Buenos Aires) of the estancias which we subsequently visited.

The Pampas—Dreamland of Cattle

We boarded our private bus and headed for the Pampas (meaning level land). We traveled to the northeast of Buenos Aires, to Venado Tuerto, a distance of more than 300 miles. The soil is a deep, black loam; and the water table is within 15 feet of the surface. Although the area is well adapted to wheat, corn, rye, barley, and oats, and vast acreages of these crops are grown, it's a dreamland of cattle and grass—the greatest cattle country that I've ever seen. There is year-round grazing on neatly-fenced, belly-deep pastures of native grass or alfalfa, and the cattle are well cared for by gauchos (Argentine cowboys). There's no such thing as winter feed, although most estancias (ranches) store up modest amounts of hay and/or silage for drought protection.

Of the South American countries, Argentina is recognized as the outstanding beef producer. In fact, taken as a whole, Argentine cattle possess better breeding and show more all-around beef superiority than do the cattle of any other country in the world. The excellence of the Argentine cattle can be attributed to two factors—their superior breeding and the lush pastures of the country. Beginning about 1850 and continuing to the present time, large numbers of purebred animals have been imported from England and Scotland, and some from the United States. No price has been considered too high for bulls of the right type; and, again and again, British and American breeders have been outbid by Argentine estancieros in the auction rings of Europe. These bulls and their progeny have been crossed on the native stock of Spanish extraction (the Criollo breed). Today, Herefords, Angus, and Shorthorns are the most numerous breeds of the country.

The large cattle breeders of Argentina formed the first aristocracy, and many of them are still of high economic and social position. Most of them live in Buenos Aires. We visited five of Argentina's noted estancias—all of them in the Pampas. Pertinent facts about each of them follow.

San Ramon

This is one of several estancias owned and operated by the Duggan family, descendants of three brothers who came over from Ireland many years ago. Sr. Jose Martin y Herrera, whose wife was a Duggan, was our gracious host. (Sr. Herrera has kept in touch with us for 30 years.)

San Ramon embraces 12,355 acres. Most of it is devoted to native pasture, although some alfalfa is

The ranch house at San Ramon.

I am driving a cart at Duggan's ranch.

also produced for pasture. They have 5,000 cattle, 2,000 sheep, and 200 horses. Most of their horses are used by the gauchos.

The cattle on San Ramon consist of three breeds—all purebreds; Herefords, Shorthorns, and Angus. Sr. Herrera made no secret of his partiality for Herefords, although he added, "the Angus make for less work." In my judgment, as a whole, their Shorthorns are of slightly higher quality than their other two breeds, although all three breeds are outstanding. I was particularly impressed with the size of their cattle. We saw several bulls which, in strong breeding condition, weighed over a ton. Their cattle also have great length. With their great size, however, they are not "leggy."

For the show cattle at San Ramon, they use two elevated (about 12 to 14 ft in the air) barns, with slotted floors (the slats are made of a very hard wood, which they call "axe breaker" wood). This type of construction (an elevated building with slotted floors) makes for good air circulation in the summertime. Also, the urine drains through the slots, thereby making for drier and less bedding.

Foot-and-mouth disease (Aftosa) is ever present. They vaccinate all cattle on San Ramon four times per year, but the vaccine isn't too good and the disease still persists.

At San Ramon, we enjoyed the first of a series of those famous South American barbecues, in which there is a bountiful choice of many meats, vegetables, and drinks, topped off by Latin hospitality and fellowship. They're experts at barbecuing meats, whether it be on an estancia or in a restaurant. For example, when it's done out-of-doors, the meat is usually on a grill which is placed in an upright posi-

Barbecuing in Argentina.

tion on the windward side, adjacent to but not immediately over live coals, with the result that ashes do not blow on the meat and fat never drips in the fire. In restaurants, barbecue grills are V-shaped, so that the fat drains away in the grill and not down on the fire.

The Firpos

We visited two estancias owned by the Firpos, La Pluma and La Danesa. At both places, we were hosted by Sr. Marcus Raul Firpo and his brother-in-law, Sr. Marcelo DuPont. Marcus is a son of Sr. Raul E. Firpo, whom I had met when he judged the Angus cattle at the Chicago International in 1951 and again in 1961.

On their estancias, the Firpos have 21,000 head of cattle, of which 2,000 are registered Angus. Marcus reported that land in the vicinity of La Pluma sells at around $140/acre, whereas the more sandy soil in the vicinity of La Danesa sells at about $70/acre. The annual rainfall at La Pluma is 33½ to 35½ inches, and at La Danesa it is 25½ to 27½ inches.

I was particularly impressed with the modern business methods (modern anywhere in the world) employed by the Firpos. They are seeking and applying the latest in research, as evidenced by their hybrid corn (seed obtained from the U.S.) and mechanical corn drying; keeping good cost records—they could quote exact costs on most items of production, and they're going to computer record keeping; leasing, rather than owning, all cropping equipment, including trucks; and weighing their show and sale bulls every 15 days.

La Pluma

At the time of our visit, 35 tractors were in operation on La Pluma, but not one of these was owned by the Firpos. Marcus quipped, "The only equipment we own is the corn drier, and we would prefer not to own it." In addition to being cheaper, Marcus pointed out that leasing equipment facilitates change; for example, should the corn export market be lost at some future time, they wouldn't have a lot of obsolete equipment on hand.

At La Pluma, they grow 8,500 acres of corn. Most of this grain is exported to Europe. Corn silage is produced on the estancia and stored for drought protection.

The Firpo's corn drier.

We also saw some excellent rye-alfalfa pastures. On one of these pastures, they had 320 head of 700- to 750-lb steers, or 1.4 steers per acre; and both the pasture and the cattle were doing fine.

In season, they pasture some straight alfalfa. But we were there in early spring, at which time the alfalfa was lush and they were fearful of bloat. They wait until about 10% of the alfalfa is in bloom before pasturing it.

The Firpo's Angus cattle.

La Danesa

Upon our arrival at La Danesa, we were served drinks and hors d'oeuvres, followed by a delicious and bountiful barbecue.

Only Angus cattle are kept on Firpo's La Danesa; and they're either registered or purebred crosses (the latter are those which have been graded up for several generations; many of them 9/10 pure breeding).

They exhibited their bulls in a number of neat corrals, surrounded by a parklike area of well-cropped turf and beautiful trees. Among the 60 good bulls being started for the 1969 Palermo show, were sons and grandsons of bulls that Sr. Firpo had purchased from Ankony Angus of the U.S. The Firpos have compiled an enviable record in the great Palermo show; among other winnings, they had a Grand Champion Angus Bull in both 1966 and 1967.

The cattle that are being fitted for show and sale are fed on alfalfa hay and a cooked mixture of ground corn, barley, oats, and sorghum. The proportion of the cereal grains used varies according to price. They add a great deal of water to their cooked grain; in fact, Sr. Firpo facetiously referred to it as "soup." Also, the animals being fitted for the Palermo show next July are on nurse cows (they do not have any milk replacers in Argentina).

They consider straw too expensive for bedding. So, they're using river sand, an idea which they borrowed from Ankony Angus of the U.S.

All of the pedigreed cows (2,000 head) and pedigreed cross cows (600 to 1,000 head) at La Danesa are bred by artificial insemination.

In Argentina (as in England), red Angus are eligible for registration in the same studbooks as black Angus; and red Angus are permitted to show in competition with black Angus.

King Ranches of Argentina

We visited Al Abolengo and Carmen, two of the four ranches in Argentina owned by King Ranch—the Klebergs of Texas.

El Abolengo

El Abolengo embraces 18,500 acres. On it, they have 11,400 cattle, 600 sheep, and 300 horses. They employ 40 men; and they and their families make for a total of 120 people. They have their own school and their own flying strip on the estancia.

Most of the cattle at El Abolengo are either commercial steers being grass-finished for market, or second or third cross Santa Gertrudis.

El Abolengo is ably managed by Sr. Armando E. Mandrilli, who is trained as a chemical engineer but now is the fourth generation of his family to be engaged in ranching. Sr. Mandrilli very much admires the United States; he even had a U.S. western saddle custom made for his personal use, and the entire family is now being privately tutored in English. The friendly Mandrilli family—Armando and Miryan, and

The Mandrilli family.

their three daughters and a son—hosted us for a bountiful noon-day barbecue.

Carmen

Here again we were much impressed with both the personnel and the cattle at King Ranch's Carmen, which is managed by Sr. Jorge O. Abelanda. Sr. and Sra. Abelanda had us in their home for refreshments following our tour of the estancia. Sr. Klaus Seeger, who speaks English and who had used my books when he was at Texas A&M, served as our guide.

Estancia Carmen consists of 24,500 acres. On it, they have 10,200 head of cattle, of which 130 are registered Santa Gertrudis. They exhibited before us four of their marvelous Santa Gertrudis bulls; among them, the 1968 Palermo Champion.

All cows at Estancia Carmen are bred by artificial insemination, and all animals are production tested—with all records on computer.

We Went to the Horse Races in Argentina

We were guests of the Jockey Club, Hipodrome de Palermo. We were told that between 42,000 and 43,000 people were in attendance that day. The races started at 10:30 in the morning, and the sixth event, which was the main event, finished at 2:30 p.m. We had lunch at the Jockey Club.

The horses raced on a dirt track, counterclockwise. The main event was 1.367 miles long. They use a starting gate, and they have a totalizer and pari-mutuel betting, much as we have in the United States. Obviously, the Argentineans love horse racing.

Liniers Livestock Market

Following our visit to five estancias in the Pampas, where we saw how cattle in the Argentine are produced, it was timely and interesting that we see how they are marketed. Thus, we visited Liniers Livestock Market in Buenos Aires, the largest market in the Argentine. We were hosted and led through the market by Sr. Alfred R. Lanusse, of the livestock commission firm of Pedro y Antonio Lanusse S. A. The market handles cattle, sheep, and hogs, but we visited the cattle pens only.

All animals are sold by the auction method; none by private treaty. Instead of moving the cattle through an auction ring, as we do in the U.S., they move the people. The ringing of large bells signals selling time. Two cattle auctions were underway simultaneously in different sections of the yards; one for the local trade, and the other for export. The auctioneer and a few people proceeded from pen to pen along a catwalk overlooking the cattle being sold, with most of the buyers astride their horses in the alley adjacent to the pen being sold. The auctioneer chanted and sold quickly, devoting about 1½ minutes to each lot of cattle. We saw two auctioneers in action; a cousin of Alfredo R. Lanusse (whose father is Chief of the Argentina Army) and Alfredo's father. The senior Lanusse has the reputation of being fast, fair, and honest; the buyers like him because he doesn't take any bids "out of the sky," as we would say.

I liked their way of auctioning. It's easier to move people than cattle. Besides, the cattle end up with fewer bruises.

International Packers, Inc.

Next, we visited International Packers, Inc., one of the largest meat packing plants (they refer to them as "factories," rather than plants) in Argentina, a giant complex covering 24 acres of floor space. In Argentina, this plant is known as Compania Swift de la Plata, S.A. It's located to the southeast of Buenos Aires, along the La Plata river, on which they export by boat. The plant has a capacity of 300 head/hour.

Their skinning facilities are excellent. Cattle are hoisted (they're never on the floor), and the workers do not have to stoop over. All carcasses are identified by number (with corresponding numbers given to the heads upon removal). Glands are carefully examined for disease. The hide from over the back area is pulled via machine. They refer to their skinning method as the "Canadian method," because the skinning machine was invented in Canada.

All carcasses are weighed, with two men present at the scales—one representing the cattle producer, and the other representing the packer. Also, all carcasses are graded hot (in the U.S., carcasses are graded after chilling, thereby permitting ribbing down the carcasses). In Argentina, government grading is required (in the U.S., it is elective).

Their coolers are very sanitary, with easy-to-clean walls and floors, and no sawdust.

Throughout the plant, there is much easy-to-clean stainless steel and tile; employees and visitors must wash their hands with chlorinated water (5 ppm) before entering certain areas; lady workers wear neat, white caps; most workers are dressed in white coats; carcasses are washed with chlorinated water; and carcasses are checked by chromatography for harmful spray residues.

Among the staff hosting us at Swift's plant was Sr. Jose M. Pellegrino, meat technologist, who studied at Ohio State University before and subsequent to our visit. He and I became warm friends.

Science and technology, much of it from the United States, is ceaselessly working away to lessen the handicaps to beef production in Argentina. Basically, they have three of the most important requisites for success in the cattle business working for them, namely good pasture, good climate, and good cattlemen. Indeed, if there be a reincarnation, and if I may choose, I would like to join a herd on the Pampas.

We had a gala dinner at Hotel Garrera with invited guests. Audrey is on the left.

Another view of the beautiful gala dinner table. I am seated at the lower right.

The Chile We Saw

We made a sightseeing tour of Santiago in our private bus. Queen Elizabeth was to visit Chile soon after us, so we saw many things being refurbished. A very large house, formerly owned by a wealthy family, was being renovated including a chandelier weighing six tons.

All of the buildings now have to be earthquake proofed because Chile is on the triangle with California and Japan.

We visited their racetrack (Club Hipico) which is nearly 100 years old. The track is 1½ miles long—all on turf. The horses on this track run clockwise, whereas in both Brazil and Argentina, they race counterclockwise. There is racing every Sunday and on holidays the year around.

Club Hipico racetrack in Santiago, Chile.

Farm (Fundo) Haras Tarapaca

In Chile, a farm is known as a fundo. So, this morning, we visited Fundo Hara Tarapaca.

On this farm, we saw Holstein dairy cattle and Thoroughbred horses. The owner of this farm, Don Alberto Solari, also owns one of the largest clothing stores in Chile. The manager of the farm is Emilio Plaza (the one who wore the manta). The farm consists of 1,250 acres, all of which are under irrigation. It is a deep, silt, loam soil, and very fertile.

Holstein Dairy

There are 100 lactating cows in this herd. They have both American and European-type Holsteins. The American-type animals are more angular and less "beefy" than the European type. The American-type animals are of Carnation breeding.

The cows graze alfalfa pasture or are given green chop alfalfa during the growing season. In the winter, they receive alfalfa hay. Also, they are fed a mixed concentrate consisting of wheat, oats, linseed meals, fish meal, and salt, with the concentrate allowance on the basis of 2.08 lb per gallon of milk.

All cows are bred by artificial insemination.

Thoroughbred Horses

There are 80 broodmares on this farm. On one alfalfa pasture, we were shown 22 yearling fillies sired by 4 different stallions. These fillies were well grown and of good type.

Thoroughbred ages in Chile are computed on the basis of July 1 (rather than January 1, as in the United States). Thus, a foal born in October, 1968 would be one year old on July 1, 1969.

Farm (Fundo) "Haras Sta Eladia,"

We arrived on this farm about noon. This large operation is owned by Sr. Benedicto Aguado. He and his family manage the several divisions; Thoroughbred horses, poultry (including a hatchery), and fruit. In addition to seeing the operation, we were served, in a beautiful parklike orchard, a most bountiful and very delicious luncheon, along with a choice of many drinks.

Thoroughbred Horses

The Thoroughbred breeding herd consists of 70 broodmares and 3 stallions.

Sr. Aguado races some horses. Also, he produces and sells horses to others for racing.

Stallions and sale animals were exhibited before us in an attractive outdoor ring consisting of turf in the center, a circular sand track, surrounded by park benches, and trees and shrubs on the outside. We were shown a few of the two-year-olds that are being fitted for the October consignment auction, to be held in Santiago.

The Aguados hosted us to a delicious luncheon.

Poultry

The poultry operation is very large. Pertinent facts about it follow: There are 150,000 layers in cages and 150,000 breeders; 600,000 baby chicks are hatched each month, on a year around basis—that's 8,200,000 chicks per year; all baby chicks are sold in Chile.

Fruit

The fruit consists of 124 acres of pears, 173 acres of peaches, 60 acres of prunes; and a fruit packing building..

A Thoroughbred stallion at Haras Sta Eladia, owned by the Aguado Family, in Chile. I am standing in the distance on the left.

Audrey among the flowering pears

The Peru We Saw

Vicente Portaro, a former California State University-Fresno student who had been at the Agriservices Foundation Headquarters when he was a student, was very helpful to us when we arrived in Lima, the capital city of Peru.

Universidad Agraria

Peru gave the world potatoes (both Irish and sweet potatoes), corn, and quinua (from which quinine is made). Their coat of arms embraces a llama, a quinine tree (quinua), and a horn of plenty.

Breed Registries

They register several breeds of livestock and issue registration certificates, for which a fee is charged.

Wool Laboratory

We visited their wool laboratory. They gave me a picture showing Alpacas at an elevation of 15,750 feet.

Swine

We saw Yorkshires, Durocs, Landrace, and Hampshires.

Dairy Breeds

Mostly Holsteins, along with a few Brown Swiss, were in evidence.

Trees in Dairy Heifer Replacement Corrals

We saw California Poplar trees thriving in cattle corrals, despite the urine. These trees were planted in 1960. Obviously, this specie will withstand animal excrement, much to my surprise.

Dairy Records

Twenty-four herds, involving 3,000 cows/month, are in their dairy improvement work, which is modeled after DHIA in the U.S., and which is on computer. A service fee is charged for same.

Milk Processing Laboratory

Their new milk processing laboratory had been open only three months. It was very clean and modern.

1,000 Head Cattle Lot

This was of circular design. Actually, there are two circles, a big one surrounding a smaller one.

Hacienda (Farm), owned by Sr. Jose Musandte

This farm is reputed to have Peru's finest Paso Fino horses; so, we were pleased to see it.

According to the university staff, with whom I visited earlier, Peru is the native home of the Paso Fino, despite the fact that the U.S. is now getting them from other South American countries, and the controversy that rages on this subject.

There were 20 Paso Finos on the hacienda that we visited. These horses are never on pasture. Most of the exercise is given by longeing in a little ring, in which there is a pole in the center.

Maranga Dairy

They produce milk and also buy from the outside, then process all of it in their plant. They make cheese and butter, as well as sell fresh, pasteurized milk.

We Were Dinner and Racing Guests of the Portaro Family

Mrs. Ensminger and I were invited by Vicente J. Portaro to be the dinner/racing guests of the Portaros (Vicente, his father and mother, and his grandfather and grandmother). It was a most delightful evening at the Jockey Club del Peru. A wonderful dinner was served at a choice location right over the finish line. The club building is new and attractive, and the night lighting is very good. Thcy usc a starting gate, and they use the tote board. Horses race counterclockwise on a dirt track. One main difference from our racetracks that we noted was the fact that part of the race crowd observes the races from their cars parked in the infield (much like our drive-in movies).

It was a most delightful evening—with good food, wonderful people, and good races. Mrs. Ensminger and grandmother Portaro picked winners. The rest of us lost; but grandfather Portaro had much fun losing as he shifted his tickets about for better luck.

Cuzco

In addition to seeing the Inca Indian Ruins, where one of the first civilizations evolved, I was much interested in seeing the following in this high altitude (11,400 feet):

Bench Terraces

The first terraces were built here. Many of them still remain. It is noteworthy, however, that they do not farm on the contour despite the terracing. Between terraces, they usually plow with the slope.

Llamas

These cloven-footed animals are members of the camel family; in fact, the natives refer to them as the "camel of the Andes." They are not ruminants as such, for they do not have a well developed first stomach or paunch. In Spanish, "llama" means light.

The Cuzco airport.

Sheep

Their sheep are small, multi-colored and undocked.

All animals graze a native type of bunchgrass, which at the time of our visit was dry-cured on the stalk. I would wager that the vegetation is low in protein and energy.

Communal Farming

The Portaros told me that the agriculture around Cuzco (the small herds and the crops) are under communal ownership and operation—a type of operation that has existed there for many years.

Macchu Pichu

We traveled via train from Cuzco to Putucusi Bridge. Thence, we traveled by bus for a distance of 5 miles up the mountain to Macchu Pichu, where we visited the lost city of the Incas. These ruins were discovered by Hiram Bingham of Yale University in 1911.

Our guide was Enrique (Henry) Miranda. At the close of the guided tour of the Inca ruins, Henry recited the Inca creed, which follows: Don't be a thief, don't be a liar, don't be lazy.

The Portaros and Stan Stout gave the following very plausible reason for the Incas selecting this location, high on the mountain side, for their head-

Macchu Pichu. At 13,000 feet, none of us felt equal to a foot race.

Macchu Pichu—what happened to the Incas?

quarters: They worshipped the sun and wished to be as near to it as possible.

Following lunch at the Hotel Macchu Pichu, we returned via bus and train to Cuzco. The next day we flew to Lima

Dinner with Vicente J. Portaro Family

We had contacted Vicente Portaro whom we had met when he was a student at Fresno State University. Vicente's father and mother invited Audrey and me for dinner in their home. It was a wonderful evening. Their hospitality was unsurpassed.

The Portaros have a beautiful home. They had invited in many of their relatives and friends, whom we enjoyed meeting. They served a wonderful dinner, buffet style. Vicente has four sisters and a brother all of whom we met. They are a handsome and closely-knit family.

The Ecuador We Saw

Upon our arrival at the airport in Quito, we were met by representatives of Metropolitan Touring and by Messrs. William C. Bowser, agricultural attaché, and Damian Miranda, senior agricultural assistant, both of the American embassy.

Actually, as we prepared to land in Ecuador, we saw a rather large military-looking group. We wondered what it was all about. When we deplaned, we were told that the other group was there to greet the new U.S. Ambassador to Ecuador. We said that we would be glad to go over and help welcome him, but we were whisked onto our bus with our own welcoming party.

Group waiting to greet the arrival of a new U.S. Ambassador to Ecuador.

Mario Miranda

Mario is the brother of Damian Miranda, the senior agricultural assistant, American embassy, who accompanied us on this trip to their family farm. Both Mario and Damian are graduates of the University of Minnesota.

This farm consists of 275 acres. We were particularly impressed with a newly seeded pasture that we saw, which they told us would carry three cows per acre the year around. The seeding used for this pasture consisted of English ryegrass; ladino; white, and red clover; and alfalfa.

Hacienda "La Avalina,"

This hacienda was established in 1600. Presently, it is leased and managed by Carlos Proano and Gustavo Fernandez (the latter served as our host).

Our first stop was at their dairy manufacturing plant, where we saw their fresh milk, butter, and cheese processing facilities.

From the dairy manufacturing plant, we went to lunch, which was delicious and enjoyable. Following lunch, I presented a *Dairy Science Handbook*, a *Light Horses* bulletin, and a Stockmen's School program to Sr. Fernandez. The latter responded warmly.

Size and Type of Enterprise

This 1,480-acre enterprise is largely devoted to dairying. There are about 1,200 head of cattle on the place, most of which are high grade Holsteins. Most of the farm is in pasture. They also produce some potatoes.

Milk Production

They are producing about 5,000 qt of milk per day.

Feeds

The cows are pastured and given green chop.

Breeding

The cows are high grade Holsteins, but not registered. Purebred Holstein bulls are used, by artificial insemination.

Calves

Calves are allowed to suck their dams for our days, following which they are placed in small, individual stalls on elevated, slotted floors. From birth to freshening, their death losses are the lowest I know of: 1% per year (or a total of 3% from birth to the first lactation). They do not feed any antibiotics. Few cases of scours are encountered.

Labor

One hundred people are employed on the farm.

Alfalfa

A cutting of alfalfa can be harvested every 50 days, the year around. Alfalfa stands are renovated every 5 years.

Santa Catalina Research Station INIAP

This station is government operated, with the assistance of the New York-based Rockefeller Foundation. The station consists of 2,225 acres. It is located at an elevation of around 10,000 ft. Research is conducted in the following areas: cereal grains, potatoes, corn, grasses, and dairy.

Potatoes

A total of 350 varieties of potatoes are under study. Each variety is evaluated on the basis of resistance to blight and other diseases, quality, and storage.

Cereals

The cereals being studied are: wheat, oats, and barley. The national average yield of wheat is 16 to 17 bu/acre. They have developed wheat at this Station which has yielded 113 bu/acre. They use a complete 10-40-10 fertilizer, applied at 280 lb/acre. Soils of the area are low in phosphorus, and they have a Ph of about 6. They seed 200 lb of wheat/acre. Their wheats are of semi hard varieties (no hard wheat is produced).

Two types of oats are being studied; one for use as green forage, and the other for grain.

Two kinds of barley are under study; a two-row barley for brewing, and a six-row barley for grain.

Gala Dinner

Our gala dinner was held at the Quito Hotel. There was good food and good fellowship. The following were our guests: Mr. and Mrs. William C. Bowser, agricultural attaché; Sr. and Mrs. Damian Miranda; Sr. Gustavo Fernandez; and Sr. Ramiro

The beautiful table at our gala dinner at the Quito Hotel.

Romero. Following the dinner, Dr. Ensminger welcomed the guests and presented a book to each Mrs. Bowser and Miranda, and sent another book with them to give to the Santa Catalina Research Station INIAP library. Mr. Bowser responded and told us more about Ecuador.

Travel to the Equator

We traveled via our private bus to the equator. En route, we stopped to see the home of an Indian family. The Indian man was making sandals on the front porch, and the mother appeared to be busy looking after the several children. Newspapers were pasted on the ceiling of the front room. There was little furniture, but it is noteworthy that there was a sewing machine.

The cookstove was without chimney, better to dry corn (which, in season, is hung on the wall above the stove), and smoke it to control insects. In the same room with the cookstove, on a dirt floor, were guinea pigs, ducks, and rabbits. The guinea pigs were happily eating away on green feed. We were told that guinea pigs are a delicacy among folks, eaten on festive occasions.

Thence, we visited the equator, where there is a monument, from which a narrow (about two in. wide), metal band on the surrounding pavement extends east-west, marking the location of the equator. Nearby, were three small, commercial establishments, catering to tourists, with souvenirs and drinks.

Our group at the equator in Ecuador.

Hog Slaughtering

Near the road, we saw four hogs being slaughtered. They would weigh 175 to 200 lb each. Hair was being removed by heating and singeing the exterior with burning eucalyptus twigs, then scraping.

Four hogs being slaughtered, roadside.

Red Flags

Where fresh meat is available, a red flag is hung in front of the place selling it, thereby advertising that buyers may come and get it. Where this custom is followed, there is no refrigeration, so the meat must move quickly to the consumer.

Social Security

Fifteen percent of all salaries goes to Social Security. Then, both men and women workers retire at age 60 or after 30 years service, on pay equivalent to the average of their best five-year earnings.

The Colombia We Saw

Upon our arrival at Bogota, Colombia we were met at the airport by Messrs. Winston Garth Thorburn and Jose Antonia Umana, of the American Embassy, and Dr. H. H. Stonaker, a longtime friend of the Ensmingers.

Gala Dinner

This evening, we had a gala dinner at the Gran Vatel Restaurant, an old and historic building in Bogota, with invited guests. Among our distinguished guests were: Mr. and Mrs. Winston Garth Thorburn, agricultural attaché, American embassy; Dr. and Mrs. H. H. Stonaker, project leader, animal science, the University of Nebraska mission to Columbia; and Dr. and Mrs. Ned S. Raun, animal scientist, the Rockefeller Foundation.

Gala dinner at the Gran Vatel Restaurant in Bogota, Colombia.

Dr. E called on each of the gentleman guests for a few words. They all responded graciously and warmly.

Study-Tour of the Bogota Area

A number of people familiar with the area joined us in our private bus for a guided tour of the area. Pertinent facts obtained and/or seen follow.

Rainfall and Humidity

The average rainfall is 60 inches, and the average humidity over 80%.

Leading Cattle Breeds

Brahman cattle lead in numbers in Colombia, followed by Charolais.

Swine Production

Swine numbers have been going down about 5% per year, due to poor management, and high feed prices.

Flower Export

Flowers are now being exported from Colombia to the U.S. by air.

Sr. Jaime Pradilla, Ganaderias Praco

This is the dairy that we visited. They have the only purebred Guernsey herd in Colombia. Also, they have Holsteins. Their Guernsey foundation stock came from the U.S. Their foundation stock of Holsteins were of Carnation breeding.

Kraus Hermanos, Gunther and Erwin Kraus

The Kraus brothers own the Charolais herd that we visited. Until 1960, they operated a dairy on this hacienda. Also, until rather recently, they were in the jewelry business.

Charolais herd at Kraus Hermanos.

They made their first importation of Charolais cattle from France in 1960.

Zipaquira Salt Cathedral

This cathedral is just what the name implies—a cathedral built within a salt mine. The deposit in the salt cathedral consists of 87% salt, with the balance made up of coal and fool's gold. Metal cannot be used in the cathedral, because of corrosion caused by the salt. Hence, all doors, statues, and other fixtures are made of salt, wood (eucalyptus), or stone.

The railing carved out of salt in the cathedral.

The Salt Cathedral is 350 ft below the surface. The largest "room" in the cathedral is 365 ft long, 210 ft wide, and 50 to 70 ft high, which is about the same size as the Notre Dame in Paris. Ten thousand people can be accommodated in the cathedral. Regular worship is held on all holidays, and there are two services every Sunday.

Santa Catalina Research Station INIAP

This experiment station was established by the government of Ecuador and is operated with the assistance of the Rockefeller Foundation. It embraces 1,250 acres. On the staff they have 30 with Ph.D. degrees, 50 with M.S. degrees, and the rest with D.V.M. or B.S. degrees. Originally, this was swampland. The soil is deficient in phosphorus, calcium, and potassium.

Dinner-Seminar in the H. H. Stonaker Home

Audrey and I enjoyed a wonderful dinner in the home of the H. H. Stonakers (Stoney and Betty). Then, following dinner I conducted a seminar relative to "the Livestock Industry of the United States." Stoney had invited a number of professional staff members of Santa Catalina Research Station, along with the men of our study-tour group. Because many of those present for the seminar didn't speak English, a translator was used in my slide presentation. I also told of the Stockmen's School and presented a set of books to the experiment station library. Following the seminar, refreshments were served.

Sightseeing in Bogota

This morning, we went on a sightseeing tour of Bogota, with stops on Montserrate, at Simon Bolivar's home, and at the Gold Museum. From Bogota, we flew to Mexico City.

The Mexico We Saw

Upon our arrival in Mexico, we were met at the airport by our good friends, Guillermo and Doris Osuna, William and Nellie Finan, and Tomas and Myrnia Castella. Guillermo Osuna and William Finan are distinguished trustees of Agriservices Foundation. In Mexico city, we stayed at the Hotel Maria Isabel.

Raul Cano's Thoroughbred Horse-Breeding Establishment

Sr. Raul Cano, the owner of this horse farm, is also the principal owner of Anaconda Copper of Mexico, and Cobre de Mexico, S.A. (a wire-coating industry). The farm is managed by Francisco Gonzales.

The farm consists of 100 acres, and between 40 and 50 Thoroughbred horses of all ages and both sexes. He has two good stallions. They race some of their young stock and sell the rest to others.

They are rightfully proud of their pastures of a mixture of tall fescue, red fescue, and perennial rye.

Tepozotlan

We visited this old cathedral and museum. The cathedral is the most ornate structure that we saw during the entire study-tour.

Estado Mayor Presidencial

This is the army post where several of the 28 equestrian teams were training for the Olympics. We were escorted about by Maria Del Carmen Cravioto, who is the commanding officer's secretary. We were told that each of the 28 teams consists of 5 to 6 horses. We saw the dressage ring and the two courses being used by jumpers.

Instituto Nacional de Investigaciones Pecuarias (the Research Station)

Dr. Pedro Solana, the director general of the station and a graduate of the University of Wisconsin, took us over the station.

We inspected their bull barn, where they collect semen for AI throughout Mexico. We saw bulls of the following breeds: Holstein, Hereford, Brown Swiss, and Charolais.

Gala Dinner, Hotel Maria Isabel

The following were our guests for the gala dinner at the Hotel Maria Isabel: Mr. Lawrence Robert Fouchs, assistant agricultural attaché, American embassy; Mr. Dale Douglas, assistant agricultural attaché, and Mrs. Douglas; William and Nellie Finan; Guillermo and Doris Osuna; Tomas and Myrnia Castella; Lauro and Susan Villalon; and Carlos Osuna (brother of Guillermo and a friend of the Ensmingers).

Dr. E welcomed the guests and thanked all of those who had done so much to make our visit a pleasant experience.

Brief talks were made by Messrs. Fouchs, Douglas, and Osuna; then a question and answer period followed. Bob Fouchs appropriately referred to the agricultural attachés as representatives of the American farmer.

Dr. E also thanked the study-tour group for their cooperation, and for being good ambassadors of the United States.

Hereford bull at Instituto Nacional de Investigaciones Pecuarias (I am on the right).

A Charolais bull at the Instituto Nacional de Investigaciones Pecuarias being looked over by me.

Pyramids

We visited the pyramids of Teotihuacan, which we found very interesting.

At noon we had lunch at the Bull Ring Restaurant. After the lunch, they invite their customers to fight a bull. First, they are kind enough to give a little instruction.

This shows the fearless bullfighters from our group. They each took a fling at it.

Rancho la Cotera

This afternoon, we visited the Holstein dairy of which Sr. Emilio Fernandez is the principal owner. Sr. Fernandez came from Spain at age 17. His nephew, Valleriano Fernandez, showed us the bulls and the circular exerciser; then Sr. Emilio Fernandez took over. Sr. Guillermo Osuna served as interpreter.

Rancho La Cotera is one of the most modern dairies to be found anywhere in the world. Also, it is noteworthy that in 1965, Sr. Emilio Fernandez received a singular citation from the President of Mexico for Holstein excellence. Only one Holstein award of this kind is given every 25 years.

General Facts

There are about 100 acres in the establishment at the location we visited. There are 610 lactating cows, 150 dry cows, plus young stock and herd bulls. About 50% of the cows are registered.

Some of our group being briefed at the dairy.

Milking Parlor

This establishment has a very modern milking parlor, with two lines of eight stalls each. All cows are washed (via jet) all over each morning. Also, prior to each milking, udders are washed with lukewarm water, followed by washing with chlorine water.

Serge milking equipment is used. The automatic feeders had been converted to manually operated feeders, because the automated equipment didn't work satisfactorily and replacement parts were too difficult to get from the U.S. manufacturer of the feeder equipment.

At la Cotera they exercise all of their bulls to keep them in good health.

Return to Los Angeles

Following breakfast at the Hotel Maria Isabel, we departed our hotel for the airport where we boarded Mexicana Airlines for Los Angeles, bringing to a close an exciting and memorable study-tour.

1970
THE SOUTH PACIFIC WE SAW

Mrs. Ensminger and I led a delegation of 48 people to Tahiti/Moorea/Fiji, New Zealand, Australia, and Hawaii, departing from Los Angeles, February 14, 1970, and returning to Los Angeles, March 11, 1970.

The Tahiti/Moorea/Fiji We Saw

Tahiti, the biggest island of French Polynesia, is in the south Pacific Ocean, about halfway between Australia and California. More later about Tahiti.

Moorea

After checking in at the Hotel Tahiti, we traveled by boat from Papeete to Moorea, a sister island to Tahiti, situated 11 miles across the channel. It was a rough crossing, with the result that many of our delegates got sick.

On the island of Moorea, we headquartered at the Hotel Bali Hai. Following a buffet luncheon at the hotel, we toured the island. The Hotel Bali Hai has a 14,000 layer (eggs) operation and produces a few vegetables. It seems obvious, however, that the future of Moorea lies in a fast rising tourism industry, rather than agriculture. The soil isn't too fertile, and arable areas are limited.

In the evening, the highlight was the Tamara (Tamaaraa) Feast, which began with the opening of the himaa (or underground earth) oven, and which concluded with the Otea, the ancient Tahitian dance of welcome performed by 40 famous Temae Dancers of Moorea. They danced, sang, and portrayed ancient legends with bodies and voices.

Some of our delegates were, rightfully, apprehensive about the "angry waves," with the result that they departed from Moorea by air prior to the feast.

Due to a severe wind-and-rain-storm, our boat was not able to find its way through the reef that night. Hence, those of us who were stranded, bedded down for a short night at the Aimeo Hotel, situated on Cook's Bay in Moorea.

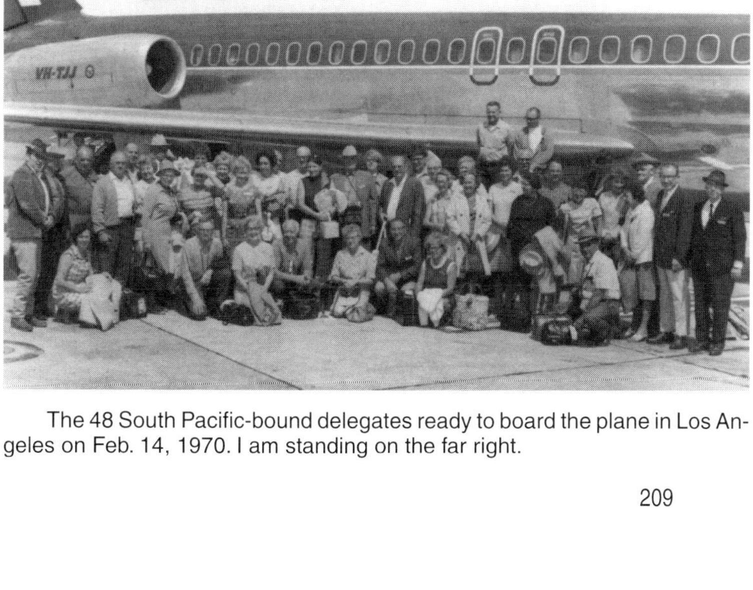

The 48 South Pacific-bound delegates ready to board the plane in Los Angeles on Feb. 14, 1970. I am standing on the far right.

More About Tahiti

In the morning, we left Moorea by boat and returned to Papeete, Tahiti. Following lunch at the LeRotui Restaurant in Taravao, Tahiti, we were briefed on the agriculture of Tahiti by Mr. Robert Millaud, Chief Engineer of Agricultural Services and Chief of Agricultural Economics, Papeete, Tahiti, and by Mr. John M. Boubee, Chief of Taravao Agricultural Experiment Station, Papeete, Tahiti. The main agriculture of Tahiti consists of coconut (for copra and refined coconut oil), vanilla, and coffee.

Fiji

In traveling from Tahiti to Fiji, we crossed the International Dateline. Hence, we "skipped" Tuesday, February 17. We stopped in Fiji both going and coming. In going, it was primarily a rest stop. In returning, we inspected the agriculture. Our reservations were at the Hotel Tanoa, Dani.

Fiji is a British Crown Colony, with a population of just over 500,000. Fiji's economy is largely dependent upon agriculture. There are two major crops—sugar and coconuts. The coconuts yield oil, copra, and meal. The principal exports are sugar, coconut products, minerals (including gold), and bananas.

On our return we visited the Agricultural Experiment Station, Sigatoka, Fiji. Mr. I. J. Partridge, the Officer in Charge, showed us the Agricultural Station.

The New Zealand We Saw

New Zealand is a member of the Commonwealth and Queen Elizabeth II, Queen of New Zealand, is represented by a governor-general.

New Zealand is the most southerly settled land in the South Pacific. It lies 1,400 miles southeast of Australia and midway between the Equator and the South Pole.

With a total area of 103,000 square miles, New Zealand is slightly larger than Britain, and about the same area as the state of Colorado. The climate is temperate, with plentiful sunshine, adequate rainfall (normally speaking, but at the time of our visit they were encountering their worst drought in 25 years), and no great extremes of heat and cold.

The New Zealand Co-operative Dairy Company Limited

This is a giant co-op that was formed in 1919 with the amalgamation of three major companies which were operating in the South Auckland district at that time. The company produces a variety of dairy products.

Ruakura Agricultural Research Center

Mr. D. J. D. Scott, scientific liaison officer, took us over the station. The center is the national headquarters of the Research Division of the New Zealand Department of Agriculture.

Although land for what is now Ruakura was set aside before the turn of the century, and a farm school and limited research were conducted at the center, the research role of Ruakura was limited until after World War II, at which time Dr. C. P. McMeekan became the director.

The Ruakura Center is appropriately located in the heart of what may be claimed the world's most concentrated area of livestock production on grass. It is estimated that within about 50 miles of the city of Hamilton, over five million sheep are grazed the year round at the rate of up to eight to the acre and nearly one million dairy cows are fully supported on grass at stocking rates of one or better per acre.

Yarndley Bros. (Bill and Sandy), Kakariki Farms

This farm is owned and operated by the two Yarndley brothers, Bill (age 29) and Sandy (age 25). Pertinent facts about the operation are:

Bobtailed Cows

The Yarndley Bros. (and we saw others in New Zealand) cut off the tails of most of their future cows (the cows are bobtailed soon after birth), as a sanitary measure.

Crossbreeding

They are crossing Jerseys X Holsteins. He likes the hybrid vigor, plus the added milk production over and above that of straight Jerseys.

Dr. C.P. McMeekan, Kohatunui Farm

Dr. and Mrs. C. P. McMeekan were our gracious hosts. Dr. McMeekan is a world-renowned animal scientist. He did graduate work at Cambridge, England, under Sir John Hammond. He was formerly the Director of the Ruakura Experiment Station, which we visited the day before. He retired four years ago, but he works 6 to 8 months each year as consultant to the World Bank.

Dr. and Mrs. McMeekan served food, which was both bountiful and delicious, along with a choice of drinks (including the traditional tea). Pertinent facts about Dr. McMeekan and his Kohatunui Farm follow:

His Book Grass to Milk

Dr. McMeekan's book, *Grass to Milk*, has been published in English, Spanish, and Russian.

Kohatunui Farm

The McMeekans bought the farm 14 years ago, then retired to it four years ago. It consists of 380

The McMeekans and the Ensmingers. *Left to right:* Mrs. McMeekan, Dr. E, Dr. C. P. McMeekan, and Audrey. Photo taken following the luncheon hosted by the McMeekans at Kohatunui Farm. Note the rolling pastures of Kohatunui in the background.

acres, on which he produces cattle and sheep. It's a one-man operation, plus four dogs.

Two or three owners just walked off and abandoned Kohatunui farm before Dr. McMeekan bought it 14 years ago. It was unsuitable for livestock production due to cobalt deficiency. Now, Dr. McMeekan applies 5 lb of cobalt per acre, as a top-dressing with phosphorus. He used to apply 200 lb of phosphorus per acre, but now he uses 300 lb per acre. Aerial spraying is used to apply it.

A Medley/On the Move

We visited Whakarewarewa Thermal Reserve and Maoria Model Pa (village); thence the Rainbow Trout Spring; thence the Rotorua Botanic Gardens. We then flew to Palmerston North; thence we traveled by motor coach to Wanganui where we visited the famous Puteki Maori Church.

Mr. J. G. Alexander, Cranleigh

On this date, we spent the day on Cranleigh, the finest Romney sheep breeding establishment in the world; and a noted Thoroughbred farm. This is the place of which Humphrey Finney, well-known American horseman, said, "As much care is used in mating the Cranleigh ewes as ever was taken by Italian master (Thoroughbred) breeder Tesio in mating the Dormello mares."

Dr. E. and a group visit a Maori village.

Cranleigh consists of 1,000 acres. On it, they have Romney sheep, Thoroughbred horses, and crossbred cattle.

About Romneys in New Zealand

Sixteen Romney ewes were imported into New Zealand, from England, in 1853. Today, 76% of New Zealand's 60.5 million sheep are Romneys. According to Mr. Alexander, the Romneys of New Zealand average 12.3 lb per fleece. He further stated that New Zealand Romneys have captured the world's strong wool (we call it "coarse" wool in the U.S.) market.

Sheep Dogs

One of Mr. Alexander's employees put on a sheep dog demonstration. He used a Border Scotch Collie dog. We were told that it takes at least six months to train a sheep dog.

Horses at Cranleigh

Mr. Alexander jokingly referred to Cranleigh as having been at the top in racing for three years, then at the bottom for 30 years.

We asked Mr. Alexander why they blanket so many horses that are out in the paddocks (pastures and corrals). The answer: flies, and dust (it's easier to groom horses that have been blanketed).

On command from Mr. Alexander, a sheep dog would go out and round up a little flock of sheep and bring them wherever he directed.

Overnight Hosting in Private Homes

We were hosted in private homes on the night of February 22. This was one of the highlights. Arrangements were made by the Wairarapa Branch, New Zealand Thoroughbred Breeders' Association. Those of us in the U.S. who host foreign groups could "take a page out of their book"—that is, we would do well to do likewise. Hosting in private homes imparted a warm, friendly feeling. Mrs. Ensminger and I were overnight/breakfast guests of Mr. and Mrs. Alister Williams, who hosted our group at Te Parae Stud the next day.

Te Parae Stud

Our delegates arrived at Te Parae Stud, following the overnight hosting in private homes. A brief of the pertinent things that we saw and did follows:

Topdressing and Spraying Demonstration

A local company put on topdressing and spraying displays, respectively; narrated by Messrs. Collins James and Clarry Wilson.

Sheep Dog Demonstration

Jim Hay, a local farmer, who competes professionally, put on a sheep dog demonstration. Sheep dogs are widely used in New Zealand as a means of saving labor. Two dogs were used: One was a Border Scotch Collie, and the other of the Huntaway breed.

Mr. Alister Williams of Te Parae Stud.

The Border Scotch Collie doesn't bark at sheep, whereas the Huntaway does.

Te Parae Stud, Masterton, New Zealand

Te Parae Stud, is owned and operated by Mr. and Mrs. Alister Williams and their sons, Thomas and Richard.

Te Parae was established by T. C. Williams, grandfather of Alister Williams, 110 years ago. Until 1938, Te Parae was devoted to the production of Romney sheep and Angus cattle. Mrs. Alister Williams founded the Thoroughbreds at Te Parae in 1938.

Te Parae has sold horses to go to the U.S., Australia, South Africa, and Malaysia.

Gala Dinner, with Invited Guests, at Hotel St. George, Wellington

The Honorable Douglas J. Carter, Minister of Agriculture of New Zealand, addressed our group. He described himself as a farmer. On his farm, he has 200 milk cows, 1,000 sheep, and some Angus cattle.

Mr. Gordon Loveless, the U.S. agricultural attaché to New Zealand, presented statistical information on United States imports from New Zealand in 1969. The grand total of all trade was NZ $169, 911,000.

Te Parae hosted us to a lovely luncheon in a beautiful garden surrounding their house.

Christchurch, New Zealand

We spent one day on the South Island, in and near Christchurch. Christchurch is know as the Garden City, Cathedral City, and English City. It's known as Garden City because of its extensive parks and reserves, and because nowhere else in New Zealand do home gardeners set such a consistently high standard; Cathedral City because of its handsome Gothic-style cathedral that rises in the central square; and English City because over a century ago its founders planned to transplant here in the Antipodes a cross-section of English life.

The winning garden at Christchurch was outstanding.

Gardening is the common hobby of the citizens of Christchurch, and prize winning gardens are selected each year. We visited the recent first-prize garden—Health Foods Limited.

Canterbury

This is the seat of the University of Canterbury. It's chief administrators are known as chancellor (an honorary position) and vice chancellor (the chief executive officer), respectively.

We visited the Canterbury Agricultural College, which lies 13 miles southwest of Christchurch, not far from the village of Lincoln. The college stands in the center of broad acres of model farmland. Lincoln College, as it is generally known, has distinguished itself by training young farmers for their careers, and by research in pasture, plant life, and animal husbandry.

Lincoln College.

The Australia We Saw

With an area of 2,974,581 sq mi, Australia is about the size of the United States and slightly more than three-fourths the size of Europe.

I have wondered how Australia manages to have more sheep than people (161,000,000 to 12,000,000)—that's 14 sheep per person vs 0.12 sheep per person in the U.S. I've wondered why and how cattle numbers exceed the human population,

19.5 million to 12 million—that's 1.75 cows per person vs 0.5 cow per person in the U.S.

Sheep and Wool

Sheep constitute by far the most important single element in the pastoral industry; and wool accounts for 28% (in 1966) of the nation's exports.

Beef Cattle

Australia is a natural cattle country, and it is free from foot-and-mouth disease. Most of their cattle are grazed the year around on unfenced ranges where they are herded by musterers—the counterpart of the American cowboy.

Shorthorns, Herefords, and Angus are the leading breeds. In the north tropical areas, Brahman and Santa Gertrudis have been introduced and are increasing in numbers. Crossbreeding is practiced widely.

Other Animal Life

The wild animals and birds of Australia are known the world over.

There's a wild (feral) dog, called the *dingo*. However, most of the native mammals belong to the more primitive class known as *marsupials*.

Australia has a large assortment of birds, no fewer than 800 species. The emu, or Australian ostrich, and the cassowary, which is also flightless, are the largest of the bird tribe. Parrots, with their brillant green, yellow and scarlet plumage, add to the color of the landscape. Then, there is the fascinating Kookaburra, which laughs instead of sings.

Plant Life

Australia produces wheat, oats, barley, corn, sorghum, rice, tobacco, peanuts, potatoes, apples, oranges, cotton, sugar, and alfalfa (lucerne).

Research, Education, and Extension Services

Research is carried out by the Commonwealth Scientific Industrial Research Organization (CSIRO), the colleges, and the state departments of agriculture. Economic research is under the Bureau of Agricultural Economics. Research is financed mainly by funds from compulsory levies on industry supplemented by grants from the government.

All of the states except Tasmania have agricultural colleges. They are primarily teaching institutions, although they are doing more and more research and expanding their graduate programs.

Marketing Boards

Marketing boards control the marketing of the main commodities. Presently, there are 11 such boards under the Commonwealth or joint Commonwealth-State Legislation.

Land Tenure in Australia

It is noteworthy that only 10.6% of the land of Australia is privately owned versus 70.0% privately owned in the U.S.

Dalgety and New Zealand Loan Ltd.

We drove to Rocklea where we visited the Wool Store (Wood Warehouse) of Dalgety and New Zealand Ltd. This is the largest and most modern wool store of its kind in Australia. This visitation was of particular interest to our group because Australia leads the world in quantity (it produces one-third of the world's wool) and quality wool production, the U.S. imports 75% of its wool requirements from foreign countries, and the wool auctions of Australia are the price barometer of the world.

The name *Dalgety* is taken from the founder of the company, who was a son of the colonel of a Scotch regiment in Canada. He came to Australia at the age of 16, and he started the business in the 1880s. Today, Dalgety is found throughout the world—Balfour Guthrie in the U.S. is a subsidiary of Dalgety. The company headquarters in London.

Gala Dinner, With Invited Guests

Mr. Doug C. Mactaggart, Mactaggarts Primary Producers, Brisbane, was our speaker.

Eidsvold Station, Eidsvold, Queensland, Mr. and Mrs. E. B. Joyce

Eidsvold Station was first operated by the Archer family in 1848. Originally, it was a sheep operation; but it was transposed into a cattle enterprise because of the spear grass problem in wool, and the "boiling down" depression of the 1890s. In 1905, Fitzpeirce Joyce, father of E. B. Joyce—the present owner, became a part owner of Eidsvold. In 1936, E. B. Joyce was called home from the Argentine to take over the management.

Mr. Joyce is as able as he is colorful; and the Joyces are most gracious hosts. Today, Eidsvold Station is one of Australia's foremost and best known stations, and a mecca for many distinguished visitors—among them His Royal Highness Prince Charles, film stars, and scientists and practical agriculturalists who wish to observe the results of current research and modern breeding practices.

Eidsvold Station consists of four separate holdings totaling approximately 36,000 acres of freehold land (fee simple title), all operated as an integrated unit with headquarters at Eidsvold Station.

Pasture Improvement

We were impressed with the pasture improvement program currently underway at the Eidsvold Station, consisting of ringbarking or applying Tordon to trees; clearing scrub areas and seeding grasses, rotation grazing; irrigation, and winter grazing crops.

We traveled by chartered plane to Eidsvold Station, Eidsvold, Queensland, Australia, owned by Mr. and Mrs. E. B. Joyce, where we saw good Santa Gertrudis cattle, good Quarter Horses, and good pasture management. *Left to right:* Dr. E, E. B. Joyce, Mrs. Joyce, and Audrey.

Eidsvold Cattle

Until 1953, Eidsvold Station ran a nationally recognized herd of Hereford cattle. In 1953, it was decided to upgrade this herd to Santa Gertrudis, because of their expected greater adaptability to the local environment. Eidsvold now has a large stud herd of Santa Gertrudis.

For the cattle, Eidsvold uses a suspension-type fence, which originated with Tom Lasater of U.S. Beefmaster fame. It looks good. It's a barbed wire fence, with steel post every 100 feet and a wood post every quarter mile.

Woodland Poll Hereford Stud, Mr. and Mrs. G. W. N. Bassingthwaighte, Greenmount, Queensland

Woodland Hereford Stud was established in 1938 by the late E. E. D. White, father-in-law of George Bassingthwaighte, the present owner.

Woodland comprises 3,000 acres, of which 600 acres is cultivated to produce cattle feed. All cultivation is on the contour, with check banks as a precaution against soil erosion. There is an average annual rainfall of 27 inches.

The following additional information was obtained at Woodland Polled Hereford Stud, "Greenmount":

Linebreeding Vs Inbreeding

Mr. Bassingthwaighte facetiously remarked: "When it's a success, it's linebreeding; when it's a failure, it's inbreeding." He went on to say that they bred rather closely with their horned Herefords, and

We visited the Woodland Polled Hereford Stud, Greenmont, Queensland, Australia, owned by Mr. and Mrs. G. W. N. Bassingthwaighte. Mr. Bassingthwaighte showed us one of his top bulls that was being fitted for the Brisbane show in August, 1970. I am standing near, and with my back to, the tree.

that he expects to do so rather soon with the Polled Herefords.

Shorthorns

Mr. Bassingthwaighte stated that, "Shorthorns will take more mistreatment than the other breeds."

Crossbreeding

Mr. Bassingthwaighte expressed the opinion that crossbreeding, in which Brahman blood is infused, has a place in tick-infested and tropical areas. He went on to quote a friend of his who used to say that, "The best cross is any British breed crossed with an oil well."

Murray Gray

This is a new Australian beef breed, developed from a Shorthorn X Angus cross.

Charsar

This is a new Australian breed, developed by one of the colleges from a Brahma X Charolais cross.

Droughtmaster

This is another beef breed, developed in Australia.

AIS

This stands for "Australia Illawarra Shorthorn," which is a dairy breed, developed in New South Wales, which resembles the Milking Shorthorn cattle of the U.S.

Thoroughbreds

Currently, they own seven Thoroughbred horses, and they race a few horses.

Tyunga Cotton Co., Brookstead; Frank K. Thomas and His Sons, Michael and Peter, Brookstead, Queensland

We arrived at Tyunga for lunch, which was served on the spacious front porch, with a number of Mr. Thomas' neighbors invited. In welcoming our group, Mr. Frank Thomas emphasized that he and his neighbors had borrowed and adapted many ideas from America.

Lunch at Tyunga.

Tyunga comprises 1,500 acres, of which 1,400 acres are irrigated. Tyunga is irrigated from the following two sources:

- **Water from the Condamine River**—Brookstead is one of five properties that developed the Leslie Dam, from which water is delivered through a system of pipes and drains to the farms. However, the Leslie Dam is dry at this time.
- **Bores (Wells)**—There are six underground bores (wells).

Mr. Thomas changed Tyunga from a livestock operation (sheep and cattle) to crops about 30 years ago, following his service in World War II. He removed all the fences; now he rides the range in a Ford V-8.

Mr. Thomas Pioneered in Cotton Production

He was one of the pioneer growers of irrigated cotton on the Darling Downs. Other crops on Tyunga, all of which are grown for marketing as seed, are: soybeans, safflower, barley, wheat, flaxseed (linseed), corn, canary seed, and sunflower. Mr. Thomas double-crops.

About the Family

One son, Ian, attended Fresno State College in California. Another son, Michael, went to Purdue. Peter has graduated from the university, but he is thinking of attending Fresno State College. They stage a "little theater" each evening as a family project.

Aerial Dusting Demonstration

He staged a demonstration. The pilot even showed how he could go under one telephone line and over another (across the highway).

Anchorfield Research Station; John E. Bligh

Mr. Bligh, the owner of Anchorfield, now lives in Sydney. He is recognized as one of Australia's foremost agriculturalists; he specializes in the seed production of wheat, oats, barley, sorghum, and soybeans. Mr. Bligh is particularly outstanding in wheat breeding.

Cooperation with the University of Sydney

Mr. Bligh works with Prof. Watson of the University of Sydney in his plant breeding work; and Anchorfield is operated as a research station in conjunction with the University of Sydney.

Seed Drying

Mr. Bligh has twelve steel silos in his seed drying complex, which was built at a cost of 24,000 pounds (A$48,960).

Soybean Yield

Mr. Bligh holds the Australian soybean yield record, with 42.7 bushels per acre. He treats the soybean area with Treflan (an Elanco product).

Lyndhurst, Perc Kruger

Lyndhurst, managed by Perc Kruger, comprises 2,300 acres, of which about 250 acres are under crop and the balance improved pasture. Water is drawn from the residue of Warwick city sewer and pumped into overhead tanks from which it is gravitated to various parts of the property. A Rainline sprinkler (similar to U.S.'s Raincat) is used to irrigate 66 acres. Lyndhurst has been well known for Thoroughbreds for over 100 years. It became famous as the home of the Buzzard, who was in stud from 1931 to 1952, and whose progeny won in excess of $850,000. The Buzzard sired two Melbourne Club winners, Australia's most prestigious race.

Dr. E (left, with notebook in hand) visiting with Perc Kruger, owner of Lyndhurst.

The Kruger family run 100 broodmares and stand three imported stallions. Mr. Kruger also makes handles for hammers, picks, shovels, and other tools. He makes two-thirds of the handles of Australia.

Neatherby Angus Stud; Mr and Mrs. H. S. Corden

Neatherby comprises 305 acres, of which 200 acres are cultivated. Eight cuttings of lucerne (alfalfa) per year are secured, without irrigation; or about eight tons per year.

Mr. Corden has exhibited and won extensively throughout Queensland. He does not production test; in fact, he does not have scales. He likes big cattle, and he selects for size at that age; he says he "likes a big beast lying down."

St. Andrews AIS Stud; Lester Brothers

The St. Andrews AIS Stud was established in 1917 by Mr. Mark C. Lester, father of Bill and Robert—the present operators. St. Andrews consists of

Dr. E (left) with Mr. and Mrs. H. S. Corden, owners of Neatherby Angus Stud. Neatherby is recognized as the best Angus herd in Queensland.

Mr. W. H. (Wally) King showing Dr. E Kengoon, an 800-acre farm. At the time of our visit, Kengoon had about 500 cattle, mostly Herefords and Polled Herefords. Also, there was a small herd of Droughtmasters, a new Australian breed of beef cattle; and Mr. King produces stock horses and polo ponies.

296 acres. They have about 60 head of AIS cows, 42 of which were in lactation at the time of our visit.

AIS (abbreviation for "Australian Illawarra Shorthorn") is the Australian Milking Shorthorn, a dual-purpose breed (bred for both meat and milk). They stem from a Shorthorn, Devon, Ayrshire (red) cross. It is the most popular dairy breed in Queensland. Currently, AIS semen is being exported to the U.S., primarily for infusion into Milking Shorthorns.

Kengoon; Mr. and Mrs. W. H. (Wally) King

The Kings showed us their cattle and horses and hosted us for tea. Kengoon consists of 800 acres, 250 acres of which are under cultivation. They grow Rhodes grass, clover, prairie, ryegrass and paspalum pastures; oats and lucerne (alfalfa) for winter feed; and Japanese millet and Caloona peas for summer feed.

Palmerstone; Mr. and Mrs. Peter Dangar

Palmerstone, which is owned by Mr. and Mrs. Peter Dangar, comprises 2,400 acres on which there are cattle and sheep.

The Polled Hereford herd at Palmerstone was established 10 years ago. Mr. Dangar formerly had horned Herefords. He shifted to Polled Herefords because, as he stated, "It was more of a challenge; more improvement needs to be made in the Polled Hereford breed than in some of the other breeds."

Moore Park Piggery; Mr. Christopher Barnes

Mr. Barnes, who came over from Herefordshire, England, and who has been in Armidale only six months, manages this piggery.

This is a very modest piggery. Mr. Barnes explained that his objective is to "make money." Landrace hogs are being raised. Currently, the herd consists of seventy-five sows.

Gala Dinner, Cotswold Restaurant, Armidale, Mr. David Wright, Speaker

Mr. David Wright is one of the owners of Mallamumbi and a member of the Australian Meat Board. As a member of the Australian Meat Board,

Mr. Wright spoke knowledgeably and persuasively on this subject.

The University of New England

The University of New England at Armidale opened in 1938, with an initial enrollment of 24 students. Today, the internal enrollment is 1,800, and there are 3,000 students enrolled for external study.

The University has five schools: Arts, Science, Rural Science, Agricultural Economics, and Economics. The School of Rural Science was established in 1955, for the purpose of integrating teaching and research in soils, pastures, and livestock.

Remarks by Prof. G. L. McClaymont, Dean of Faculty and Head of School of Rural Science, the University of New England

Prof. McClaymont referred to the three broad kinds of Australian agriculture:

- **The Soil-Plant-Animal Area**—Comprising 70% of Australia. This group is adapted only to sheep, wool, and beef production. The wool producers are experiencing severe economic problems; many of them must shift to beef production to survive.

- **The Better Watered Areas**—The better watered areas of Australia are devoted to pasture, livestock, and grain growing.

- **The Intensive Type**—This embraces the fruit, vegetable, poultry, pig, and dairy producers. The small producers among these must get big in order to survive. Many dairymen will switch to beef.

Remarks by Prof. N. T. M. Yeates, Professor of Livestock Husbandry, the University of New England

Prof. Yeates is the author of the book entitled, *Modern Aspects of Animal Production*. He gave a slide presentation of the environmental studies being made in central Australia, in the hot, 10-inch rainfall area. He also stated that water bores are costly; hence, the need is for cattle that will graze as far distant from water as possible.

Dr. Philip A. Wright, Wallamumbi

We visited Wallamumbi, which is owned and operated by Dr. Philip A. Wright and his three sons—Bruce, David, and Peter. Dr. Wright is also Chancellor of the University of New England.

En route to Wallamumbi, we saw some kangaroos.

Wallamumbi consists of 10,000 acres. It is operated in conjunction with Jeogla Station, the adjacent property on which Mr. Bruce A. Wright, son of Dr. Philip Wright, lives. On the two stations, they run 6,000 to 7,000 cattle plus several thousand sheep.

The Cattle at Wallamumbi

The Hereford herd at Wallamumbi was founded in 1827, when an ancestor of the present owners imported five cows and one bull from England. These were the first Herefords brought to Australia. Today, the 600 head of registered Hereford brood cows are rich in Vern breeding (the breeding made famous by the late Capt. deQuincy of Herefordshire, England). It is largely a horned Hereford herd, although a few Polled Herefords are being bred. They have scales; and the registered Herefords are performance tested for rate of gain, feed efficiency, and fertility. All cows must milk well and raise a calf.

Dr. Philip A. Wright, Wallamumbi Farm as well as Chancellor of the University of New Zealand (without hat), with Dr. E on his right.

Wallamumbi Herefords.

The Sheep at Wallamumbi

Dr. Wright brought up a band of 2,000 wethers (all-wether band) for us to see.

Gunnedah Weekly Fat Stock Sale

Just outside Gunnedah, we made a brief stop to see the Gunnedah Weekly Fat Stock Sale, which was in progress. They were selling cattle; that afternoon, they were also scheduled to sell sheep. Fat cattle weighing about 700 lb on foot (350 to 400 lb carcass weight) were selling at U.S. $155 per head.

Instead of moving the animals into a sale ring where buyers are seated, they moved the people. That is, the animals were left in pens; the auctioneer and clerks operated from a catwalk over the pens; and the buyers stood outside the pens or on the catwalk. Then, the people moved from pen to pen. Their system results in less shrinkage and bruising of animals than our system; and it's easier to move people than animals.

Wee Waa, in the Fertile Namoi Valley

We visited this fertile valley, in which Americans (from California) initiated the growing of cotton. The Australians point with pride to the "American Colony," and to their fabulously successful cotton venture. Today, both Americans and Australians are engaged in cotton production in the area. Currently, 47,000 acres of cotton are produced in the Namoi Valley.

Cotton at We Waa.

Wee Waa Cotton Gin

We were told that the gin (actually, the operation that we visited embraces two gins, side by side) that we visited is one of the largest in the world. At full capacity, it has a 45-bale (each bale weighs about 500 lb) capacity.

Dr. Larry Davis, Gunedra

Dr. Davis is a son of T. A. Davis, McFarland, California. He has his doctorate degree in plant physiology from the University of California, at Davis. He has been in Australia two years, developing new land. The Davises own and develop the land, then lease it on a sharecrop basis. For example, Phil Kniesley and Allen Young sharecrop the Red Camp property.

At the end of our tour, these gracious transplanted Americans hosted a tea for our group.

Auscott, Owned by J. G. Boswell

We made a brief stop at the Auscott office of J. G. Boswell, a California businessman. Pertinent facts about it:

Number of Properties

Boswell now owns five properties in Australia, nearly all of which consist of freehold land.

Size of Auscott

It embraces 9,000 acres of cotton, with about 100 people employed. They farm most of it, but some is sharecropped. On developed land, the sharecropper gets 85% of the crop, and the owner 15%.

Sir Walter Merriman, Merryville and Hillview

This afternoon, we traveled to Sir Walter Merrimans' two breeding establishments, located about 30 miles from Canberra. At Hillview, we inspected his Polled Shorthorn cattle, and at Merryville we inspected his Merino sheep, and were served tea. Sir Walter is now 88 years old. In 1940, he was knocked down by a ram, which broke his neck and destroyed his voice box. As a result, it is very difficult to communicate with him. But what a wonderful gentleman!

About the Merryville Merinos

Sir Walter Merriman's father established a Merino stud, known as Ravensworth Stud, in 1865. The Merryville Stud, based on Ravensworth breeding, was founded in 1903, when Sir Walter Merriman was 21 years of age.

When he was in his teens, Sir Walter formulated in his mind a clear picture of the kind of sheep that he wanted to produce; and he has stuck by this ideal ever since.

A white Polled Shorthorn bull at Hillview (farm), owned by Sir Walter Merriman. Dr. E (wearing coat) is standing nearest the handler of the bull.

Sir Walter Merriman and his sheep.

Sir Walter hosted us for tea upon our arrival. With rightful pride, he showed us one whole room in his house which is devoted to an exhibit tracing the history of the Merryville Merinos. Following tea, Sir Walter took us on a tour of the sheep headquarters, where we saw the rams and ewes that are being fitted for this year's shows and rams being "stubble sheared" (sheared with hand shears, but leaving one-half inch growth) for showing. I was impressed with the relatively smooth bodied Merinos with exceptionally high quality fleeces of long staple length.

Gala Dinner Address by Fred M. Lege III, Agricultural Attaché

Mr. and Mrs. Lege were our guests at the gala dinner in Canberra.

Pertinent information presented by Mr. Lege follows:

Investing in Australia

Mr. Lege stated that of all the countries that he has been in (61 different countries), Australia is the only nation other than the U.S. that he would invest in. His stated reasons for liking the investment climate of Australia:

- The political stability of the nation.
- Basically honest people.
- Money can be taken out.
- Not an AID country; they don't want a hand-out from anyone. All they want is business.
- They have always stood side by side with the U.S. in combat; and this includes Vietnam.

King Ranch

They now have 11,000,000 acres in Australia, and they have pumped in $51,000,000 to date.

Fonthill Stud and Springfield Saxon Stud, Jim Maple-Brown

This morning, we visited Fonthill Stud on which a dual-purpose type of Merino is being developed—a sheep suitable for both wool and mutton production.

The two stations—Fonthill and Springfield—embrace 32,000 acres and carry 22,800 sheep.

Mr. Jim Maple-Brown, the owner, contends that the Australian Merino is not meeting the farmer's requirements, as evidenced by the swing to cross-breeding for meat production.

The inspiration to develop a new Merino type to fit the changing needs came in 1967, when Mr. Jim Maple-Brown visited South Africa and saw the Letelle Merino. However, the Fonthill Merino program was actually started in 1954, at which time Saxon Merino ewes were mated to Rambouillet rams that had come from Texas.

The Maple-Brown house and garden.

Dogs working Maple-Brown sheep.

King Ranch (Australia) Pty. Ltd.; Retford Park and Milton Park, Mr. Peter Baillieu, Manager

At the time of our visit, we met the following key personnel: Peter Baillieu, manager; Martin Lemann, assistant to general manager; Dr. Glenn Murray, veterinarian; Greg Gilpin, horse manager; and Frank Badman, manager of show and sale cattle.

We visited Retford Park and Milton Park, owned by King Ranch (Australia). Retford Park and Milton Park consist of 3,000 acres. Milton Park (where we had tea and saw the huge garden), situated 6 miles from Bowral, was purchased by King Ranch (Australia) in 1960. Retford Park was acquired later.

Initial Santa Gertrudis Shipment

The initial shipment of Santa Gertrudis was made from King Ranch, Texas, in 1952. It consisted of 75 bulls and 200 heifers. In 1954, a second shipment was made, prior to a ban being placed on all cattle importations to Australia from the U.S., due to the disease bluetongue.

Dr. E (right), Peter Baillieu next to Dr. E, then Mrs. Baillieu, at King Ranch, Australia.

Initial Quarter Horse Shipment

Four King Ranch, Texas, Quarter Horse stallions were imported in 1954. A second importation of Quarter Horses followed in 1961.

Beef Cattle Science *to the Rescue*

Frank Badman, manager of the show and sale cattle of King Ranch (Australia), greeted me by exclaiming: "You saved my life!" Then, he went on to explain that, prior to being offered the beef cattle job at King Ranch, his training and experience had been entirely with sheep, so, he went to the local library where he learned of a book called *Beef Cattle Science* by M. E. Ensminger, following which he obtained a copy at the bookstore. He went on to say that he studied and followed *Beef Cattle Science* "religiously"; and that "it worked." Today, Frank Badman is recognized as an expert cattleman.

King Ranch, Australia, Quarter Horses.

Following an informative guided tour of the Santa Gertrudis cattle and Quarter Horses, Mr. and Mrs. Peter Baillieu graciously hosted us for tea in their beautiful home and showed us their big and beautiful garden.

The University of Sydney; University Farm, Prof. H. J. Geddes

This morning, we met with Prof. H. J. Geddes, The University of Sydney, University Farm, Camden. Prof. Geddes supervises the five farms of the University of Sydney, in the Camden area of N.S.W.

In particular, Prof. Geddes told us about "water harvesting"—the collecting of surface water and using it for irrigation.

The harvesting of water grew out of an accidental experience in 1952 when a 3½ acre paddock (pasture) of subterranean clover, top dressed with phosphorus, irrigated from a farm dam, fed 45 cows for 60 days and returned 174 lb (U.S. $417.60) per acre. The cows were rotated, with 45 cows per 1/10 acre; that's 450 cows/acre. As Prof. Geddes put it, "With that concentration of cows, they scarcely have room enough to breath." The results of the above study: The practice of harvesting water is now followed by 80% of the farmers in the area; and on the five University farms, they have constructed 33 dams with a total storage capacity of 225,000 gallons of water.

A Novel Horse Training Method

Prof. Geddes told of a horse training method based on psychology, which he had obtained from an old man (who continued to practice it until age 81). Through this method, within 20 to 35 minutes a horse can be tamed and ridden bareback.

Step one consists of lassoing from horseback the horse being trained; then the program of training progresses from getting the horse to face the trainer, slow movement toward the horse, rubbing the horse, mounting bareback, and ending with the trainer sliding down over the horse's tail.

Rose Hill Racecourse

We went to the running races at Rose Hill Racecourse, in Sydney. We also had lunch there. We were guests of the Sydney Turf Club.

Gala Dinner, Menzies Hotel, Sydney

This evening, we had a gala dinner, at the Menzies Hotel, Sydney, with invited guests. David Landa, attorney and consultant, and an old friend of mine, addressed our group.

The Hawaii/Parker Ranch that We Saw

We visited famed Parker Ranch, which was founded in 1837 by Palmer Parker, great-great-grandfather of the present owner, Richard Palmer Smart. Due to labor union negotiations, neither the owner, Mr. Richard Smart, nor the manager, Raleigh Greenwell, could be with us. However, we were ably shown about by Stella Okana, public relations director.

Vital statistics relative to Parker Ranch follow: acres, 227,000; cattle, 48,500; horses, 1,500.

Cattle Feedlot on Parker Ranch

We visited the cattle feedlot on Parker Ranch, a 1,200 head capacity feedlot in which cattle are fed a starter ration for 45 days.

Mauna Kea Beach Hotel

In 1961, Lawrence Rockefeller signed a 99-year lease on some of the Parker Ranch lands for the development of a multimillion dollar resort area. The Mauna Kea Beach Hotel, where we had lunch, is a part of that resort complex. It was built under the personal supervision of Mr. Rockefeller at a cost of $100,000 per room.

Here are some happenstances that kept us laughing:

When the group who had flown back from Moorea to Tahiti because of the storm formed the Chicken Club, complete with officers.

When Berneice Runyan lost her dental bridge down the drain at Papeete, Tahiti, and it was recovered by a handyman, just in time to catch our plane for Fiji.

When Oscar Burroughs said he was sorry that the Stewarts finally showed up (they misread the date of departure), because it had been so exciting with the conflicting reports we had been receiving as to their whereabouts.

When Mildred Selkirk lost a sock down the drain—they had such terrific suction that this was easy to do.

When John Wilkinson said, on the bus, returning from Eidsvold to the Gayndah airport, that we were becoming "jet setters," and we looked anything but "jet setters."

When Fred Milnes washed all his clothes in one batch and they all turned green from one green shirt.

When Russ Selkirk was at the trotting races with Mildred Selkirk's name tag on.

When George Neuner tried so hard to keep his wife out of the stores, and everyone gave Grace encouragement.

When, at the Canberra Rex Hotel, Carol and Monica (our two teenagers) found themselves in the men's room, instead of the stairway.

When Grace Neuner, tired at the end of the trip, and at the last gala dinner, called herself the husband of George.

Seeing Bryan Runyan (a sheepman) eating all the lamb he could, so Australia and New Zealand wouldn't have any left to export to the U.S.

In retrospect, I believe that the South Pacific trip was one of the most enjoyable trips we ever had. We had an extremely congenial group of traveling companions. The climate was excellent and our hosts were superb. Besides, when we ended on the Island of Hawaii, we were treated to the world famous Hawaiian hospitality. Harry and Kapau Heuer hosted a fabulous gala dinner in their home in Hilo, Hawaii.

AHE

1971
AROUND THE WORLD WE SAW

Mrs. Ensminger and I led a delegation of 26 people around the world in 26 days, October 22 to November 16, 1971, with stops in Japan, Taiwan, Hong Kong, Thailand, Nepal, India, Iran, and Greece.

We saw history in the making! And we barely escaped becoming a part of it! We saw the miracle of Japan; we were in Taiwan just three days after it had picked up its "marbles" at the United Nations and gone home; we saw rifle-toting Hong Kong and mainland China soldiers patrolling the Sham Chun River, the border area between Hong Kong and the People's Republic of China; we visited Thailand (Siam) two weeks ahead of a bloodless military coup; we toured Nepal, a forgotten land, until 1950, shut off from the rest of the world; we experienced blackouts and hidden cameras in India, just three weeks ahead of their shooting war with Pakistan; we were in Iran (Persia) two months following the big bash celebrating the 2,500th anniversary of their monarchy; and we were in Greece. Country by country, here is what we saw and the impressions that we gained.

Our group of 26 around-the-world travelers.

The Japan We Saw

The Japanese miracle, so we found, is simply the hard work of a dedicated people, pulling together. Japan has few natural resources other than people.

Japan! More than 103 million people living on four major islands with a total land area slightly smaller than the state of California.

Japan! An industrious, prosperous people. Today, they are the world's second largest auto producer, exceeded only by the U.S. It's predicted that their Gross National Product (GNP) will outrun the U.S. in the next decade.

Japan! Melting pot of the East and the West, for the old and the new. The old traditional things still remain, even in their original forms, while all around them and parallel with them an ultramodern technology is being developed.

Japan! Land of chopsticks and rice. But the taste buds of people and races are much the same—only their pocketbooks differ. With their prosperity, the Japanese people are demanding, and getting, more steaks, similar to their famous Kobe beef, which, today, is beer-fed and hand-massaged in legend only. Their dilemma: Either cut steaks in small pieces, adapted to chopstick eating, or go to knives and forks. One way or another, I predict that more and more Japanese mouths will be fed high-quality steaks; some cattle will be fed in Japan, but, in my opinion, the bulk of their beef will eventually come from Australia.

Japan! A constitutional monarchy lying in the northwestern Pacific

Ocean. The Japanese people call their country Nippon, meaning "Land of the Rising Sun," because the continent of Asia to the west sees the sun emerge from the myriad islands of Japan. Capital and largest city, Tokyo; religion, primarily Shinto and Buddhist (there are more than 100,000 Shinto shrines and 106,634 Buddhist temples); Emperor, Hirohito—the 124th of his line; there is a prime minister and a Parliament of two chambers.

Japan! Where pollution increased with industrialization and modernization. Today, pollution is recognized as a major problem in Japan, just as it is in the U.S. One native put it this way: "Tokyo is so polluted that even the bacteria can't live."

About Horse Racing in Japan

Here is what we learned about the history and current organization and method of operation of horse racing in Japan:

- Horse racing had its beginning 1,200 years ago in court functions, as an integral part of sacred shrine ceremonies.
- Pari-mutuel betting was initiated in 1888. In 1908, the government prohibited pari-mutuel betting; but it was resumed again in 1923.
- A computerized totalizator was first installed at the Nakayama Race Course in 1957.

Equestrian Park, Tokyo

We visited Equestrian Park, which is operated by the Japan Racing Association, and is the center of horsemanship in Japan. It has endeared itself with horsemen and the general public.

Equestrian Park was established in 1940. It is a unique 51-acre facility, located about 10 miles from downtown Tokyo. It has the necessary facilities, horses (120 head presently), and staff for the following program:

The Jockey School

This is a program in which most of the jockeys for National Racing are trained. We saw the current 10 "red hats" (neophyte jockeys in training) in the ring, receiving instruction. Also, we were shown a movie, depicting the training in the two-year course.

Racing is a contest among horses and jockeys; and the jockey is the man who makes the horse run. To assure exciting and fair racing, jockeys must be outstanding in both mind and technique. In order to have outstanding jockeys, the jockey training program at Equestrian Park was instituted. The instruction program lays special stress on molding of individual character. Also, trainees are taught academic subjects, riding technique, sportsmanship, self-reliance, the spirit of hard work, and rigid discipline.

Dr. E with Mr. Takehiko Shinjo, Jockey School Master at Equestrian Park.

The Equine Health Laboratory

Equine veterinary research is carried out in this laboratory, which was established in 1959. The laboratory is unique in that it specializes in the study of racehorse diseases and health.

Light Breed Horse Registration Association, Tokyo

Horse racing in Japan was promulgated with the Horse Racing Law of 1923. From that date until 1936, horse registrations were handled by the Imperial Horse Association. From 1937 to 1948, registrations were handled by the Japan Racing Association. Since 1948, the Light Breed Horse Registration Association, which was established that year, has carried out registrations.

The Tokyo Race Course

At the Tokyo Race Course, we were guests (luncheon, and an afternoon at the races) of the Japan Racing Association. The grandstand of this huge facility, which can accommodate over 100,000 people, was completed in 1968. The facilities and the races are much as they are in the U.S. However, their best races are run on turf. Also, in the same afternoon at the same track, we had the experience of witnessing horses run both clockwise and counterclockwise. I don't know of any other place in the world where this sort of thing occurs; that is, at the same track and on the same day.

Nihon Nosan Kogyo K.K. (a commercial feed manufacturer), Yokohama

Nihon Nosan Kogyo K.K., established in 1931, is the largest commercial livestock, poultry feed, and pet food supplier in Japan and the Far East. Its products include feed for livestock, swine, poultry, horses, fish, mink, and pets. The feed plant produces 20,000 tons of feed per month. The plant is in a six-story building on Yokohama Bay.

Dr. E with Mr. Itsuo Iida, Manager, Nihon Nosan Kogyo K.K., Yokohama, Japan, the largest commercial feed plant in Japan. Mr. Iida had visited the Ensmingers in California at an earlier date.

Mr. Iida later came to our hotel for lunch accompanied by his wife and daughter. I presented him with a copy of *The Stockman's Handbook.*

Soga-No-Ya (House of Soga) Swine Business, Kanagawa Pref

This embraces a number of swine operations throughout Japan, along with integrated wholesale and retail marketing of pork, all under the ownership of Mr. Tatsuo Soga.

We visited two of these huge operations; namely Hiratsuka Finishing Unit, and Kiyokawa Pig Breeding Center, which market 24,000 hogs per year.

I had met Mr. Soga earlier. Additionally, the following two old friends of mine joined us for the visit to Soga-No-Ya: Terry T. Hashida, in charge of research, development, and planning, Soga-No-Ya; and Karl H. G. Sera, an Iowa State University graduate, in charge of the feed and meal department, American Soybean Association, Tokyo.

A deep sense of responsibility came over me when Mr. Soga, president of the swine company, greeted us by saying, "I use Dr. Ensminger's *Swine Science* book for guidance in my operation." Anyway, with a net profit of $25 per market hog, he's doing all right. Mr. Soga is integrated; he produces hogs, operates a wholesale meat business, and owns a chain of supermarkets. By 1980, his goal is to market 10,000 hogs/month—that's 120,000 hogs/year. Also, he plans to integrate still further, by having his own packing plant; and he plans to diversify by feeding cattle.

Mr. Soga has straightbreds and crosses of three breeds: Hampshire, Yorkshire, and Duroc. Much of his foundation stock came from the U.S.

Tokyo Central Fish Market

We went through the Tokyo Central Fish Market, which was established in 1935. Today, it is the world's largest fish market. It handles 2,800 tons of fish each day, comprised of 450 different kinds. A total of 1,300 jobbers, each with a stall, buy from wholesalers and sell to retailers. Transaction between wholesalers and jobbers is by means of public auction, the announcement of the start of which is signaled by a bell. Fish auctions are conducted much like an American livestock auction.

In addition to fish, the Tokyo Central Fish Market handles vegetables, fruits, eggs, and pickles.

Gala Dinner, with Invited Guests, Hotel New Japan

Seven-minute addresses were made by each of the following: Matsukichi Amano, Resident Director, Japan Study Center, Tokyo; Thomas D. Templeton, Assistant Regional Director, Wheat Associates, U.S.A., Tokyo; and Dr. Yoshimasa Matsuo, Manager, International Section, Japan Racing Association, Tokyo.

Gala dinner in Tokyo.

At breakfast Mr. Elmer W. Hallowell, U.S. agricultural attaché, briefed our group on the agriculture of Japan. Dr. E is shown presenting one of his books to Mr. Hallowell.

The Taiwan (Formosa) We Saw

Robert and Phyllis Hall met us upon our arrival in Taiwan, and stayed with us throughout our study-tour of Taiwan. Mr. Hall is employed by the U.S. Agency for International Development and stationed in Taiwan. Phyllis Hall was a student of mine at the University of Massachusetts.

Taiwan (Terraced Bay) consists of the islands of Formosa (meaning "beautiful" to Portuguese explorers) and Quemoy, and other surrounding islands. The Taiwan Straits separate Taiwan from the Chinese mainland, 100 miles to the west. It's the seat of the Republic of China (Nationalist China).

Taiwan, which is 245 miles long and 90 miles wide at the widest point, totals 13,887 square miles. Capital and largest city is Taipei (pronounced Tie-bay).

Main Exports

Taiwan's main exports are fruit and vegetables; textile yarns and fabrics; clothing; telecommunications equipment; plywood; and sugar. The balance of trade of Taiwan is favorable, except with Japan.

Farms

The farms average 2.5 acres with over half of the

Luncheon in Taiwan. *Left to right*: Phyllis Hall, Robert M. Hall, Dr. E, Mrs. Pettipaw, U.S. Agricultural Attaché Norman J. Pettipaw. At the time, Mr. Hall was the Taiwan rice advisor of the U.S. Agency for International Development. The Halls were students at the University of Massachusetts.

farms less than 1 acre. Eighty percent of the farmland is owner-operated; 11% part owner-operated; and 9% tenant-operated. Taiwan farmers get up to 4 crops peryear. They apply up to 1 ton of fertilizer, or 35 tons of manure, per acre.

Hogs have long been vital to Taiwan's small, intensive farms, ranking second to rice in value of production. Because of the dietary preference of people, they supply the bulk of animal protein for Taiwan. Hog manure is also essential, since Taiwanese farmers produce up to four crops a year on the same land. Many farmers keep hogs to produce manure, to grow more crops, to produce more manure; after which the hogs may be slaughtered when cash is needed.

Briefing at Taipei, Taiwan

At the noon luncheon today, Mr. Norman J. Pettipaw, our agricultural attaché, American Embassy, Taiwan, briefed us.

Co-ops

100% of agriculture is in co-ops.

Livestock Dominate

One-third of the farm income is from livestock.

Pineapples Exported to U.S.

Since their pineapples go by boat, they can lay them into the U.S. mainland cheaper than Hawaii can.

Imports From The U.S.

Taiwan is importing considerable soybeans and cotton from the U.S.

Taiwan's Land Reform

Mr. James P. Y. Lee, Chief, Administrative Division, Land Reform Training Institute, Taoyuan, Taiwan, told us about Taiwan's successful land reform, which was initiated in 1949. Pertinent information which he presented follows:

Areas of Land Reform

Their land reform has been in the following three areas: rent reduction, sale of public farmland, and the "land-to-the-tiller" policy.

These changes in Taiwan have been carried out in a peaceful, gradual, and bloodless way.

What's Happening in Land Reform in Asia and the Far East

Most countries of Asia and the Far East have introduced programs of land reform in the past 20 years. Two reasons have prompted such reforms: social justice, and to avert the threat of a world food crisis facing a growing population. Many of these adopted land reform programs have been within the framework of democracy—gradual, peaceful, and without bloodshed; some have been of a drastic nature; while others fall between these two typologies.

As in all other aspects of democratic government, land reform through democratic means is complex; it involves serious legal, organizational, procedural and practical problems when implemented. It needs thorough planning and preparation—trained personnel is one of the most important requisites for successful land reform. To meet the latter need, the Land Reform Training Institute was founded.

The Land Reform Training Institute

In response to the need for trained manpower in land reform, the John C. Lincoln Institute, University of Hartford, Hartford, Connecticut, U.S., and the Council for International Economic Cooperation and Development of the Republic of China in Taiwan, signed an agreement in 1968 to establish a training program in land reform for the developing countries of Asia and the Far East.

The Land Reform Training Institute (LRTI) commenced its first training session in April, 1969. Since then, it has become a major force in the field of land reform.

VACRS Honour Rug Factory, Chungli

During our visit to this rug factory, we obtained the following information:

The Chung Li Rug Factory (VACRS) pioneered in the manufacture of Chinese carpet in Taiwan more than a decade ago. It was established as a vocational assistance program for the wives and children of retired servicemen. Some of the children that we saw working were very young.

Taiwan Sugar Corporation (TSC) Farm Animal Breeding Station (Swine), Chu-Nan, Mioli

Taiwan Sugar Corporation (TSC), a large government-owned sugar company, founded the swine project in 1953.

TSC's purpose is to supply improved breeding stock for 16 breeding and finishing farms, scattered over Taiwan, which, in turn, utilize sugar byproducts and produce manure for TSC's sugarcane plantations.

United Nations Development Program

We saw a large, new building that we were told is a United Nations project. It is a part of the newly established Swine Science Research Institute, a project jointly financed by the government of the Republic of China and the United Nations Development Program. Its purpose: To train Chinese swine specialists, conduct research, and give technical assistance. It is intended that swine research scientists from other countries will be invited to work on research problems in breeding, nutrition, diseases, management, marketing, slaughtering, and pork.

Art House Wood Carving Co., Ltd., Hsin Chu

We visited this small factory where wood carvings and furniture are made from seasoned teakwood, rosewood, and camphorwood by skilled workers who are well known for their carving arts.

One of the favorite stops for the ladies was a ceramic factory. There are many in Taiwan and China—the land where "china" was first made.

We visited this china factory in Taipei.

The Hong Kong We Saw

Hong Kong, a British Crown Colony, is about 90 miles south of Canton. Area, 400 square miles; population, 4,089,000; capital, Victoria, with a population of 646,800. Governor Sir David Trench is the Queen's representative. They were already preparing for the eventual handover to the People's Republic of China.

The main exports of Hong Kong are clothing 29%; plastic manufacturers 9%; textile yarns and fabrics 9%; electrical equipment 8%. Tourism (1968): visitors arrived, 618,400; gross receipts from tourism, US $160 million.

Hong Kong Fibres Industrial Ltd.

Mr. George C. J. Huang, whose uncle completed his doctorate degree under my supervision at Washington State University, showed us through the fiber company of which he is the manager. They manufacture nylon and polyester products.

Sea Cruise

Late this afternoon, we took a sea cruise, on a junk, and covered the water cities of Victoria Harbour. The points of interest were: Yaumati "Water City" (floating population); Stonecutter's Island; Kennedy Town, a Chinese district symbolic of old Hong Kong; Green Island; and Aberdeen, with dinner aboard the Floating Sea Palace Restaurant.

Kowloon and New Territories

This morning, we toured the Mainland of Kowloon and the New Territories.

The Resettlement, Multistoried Apartment Houses

This is a Hong Kong government project. These are multistoried apartments. Ground floors are set aside for offices, markets, shops, schools, clinics, community centers, and transport services. The rooftops are used by voluntary agencies who operate schools and children's clubs under the guidance of the Education or Social Welfare Departments.

Un Long (the Great Embankment)

An important rural district town, in a productive agricultural area, devoted primarily to vegetable crops. We also saw ducks and two or three riding stables.

Lok Ma Chau

This is the border area (separated by Sham Chun River) between Hong Kong and the People's Republic of China. It's patrolled by both sides; and gates close off roads.

At the blocked-off road, there were two wary police (Hong Kong). I asked them if we might take their pictures; one declined, the other permitted us to do so—but he added *one picture only*.

Hong Kong Island

We made the following stops on Hong Kong Island:

Victoria City

It's a city characterized by modern skyscrapers in the midst of old colonial-styled buildings, and pitiful slums.

The Peak

We took the Peak Tram to Victoria Peak (1,809 feet), where we looked out over Victoria City.

Tiger Balm Garden

The gardens are the legacy of the deceased multimillionaire philanthropist, Mr. Aw Boon Haw, who made a fortune out of a patent medicine known as Tiger Balm Oil, claimed to be a panacea for all ills.

Dr. E and "Little Audrey" in Hong Kong.

The Chinese guard at left allowed this one photo of him with Audrey and me. Little did we know that we would be traveling into China the next year.

We saw the sights of the White Pagoda and the fantastic figurines on the walls of heaven and hell.

Aberdeen

This is a fishing village. Here we saw the floating restaurants (including the Sea Palace Restaurant, where we had dinner on Friday night, and the near-complete new one that burned). Access to these restaurants is by sampans. Here, too, is the home of the Tanka (water folk), who live their entire lives on junks and earn their livelihood by fishing.

Porfulam Dairy (on Victoria Island, near Aberdeen)

Our group visited this dairy that is owned by a stock company. There are 2,400 head of cattle, mostly Holsteins.

■ **Housing and Corrals**—The cows are housed in small barns each holding 40 to 60 cows. The buildings are located on very rough terrain, on the hilltops and hillsides. Cows are turned out in the corrals for two hours daily.

■ **Feed**—A very low grade roughage (elephant grass, or napier grass) was being fed. However, the fact that the cows were in good condition gave evidence that they are fed a high concentrate ration and a minimum of roughage.

■ **Cleanliness**—Both the cattle and the barns were clean, giving evidence of a good sanitation program.

Repulse Bay

They served a lavish buffet in this old English hotel, which was used by the Crown Colony residents during the days of the British Army.

On our trip, Audrey did all of the photo work. This photo, taken in Hong Kong by a professional photographer, was used by Jason Gaillard, the artist, when he painted Audrey in the beautiful mural for the Ensminger room in Kildee Hall, Iowa State University.

Deep Water Bay

This is where the movie *Love is a Many Splendored Thing* was filmed.

We also drove by a Chinese Cemetery, where we saw the armchair graves of the deceased rich; and the new buildings of the University of Hong Kong, where they have facilities for medicine, engineering, science, arts and architecture, for approximately 2,000 students.

My general impressions of Hong Kong: Skyscrapers and junks (floating houses); teeming with people; cars everywhere; a city of signs and shops—clean and unclean; a shopper's paradise—but you had better know how to bargain; and prospering on tourism.

The Thailand (Siam) We Saw

We found Thailand a delightful place. It's the "land of smiles." We were impressed with the pleasantness and cheerfulness of the Thai people. "Mai Pen Rai," which means "never mind," is one of the popular Thai sayings.

Floating Market

Bangkok's markets are different! Many of them are floating. This morning we traveled via private motor launches up the Chao Phya River and the klongs (canals), passing floating markets. We saw merchandise, fruit, and vegetables being sold; from boat to boat, as well as from small stores ashore. The klongs were crowded with boats of every size and description. Also, interspersed among the markets were houseboats; houses on piles and stilts; boat cafeterias; people bathing, washing their hair, doing their laundry, cooking, eating, and washing their dishes—all in the same murky water of the klongs; monks and monasteries; nuns and nunneries; Buddhist temples; and dogs.

Mr. Norman Luis Smith, First Secretary of the Embassy of the United States of America, briefed our group. Also, that same afternoon, I traveled to the American Embassy, where I visited the office of Mr. William E. vonSeggern, Jr., agricultural attaché. The following pertinent information pertaining to Thailand was obtained from these two sources:

Economic Problems

Depressed world prices for rice, rubber, and a number of other major Thai export products, balance of payment deficits, and mounting revenue needs are claiming the government's attention.

The "Green Revolution"

The so-called "green revolution" that's occurring in many countries of the world is hurting Thailand since it means less demand for its products, especially rice. For example, the Philippines are becoming self-sufficient in rice as a result of a new variety of rice, and India is becoming self-sufficient in wheat as a result of a new variety of wheat.

Farms

There are 2.2 million farms, with an average size of 10 acres/farm; 82% of the farmers own their land.

Pollution

They are concerned about pollution, yet they feel that they have other more pressing problems.

Monks

Buddhist monks play an important part in Thai life. Young men, regardless of their social status, are expected to spend a minimum period of three months as monks. In early morning, the barefoot, golden-robed priests appear on the streets, their bowls generously filled with food by the people who gain merit through their generosity.

Loy Krathong Festival (The Festival of Lights)

We were in Bangkok on November 2, the date of the annual Loy Krathong Festival, an old festival dating back to ancient times. It's a Buddhist holiday. We saw the people give *thanks to the life-giving waters*. "Karathongs," which are small vessels decorated with candles, flowers, and incense sticks, were placed upon the waters of rivers, streams, and ponds, amidst singing, dancing, and merriment.

The Nepal We Saw

Nepal has two chief claims to fame: It's the birthplace of Buddha, the founder of Buddhism, one of the great living religions of the world; and it has Mt. Everest, the highest peak in the world (29,082 ft). Until 1950, it was a "forgotten land," shut off from the rest of the world. Even today (1971), only about 40,000 tourists go there each year.

Facts about Nepal: It's only 530 miles long and 95 to 150 miles wide; area, 54,362 square miles (about the size of Arkansas); population, 11,044,034; capital and largest city, Kathmandu; language, Nepali (official), but English is taught in the schools.

Main Exports

Nepal's main exports are food and livestock 67%; manufactures 23%; crude materials (including timber and jute) 7%.

Agriculture Production

The economy of the country is based largely on agriculture, which absorbs 9 out of every 10 people. In metric tons, annually Nepal produces 2,475,000 tons of rice, and 35,000 tons of jute.

Food

Rice is the staple food of the people in the tropical and central regions, and millet and corn in the northern region.

The Kathmandu Valley

This fertile valley was once an ancient lake. It embraces 342,000 square miles and has 600,000 people. The valley is dominated by three main towns—Kathmandu, Patan, and Bhadgaon—all of which we visited.

Literacy

Only 12% of the people can read and write.

Swayambhu

Reputed to be 2,500 years old, this is one of the world's most glorious and oldest Buddhist Chaityas (shrines). It is situated on a high hill 1½ miles west of the city of Kathmandu. It is characterized by the all-seeing eyes of Swayambhu-Nath. Included in the complex are other temples, Tibetan monasteries and images.

Hanuman Dhoka

Hanuman Dhoka is the durbar or residential area of the ancient kings of Nepal.

Abode of the Living Goddess

We stood in a courtyard and looked up at intricately carved wooden balconies and windows. The present living goddess, a 4½ year-old girl, garbed in red and with painted cheeks and lips, appeared at the window. Photographs of the living goddess were not allowed, but contributions were requested. The living goddess, who rules to the age of puberty—at which time a new goddess is selected—is a sex symbol and advisor to all who seek her counsel—including the king.

The Old Wooden House, Known as "Kasthamandap"

This house was built from a single tree in 1396, by King Laxmi Narsing Malla. The city of Kathmandu derives its name from this structure.

The Bazaar Area

This is the main market area of Kathmandu.

Patan

This morning, we visited Patan (Lalitpur). It was founded by King Veera Deva in 299 A.D. and given the name Lalitpur. It's known as the city of fine arts. It is a most interesting city, full of Buddhist monuments, temples, buildings ornamented with elaborate carvings and intricate sculptures in stone, clay, wood, and metal. The streets in Patan are narrow and paved with stone.

We visited the Tibetan factory, just outside the city of Patan, where rugs and sweaters are manufactured. Here, several hundred Tibetans, who were displaced from their homeland in 1959, have set up a small community. Half the population sat cross-legged as they chanted and transformed wool into carpets and sweaters.

More About Nepal Agriculture

Dr. Raymond E. Fort, Chief, Food and Agriculture Division, U.S. AID, gave an excellent briefing on Nepal's agriculture, supplemented by a handout. Dr. Fort, who is a graduate of Kansas State and Cornell, has been in Nepal for five years. He's knowledgeable.

Transportation

Transportation into much of the hills area is by "human trains," a few mules, and some sheep (the latter carry a 22-lb load). It's costly and unreliable. There is need for mule trains (for packing), and jeep roads where possible in the hills area.

Crops

Nepal produces potatoes, oranges, tobacco, jute, sugarcane, rice (77% of the Kathmandu Valley is devoted to rice), wheat, corn, barley, and millet.

Fertile Kathmandu Valley

Dr. Fort referred to this valley as "the most fertile in the world"; and it looks the part.

The Peace Corps in Nepal

Mr. Jim Martin, a friend of Les and Ruth Leachman (members of our group) and Deputy Director of the Peace Corps for Nepal, told of the Peace Corps work in Nepal.

Peace Corps Workers In Nepal

They have 15 Peace Corps workers in Nepal, of whom 15 are women. Peace Corps workers train and assist the local people. They learn the language.

Four Primary Programs

In Nepal, Peace Corps workers are assigned to one of the following primary programs: agriculture, fisheries, rural water supply, and education.

Life of a Volunteer

Travel to posts is difficult. Most of them walk from one to eight days from where they land by air. At their posts, they may live in one room with a family or live alone; sleep on a straw mat, in a sleeping bag; have just the bare necessities—outdoor plumbing, and the like.

The life of a Peace Corps worker in Nepal is the most challenging Peace Corps assignment in the world. Most stay only two years, but they have one who is staying five years.

The India We Saw

India was preparing for war against Pakistan, which we were told was imminent. When flying in and out of the airports of Calcutta, Banaras, Agra, Jaipur, and New Delhi, we were required to observe the "no camera—no picture rule." In Calcutta, I got off the plane to stretch my legs, only to find myself flanked by two rifle-toting soldiers. They came aboard the plane and gave us all "the once-over."

Three weeks after our departure, a shooting war between India and Pakistan erupted. Nevertheless, the Indian people gave us a warm, friendly welcome. One of their poets even composed a poem in our honor. They were wonderful.

India! One-third the size of the U.S., but with 524,080,000 people—2½ times our population. One of the oldest civilizations in the world—tracing back for at least 5,000 years.

India! Land of contrasts. Abject poverty and beggars—you would have to see it to believe it. Yet, there are magnificent palaces, forts, tombs and temples; most of them constructed by former emperors and maharajahs, relics of a glorious past. Greatest of all is the Taj Mahal.

India! A country of villages. Eighty two percent of the nation's people live in 550,000 villages; hence village life is very important. We visited the villages of Chattarpur, Panachayat, Raipura, and Sultanpur. Although the industries differ somewhat from village to village (much as the industries of U.S. towns differ), between these four villages, we visited the following: schools (both high school and kindergarten), bank, pottery making, feed store, rug weaving, glass making, poultry production (layers and broilers), vegetable gardens, roses produced commercially, and demonstration crop plots.

India! Where the Ford Foundation and Dr. Douglas Ensminger are respected names. The Ford Foundation program in India was initiated in 1951 under the leadership of Dr. Douglas Ensminger, my

I am standing alongside horse statuettes which adorn the conference room of the Ford Foundation Building in New Delhi, a new $1.85 million structure. Dr. Douglas Ensminger, my horse-loving brother, initiated and supervised the huge Ford Foundation program for all of India for 19 years, during which period the foundation spent U.S. $127 million. Presently, they have a staff of 500.

brother. He continued to direct the program until August, 1970. When we visited, Dr. Doug was a living legend and even revered, in India. Truly, he made a lasting name and fame. Mr. Harry Willhelm, who succeeded Dr. Doug, briefed us on the foundation's program and the Pakistan refugee problem—involving 9½ million people who fled from Pakistan to India.

India! Where I saw the green revolution in progress. It's changing the farming of India and feeding more hungry people. The goal: self-sufficiency in food production.

Sacred Cows

The sacred, humped cows of India pillage crops in rural areas and roam the streets of villages and cities—gentle and traffic-wise. Some are homeless; others are turned loose by owners who do not wish to pay for their keep. To the Hindu (approximately 80% of India's population), the cow is regarded as a mother and an object of reverence; and the eating of beef is taboo. Although India's cattle population puts a serious drain on the nation's resources, no politician dares twist a cow's tail, or even flick a hair, to do so would be like an American political campaign against motherhood.

The Bos Indicus

Bos Indicus cattle of India, of which there are more than 30 breeds, have made a tremendous contribution—to India and the world. Through the years, and even today, they are the chief source of agricultural power in India. Also, the U.S. owes a debt of gratitude to India for having provided the seed stock from which our Brahman breed of cattle originated.

About Lord Buddha

This afternoon, we traveled to the buried Buddhist city of Sarnath (meaning dear Lord), where Lord Buddha delivered his first sermon 2,500 years ago.

Gautama (the family name), who became the Buddha after attaining enlightenment under a sacred bo-tree, was born in 563 B.C., and died at the age of 80. Today, the religion and teachings of Buddha are known as Buddhism. It is noteworthy that Buddhism arose as an offshoot of the Hindu religion which prevailed in north India at the time, and in his life and teachings, Buddha was more like Christ than any of the other founders of living religions. The five great commandments of Buddhism forbid killing, stealing, adultery, lying, and drunkenness.

The Ganges River

This morning, we took a boat excursion on the holy river Ganges to see the bathing ghats (bathing steps). We watched people bathing and worshipping at the ghats.

The Ganges impressed me as being the world's biggest and most versatile bath tub. We saw thousands of people there; bathing, worshipping, brushing their teeth, doing their laundry, filling their jugs with holy water to take home to drink, visiting neighbors and friends, seeing the priests, cremating the bodies of departed loved ones along the banks, selling souvenirs, or begging. One human body even floated by our boat, with a crow perched on top of it. Pollution? We were told that, in some mysterious manner, minerals and divine power purify the holy waters of the Ganges, but I'd have to see a bacteria count to believe it.

Taj Mahal

This afternoon, we visited the Taj Mahal, a

We visited the Taj Mahal, a "dream in marble."

"dream in marble," finished with semiprecious stones. The Taj Mahal was built by Emperor Shah Jahan to enshrine the mortal remains of his beloved wife, the Empress Mumtaz Mahal. Construction on the edifice was started in 1631 and finished 22 years later, during which time 20,000 workmen were employed on it daily. It's regarded as one of the Seven Wonders of the World.

Mumtaz Mahal was married at the age of 19, gave birth to 14 children (8 sons and 6 daughters), and died at the age of 36. She was noted for her beauty, accomplishments, and tenderhearted sympathy for the poor and distressed.

Shah Jahan's son, Aurangzeb, put all his brothers to death (in order that there should not be any dispute for the throne); usurped the throne in 1658; and imprisoned his father for the rest of his life (7 years), thereby stymieing his plans to construct a second mausoleum in black marble, to be located alongside the Taj Mahal, for his own remains.

I make a little hay! I am seated on a lawnmower powered by this handsome yoke of oxen. Picture was taken on the front lawn of the Taj Mahal, near Agra, India.

Upon the passing of Shah Jahan, his son did carry out his last wish—that he be buried beside his beloved wife, in the Taj Mahal.

Agra Fort

This palace fortress, in sight of the Taj Mahal, was built by Akbar the Great and later improved by Shah Jahan. A double wall of red sandstone surrounds the fort; the outer one is 40 feet high, and the inner one 70 feet high. A water-filled ditch 30 feet wide and 35 feet deep flanks the outer wall externally. The entire structure is of red standstone, inlaid with white marble.

Shah Jahan died in the palace fortress in 1666, where he had been imprisoned for seven years.

Among the facilities of this relic of former grandeur are: quarters for two queens and 600 concubines; the Hall of Special Audience (where the emperor used to receive kings, nobles and ambassadors, and transact the most important affairs of state); the king's bath; and the private chapel of the emperors.

To reach Agra Fort, which is atop a very steep hill near Jaipur, India, Audrey and I rode a powerful, ash-colored elephant, handsomely decorated and covered with dazzling cloth. The Indian handler's aids—the mutual language between him and the elephant—consisted of his legs, a small stick, and a quiet voice. Without bridle, bit, or reins, the ponderous beast was put in motion, guided, and stopped at will—under perfect control at all times.

Agricultural Research Station, Durgapura, Jaipur-4, Rajasthan

We visited the Agricultural Research Station. Although it was Sunday, we were pleased and honored that 23 of their top scientists were there to greet us and tell us about their agricultural program.

The primary objective of this station, which is devoted entirely to plant studies, is to achieve higher food production better to feed India's human population. This station, along with other research stations in India, is a major force in the green revolution now sweeping across Asia. The experimental approaches being pursued by the Agricultural Research Station to obtain more human food are: new and higher yielding varieties of different crops, increased irrigation, soil testing and use of manures and fertilizers, control of plant insects and diseases.

Maharajah's City Palace

The City Palace, which we visited, was once the home of a Maharajah. It was built by the founder of the city of Jaipur, thence passed along through the eldest son of subsequent generations. The last Maharajah, who occupied it only when special events were underway in Jaipur, died earlier in 1971 while playing polo in England. The City Palace possesses grandeur and grace. It's full of treasures; among them, a rare collection of books and manuscripts, priceless paintings, and historic garments.

I am shown visiting with the scientists at the Agricultural Research Station, Durgapura, Jaipur-4, Rajasthan, India.

I take a spin! In Jaipur, India, I went for a ride in a bicycle-type jinrikisha, a common mode of transportation in the area.

Maharajah Jaisingh's Observatory

This unique observatory is situated at City Palace. It was constructed by Maharajah Jaisingh II during 1718–34 A.D. It contains huge astronomical instruments, is built of masonry and was devised to determine and study the location and movement of the sun, moon, and other celestial bodies.

The Museum of Jaipur

This building, which was constructed in 1876–87, houses a magnificent collection of art and architecture.

Water Buffalo Dairy and Sale Animals

We stopped in the city limits of Jaipur, where we inspected an unfenced, dry lot full of Water Buffalo cows. We were told that these cows were the property of several owners, with each owner possessing one or a few head. Also, these particular cows were dairy animals, kept primarily for milk production; and some of them were for sale (one owner was washing his animal, better to present her to prospective buyers).

Indian or Water Buffaloes are characterized by a

thin, black coat; absence of sweat glands; a love to wallow in the mud; being quiet and amenable when handled by familiar caretakers, but often hostile and even dangerous with strangers; not crossing with cattle; and a gestation period ranging from 287 to 340 days.

Amber Palace (Fort)

Amber is located five miles from Jaipur. This fort was commenced in 1600 A.D. by Maharajah Man Singhji and completed in the 19th century, during Sawai Jai Singh's reign. It formerly contained many fine temples, but most of them are now in ruins. Amber lies on the slope of a very steep hill.

Mr. Bhonrilal Golimar, Jaipur

We visited Mr. Bhonrilal Golimar, Golimar Garden, Amber Road, Jaipur, who is one of the most outstanding farmers in India.

The late Mr. Nehru, former prime minister of India, visited Mr. Golimar in 1954 and cited him. Likewise, Mr. Bulganin, former premier of the U.S.S.R., visited him, as did Jacqueline Kennedy. This gives evidence of the stature of Mr. Golimar in India. Mr. Golimar formerly produced much cauliflower and cabbage. Today, most of Mr. Golimar's land is devoted to fruit production. Mr. Golimar is also a poet of note, as well as an outstanding agriculturist.

I presented a copy of my book, *Animal Science* to Mr. Bhonrilal Golimar, of Jaipur, India, "the Luther Burbank of India."

Left to right: Mr. Golimar's friend, Mr. Golimar and Dr. E.

Delhi

We saw some of Delhi, including the following.

House of Parliament

A circular edifice, one-half mile in circumference, in which India's Upper and Lower Houses of Parliament meet.

The Secretariat Building

These buildings, which were completed in 1929–30, consist of two blocks—known as North Block and South Block. These two blocks house the offices of all the ministries, libraries, and other government institutions.

The Office of the Prime Minister

We drove by this building in which Mrs. Indira Gandhi, the current prime minister of India, has her offices.

Rashtrapati Bhavan

This is the official residence of the president of India. It occupies an area of 330 acres and has 340 rooms and 37 fountains. The "Star of India" can also be seen from here.

It's feedbag time! In New Delhi, India, this carthorse, parked near the monument of Mahatma Gandhi, and with no caretaker in sight, was placidly munching his noontime meal from a feedbag strapped to his bridle.

Raj Ghat

This is a national monument to Mahatma Gandhi, the father of India, whose cremated remains are buried here. Mahatma Gandhi was assassinated on January 30, 1948. Trained as a lawyer, he championed home rule (independence from England) by means of nonviolence and noncooperation.

Jama Masjid

This is the best and biggest mosque of India. It was built in 1650–1658. Twenty thousand people can pray in the courtyard at one time.

Mr. Kanlar Mahinder Pal Singh's Farm

En route to Mr. Singh's farm, we saw and obtained pictures of a camel caravan, a Persian water wheel powered by a blindfolded camel, and ladies at the well.

Mr. Singh's farm is located about 40 miles from New Delhi. He came from Pakistan 12 years ago, where he operated a 10,000-acre farm. His father was once the Secretary of Agriculture of India.

Mr. Singh impressed us as being as able as he is colorful and articulate.

The productive farm that we saw was once (as recently as 12 years ago) wasteland—too alkali to farm. However, through proper drainage, application of gypsum to increase percolation, subsoiling (deep tillage), and farm management, it's a productive farm today.

Mr. Kanlar Mahinder Pal Singh (wearing turban), whose father was once Secretary of Agriculture of India, and whose farm is located about 40 miles from New Delhi, told the Agriservices Foundation tour-study group and me about his operation. On his farm, he has some wheat, peas, clover, mangels, and citrus (grapefruit, oranges, and lime). It's men like Mr. Singh who are making the "green revolution" in India—and throughout the East. It was always a pleasure to meet with farmers like Mr. Singh and his neighbors and to exchange ideas, even when it meant sitting out in the fields.

I gave Mr. Singh a copy of my book *Animal Science*.

Mr. Singh credits Mr. Norman E. Borlaug, the 1970 Nobel Prize winner (Peace), for much of his success.

It's men like Mr. Singh who are making the green revolution in India. His farm shows what can, and must, be done in Indian agriculture. Moreover, in his printed literature, there is the following refreshing statement: "This farm has been developed from a once saline, water-logged waste land to produce bumper crops, without any aid or loans from any source."

In a very touching ceremony at the grammar school of the Village Chattarpur, in India, I received the blessings. This very pretty little girl, carrying a tray on which there were lighted candles, "blessed" me by putting a red dot on my forehead (a ritual known as "Tilak"). During the ceremony, I shed tears—unashamedly.

Village Chattarpur

Our visitation to Village Chattarpur included the following:

The Grammar Schools (Boys and Girls)

Miss K. Haridao, the principal, greeted us upon our arrival. Obviously, they had gone to a lot of effort in preparation for our visit. The program and visitation here included the following:

■ **Drum-formation**—Upon our arrival, a special formation of students, accompanied by a drum, was presented.

■ **Welcome song**—A group of girls sang for us.

■ **Blessing; lei**—A very pretty little girl, carrying a tray on which there were lighted candles, came forward and "blessed" me by putting a red dot on my forehead. (The ritual of putting the red dot on the forehead is known as "Tilak.") She was followed by a second girl who put a beautiful lei around each of our necks. It was very touching.

The children were all dressed up for our visit. Also, we were impressed with their discipline; for example, when we entered a classroom they arose. And there was no giggling!

The Kindergarten

The kindergarten consisted of one large room, in which most of the youngsters were seated on the floor, and a small separate nursery, where they care for babies of working mothers.

During the time of our visit, each youngster was given a small bowl of oatmeal porridge.

Bank

We visited the Syndicate Bank of Chattarpur where we met the manager, Mr. M. S. Hebbar. Mr. Hebbar told us that the Syndicate Bank is a government bank, with 500 branches in India.

Village Panchayat

Next, we visited Village Panchayat, where we saw the following village industries and cooperatives: pottery, feed store, rug weaving, glass factory, poultry, and vegetable gardens.

Village Rajpura

At Village Rajpura, we saw the roses. We were told by Dr. Chandra, extension horticulturalist at the Indian Agricultural Research Institute, that a good rose farmer can net US $2,666 off an acre of roses in one season. Their best market for roses is in Europe, especially Germany and France.

Mr. Hebbar of the Syndicate bank with Dr. E.

Village Sultanpur

At this stop, we visited a National Demonstration plot and cropping system of a small, 2½-acre farm. We were told that this small farm produces four crops per year; namely, maize (corn), radishes, wheat, and green grain (MVNG).

Indian Agricultural Research Institute, New Delhi

Upon our arrival, we were greeted by Dr. M.S. Swaminathan, director of the institute. Dr. Swaminathan briefed us.

Visit the Central Library and Museum Of IARI

The IARI librarian reported that they have 200,000 books and 5,000 periodicals. He showed me

I am shown introducing Dr. M. S. Swaminathan (seated to my left), Director of the Indian Agricultural Research Institute (IARI), near New Delhi. Seated near camera is Dr. Bert A. Krantz, soil and irrigation specialist, on leave from the University of California at Davis and working on irrigation at the IARI.

9 cards cataloguing research reports by me that are on file in the library.

I promised to send them a complete set of my books. The museum is primarily a story in pictures—and the pictures are excellent.

IARI Farm Visit

We drove out to the "crop cafeteria," to see the place where different treatments are applied to a given crop. I was impressed with their charts located adjacent to the plots, to facilitate presentation.

Water Management Demonstration Center

At this point, we were told that 21% of the total acreage of India is under irrigation. India has the largest acreage under water of any country in the world.

We inspected different types of water gates; flumes; methods of getting the water on the land—ranging from drip irrigation to the Persian wheel; a well drill; cultivating equipment; and laboratory equipment used by the graduate students.

Livestock Markets

Scattered about India, cattle and buffalo markets are held once a week, with buying and selling taking place on a private treaty basis (such markets are known as "Shandy" in India).

Gala Dinner

This evening, we were addressed by several distinguished and knowledgeable persons. A brief summary of what each of them said follows:

Mr. Galen Stone, Deputy Chief of Mission, American Embassy

Mr. Stone commented on the present India-Pakistan problems, which have also strained the relationship between the U.S. and India.

Mr. James Boulware, Agricultural Attaché, American Embassy

Mr.Boulware reported that rice is the most important food grain produced in India, accounting for 40% of the total grain production.

Mr. Howard Ray, Deputy Team Leader, Ford Foundation

Dr. Ray paid high tribute to the work done in India by my brother, Dr. Doug Ensminger. He reported that the Ford Foundation has 60 active projects at this time; and that the following kinds of projects are supported: agricultural and water resources; education, social sciences, humanities, and arts; population, health, and nutrition; development planning and management; and projects in village extension.

Mr. Johnson Douglas, Rockefeller Foundation, New Delhi

Mr. Douglas stated that, "Cereals constitute the major share of India's food. Hence, increases in yield and nutrition quality can overcome the country's food deficit in large measure."

Poem By Jagat L. Bright; Read By K. N. Srivastava

Mr. Jagat L. Bright, an Indian poet, composed a poem in honor of the visit to India of the Agriservices Foundation group. The poem was read by Mr. K. N. Srivastava.

The Iran (Persia) We Saw

About two months prior to our visit, Iran celebrated the 2,500th anniversary of its monarchy. This celebration was much more than a glorification of monarchy; it was a time in which they took stock of the progress of the recent past—when they evaluated the "white revolution" that's been going on in Iran under the leadership of His Majesty, the Shah of Iran, as a means of preventing a "red revolution." The shah has been very progressive. His improvements include major land reform, introduction of industry to towns, the spread of literacy, and drastic gains in women's rights. The shah divorced his first two wives who failed to produce a male heir, because no shah can be crowned until a male succession is assured.

Gala Dinner, Tehran

Following the dinner, Mr. William W. Lehfoldt, American Embassy, counselor for economic affairs, presented the following information relative to Iran:

Population Engaged in Agriculture

Forty-six percent of the people are engaged in agriculture versus 18.2% in manufacturing.

Landmark of Modern Iran's History

In 1941, Britain and the U.S.S.R. entered Iran, to assure supply lines for the so-called "bridge of victory across Iran." They deposed Reza Shah; and the

Our group at the Animal Husbandry Research Institute, Tehran, Iran. I am in the dark suit with notebook in hand.

present Shah Mohamad Reza Pahlavi ascended the throne.

The Economy

The Iranian economy has increased rapidly. For the past ten years, the Gross National Product (GNP) has increased 10% per year. Much of this growth has come from the utilization of Iran's oil revenues.

Currently, agriculture and irrigation are receiving the lion's share of government investment, followed by industry and mines, roads, ports, and airports.

Agriculture

Only about 11% of the land is arable, and insufficient water restricts actual cultivation to about 4%.

Wheat is Iran's principal crop, followed by barley, rice, cotton, dates, sugar beets, fresh and dried fruits, vegetables, pulses (legume seeds), oil seeds, tobacco, and sugarcane. The main cash crop is cotton.

Petroleum

It's the principal resource and largest foreign exchange earner.

Razi Institute, Tehran

This institute is devoted to the production of serums and vaccines for the prevention and control of both animal and human diseases.

Snakes

We visited their snake laboratory, where they put on a demonstration of milking the venom from a cobra.

We saw cobras and vipers in a pit. Also, we inspected their museum where they have specimens of 56 species of snakes, 17 of which are dangerous.

They prepare serum at this laboratory for use when people are bitten by snakes. This serum is in stock at various health laboratories throughout Iran.

Animal Husbandry Research Institute, Tehran

Next, we visited the Animal Husbandry Research Institute, which is an impressive animal research establishment. Because of the interests of our group, we concentrated on dairy cattle and sheep.

Sheep Breeds

They have the following four, fat-tailed breeds, which comprise 70% of the sheep population of Iran: Kellakvi, Kizil, Bakhtiari, and Baluchi.

Dairy Cattle

They have approximately 100 total head of the following breeds: Holstein, Brown Swiss, and Jerseys.

The Greece We Saw

Greece and the Acropolis are synonymous. Built between 447 and 406 BC it is a witness to the artistic creativeness of ancient Athens, and to human culture in general. It's located atop limestone rock which rises 230 feet above the surrounding city of Athens. As every schoolboy knows, this hill was rendered sacred by its temples and much venerated sanctuaries of the gods, especially of Athena, divine protectress of the city.

Agriculture

Greece is still largely agricultural, but only one-fourth of the total area is arable.

Although revering the past, modern Greece is not living in it. For example, we visited the modern 500-sow swine establishment owned and operated by Mr. Alex Zagares, located about 20 miles from Athens. Both straightbreeds and crossbreeds of the Landrace and Yorkshire breeds are produced.

Achievements

The achievements of ancient Greece in sports, art, architecture, science, mathematics, philosophy, drama, literature and democracy became legacies for succeeding ages. Greece reached the height of its glory and power in the 5th century B.C.

In Greece we visited the Acropolis of immortal fame. I am shown walking among the sacred ruins.

Alex Zagares (Swine), Marathon-Attikis

This afternoon, we visited the modern 500-sow swine establishment owned and operated by Mr. Alex Zagares, which is located about 20 miles from Athens. Mr. Zagares appears to be doing all right, as indicated by his plans to add another 500-sow unit.

More About Mr. Zagares

His father was in the hog business. In addition to the hogs, we inspected his feed mill. Also, we were advised that he has a 9,000-hen (layer) operation.

Marathon

This afternoon, we saw and/or were told about three marathons:

■ **The Monument to the "Battle of the Marathon"**—This is a 39-foot high mound erected over the ashes of 192 Athenians who lost their lives at the Battle of the Marathon—a battle against the Persians.

■ **The Marathon Race**—This is still an endurance test at sporting events. It was inspired by the marathon race to Athens following the victory of the Athenians over the Persians, in the Battle of Marathon; although the messenger sent to Athens died after announcing the sensational victory.

■ **Marathon Lake**—This is a large artificial lake. It is the source of the water supply for Athens.

Gala Dinner, in Athens

Our gala dinner in Athens was truly a gala affair, enhanced by the presence of the most distinguished agriculturalist of Greece, His Excellency, Mr. Panayotis Papapanayotou, minister of national economy, whose position in Greece is comparable to that of secretary of agriculture in the U.S. In his address, the minister alluded to the kindred spirit that exists between farmers throughout the world, thanked America for the great contributions in technology that it made to agriculture in Greece following World War II, and told of their need to increase the income of the farmers of Greece and produce more food. He seemed to be especially interested in increasing beef cattle numbers and producing more beef. The minis-

Dr. E is shown presenting a copy of his book, *Animal Science*, to Mr. Panayotis Papapanayotou, Minister of National Economy, Athens, Greece. The minister's position in Greece is comparable to that of secretary of agriculture in the United States. The occasion was a gala dinner in Athens, hosted by the Agriservices Foundation study-tour group and attended by 20 distinguished Greek officials. Minister Papapanayotou extended a warm welcome to the Americans.

impressed us as a very able and knowledgeable person, and a warm, friendly personality.

So Long Delegates

Mrs. E and I never say good-bye to our delegates, because they are alumni of Agriservices Foundation and members of the Ensminger family. Instead, we part with a fond "so long until we meet again." The group flew back to the USA the next day, while Audrey and I flew to Milan, Italy to take care of my consultant client, Dr. Hugo Galassi.

1972
THE NORTH SEA COUNTRIES WE SAW

The Norway We Saw

Upon our arrival in Norway we were met by Dag Ryen and his wife Grethe. Dag is a son of Kob Ryen, a Lexington, Kentucky horseman and friend of mine. Dag arranged our schedule in Norway and served as our interpreter.

Gala Dinner in Norway

Mr. Torstein Treholt, Minister of Agriculture of Norway, addressed our group. Dag Ryen and Minister Treholt provided most of the facts and figures pertaining to Norway.

A popular impression of Norway is that of a beautiful but lost country in the frozen north, living its own hard life, yet offering a warm welcome to those brave enough to visit its fjords and mountains in search of a summer vacation far from the noise and cares of modern civilization.

Yet its people have made Norway a modern nation, and this despite the severity of its climate and the vagaries of its topography—a nation that takes its full place in the political and economic life of the community that is Europe.

The Honorable Torstein Treholt, Minister of Agriculture of Norway, at a gala dinner, in Oslo, with Dag Ryen serving as interpreter. Les Leachman, of Hudson, New York, is seated on the minister's right, and Dr. E is seated on his left.

I presented five of my books to the honored guests. Here I am presenting *Animal Science* to the minister of agriculture.

One-third of Norway lies within the Arctic Circle; and it is the same latitude as Anchorage, Alaska.

The brightest picture on the horizon is oil production in the Norwegian sector of the North Sea. The midnight sun is a phenomenon of the North Cape area. The sun does not set from the middle of May until the end of July, nor does it rise above the horizon from approximately November 20 to January 24. The Northern Lights are visible in winter.

City of Oslo

We toured Oslo, including stops at the following places.

The Viking Ships and Archaeological Finds

These remarkable relics of the Viking Age, which include the Oseberg ship, the Kokstad ship, and the Tune ship, were all found near the Oslo Fjord. The Viking ships also brought to light a collection of household articles and garments; a treasure large and varied enough to give us a good idea of daily life in ninth century Norway. The Norwegians make it clear that the Vikings, not Columbus, discovered America; and a number of historians are now inclined to agree.

The King's Farm

We made a roadside stop as we drove through the king's farm. On one side of the road, we inspected a herd of 20 to 30 dual-purpose type cows of the Norwegian Red-and-White breed. These are marvelous big cows, with large udders, and they are red in color, although some of them have white spots. They are a horned breed. On the other side of the road, we saw some of the king's horses. These are a draft breed, chestnut in color. These horses were on pasture, but they were in high condition. The breed is known as Norwegian Valley Horse (or Dole) in Norway.

We also saw an area close to town where the king's sheep are pastured. I am shown behind one of them.

Nobel Institute

This is an unpretentious building, erected in 1905, on the outside of which is a bust of Alfred Bernhard Nobel, who made a fortune of his discovery of dynamite. Only the Nobel Prize for Peace is awarded in Norway. This happened because once Norway was a part of Sweden. With the separation of the two countries, Norway retained the peace prize, whereas the rest of the Nobel prizes (physics, chemistry, physiology or medicine, and literature) are awarded in Sweden. Each year, a committee elected by the Norwegian government selects the recipient of the Nobel Prize for Peace and the King of Norway makes the presentation. Each Nobel award recipient receives a gold medal and a sum of money.

Ski Jump and the Ski Museum

The Holmenkollen Ski Jump is, without doubt, the most famous ski jump in the world. The original jump was erected in 1882, but many improvements and enlargements have been undertaken subsequently. The Ski Museum, which was opened in 1923, and which is located under the Holmenkollen Ski Jump, is the world's oldest ski museum.

The Agricultural College of Norway

We visited the Agricultural College of Norway, which is located about 20 miles south of Oslo.

General Information

The Agricultural College of Norway is a State College, and the only agricultural college in Norway. It has had university status since 1897. Today, the college has five divisions: agriculture, dairy industry, forestry, horticulture, and land consolidation and surveying.

Department of Animal Genetics and Breeding

This department is headed by Professor, Dr. Harald Skjervold.

Cattle

Professor Skjervold reported that at one time there were eight different breeds of cattle in Norway. Today, the Norwegian Red-and-White has practically taken over all of the cattle breeding of Norway.

View of the Agricultural College of Norway with some of the buildings in the background.

Dr. Harald Skjervold, Head, Department of Animal Genetics and Breeding, Agricultural College of Norway, took us on a walking tour of the college farm. He is shown pointing to an object of interest. I am on the right doing my thing—taking notes. Dr. Skjervold studied under Dr. Jay Lush, Iowa State University.

Sheep

The department has about 50 sheep, of the Oxford Down and Dala breeds.

Industry Relationship

The Department of Animal Genetics and Breeding has a close working relationship with cooperative farm organizations, including breed registry associations, as evidenced by the fact that the industry provided the funds with which their new building, now six years old, was built.

College Farm

The college farm consists of 1,457 acres.

The Farm, "Maarud Bedrifter," Owned by Mr. Ole A. Stang

We visited Mr. Stang's operation, which includes the manufacture of cheese, potato chips, and snacks.

Mr. Ole A. Stang

Mr. Stang is 49 years of age. He studied in the United States; he completed a B.S. degree in business at the University of Kansas in 1948. Mr. Stang took over the business in 1960.

We visited Maarud Bedrifter Farm, owned by Ole A. Stang. At the time of our visit, Mr. Stang was conducting an $8 million per year industry on the farm, producing cheese, potato chips, and snacks. I am shown presenting a book to Mr. Stang.

Maarud Farm

The word *Maarud* means flat land, cleared. The land, which now constitutes this farm, was originally cleared around 800 AD. The present owner's grandfather acquired the farm in the 19th century. However, the real expansion took place under his father, Thomas Stang, who returned from the U.S. in 1922, after completing a master's degree in forestry. Thomas Stang's idea was, from the beginning, that raw materials should be processed on the farm and taken to the consumer. Hence, production of meat products, chicken and eggs, fresh cream, margarine, potato chips, cheese, houses, grass-meal, sawed and planed lumber, vacation houses and other wood products were gradually started. Today, Maarud Farms consists of 7,300 acres. It does a gross business of $8 million per year. Today, most of the business consists of cheese and snacks.

Cheese

Maarud Farm produces Camembert, Brie, and three types of cream cheese.

Potato Chips

Maarud processes about 14,000 tons of potatoes

per year, of which only about 5% are grown on the farm.

Other Snacks

Other snacks produced at Maarud include popcorn and bacon crisps. More products are planned in the future, including peanuts.

Other Products

Maarud also produces barley and wood products. Forests require about 80 years per rotation.

Horse Racing at Ovrevoll

We went to the races at Ovrevoll, as guests of the Norwegian Jockey Club. Mr. and Mrs. Hans Thorbjornsen hosted us. Mr. Thorbjornsen is the public relations director for the Norwegian Jockey Club.

Ovrevoll race course is beautifully situated in picturesque countryside only five miles from Oslo City Center, and is easily accessible by road and rail. The horses race uphill and down. They use a starting gate very much like those used in the U.S. There is pari-mutuel betting. The Norwegians love horse racing.

The Sweden We Saw

We flew from Oslo, Norway to Stockholm, Sweden. In the evening, we had a gala dinner, with many distinguished guests.

The government of Sweden is a constitutional monarchy, with King Gustaff VI on the throne. Sweden is larger than California, but smaller than Texas. It borders Finland and Norway.

The chief agricultural products of Sweden are: cheese, butter, beef, pork, wheat, rye, potatoes, sugar beets, vegetable oils. The main natural resources area: forests, iron ore, water power.

The average farm today is still generally a family enterprise, although nowadays some food processing industries grow primary products on their own farms.

Reindeer

The number of reindeer in Sweden is estimated at 250,000 head. Increased productivity is aimed at through improved breeding and management.

Dr. E (left) introduced the Honorable Ingemund Bengtsson (right), Minister of Agriculture of Sweden, who addressed the Agriservices Foundation tour-study group at a gala dinner, in Stockholm, Sweden. Dr. E also presented one of his books to the minister.

Better Livestock

The National Board of Agriculture issues direction for livestock control, breeding, and artificial insemination.

Smaller Farm Workforce, but Bigger Production

Today, the number of people employed in agriculture constitutes only about 5% of the total workforce. However, this small group produces a greater amount of agricultural products than was the case when 70% of the population was engaged in agriculture.

Special Supports Accorded Northern Sweden

Because of the short growing season and cold climate, special supports are accorded northern Sweden in order to keep agricultural production at satisfactory levels.

The City of Stockholm

We got a "bird's eye view" of Stockholm, with stops made at the following two places:

The Royal Palace

The Royal Palace was built between 1697 and 1754. It is famed for its exquisite interior with baroque and rococo decorations and fine collections of tapestry and china. This is really a castle which is lived in, for the King of Sweden resides here most of the year. The present King uses only about 40 of the 608 rooms.

Millesgarden

This was originally the home of Carl Milles, the great sculptor. The terraces of Millesgarden are lined with columns that conjure up visions of ancient days. There are fountains and reflecting pools, small pathways lined with sculptured figures and monumental groups in bronze, granite, and marble nesting among the birch trees and pines; the gray of the rock broken by the color of summer flowers.

Federation of Swedish Farmers, Address by Mr. Thorvald Persson

At breakfast this morning, we had with us Mr. Thorvald Persson, agronomist, Federation of Swedish Farmers.

Origin of Sweden's Co-op Movement

Co-ops started over 100 years ago in Sweden. More specifically, the first known co-operative association—a mortgage society—was formed in 1836. The Federation of Swedish Farmers now embraces all production and marketing associations. More than 80% of Swedish farm produce is handled by the agricultural cooperatives.

Erstavik Estate, at Saltsjobaden

We visited Erstavik Estate, at Saltsjobaden. This estate belongs to a Swedish noble family, Major and Mrs. Magnus af Petersens. The Petersens are especially interested in recreational development and environmental control.

Erstavik was first mentioned in the literature about 1380. It has been owned by the Petersens family since 1762. The main products are dairy products, meat products, and wood products. The estate is about 6,000 acres.

What's Unique About Erstavik?

The unique thing about Erstavik is that it is an example of how leisure activities can be combined with agriculture. Wood (timber) is the main agricultural production. However, Erstavik is the most important leisure area near Stockholm. Over one million people walk, ski, swim, or otherwise enjoy nature in Erstavik. Also, it would appear that the development of recreational possibilities on an estate like Erstavik offers the only hope of keeping up with higher tax rates, especially when the farm is not suited to cultivation.

Hamra Farm, Alfa-Laval's Experimental and Demonstration Farm

It all started with the invention of the centrifugal cream separator, by Dr. Gustaf de Laval. Alfa-Laval was founded in 1883, and Hamra Farm was purchased in 1894. Hamra Farm has developed a reputation as a prominent cattle breeding station and research center.

Milking Equipment

Pipeline milking is used in the stanchion barn, and a double-five Herringbone parlor (five cows on each side) is used for the animals in the loafing shed.

What's Unique About This Operation?

Alfa-Laval (de Laval) is using this farm as a test plant for milking machines, cooling equipment, feeding equipment, manure disposal equipment, and manure treatment methods.

Agesta Gard (Farm); Gotland Horses

We visited this farm for the purpose of seeing Gotland horses, which originated on the Gotland Island, off the coast of Sweden. Thus, they are a native breed to Sweden. Mr. and Mrs. B. Von Krusenstjerna provided the following information about this farm:

Agesta was named for the first time in 1540. Its main source of income is riding school instruction and breeding Gotland horses.

What's Unique About This Operation?

The unique thing about this operation is that 22 head of the Gotland horses that we saw all stemmed from one mare that was bought in 1956. Although this mare died about two weeks prior to our visit, she left a great bunch of progeny.

Dr. E is shown visiting with Mr. and Mrs. Von Krusenstjerna, owners of Agesta Gard farm.

Gotland horses at Agesta Gard farm. Our group enjoyed walking amongst these gentle horses.

National Veterinary Institute

The institute, which was founded in 1991, comes under the Ministry of Agriculture. The following divisions operate under the director: pathology, virology, bacteriology, chemistry, parasitology, advisory, epizootiology, and production.

The Disease Situation in Sweden

Sweden is entirely free of many of the dreaded animal diseases that exist in other parts of the world. Among the diseases *not* present in Sweden are brucellosis, tuberculosis, rabies, rinderpest, and foot-and-mouth disease.

The Finland We Saw

We flew from Stockholm, Sweden to Helsinki, Finland. Finland is about half the size of Texas. It is bordered by Sweden, Norway, and the U.S.S.R.

At the time of our visit, Finland was dominated by agriculture, although rapid industrialization was taking place. About 70% of the land is forested.

The co-operative system is carried on in Finland with marked success.

Taivalahti Church

This is known as the "Cliff Church," because it is carved into a cliff. Except for the copper and glass roof, the church was hewn out of the rock in a cliff. It is very modern and beautiful, with red cushioned pews.

Sibelius Park

The center of attraction in this very beautiful park is the abstract monument of Sibelius, which literally floats in the air. Jean Sibelius (1865–1957) was affiliated with European music.

The Statue of Paavo Nurmi

In three Olympics (1920, 1924, and 1928), Nurmi, the "flying Finn," won a total of nine gold and three silver medals.

Agriculture Research Centre, Tikkurila

Prof. Dr. Kalle Maijala showed us this station, which means to Finland what the Beltsville Station of the U.S. Department of Agriculture means to the United States. The station operates under the Ministry of Agriculture. It has the following nine different departments: Agricultural Chemistry, Plant Pathology, Physics, Pest Investigation, Soil Science, Horticulture, Plant Science, and Animal Science.

University of Helsinki Experimental Farm

Next, we visited the University of Helsinki Experimental Farm, which is about a 20-minute drive from the Agricultural Research Centre. We were shown over this experimental farm, which covers 1,178 acres, by Pekka Ahtiainen.

Gala Dinner

This evening, we had a gala dinner in Helsinki, with distinguished guests. At the dinner, Antti Nikkola represented the Minister of Agriculture of Finland and warmly welcomed us; and Prof., Dr. Kalle Maijala sang two Finnish folk songs.

Lounais Suomen Osuusteurastamo (L.S.O.)—A Hog Packing Plant

This morning, we visited the hog packing plant known as Lounais Suomen Osuusteurastamo (L.S.O.). This plant is the largest and most modern pig packing plant in Finland today.

Number of Hogs Slaughtered

They have a capacity of 145 hogs per hour. Also, we were told that they slaughter from 1,000 to 1,500 hogs per day.

Plant Ownership

The plant is a farmer-owned co-operative. The plant assures itself of a continuous flow of hogs at all times through contracts with its member producers.

Rauhalinna Society Breeding Service, Jalostuspalvelu

We were shown through this animal breeding establishment by Mr. Bo Holmstrom, a native of Finland who speaks very good English. This breeding service was founded in 1946. In the area which they serve, 100% of the cows are inseminated, and 35% of the sows are bred AI.

Humppila Testing Station, Tikkurila

This station is used for the performance testing (rate of gain) of future AI bulls in Finland. Since the end of 1965, the development of beef producing characteristics has been included in the breeding programs of the three Finnish dairy breeds—Ayrshire, Finn Cattle, and Friesians. Because of this, attention is paid to the size and growth of the bulls. For this purpose, two performance testing stations are operated in Finland, where future AI bulls must pass a growth trial before their final selection for AI use. The growth trial starts at 60 days of age and ends at one year of age.

At the Humppila bull testing station, Tikkurila, Finland, Mr. Veikko Kivipelto (left), director, showed us through the young bull testing barn, following which I presented one of my books to him.

The U.S.S.R. We Saw

This was our second study-tour of the U.S.S.R.; we first visited there in 1966.

The common enterprises of collective farms and co-operative organizations, their output and common buildings constitute their socialized property. Members may use small plots of land attached to their dwellings.

"Backyard" farms, from which farmers may sell produce and keep the profit, increased in size and number in the 1960s.

Leningrad

Peter the Great, after whom the city was originally, and is presently named, is extolled as the greatest of all their czars. This city has had four different name changes; in order: St. Petersburg, Petrograd, Leningrad, and St. Petersburg. At the time of my 1966 and 1972 visits, it was Leningrad.

Leningrad University

Leningrad University occupies the 12 buildings which formerly housed the "Twelve Collegia" as the ministers were called at the time of Peter the Great.

Peter and Paul Fortress

Peter the Great laid the foundation for this fortress on May 16, 1703. The stone bastions of the fortress were intended to defend the city of St. Petersburg (as it was known in that day) from enemy attacks. Soon, however, Peter and Paul Fortress was converted into a prison. Three generations of Russian revolutionaries were jailed in its cells. The fortress is now a museum.

Winter Palace (Hermitage)

This was the former residence of the czarist family. This huge building is one of the masterpieces of the famous architect B. Rastrelli. It was built in 1754–1762.

It has ceilings ornamented with stucco molding, walls covered with murals; and its floors, inlaid with precious woods, are works of art. A walk through all its halls would mean covering a distance of nearly 18.6 miles.

Today, the Winter Palace and the buildings adjoining it, house the Hermitage. There are 2½ million exhibits on view in this museum, among them works by Leonardo da Vinci, Titian, Rembrandt, and Rubens; sculptures and art objects of Ancient Egypt, Greece, and Rome. It is the richest and largest of Leningrad's museums.

Petrodvorets (Grand Palace)

This palace is located about 20 miles west of Leningrad. Its construction was started in the first quarter of the 18th century when, after the victory of 1709 in the Northern War, Peter I ruled that a gala summer residence be built on the coast of the Gulf of Finland. The work and art of several generations of craftsmen went into the development of Petrodvorets.

The most beautiful of the numerous gardens of Petrodvorets is the Lower Park.

In the center of the ensemble stands the Grand Palace designed for ceremonial receptions. The palace, towering over the tree tops, spreads its wings along the terrace dominating a graceful array of avenues and fountains.

The ingenious fountain system of the park was created more than 200 years ago. It consists of a 13.7 mile gravity water conduit.

Pyatigorsk

We flew from Leningrad to Pyatigorsk, a noted livestock area, a distance of about 1,200 miles. Actually, we arrived in Mineralnye Vody, then we went by bus to Pyatigorsk, a distance of about 16 miles. Pyatigorsk is situated at the foothills of the Caucasian Range, and not far from the Black Sea.

Upon our arrival by plane in Mineralnye Vody, we were met by my good friend, Mr. Yuri V. Borschenko, whom I first got acquainted with in 1966. Mr. Borschenko presented flowers to Mrs. Ensminger and his limousine and driver to me. Also, he proudly showed us the gold pen and pencil set that Mrs. Ensminger and I sent to him following our 1966 visit.

During our 1972 visit, Mr. Borschenko arranged

Mr. Yuri V. Borschenko, Manager of Intourist, Pyatigorsk (left) and Dr. E inspecting a field of corn (maize) in the Pyatigorsk area.

for me to conduct a seminar before a group of chairmen of collective and state farms of the Pyatigorsk area—the first time since their 1917 revolution that an American agriculturist had been invited to conduct a seminar before such a group in the U.S.S.R.

What a difference a friend can make! It took much, much doing on my part to meet Mr. Borschenko and to visit state and collective farms in 1966. But, from that date forward, Mr. Borschenko and I became warm friends.

The city of Pyatigorsk, a popular health resort, was founded 150 years ago. It is situated on the bank of the Podkoumok River at the foot of the five-peaked Mt. Beshtau. Among the resorts of the Caucasian Spas, Pyatigorsk ranks first for the number of mineral springs, diversity of mineral water types, and its reserves.

Pyatigorsk has 11 large specialized sanatoriums, several hydropathic establishments (baths), a mud-bath center, a radon hospital, inhalation facilities, and a general polyclinic; all staffed by highly qualified specialists.

There is also a racetrack not far from Pyatigorsk.

"Collective Farm 40 Years of the Great October"

This is the name of the collective farm we visited. A gateman was present at the entrance to the collective farm. We were advised that this precaution was being taken for the purpose of stopping animals, people, or vehicles that might carry foot-and-mouth disease.

Mr. Vasil Burlak (left; with Dr. Ensminger standing next to him), chairman, "Collective Farm 40 Years of the Great October," Stavropol territory, U.S.S.R., and the members of the Agriservices Foundation tour-study group. We donned white lab coats and rubber footwear before being permitted to enter the barns of the 4,000-head confinement cattle finishing operation.

I am meeting some of the workers at 40 Years of the Great October Farm.

The spirit of our host, and the warm welcome that we received, can best be expressed by quoting the toast which Vasil Burlak, chairman of the collective farm, gave during the bountiful and delicious luncheon that he hosted in our honor at the collective farm.

> Every time the American people come to us, we get more and more convinced that our two nations can live in peace. So let us do all in our power to preserve peace between our two great countries.

Although many of the collective farms in the former U.S.S.R. have now been broken up, in1993 we

Late in the afternoon, they served a bountiful meal, after which we took group pictures.

found that the collective farms were still in place in the Stavropol area. They explained that they felt because it was a successful system, they did not see why they should change it.

Gala Dinner—Seminar

We had our gala dinner at the Mashuk Hotel in Pyatigorsk, with invited Russian guests. The head table was decorated with "Old Glory" and the U.S.S.R. flag, side by each. There were nine distinguished guests at this gala dinner; among them, Mr. and Mrs. Yuri V. Borschenko and Peter Strahov, the able Director of Stud Farm 169, Terksy Stud, which we visited in 1966.

Following dinner, we proceeded to a separate room in the hotel, where, at the invitation of the Russians, I presented a seminar on "The U.S. Livestock Industry—a panoramic view." In order to minimize the language barrier and interpretation, I used 160 slides, then gave our Russian guests a 74-page booklet which contained the facts, figures, and charts that I presented (actually, the booklet contained everything but the pictures). Messrs. Borschenko and Prockopoy (our Intourist guide) served as interpreters. The Russians were much interested in the seminar report.

Following the seminar, Mr. Semen Lutchenco, retired chairman of a collective farm, Stavropol Territory, Predgorny region, Proletarskaya Volja, and decorated "Hero of Socialist Labor," decorated me with a medal. Said he, "This medal is presented to you, Dr. Ensminger, in recognition of your outstanding work in agriculture."

Krasnodar

We flew to Krasnodar, in the heart of the Caucasus, probably the best agricultural area in the U.S.S.R. Our reservations were at the Caucasus Hotel.

Trees and Other Vegetation

Krasnodar is a beautiful city. The streets are lined with trees of various kinds—oaks, ash, maples, lime trees, acacias, chestnut trees, and others.

Crops

The major crops of the area are wheat, barley, sugar beets, rice, sunflowers, and tea (the latter, along with coffee and tobacco, grow near the Black Sea). They also grow grapes and make champagne and wine. The whole area reminded us of the San Joaquin Valley of California.

The Circus

We went to the Filatov Bear's Circus (a Moscow troupe) in Krasnodar. It was held in a well-designed and attractive new building, which was air conditioned, and which we estimated would seat 2,000 to 2,500 people. There was a full house.

Two bears on a bicycle built for two.

The State Farm "Kubanets,"

En route to the state farm, "Kubanets," which is about an hour-and-10-minute drive to the north of Krasnodar, "Nellie," our local Intourist guide, told us that her salary is U.S. $180 a month, and that she pays U.S. $13.20 a month tax.

At "Kubanets," the director, Mr. L. P. Yulov, presented the following information as he led us on a conducted study-tour of the state farm.

General Facts About "Kubanets"

This State Farm was founded in 1932. It produces cereal grain, milk, and meat.

Net Profit

Last year (1971), the farm showed a net profit of U.S. $1,560,000 before taxes, and taxes totaled U.S. $34,800. Taxes on state farms in the U.S.S.R. are less than on collective farms, because state farms do not pay land taxes whereas collective farms do. The prof-

Dr. E is shown introducing, and presenting a copy of one of his books to, Mr. L. P. Yulov, Director of the state farm, "Kubanets," a 17,290-acre farm. This is in the heart of Krasnodar territory, known as the "Gem of Russia," because of the fertility and productivity of the area.

As a disease preventive measure, all of the tour-study members were asked to put on lab coats before entering the hog barns on the state farm "Kubanets," where they produce 50,000 market hogs annually. Dr. E is front and center and Mr. L. P. Yulov, Director of Kubanets, is on Dr. E's left.

"Kubanets'" Director, L. P. Yulov (in white shirt) points out the features of a new "tandem type" milking parlor, with provision for milking three cows on each side, near completion and scheduled to be in operation about a month following our visit.

At the state farm "Kubanets," near Krasnodar, Mr. L. P. Yulov, Director (left) showed Dr. E (notebook in hand) corn being harvested for silage.

its are used to increase production, improve dwellings, for cultural and other needs of workers, and as bonuses.

2:30 p.m. Dinner

Following our inspection of the state farm, we were served a bountiful dinner. It consisted of six courses, and it included 20 different dishes. Both champagne and vodka were served; and there were many toasts by both our tour-study group and our Russian guests. Through all the toasts, there was the wish for peace and friendship between the peoples of our two great nations.

The auditorium of the school of the state farm, "Kubanets." Standing left to right: Dr. E, Audrey Ensminger, and the director of the school. They have 32 teachers and 600 students—a ratio of one teacher to 20 students. Three languages are taught: Russian, English, and German.

Research Institute, Oil Seed (Sunflower) Breeding, Krasnodar

I had the opportunity to visit the research institute where Famed Dr. V. Pustovoit pioneered in research with sunflowers, once considered a worthless weed in its native North America—research that resulted in sunflower seed which yielded more than 50% high quality oil, and in sunflower oil ranking third as a vegetable oil, worldwide. A statue of Dr. Pustovoit stands near the front entrance of the main building. Research work at this institute was started in the present century. Dr. Pustovoit is 86 years old and in the hospital at the present time.

Research Responsibility

This institute is responsible for all oil seed studies in the U.S.S.R. It has 98,800 acres of land, part of

The research institute in Krasnodar.

which is located in different areas and operated as branch experiment stations.

Oil Plants Studied

The institute studies sunflowers, castorbeans, soybeans, mustard, flax, peanuts, and sesame.

Magnitude of Sunflowers in the U.S.S.R.

Eighty percent of the vegetable oil produced in the Soviet Union comes from sunflowers. The new varieties, not yet released, run 56 to 58% oil content.

Exports of Sunflower Seed and Oil (Mostly Seed)

They export sunflower seed, and a little oil, to the U.S., Canada, France, Turkey, Western Europe, Pakistan, Argentina, and Cuba.

Availability of Seed

We were advised that seed of their new 56% to 58% oil content varieties may be obtained provided their Minister of Agriculture approves, and our U.S. Department of Agriculture grants permission to bring it in. These five scientists seemed to be very appreciative of our visit. They presented a book in Russian on sunflowers to me; along with a flier, which is also in Russian.

Moscow

This morning, Mr. G. Stanley Brown, our agricultural attaché in Moscow, came aboard our bus to extend greetings. He explained that negotiations have been finalized for the marketing of $750 million worth of grain (wheat, corn, and soybeans) from the United States to the Soviet Union over a period of three years; and the figure may reach $1 billion.

Armory Museum

This morning, we went to the Armory Museum, which houses the "finery" of former Russian czars. As an animal husbandman, I was particularly interested in the ornate carriages, saddles, and other tack. We were told that some of these royal stables had as many as 20,000 horses. Of course, the czars lived in a horse and buggy era. They had no other method of transportation. Imagine having trappings—everything from saddles to blankets to carriages—covered with precious stones!

Permanent Agricultural Exposition

Following lunch at the Zolotoy Kios Restaurant, we saw a bit of the Permanent Agricultural Exposition. Mrs. E. and I visited the horse barn, the swine barn, the cattle barn, and the sheep barn. We were unable to get pictures of the horses through their screened stables, but they had both light and draft breeds.

In the sheep barn, I observed representatives of the following breeds: Rambouillet, Merino (smooth bodied), Hampshire, Karakul, and Suffolk. Also, there were other breeds, including some fat-tailed sheep, which I was not able to identify. There were Angora goats, too. I was particularly impressed with the size and scale of the Rambouillet sheep.

The Permanent Agricultural Exposition is beautifully done, with permanent buildings, and all sorts of exhibits, which would take several days to go through with care. Also, they seemed to get enormous crowds.

Friendly People Everywhere

We found friendly people everywhere. This was particularly true in the down-country areas of Pyatigorsk and Krasnodar, especially on the farms. The farm folk—men, women, and children—gathered along our line of travel to exchange smiles and to wave; and they were overjoyed when we shook hands with them. Indeed, it imparted a warm, friendly feeling.

The Poland We Saw

In Poland, I saw much of their agriculture being powered out of a different period of history. I saw horse-drawn equipment much like I first used in 1919 as a nine-year-old boy on a Missouri farm. Poland is about the size of New Mexico. Bordered by the Baltic Sea, the U.S.S.R., Czechoslovakia, and East Germany.

Warsaw

Warsaw was almost completely destroyed during World War II. But with great courage and hard work—traits of which the Polish people possess a super abundance—the city was rebuilt. Although many cities in Europe have been rebuilt since the Second World War, none has been reconstructed in such a painstaking manner as Warsaw. Today, the city is bristling with activity.

Kolonia Bialka

We visited this farm owned by Mr. Edmund Olesiejuk. It is located about 120 miles east of Warsaw, and within 4 to 5 miles of the U.S.S.R. border.

Upon our arrival, we were served a bountiful Sunday dinner. This is an orchard operation about

Our group enjoyed a home-cooked dinner.

which the following pertinent information was given.

Size and Crops

This farm consists of 39.5 acres, on which the following are grown: 24.7 acres orchard, 7.41 acres meadow, and 7.41 acres cultivated—including potatoes.

Varieties of Apples

Fifty percent of the apples are McIntosh. Also, they produce Jonathan and other varieties.

Market

The fruit is marketed through a co-op, which, in turn, sells the apples for export.

Refrigeration Is Being Added

At the present time, the owner is building a refrigeration room for storage of his apples. Also, he plans to add a grading and polishing machine.

Cielesnica State Farm

Late in the afternoon, we visited the Cielesnica State Farm, of which Mr. Stanistlaw Koeiubinski is the manager. Mr. Koeiubinski arranged for a reception for us, during which time he also briefed us pertaining to Cielesnica State Farm. The farm embraces 2,223 acres, in addition to some industrialization. The crops grown are: orchard, 123.5 acres; cherries, 24.7 acres; berries, 14.8 acres. Additionally, some certified seed is grown and they produce potatoes.

Fish Production

Nearly 2,000 acres are devoted to water for fish production. Currently, they are marketing 30 metric tons of fish per year.

Cattle

There are 600 head of cattle on the place. One hundred head of these cows are now in lactation. We visited the dairy barn where we saw the 100 cows, and 16 head of springer heifers. All of the cattle are of the Black-and-White (Holstein) breed.

Janow Podlaski, State Stud Farm

Upon our arrival in the little town of Janow Podlaski, which is located near the U.S.S.R. border, we were surprised that so many people of the village turned out to see, wave, and smile at us. An occasional one could speak a little English. We were a curiosity.

On this date, we visited the famous Arabian stud farm located at Janow Podlaski, Poland. It's the best known stud farm in Poland. We were shown over the establishment by Dr. Andrzej Krzysztalowicz and his staff. The following pertinent information was obtained or observed:

Historical

This stud farm is 160 years old. During most of its entire existence, it has been owned by the state.

Breeds

Arabians and half-breds.

Exhibit of Animals Under Saddle

Five of the horses were exhibited under saddle.

Dr. Andrzej Krzysztalowicz, Director, famed Arabian Stud Farm, Janow Podlaski, Poland. Dr. Krzysztalowicz is holding two of my books that I presented to him.

We toured the state stud farm in two-seated vehicles (with seats facing each other), with pneumatic tires, drawn by Anglo-Arab horses.

A Vehicle Ride over the Farm

We were taken over the farm in vehicles—six of them. These vehicles were two-seaters (with the seats facing each other) equipped with pneumatic tires. Each vehicle was drawn by a team of Anglo-Arab horses.

Horses

In one field, we saw a band of 80 mares. In another field, we saw 45 stud colts.

Fencing

We observed both steel-pipe and pole fencing.

Przewalsky's Horse

In one field, we observed a stallion of Przewalsky's horse, which belongs to a zoo in Warsaw.

The only surviving species of original wild horses—not feral or escaped from domestication—known to exist at the present time is Przewalsky's horse (or the Asiatic wild horse). This is the wild horse discovered by the Russian explorer, Przewalsky, in 1879, in the northwestern corner of Mongolia. It is a small, stockily built, and distinctly yellowish horse, with an erect mane and no forelock. There is usually a dark stripe on the shoulders and down the middle of the back. Like the wild mustang or feral horses of the frontier days, Przewalsky's horses separate into bands, seldom more than forty in number, with a stallion leader in each group. At the present time, it is reported that only three wild bands remain. Fortunately, however, live specimens have been brought to Europe and America where they are being preserved and propagated successfully in captivity.

German Occupancy

In 1944, the Germans took all the horses from this stud farm to Germany, and they burned down 16 of the buildings when they left.

About Director Krzysztalowicz

We learned that he grew up in the horse business, that he came to this particular stud farm as a student in 1938. He became the director in 1956. In 1944, when the Germans took all the horses, they took him with them. Further, the British returned him with the horses in 1946.

Gala Dinner

At the banquet, our Polish guests informed us as follows: There are in Poland 2½ million horses at the present time; there are 30 stud farms and 13 stallion stations (depots); the breeds in Poland include Arabians, Thoroughbreds, Trakehner, Anglo-Arabs, Oldenburg, and draft horses (breeds of the latter were not named).

Sluzewiec Race Track

This morning, we visited the Sluzewiec Race Track, the leading racetrack of Poland.

Historical

This track was built in 1938, prior to World War II; and it was not damaged during the war.

Race Breeds

In Poland, Arabians, Thoroughbreds, and half-breds are raced; with each breed raced separately.

Here is a racehorse that they led out for us to see.

Magnitude of the Horse Business in Poland

We were told that Poland has the greatest horse concentration of any country in Europe. This stems primarily from the number of horses still used on the farms, because of inadequate automation. However, a number of light horses are bred in Poland.

People Employed

A total of 1,000 work at the track. Each groom cares for three horses.

Racing Distance

Arabians race from one mile and up. Thoroughbreds race from 5 furlongs and up.

In 1972, large numbers of horses were being used on the farms and city streets of Poland. I took the lines of this horse in Warsaw. Kapua Heuer, of Hilo, Hawaii, is standing in the back.

The Denmark We Saw

The Denmark we saw was the cleanest (from a litter and sanitary standpoint) country in the world. I saw their famed Danish Landrace swine and Red Danish cattle. I saw straw, straw everywhere.

The government of Denmark is a constitutional monarchy, with Copenhagen as its capital and largest city.

It is about the size of New Hampshire and Massachusetts combined; it lies between the North and Baltic Seas.

Briefing Relative to Danish Agriculture by Mr. Harlan J. Dirks, Agricultural Attaché, U.S. Embassy

Nearly three-fourths of the land area is devoted to agriculture.

Although only about 6.5% of the gross national product in 1970 was of agricultural origin, agriculture supplies the nation's major food requirements and much of the exports.

The average size of a Danish farm is approximately 50 acres.

Type of Farming and Crops

Danish agriculture is primarily dependent on a livestock economy supported by domestically-grown feed but supplemented by imported concentrates, especially oilseed meals.

Livestock

Red Danish cattle are the dominant breed in Denmark, accounting for about 40% of the cows in 1969. However, the number of Black-and-White (Holstein Friesian) cows is increasing. Both of these breeds are of the dual-purpose type with high butterfat production.

Agricultural Co-operatives

The co-operative movement in Denmark has influenced the development of agriculture greatly and has been a most important factor in the advancement of Danish agriculture. The principles of cooperation have been successfully applied to all branches of agriculture, such as production activities, foreign trade, domestic marketing, purchasing, plant and animal breeding, various types of research, credit, and insurance.

Agricultural Research

Although the Ministry of Agriculture plays a relatively small part in the farm advisory service, it is greatly concerned with agricultural research. There are government research stations covering virtually every aspect and the ministry also supports research undertaken by farmer organizations with treasury grants.

Social Legislation

Membership of a local health insurance society is compulsory to Danish citizens. The insurance society will cover expenses in connection with hospitalization and medical treatment. Persons in higher income groups must pay part of their expenses for medical treatment.

Danish citizens above 67 years of age have, irrespective of their income, a right to senior-citizen pension.

Gala Dinner in Copenhagen

The Honorable Ib Frederiksen, Minister of Agriculture, made the following statement in his address at our gala dinner:

The Honorable Ib Frederiksen, Minister of Agriculture of Denmark (left), shown accepting a book from, and being introduced by, Dr E. The Minister addressed the visiting Americans at a gala dinner in Copenhagen.

Dr. E is shown introducing, and presenting two of his books to, Mr. Harlan J. Dirks, Agricultural Attaché, U.S. Embassy, Copenhagen, Denmark. Mr. Dirks briefed our group on Denmark.

> The Danish farmer is looking forward to access to a larger European market for agricultural products through entry into the common market (EEC). Final decision on joining the EEC will be determined by referendum on October 2 of this year.

Mr. Harlan J. Dirks, Agricultural Attaché, American Embassy, had the following to say in his address at the gala dinner:

> Denmark's farmers, as a whole, want to go into the common market. However, Norway's farmers are opposed to going into the common market. The latter situation is understandable because, were Norway to enter the common market, prices for its farm products would drop by 60%.

"Hjortlundsgaard," Farm Owned by Holger Petersen, Where We Saw Oldenburg Horses

This morning, we visited Hjortlundsgaard farm, primarily for the purpose of seeing representatives of the Oldenburg breed of horses. This farm, which is located approximately 31 miles southwest of Copenhagen, consists of 59.2 acres, and has 22 horses. The following additional facts are pertinent to this horse farm:

Dr. E greets Mr and Mrs. Petersen and presents them with a book.

House

The house, in which we were served refreshments, is over 200 years old. It has a straw roof, which we were told is about 30 years old. We observed the very short doors. Two hundred years ago people were much shorter.

Purebred Oldenburgs

We were shown some purebred Oldenburgs. The Oldenburg is a draft breed. In type, they are "farm chunks" and "cobby" in formation. Mature horses weigh about 1,800 lb.

Oldenburg horses owned by Holger Petersen, Hjortlundsgaard Farm.

The Farm "Juellund," Managed by Dr. H. O. Nielsen, DVM

There are actually three farms: a 6,000-acre unit (3,000 acres of which are in timber) owned by a count who is now 90 years old, a second unit consisting of 1,000 acres, and a third unit consisting of 168 acres; and it is very diverse.

Crops Grown

Crops grown here are wheat, 840 acres; barley, 86.5 acres; alfalfa, 210 acres; other crops, 59 acres. Additionally, 1,482 acres of alfalfa are produced under contract.

Swine Operation

Hogs of the Danish Landrace breed are produced for the British market.

"Bellinge"; Red Danish Cows, and an AI Center

We visited the farm "Bellinge," which is located on the island of Lolland-Falster. It is managed by Mr. C. O. K. Hafstrom. The farm consists of 420 acres, all of which is cultivated.

Stanchion Vs Loafing Barn

In 1967, a new cow barn was built for the purpose of comparing a stanchion-type operation vs a loafing barn type of operation. This study was initiated in 1969. One hundred Red Danish cows are used; 50 are housed in a stanchion barn, and 50 are housed in a loafing barn—the latter on slotted floors plus individual, loose stalls. This study has now been underway about 2½ years. Mr. Hafstrom reported the following results to date:

> During the first year, the stanchioned cows out produced the loafing barn cows—the stanchioned cows producing 519 lb of butterfat per year vs 466 lb of butterfat per year for the loafing barn cows. However, this gap is gradually closing, which, according to Mr. Hafstrom, is interpreted to mean that the cows are gradually getting accustomed to spending their life in a loafing barn. The really big finding of this experiment is the difference in the man-hours of labor required. In the stanchion barn (tie shed), 10.58 minutes of labor are required per cow daily, vs

6.59 minutes per cow in the loafing barn. In hours per day for 50 cows, this means 9.0 for the stanchioned barn vs 5.7 hours for the loafing barn.

Based on the above, it appears that a loafing barn is favored, primarily because of the saving in labor.

The AI Center at "Bellinge," Directed by C. O. K. Hafstrom

Twenty-five bulls are used in the AI Center, embracing the following breeds: Red Danish, Black-and-White (Holstein), and Jersey. We inspected the bulls. They were staked out in a pasture by means of a nose ring attached to a weighted chain.

"Assendrup Hovedgard," Managed by Mr. Harold Johansen

This establishment is operated under a foundation whose purpose is to promote the Red Danish breed of cattle and give young people (students) an opportunity to study agriculture. Also, the farm conducts research on cattle and farm buildings. Mr. Harold Johansen, the manager, showed us their 525-acre facilities.

Barn

The new and modern barn that we saw was opened in January 1972. Its unique features are:

■ **Kind**—It's a loafing type barn with individual loafing stalls; slotted floors; maternity stalls and hospital pens; two Herringbone milk parlors, each with five units on a side (which means that 20 cows can be milked simultaneously); both individual and group pens for rearing calves; and feed storage in one end.

■ **Slotted Floors and Manure**—The slats are concrete, 7.5 in. wide, and with 1.65 in. slots. Under the slots, there is a pit which is 5.4 ft deep, sufficient storage for manure for six weeks. The manure is flushed out at intervals, handled as a liquid, and put on the fields.

Loafing Barn Vs Stanchioned Barn

Mr. Johansen favors the loafing barn over their former stanchioned barn. He cited the following "plusses" after he changed from a stanchioned to a loafing barn: 10 to 12% increase in milk, increased feed efficiency, and improved herd health.

"Gramrodegaard," Owned by Ole Due

The farm, "Gramrodegaard," is owned by Mr. Ole Due. Mr. Due came in possession of the farm from his father, in 1946, who, in turn, took possession of it in 1906. However, we were told that it was first known as a farm back in 1671.

An Oldenburg X Thoroughbred cross at Gramrodegaard, owned by Ole Due and trained by his daughter, Kirsten (exhibiting this horse). Such crossbreds are used for jumping, dressage, and pleasure horses.

Horses

There are 22 horses of all ages and both sexes. Most of the horses are Oldenburg X Thoroughbred crosses. They are used as jumping, dressage, and pleasure horses.

Roe Deer

Mounted on the wall in the front room, we saw the small skulls, with horns (the horns indicating males) of 170 Roe Deer. We were told that these males probably averaged about 66 lb in weight.

"Klejsgaard," Owned by Fred Hansen

Next, we visited the swine establishment owned and operated by Fred Hansen who was born on this place.

This 333½ acre farm produces mostly pigs and fruit (primarily apples).

Fred Hansen, Klejsgaard, shaking hands with Dr. E as he is presented with a book.

There are 100 brood sows, and they market about 1,700 bacon pigs per year.

This impressed all of us as a very fine operation. The hogs were very clean, the buildings were well maintained, and the gardens were beautiful.

Copenhagen

We spent the morning in Copenhagen, resting, packing, and shopping. Early afternoon, we traveled to the airport where we learned that our plane was three hours late. Unfortunately, we couldn't reach any of our contacts in Edinburgh to cancel the gala dinner that was scheduled for that evening, which was distressing.

The Scotland We Saw

Scotland, the land of colorful kilts and bagpipes, created for the world the following equally colorful and stylish breeds of livestock: Clydesdale horses; Ayrshire, Angus, Scotch Highland, Galloway, and Belted Galloway cattle; and Cheviot and Scotch Highland sheep. In addition to having an eye for beauty and style, the stockmen of Scotland possess an inborn love for animals and the ability to handle them.

Bonhard Farm, Owned by Mr. and Mrs. Roley L. Fraser

Our first stop was at Bonhard Farm, owned by Mr. and Mrs. Roley Fraser, where we saw their purebred Shorthorn and Polled Hereford herds, and were served refreshments. Mr. Fraser is one of Scotland's leading livestock auctioneers. Mrs. Fraser, who is an able lady in her own right, operates a 100-cow Jersey dairy, in addition to assisting her husband with the two beef herds.

The Frasers operate two farms; Bonhard Farm, which we saw and to which they will soon move, and Parkfield. In total, the two farms have 300 acres of land.

The Scottish Milk Marketing Board, Newlands Cattle Breeding (AI) Center, Perth

The Scottish Milk Marketing Board, which operates this AI center at Perth, also operates an AI center at Glasgow. From these two AI centers, the Scottish Milk Marketing Board provided the semen with which to breed a total of 175,000 cows last year.

Shorthorn bull at Newlands Cattle Breeding (AI) Center, Perth, Scotland.

C. C. (Contemporary Comparison) of Dairy Bulls; Commonly Referred to as "Herdmate-Daughter Comparison" in the U.S.

A contemporary comparison is the number of pounds by which a bull's daughters exceed or fall below the yield of other heifers by other bulls milked at the same time in the same herd(s).

Tethering Equipment

We were quite impressed with the Taylor Bull Tether, which is in use at this AI center. It was designed by a foundry operator in England. The revolving wheel in the center is equipped with a protruding arm that sticks into the ground and holds it in place. However, it can be turned on its side and used as a wheel when it needs to be moved.

Blackface Highland (Scotch Highland) ewe lambs on Kingoldrum Farm, owned by James G. Findlay, Angus, Scotland. These lambs will be sold for breeding purposes.

The Farm Operated by Jamie E. Gammell

We drove through the "lower farm" that is owned by the Gammell family and managed by James E. Gammell. Jamie gave us the following information pertaining to this operation: Their holdings total 4,000 acres; they have 550 commercial breeding cows and 1,100 breeding sheep—all operated as a commercial enterprise.

Gammell's black-faced sheep.

Border Leicester ram lambs.

"Kingoldrum" Farm, Owned and Operated by James G. Findlay

"Kingoldrum" Farm is owned and operated by an unmistakable Scotsman, Mr. James G. Findlay.

County Award

Recently, Mr. Findlay was the recipient of the county award for the best operated farm in the county. This award is based on quality of stock, land use, and intelligent use of capital.

Blackface Flock

Mr. Findlay has 300 purebred Blackface ewes. He keeps ewes until they are five years of age. He plans on 80 replacement ewe lambs each year.

Border Leicester

Mr. Findlay has a flock of 70 purebred Border Leicester ewes. We saw 17 ram lambs of this breed, dropped in February and March of 1972, that had been prepared for sale. The lambs had been washed, dipped, and colored (with a yellow coloring). Each of these rams was wearing a cloth "blinder," in order

Our travel group on St. Andrews golf course, where golf began. Audrey is on the right, and I am sixth from the right.

to keep them from fighting and possibly breaking their necks.

"West Drums" Farm; Mr. Frank Lightfoot

We visited "West Drums" farm where we were shown about by Mr. Frank Lightfoot.

Acreage and Crops

There are a total of 450 acres in this farm. This year, they had 150 acres of barley, 30 acres of wheat, 30 acres of oats, 30 acres of potatoes, and 8 acres of raspberries.

Angus Herd

The Angus herd was founded in 1948.

Simmental

They have 11 head of Simmental cows. These were purchased in Bavaria (Germany).

St. Andrews

Tonight, we stayed at the historic Old Course Hotel, which is located by the sea and in famed St. Andrews golf course. The first formal golf club was established in Edinburgh, Scotland, in 1744. However, the Royal and Ancient Golf Club of St. Andrews, established 10 years later at Saint Andrews, Scotland, became the official ruling organization of the sport, and ranks as the world's oldest golf club in continuous existence.

Travel to Glasgow

We took a scenic route back to Glasgow, with a stay at Sterling, Scotland, for lunch at the Golden Lion Hotel. Then, we drove to the nearby airport for our flight back to New York City.

1972
THE CHINA WE SAW

In a letter to the China Travel Service dated February 23, 1971—a full year ahead of the historic President Nixon/Secretary of State Kissinger visit to China, February 21–18, 1972—I initiated a request to make a study-tour of China. Then, a "long march" followed, which, 1½ years later, culminated in approval for Mrs. Ensminger and me to visit China, October 5–19, 1972.

China had long used my books; and I had Chinese friends in powerful positions all over China, but we were separated by the bamboo curtain for 23 years. Details of my maneuvers to visit China follow.

Dr. E atop the Great Wall in 1972—the most colossal line of defense in the world. The Great Wall winds serpentine-like over the mountains and through the valleys, never beginning and never ending. Built more than 2,000 years ago by forced labor, it extends over 3,728 miles—greater than the distance from the East Coast to the West Coast of the United States.

Mr. and Mrs. Huang Hua

Through our request to visit China, Mr. and Mrs. Huang Hua and the Ensmingers became old and dear friends.

On our return trip from around the world, we flew to Ottawa, Canada from Italy. We had been invited by the Huang Huas to do so. As we traveled around the world, we read in the newspaper that Mr. Huang Hua had been made Ambassador to the United Nations in New York City. Unfortunately, we already had our tickets and couldn't change our flight. When we arrived in Ottawa, we called the Chinese Embassy, and Mrs. Huang Hua invited us to come for lunch. We were surprised and delighted.

Prior to the luncheon, we sent a dozen beautiful yellow mums to Mrs. Huang, along with the following message:

> It was very gracious of you to invite us for a 12:30 luncheon today at the Chinese Embassy which we accept with pleasure. We are looking forward to meeting and visiting with you.

We had a delightful luncheon including 100-year-old eggs (a Chinese delicacy), and a productive meeting with Mrs. Huang Hua and Mr. Yao Jen-Liu. Mr. Yao is the cultural attaché at the Chinese Embassy. Mrs. Huang Hua told us she will join her husband in New York City next week, where Mr. Huang will be China's Ambassador to the United Nations. In addition to activating the visa request for the Ensmingers to visit China, this marked the beginning of a long and warm friendship between the Huang Huas and the Ensmingers.

On July 16, 1972 the Embassy of the People's Republic of China in Canada responded to our request for Mrs. Ensminger and me to visit China August 22–September 5, 1972.

> We are very glad to inform you that your application to visit China, as well as Mrs. Ensminger's, have been approved.

Mrs. Huang Hua, Dr. E, and Audrey at a luncheon hosted by Mrs. Huang Hua at the Chinese Embassy, Ottawa, Canada.

> It would be much appreciated if you could make this trip from August 22nd until Sept. 5th of this year. Please cable "LUXINGSHE PEKING" (which is China International Travel Service) as soon as possible in confirmation of above date, and informing them of your entry and exit ports (if via Hong Kong, it should be ShumChun). An amount of two hundred seventy-five British sterling pounds should also be remitted to the account of China International Travel Service in Bank of China, Peking.
>
> We are enclosing four copies of application forms to you. Please fill out in duplicate, and mail them back to this office together with your passports, two photographs for each and five dollars of visa fees for each person.

I responded on July 19, 1972 with a request for a change in dates from August 22–September 5 to October 5–19, 1972.

> Accept your invitation to visit your country. But due to commitment to be in North Sea Countries at that time, respectfully request date of our visit be changed to October 5 to 19. Will enter and exit via ShumChun. Two hundred and seventy-five British sterling pounds remitted via cable to account of China International Travel Service in Bank of China, Peking, on this date.

By way of the grapevine, I received word to the effect that the China Academy of Agricultural and Forestry Sciences would like that I conduct a seminar, and that they would have a projector and screen available.

A Dilemma

In a letter dated September 1, 1972, Mr. Yao Jan-Liu, Attaché, Embassy of China in Canada, advised us that our passports were unacceptable because they were stamped showing that we had been in Taiwan in 1971. Thereupon, Audrey and I immediately traveled by car to San Francisco and obtained new passports. On September 13, 1972, our new passports were airmailed to Mr. Yao Jan-Liu in Ottawa, following which he sent visas and returned our passports.

China Synopsis

As indicated, what follows is a **synopsis**. A much more complete story of the China that we saw in 1972 is reported in our book, *China—the impossible dream*.

We didn't go to criticize, for we can find plenty of things in the United States that need rectifying. Rather, we went for the purpose of making an in-depth study of China's agriculture, of its current status and future prospects. Also, we went for the purpose of studying the customs, traditions, and current thinking of the Chinese people, particularly as they may affect the relationships between our two nations in agriculture.

Reliable statistical information in China is hard to come by. Hence, an evaluation based on observation is important.

We Were Prepared For the Worst

The old China was a troubled place characterized by warlords; large and rich landowners and poor peasants; national disunity; civil war; imperialism; unequal treaties; Japanese aggression; ruinous inflation; underproduction; ravages of typhoons, floods, droughts, and locusts; famines, with millions of people starving to death; grinding poverty; disease; illiteracy; child selling; prostitution; callously rapacious rulers; and corruption. The peasant's (farmer's) life was hard, and without hope. What nature didn't destroy, man finished. The tax collector took most of his produce and the warlords and landlords seized the rest. He became a mere laborer, deeply indebted to a rich landlord to whom his life was mortgaged for years ahead. Knowing this background, we were braced for the worst as we peeped through the bamboo curtain.

We visited the cities and surrounding areas of Canton, Shanghai, Soochow, and Peking. We trav-

The four children who escorted Audrey and me through the Children's Palace in Shanghai *left to right):* Wu Xiu-ting, Tang Lan, Dr. E, Cho Li-gao, and Chien Feng.

eled by airplane, train, and car. We visited four communes, where we studied huge agricultural complexes; where we saw their crops, animals, machinery, factories, reservoirs, irrigation, and drainage systems; and where we visited in peasants' homes. We saw the Great Wall, museums, palaces, and exhibitions. We visited their stores and shops. We went into a hospital where we witnessed their amazing acupuncture anesthesia used in major surgery, and we visited with their doctors and "barefoot" doctors. We visited a Children's Palace and a kindergarten. We visited Peking University, and their agricultural research stations and institutes. We visited with people in all walks of life. We spent a full day with the top scientists of the China Academy of Agricultural and Forestry Sciences, before whom I gave an invitational lecture, and with whom I exchanged ideas in a spirited question/answer session—the first such lecture-seminar conducted by an American agriculturalist in China for 25 years.

We liked what we saw! We saw history in the making. We saw a sleeping giant of a country coming awake. We saw a new China emerging. We saw a nation of 750 million people that is fairly well fed, with neither hunger nor famine stalking across the land, and that is adequately clothed and reasonably well housed; this within itself is no small accomplishment. And we didn't see one beggar or one drunk. We saw a nation with compulsory education for all, beginning at age seven; we saw illiteracy disappearing with the passing of the older generation. We saw people who are getting more and more of the good things of life, all because they are willing to work. We saw a relatively prosperous people. We saw a united, confident country. We saw clean cities; we saw tree-lined roadsides and boulevards; we saw peasants joined together in well-managed and prosperous communes that are automating, and doing more and more irrigating and flood control work; we saw a nation that is on the way to industrialization; we saw hardworking people, with full employment, pulling together to improve their lot in life; we saw the most enthusiastic population that we have seen in any of the 40 countries that we have visited in the past six years. We saw a country that is well on the way to becoming a leader among nations. And our hosts were wonderful! We were particularly grateful to our guides/interpreters of China International Travel Service, who were able professionals and great people to know: Mrs. Ke An-Lin, Mr. Lee-yao, Mr. Yu Shih-teh, and Mr. Yen Chao-hua.

China recognizes that it has a long way to go. Per capita income is low, and there are few luxuries. But remember that only 23 years have elapsed since China's liberation, whereas nearly 200 years have transpired since we gained our independence.

I predict a bright future for China in the years ahead. Also, we can learn from each other. For example, acupuncture anesthesia is undeniably a successful medical technique for both humans and ani-

The Ensmingers with a few of the 2,200 staff members at Peking University. *Front row, left to right:* Audrey Ensminger; Dr. Tsung Hsun-tsao, who completed a doctorate degree at the University of Wisconsin in 1948; Dr. E; and Prof. Chen An-mei, who completed a B.S. degree at the University of Illinois in 1953. Both of the U.S.-trained staff members are now in the Biology Department of Peking University.

mals. And we may have much to learn from the Chinese about the role of science and technology in society. Indeed, there is much to be gained from opening the door wider between the two nations.

Chinese Agriculture

Farming is the backbone of China. Providing food, clothing, and shelter for people—now 750 million, and still growing—is an awesome task.

Chinese agriculture is characterized primarily by its intensity. Every inch of arable land is cultivated; and every slope is terraced and producing plants or trees. Where the weather permits, three to four crops are grown per year. This is made possible only by the unremitting labor which the struggle for existence demands and the traditional skill of the Chinese born of 40 centuries of experience. Straw-hatted peasants, working in groups, bend over the never-ending task of seeding, cultivating and harvesting—spreading the night soil, transplanting rice seedlings, weeding the corn, hoeing the vegetables, and scything the ripe grain at harvest. The Chinese peasant is the hardest working person in the world.

Automation is coming in, but it will take time. In the south of China, roughage-burning water buffalo that have not taken a hurried step for 20 centuries pull the farm implements. In the north, power is by horse, donkey or mule, and bullock—sometimes all three in combination.

Farming is held in high esteem. In the days of the empire it was the custom each year for the emperor to open the agricultural season by turning a furrow and sowing some seed.

In southern China, we saw water buffalo that have not taken a hurried step for 20 centuries pulling plows.

The land of China has been cultivated for thousands of years, yet its fertility is not exhausted for two reasons: the hills and slopes are terraced and rimmed, thereby conserving the soil and water; and night soil (human waste), and every other kind of manure, is applied to the land in primitive, but effective, fashion. Even today, many of the smaller cities and communes have no sewage system. In the early morning hours, before dawn, the farmers' boats enter the canals of the city and glide here and there, collecting the refuse of every sort for fertilizer purposes. In the larger cities, night soil is treated to control disease, and, in some cases, transported to rural areas.

Arable Land; Kind of Crops

The majority of China is either too dry, too hilly, or too cold for farming. Only 11% of the area is cultivated. But this 11% is the land of rice and fish. It's fertile, blessed with a good climate, and 40% to 50% of it is under irrigation.

Subsistence crops come first. Rice alone occupies an estimated 28% of the cultivated land, and has first choice of the soil. Wheat ranks second to rice and replaces it as a food crop in north China; in some areas, it occupies 40% of the land. Today, there is about as much corn (maize) as wheat in China. Millet and sorghum (kaoliang) are more widely distributed than wheat and corn, but they occupy a smaller acreage.

Tea has long been the chief beverage of China. Since the 8th century A.D., its cultivation has been a great agricultural industry.

Of course, China's most far-famed and ancient industry is the production of raw silk from silkworms, for which it enjoys many advantages: Two or more leafings of mulberries per year, and abundant, cheap, and skilled labor in manipulating cocoons and weaving.

The most remarkable development in China during recent years has been the rapid growth of the bean industry. Beans are staple food. Their high food value and cheapness make them an effective substitute for milk, meat, or grains. They now rank next in importance to rice, wheat, corn, and millet.

Cotton is important as an industrial crop. The Yangtze Valley is their main cotton area, and Shanghai is their great textile center.

Other important Chinese crops are: soybeans, ramie (a fiber crop), tobacco, barley, buckwheat, peanuts, sugarcane, many kinds of vegetables, and a great variety of medicinal plants and spices.

China's Livestock Industry

The chief role of the livestock industry is to provide draft power for the fields, transportation on the roads, and manure for the crops.

Swine, poultry, and goats, which can subsist on byproducts and live in the farmyards, are kept in large numbers. China ranks first in world swine numbers, with an estimated 275,000,000 head (vs 63,000,000 in the U.S.). Moreover, the People's Republic of China has set a goal of "one pig per person" on the communes. Think of it! That would mean 600 million hogs—as many hogs as there are in all the rest of the world put together. Even if China's swine numbers stabilize at 300 million, that's a lot of hogs. It would increase the animal protein in the diet, provide pork for export, and produce more manure. One commune chairman pointed up the importance of pigs for manure production by putting it this way: "The more pigs we produce, the more manure we shall have to put back on the land."

Communes and Incalculable Human Toil

The whole countryside has been transformed. The communes have replaced the patchwork of little farms and made the land into larger and more efficient fields and units. By incalculable human toil, dams have been built and water impounded for irrigation, flood control and generating electricity; canals have been dug, dikes have been heightened and widened, land has been drained and reclaimed, telephone and power lines have been constructed, and pumps have been installed.

I Gave an Invitational Lecture Before the China Academy of Agricultural and Forestry Sciences

Upon my arrival in Peking, I was formally invited (although I had received informal notice via the grapevine much earlier) by the China Academy of Agricultural and Forestry Sciences to deliver a lecture and conduct a seminar before the leading agricultural scientists of China. I accepted, fully cognizant of my responsibility, for this was the first lecture given in China by an American agriculturalist in 25 years.

My lecture/seminar was scheduled for Monday, October 15. I was apprehensive about the meeting room, the projector, and the screen. So, I asked to see the facilities the day before my scheduled lecture. The ever polite Chinese friends happily accommodated us. On Sunday, October 14 (the day before the lecture/seminar), they drove Mrs. Ensminger and me to the Cultural Palace for Nationality to see the facilities and equipment. The meeting room was adequate in size, but it had many, many, windows, all without shades or draperies with which to darken the room for presentation of slides. So, I suggested that they cover the windows with brown paper, to which they happily agreed. The little projector, which was sitting on the floor in the middle of the room, was a hand-operated, wood-shuttle machine similar to what we used at the turn of the century. I assured them that it would be just fine, but I suggested that it would be easier for Mrs. Ensminger to operate it if it were placed on a table; they happily agreed. The screen was a sheet on the wall. These facilities and equipment were the best that they had; so, they were good enough for us.

On Monday, October 15, the meeting got underway at 9:00 a.m., and lasted until 5:00 p.m. The program consisted of the following in order of presentation: my questions asked of them, my illustrated lecture, and their questions asked of me.

My illustrated lecture was on the subject, "The U.S. Livestock Industry—a panoramic view." By using a booklet by this title, which I had prepared in advance of my visit, along with 88 slides portraying

The Cultural Palace for Nationality

the U.S. livestock industry, it minimized the language barrier.

In my introductory remarks, I paid tribute to China as follows: "You helped make us what we are. You gave us, and the world, Peking ducks, Cochin chickens, azaleas and rhododendrons, peaches, and oranges. You Chinese were the first to use gunpowder, paper, silk, movable blocks for printing, and the magnetic needle. You gave the world exquisite paintings, superb porcelain, graceful statues, and profound systems of thought. Your silks and embroideries are marvels.

My lecture, which had to be interpreted, took 1½ hours. Then, the balance of the day was devoted to a question-answer session, with a free and spirited exchange between us. At 5:30 p.m., the session didn't really end; I invited them to come to the United States in order that we might continue it. My evaluation: It was a distinguished, scholarly, and stimulating group. We learned from each other.

At the China Academy of Agricultural and Forestry Services, I was particularly pleased to meet many of China's leading animal scientists, whose works I had known; among them: Prof. Dr. Cheng Pi Liu, who took his doctorate at the University of Wisconsin under Dr. L. E. Casida with whom I shared a bachelor's apartment when we were students at the University of Missouri. I reported some of Dr. Cheng's research in the first edition of *Horses and Horsemanship* in 1951; and Prof., Dr. C. H. Liu, who took his Ph.D. at Cornell University; and Prof. Dr. L. R. Qin, Department of Animal Husbandry and Veterinary Medicine, Huazhong Agricultural College, Wuhan; a brother-in-law of Dr. T. C. Huang, who took his doctorate under me at Washington State University.

The next evening, the academy members and the China International Travel Service, jointly, hosted a dinner at which Mrs. Ensminger and I were the guests of honor.

Peking University

We visited Peking University which was founded in 1898. Today, the university has an enrollment of 4,300 students. It has what our hosts referred to as a

Part of the members of the China Academy of Agricultural and Forestry Sciences before whom Dr. E gave an invited lecture on October 15, 1972; and with whom a spirited exchange of ideas and questions-answers was conducted the rest of the day. Professor Chin Shan-pao, leading member of the academy, is standing between Dr. and Mrs. Ensminger. On Dr. E's right is Professor Cheng Pi-liu, member of the academy, and on Mrs. Ensminger's left is Mr. Yue Dai-hun, leading member of the head office, China International Travel Service. The next evening, the academy and China International Travel Service co-hosted a dinner at the famous Peking Rose Duck Restaurant, with the Ensmingers as guests of honor.

"new look in education, which is still in the experimental stage."

The two main objectives of the Peking University program are to obliterate the former ivory tower concept of the university—that the university is a means of escaping from the life of the worker; and to promulgate courses that will make for expertise in the production line—that will permit, and even require, that the students return to the communes and factories.

Acupuncture Anesthesia

Acupuncture (the placing of needles in the body) is another treatment and method of anesthesia for both people and animals. As a general painkiller, it has a history in China going back 2,000 years. Since 1958 it has been used as anesthesia in 500,000 operations in China, including 30 involving open heart surgery. Moreover, we were advised that it works very well as anesthesia for horses and cattle; in fact, a new motion picture of horse acupuncture anesthesia is soon to be released. Hence, Mrs. Ensminger and I were delighted to be invited to famed Wha-Shan Hospital, in Shanghai, where we saw and photographed this amazing technique used as anesthesia on two different patients; one for the removal of a brain tumor, and the other for removal of a thyroid tumor.

Chairman Mao and Premier Chou

No discussion of modern China would be complete without recognition of the present leaders of China—Chairman Mao Tse-tung and Premier Chou En-lai.

Chairman Mao is revered. He's a legend in his own time. He's the "savior" of the masses—especially the 600,000,000 peasants. He delivered them from the bondage of the landlords; he gave them security—assurance of work, food, clothing and shelter; and he provided them free medical service and education. No one has ever done so much for so many.

No Chinese other than Mao is ever pictured in public. He shares history only with Marx, Engels, Lenin, and Stalin. In each square or building, Mao and his quotes are accorded the "center stage."

Premier Chou is the sophisticated government chief, an able administrator, and the person responsible for setting China on a more moderate course.

Warm Welcome; Convey Greetings

At each of our stops—communes, factories, the Children's Palace, the hospital, the Chinese Academy of Agricultural and Forestry Sciences—we were warmly welcomed by words, actions, and/or signs; and in a very deep and sincere way, they asked us to convey their greetings to the American people.

Literacy

In the old China, not more than 10% of the people could read and write. Today, education is compulsory, beginning at age seven—and it's free. Hence, there is practically no illiteracy among the younger generation of China.

"To Each According to His Work; from Each According to His Ability"

This phrase was echoed over and over on the communes, as the basic philosophy back of the point system and wage scale. Although the Chinese system calls for equal pay for all, and no incentives, in practice there are both salary differentials and incentives on the communes based on work points; although both are infinitesimal in comparison with ours.

"Barefoot" Doctors

These practitioners bridge the gap between the masses and the limited number of medical doctors. In many of the remote areas of China, they are the only medical aides.

"Barefoot" doctors usually have three to four months' hospital training—particularly in acupuncture, herb treatment, and some western medicines. They dispense birth control pills, prescribe for such minor ailments as headaches, and conduct campaigns in health care. Also, they decide whether a patient needs higher medical treatment at a clinic or hospital.

United States-China Agricultural Trade

China is fast moving into the economic world, to play a role that they believe the nation's status deserves and her interests require. It is rapidly developing the necessary sophisticated technology to make it fully capable of competing with other nations of the world; and its cheap and abundant labor places it in a good position to enter the world market.

China—the impossible dream

Mrs. Ensminger and I not only made history, we became a part of it when we visited China in 1972. Our book, *China—the impossible dream*—311 pages, hardback, 300 pictures, 85 of them in color—is recognized as one of the most accurate works ever, in pictures and words, of the old China. In recognition of this fact, the University of Michigan, at Ann Arbor, requested that the original documents and records that we collected in 1972, out of which evolved *China—the impossible dream*, be preserved for scholars and posterity in their National Archives on Sino-American Relations, Center for Chinese Studies. We were pleased and honored to comply.

Following are what has been said about *China—the impossible dream*:

Mrs. Huang Hua, China Consul
United Nations
New York City

It is very delightful and well written; I like it. The pictures are wonderful. It will help relationships between our countries. You are to be commended.

President Richard Nixon
The White House
Washington

This is to express my thanks for the copy of your new book, *China—the impossible dream*. I deeply appreciate the thoughtful interest which prompted you to remember me with this account of your visit to the People's Republic of China. Cooperation is the tie that binds people together. It is my hope that efforts like yours will lead to the peace and progress that all of us seek.

Mrs. Nixon joins me in sending best wishes to you.

Henry A. Kissinger
Secretary Of State

Thank you for your book, *China—the impossible dream*. It is a beautiful work and certainly a tribute to the People's Republic of China and to the scientific and cultural exchange between our two countries. I appreciate your thoughtfulness in sending me an early copy.

With warm regards and best wishes for the success of your book.

Earl L. Butz
U.S. Department of Agriculture

What a beautiful book you have written! The printing and typography are appealing to the eye; the text is understandable; and the subject matter treatment is a joy to read.

Mary Emma and I will enjoy *China—the impossible dream*, not only once, but time and time again in the years ahead.

Thank you so much for your thoughtful gift. It will become a treasured part of the Butz library.

Bing Crosby

Thank you for sending me the book, *China—the impossible dream*.

China has always been a tremendously in-

Left to right: Mrs. Huang Hua, Dr. E., Audrey Ensminger, and Mr. Huang Hua. This photo was taken in the Biltmore Hotel in Los Angeles, in 1991. The Huang Huas and the Ensmingers are longtime warm friends.

Dr. E in front of the Chen Hai Tower Museum (the five-story building), Canton. An-Lin, our head guide, is on the left.

teresting country to me—as it must be to everybody who has an interest in the future, because China is going to be a considerable part of that future.

Very best wishes to you and Audrey.

Audrey among the lotus. Photo taken en route to the Seven Star Cliffs. The lotus, which has a huge leaf and a big flower, grows in water. The root is used for human food.

Straw-hatted Ensmingers with Chinese guides at the Seven Star Cliffs, a beautiful resort area, October 6, 1972.

The Canton Area/Kwang Li People's Commune

Dr. E presented a copy of his book, *Swine Science,* to Mr. Lian Wei-wen, Vice Chairman of the Revolutionary Committee, Kwang Li People's Commune, Kaw Yao County, Kwang Tung Province, a 61,496-acre commune, on which there are 13,700 workers. The vice chairman is 42 years of age, married, and the father of four children.

A hog-fish combination on Kwang Li People's Commune, Kaw Yao County, Kwang Tung Province, where, in 1971, they produced 49,700 pigs and had a fish catch of 863,000 pounds. The fish are fed entirely, and solely, on pig manure flushed from the hog barns directly into the fishponds, plus grass clippings from the pond banks. Hence, they have solved their own pig manure pollution control, and, at the same time, recycled and used the feed twice—first through hogs, and second through fish.

Brood sows on Kwang Li Commune. Dr. E, who is shown inspecting them, described these hogs as "very similar to our Chester Whites in the United States." In China, hogs are fed minerals (bone meal and ground sea shells), but no synthetic vitamins.

Dr. E met with the Kwang Li Commune leaders in 1972.

Dr. M. E. Ensminger and Chen Tung Shen, chief veterinarian on Kwang Li People's Commune, Kaw Yao County, Kwang Tung Province. Translated, the following statement by Chairman Mao appears on the side of the building: "A national economy without animal husbandry is incomplete."

The Ensmingers receiving a Buddha Hand at the Kwang Li Commune in 1972.

The Ping Chou People's Commune

Mr. Chen Yun kwang, Vice Chairman of the Revolutionary Committee, Ping Chou People's Commune, Kwang Tung Province, shows Dr. E their method of handling liquid nitrogen fertilizer in jars, with each jar holding 66 lb of fertilizer.

Herbs are used extensively in both human and animal medication. Adjacent to this hog barn, on either side of the narrow road, are some of the herbs grown on Ping Chou People's Commune, Kwang Tung Province, for use in their swine health program. Dr. E was shown the herbs by the veterinary staff.

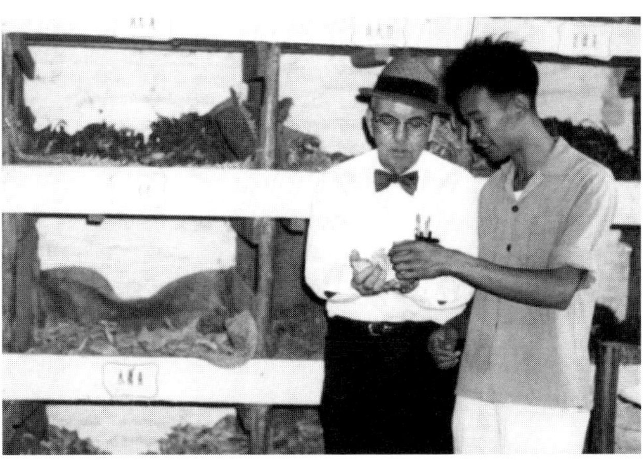

The dried herb room on Ping Chou People's Commune, Kwang Tung Province, showing different dried herbs in labeled bins. Mr. Kao Ka-yia (right), head of the veterinary staff of the commune, showed Dr. E a special dried herb called "Mu-I-Chun," which, to the uninformed, looked like yellow wood chips.

Herb processing room on Ping Chou People's Commune, Kwang Tung Province. Most of the woody herbs are boiled in water to prepare the liquid herb medicine. The veterinary staff showed Dr. E how it is done.

Dr. E, who followed a "footburner" as a boy on a Missouri farm, tried his hand with a one-handled stick-plow pulled by a water buffalo. This was on the Ping Chou People's Commune.

Dr. E at the Ping Chou People's Commune shop in 1972.

The Shanghai Area/Shu-hong People's Commune

Upon arrival at Shu-hong People's Commune, near Shanghai, Dr. E presented a copy of his book, *Animal Science,* to Mr. Cheng Ping-Shi, Vice Chairman of the Revolutionary Committee. The sign to the right reads: "Warmly welcome American friends."

Dr. E inspecting cotton on Shu-hong People's Commune, near Shanghai.

Dr. E inspecting threshing machines on Shu-hong People's Commune, near Shanghai.

The Peking Area/Sino-Albanian Friendship People's Commune

At the Sino-Albanian Friendship People's Commune, near Peking, Dr. E presented a copy of his book, *Swine Science,* to Mr. Chen Chao, Vice Chairman of the Revolutionary Committee (second from left). The sign in back reads: "Our friends are all over the world."

Ox-drawn cartload of manure, which had been hauled to this field. Dr. E is standing to the back of the cart.

A Russian-bred stallion on Sino-Albanian Friendship People's Commune, near Peking. He's a sorrel with flaxen mane and tail. This stallion is on the small side (about 14-2 hands) and chunky (cobby).

1973
THE AFRICA WE SAW

This was an in-depth study-tour, accompanied by 29 delegates, of Ethiopia, Tanzania, Kenya, South Africa, and Rhodesia, during which I also conducted seminars. A record of what we saw, did, and learned, country by country, follows.

Rome was not a primary stop as such. But because it was necessary to pass through it en route to Africa, we took advantage of the opportunity to see the city. Known as the "Eternal City," Rome is for many reasons among the most interesting of the world's cities. It was the capital of the ancient Roman Republic and of the Roman Empire. Very early, it became the headquarters of the Christian church. Today, it stands as one of the greatest cities of romance and power, and as the center of the Roman Catholic Church, the holy city toward which the eyes and thoughts of millions of people are directed.

We had a gala dinner at the Tempio Di Giove, a famous restaurant. Following dinner, Dr. R. L. (Berk) Berkenkamp, Agricultural Attaché, American Embassy, Rome, Italy, addressed our group. He told about the agriculture of Italy, and about the imports of meat and animals from the United States.

Dr. Ugo Galassi also addressed our group. He told of his farm, Aimonetta, near Alexandra, Italy, for which I served as consultant for many years.

Please note that we could not visit the countries in order from north to south. We had to visit South Africa before Rhodesia because South Africa did not allow anyone with a visa stamped by Rhodesia into the country.

Dr. E visiting with three blind law students at Haile Selassie I University. The university is located in Addis Ababa, not far from the center of the city. At the time of our visit, it had an enrollment of 4,500 students plus an extension enrollment of 1,500.

The Ethiopia We Saw

Ethiopia is a constitutional monarchy derived from a number of earlier kingdoms. Emperor Haile Salassie I was crowned November 2, 1930.

Ethiopia is about the size of Texas, Oklahoma, and New Mexico.

Gala Dinner at the Hilton Hotel

Our guests of honor were: Mr. Charles A. Tem-

Dr. E examining a sheep at a market on the outskirts of Addis Ababa. The sheep market was a place where sheep for sale were displayed in little groups along the roadside. It was a place where buyers and sellers of sheep met.

Dr. E is presenting one of his books to Mr. Charles A. Temple, Plant Production and Protection Advisor, Agency for International Development, Addis Ababa. The occasion was our gala dinner at the Hilton Hotel.

ple, Plant Production and Protection Advisor, Agency for International Development, Addis Ababa; Dr. Taye Bezuneh, Director, Agricultural Experiment Station, Debre Zeit; and Mr. Kevork Sevadjian, Addis Ababa. Greetings were extended by each of our three distinguished guests, but there were no speeches.

Visit to the Ethiopian Spice Extraction Share Company

We were briefed upon and shown this spice extraction plant by Dr. Seleshe Kebede, Deputy Manager, who has his doctorate degree from Michigan State University. The Ethiopian red chili is their main product. It is used in the United States for coloring and flavoring meats and other food products. Other products that are processed throughout the year are black pepper, turmeric, ground pepper, and paprika. In 1972, the plant produced 3,000 tons of extract, enough to change the taste of an entire nation (the U.S.), plus a sneeze for all those who come near the plant.

Vineyard Owned By Dimitri Varelas

Mr. Varelas was born in Greece. His vineyard consists of 34.6 acres, on which he produces both wine and table grapes. They have a bird problem, which they control by stationing two men on a raised platform about 20 to 25 ft high, who frighten the birds away by cracking a blacksnake whip.

Dr. Seleshe Kebede *(left)*, Deputy Manager, the Ethiopian Spice Extraction Share Company, is telling about the spice extraction plant and Dr. E is taking notes.

Agricultural Experiment Station at Debre Zeit

Dr. Taye Bezuneh, director of the station, showed us about. Dr. Bu also mentioned that my book, *Animal Science*, is used as a textbook at the University of Ethiopia from which he graduated.

The experiment station is a branch of Haile Salassie I University. The staff consists of 10 professionals and 40 supporting staff. The sections of the station are: animal science, agronomy, horticulture,

Barkas heifer at the Agricultural Experiment Station at Debre Zeit, Ethiopia. The Barkas breed is native to northern Ethiopia. The people, left to right: Mr. Goshu, who is in charge of the dairy program at the experiment station; Dr. Taye Bezuneh, Director of the Station; Dr. E; and Mr. Kevork Sevadjian, prominent farmer and businessman of Addis Ababa.

agricultural economics, agricultural engineering, and farm management. The station embraces 200 acres.

Fairfield Farm, Owned By Haile Salassie I, Emperor of Ethiopia

Privately, I was informed that the Ethiopians never refer to this farm as owned by the emperor, for reasons that I did not understand. Instead the natives refer to it as "Minister of Palace." Mr. Alfred H. Borwick, who showed us about, gave us the following information about the farm: size, 99 acres; number of animals, 235; breed, grade Holsteins; milking, by hand two times daily, with each milker milking 15 cows.

California-Ethiopia Co. Farm

Presently, this farm is owned by a group of American investors. At the time of our visit, there were 2,000 pigs on the farm, of the Large White (Yorkshire) breed.

Adami Tulu Cattle Livestock Station (Abernosa Ranches)

This is a beef farm operated under the Ministry of Agriculture, which means that Emperor Haile Selassie I owns it. It was established in 1958. They experiment with crosses of native Borona cattle and European breeds, and distribute improved strains to farmers. The following information was given to us about the Tulu Station: Size, 5,928 acres; breeds, primarily Borona and Borona X Holstein crosses.

Teff Threshing

Teff is an important cereal grain of Ethiopia. When ripe, the grain is harvested by small hand sickles and threshed by treading with cattle. We saw a dozen oxen being driven round and round, threshing teff. The straw was thrown into the air by means of a wooden-tined fork to separate the grain from the straw. Following threshing, women grind the grain on flat stones to make flour, which is baked into large, flat pancakes called injara.

Threshing teff in Ethiopia by treading with oxen driven round and round.

Awassa Agro-Industrial Share Co., Awassa, Sidame

This is a government station located 171 miles south of Addis Ababa. Its purposes: advancement of agricultural research, help the people of the area, and create jobs. The complex embraces 24,700 acres. They grow corn, peppers, beans, sunflowers, tomatoes, rapeseed, and sisal.

The station grows 4,446 acres of sisal. The sisal is processed by the station's own sisal factory.

The people on the station possess a missionary zeal—and with reason. They are most proud that they have created jobs and improved crop production, and that they are not subsidized by the government. They stated their philosophy as follows:

> Give a man a fish, and he will eat it at once. Teach him to fish, and he will eat fish his whole life.

Sisal growing on the Awassa Agro-Industrial Share Co., Awassa, Ethiopia, about 170 miles south of Addis Ababa. Dr. E is nearest, and with his back to, the camera—taking notes.

Tukul House

We visited the Tukul House of an African family, consisting of a man and wife and three children. Also, animals were kept therein, in a stall. Both people and animals ate and slept in the Tukul House. Tukul houses are round, built of eucalyptus framing covered with grass, and lighted by a gas lamp.

Coffee

Ethiopia is the only country in the world where wild coffee grows in profusion. Most of the nation's coffee is picked from bushes growing in forests.

Men with Spears

The spears carried by the men are used to ward off jackals, monkeys, baboons, and foreign people.

The Tanzania We Saw

Tanzania is slightly larger than Texas and Oklahoma combined. Almost two-thirds of the country has virtually no agriculture because of tsetse fly infestation and lack of water. It produces the bulk of the world's supply of cloves and olive oil.

Tanzania has majestic snow-capped Mt. Kilimanjaro, tallest in Africa, in the north. Nearby are the famed Serengeti Plains, teeming with vast herds of wild animals. Safaris, sport fishing, and mountain climbing are among the attractions.

Arusha

This was formerly a trading post. Today, it is the safari capital of northern Tanzania. Arusha is a colorful town with blue flowering jacarandas, poinsettias, banks of canna lilies, and avenues of scarlet African flame trees. On bustling market days, the local farmers and picturesque Masai crowd into town. The nomadic Masai raise large herds of cattle, sheep, and goats; and their womenfolk make beautiful beadwork for sale in Arusha.

Research and Training Institute

This morning, we visited the Research and Training Institute, where we were briefed upon, and taken on a guided tour of, the institute by Dr. B. Simon, the director. Dr. Simon has a Ph.D. degree from the University of London.

In addition to conducting research, the institute has a one-year training program.

At the Research and Training Institute, Moshi, Tanzania. *Left to right:* Mr. I. S. Tema, farm manager of the institute; Dr. E; and Dr. B. Simon, director of the institute. In the background is a planting of 25 types of bananas. (They do not call them varieties until they are released.)

Dr. E making notes relative to a field of wheat at the Research and Training Institute.

The institute has 616 acres. Research is conducted on the following crops: coffee, bananas, wheat, cardamon (spice), and citrus. Coffee is the farmer's most profitable crop.

Small herds of Jersey and Red Poll cattle are maintained at the institute.

The Tanganyika Coffee Curing Co., Ltd.

We visited this interesting coffee processing company. We were taken on a guided tour of the plant by Mr. E. A. Kyendesya, the manager, who is trained as an engineer. The plant has been nationalized, which means that it is government owned and operated.

Gala Dinner

We had a gala dinner in Arusha. Following dinner, Mr. Warren C. Putnam, Project Coordinator, Masai Range Project, addressed our group. Mr. Putnam is an employee of the Tanzanian Government. He is a graduate of Rutgers University in New Jersey.

Mr. Putnam is working with the Masai. He is establishing ranching associations of about 400,000 acres each. They now have eight such ranching associations.

The biggest problem is to get the Masais to market their cattle; to them, cattle are like money in the bank. They never feed salt or other minerals. Water is difficult to come by, so cattle frequently go without water for three days. When they do water, the well disciplined cattle come up orderly—if there is a small trough, for example, they may come to the trough by fives; as each group of five is filled, they drop back and a new group comes forward.

They are getting dipping vats and dams constructed. In the future, they hope to set up marketing associations. At first the Masai resisted, but they are now accepting vats.

More cattle watering areas are sorely needed as a means of distributing cattle and avoiding overgrazing.

George Damm, G & J Farming, Ltd., Arusha

Mr. George Damm is, without doubt, the most progressive agriculturalist in Tanzania. It was our pleasure to visit his farm, and to learn about his program. He and his secretary, Ms. W. Kotschy, served refreshments in the attractive home upon our arrival, following which Mr. Damm took us over the farm. Pertinent information relative to Mr. Damm and the farm follows:

Mr. Damm is of German descent, married, and has four children. Mrs. Damm and the children were in England at the time of our visit.

George Damm *(right)*, G & J Damm Farming, Arusha, Tanzania, showing Dr. E a herd of Manyara Zebu cattle, a breed that Mr. Damm developed.

Mr. Damm has lived in eight different countries. Tanzania is the nation of his choice.

When I asked about the possibility that his farm might be expropriated (taken over) by the government and nationalized, he replied: "The only security is the grave!" Then, thoughtfully, he added, "If my farm is expropriated, I'll have it back two days later" (obviously alluding to his government connections).

Six months after our visit, I received the following shocking news: George Damm's farm was expropriated, along with his great cattle herds and sheep flocks, without any chance to get it back. He was found in bed, beheaded by someone who was very good at it.

Lake Manyara National Park

Following the visit to the George Damm farm, we drove to the Lake Manyara Hotel, where we had lunch. Thence, we visited the Lake Manyara National Park.

This park of 123 sq. mi. is 75 mi. southwest of Arusha. It is chiefly noted for its breeding herds of elephant, large numbers of buffalo, the famous tree-climbing lion, impala, giraffe, zebra, bushbuck, reedbuck, yellow and olive baboon, the handsome blue monkey, the mischievous little black-faced vervet monkey, and occasionally rhino and leopard.

The forest trees include wild fig, wild mango, tamarind, many species of acacia, wild date palm, the strange "sausage" tree, and the grotesque thick-trunked baobab, which looks as if it has been planted upside down.

Amboseli Game Reserve

This famous Masai owned and managed reserve, covering 1,259 sq. mi. borders Tanzania and Kilimanjaro, Africa's highest mountain. The reserve takes its name from Lake Amboseli.

Amboseli is probably the best area in Kenya to see large herds of elephant, buffalo, zebra, wildebeest, hartebeest, impala, and gazelle. Rhino, oryx, eland, giraffe, waterbuck and the delicate long-necked gerenuk live alongside the predators—lion, cheetah, hyena, jackal, and occasionally the African hunting dog.

Bird life is abundant and includes water birds and migratory species. Ostriches, bustard, plover, and sandgrouse are found on the plains, and birds of prey include eagle, buzzards, hawks, and vultures. The black ground hornbill is often seen in the acacia woodland. Near the lodge, there are colorful African hoopoe, iridescent blue green starlings, brilliant yellow weaver birds, the tiny red-cheeked cordon bleu, and African firefinch.

Amboseli is dominated by the snow-covered dome of Kilimanjaro, soaring majestically into the sky from the dusty plains below.

Why Patrick Can't Get Married

Patrick, one of our bus drivers, has a girlfriend. Patrick's last name is Gathogo. He's a member of the Kukuyu tribe; and he's 27 years of age. But Patrick cannot get married until he collects a dowry that the father demands. The future father-in-law is willing, however, to go along on the basis of half of the "bounty" now, with the other half paid on an installment plan. Even with a credit arrangement of 50%, it will take Patrick several years to accumulate so much wealth. His salary is only U.S. $66.66 per month, and living costs are high. Income tax takes U.S. $8.30 per month, room another U.S. $8.30, and it costs U.S. $5.83 for a shirt. Then, there is the ever present hazard that another man may come up with the dowry in the meantime, and that the girl's father may accept it.

Levi McKee of Amity, Oregon, member of the study-tour group, counseled Patrick, native of Kenya and one of our bus drivers, about his marriage problem.

Such marriage stipulations serve to control population increases because it makes for late marriages, simply because it may take ten years, or more, for a young man to accumulate sufficient wealth. They also help to control the economy of the nation by concentrating wealth in the hands of those who have many daughters, and making for hording until the necessary loot is collected.

Patrick's Agriservices Foundation bus group gave him a new bicycle. So, henceforth he can go courting in style, without walking. Likewise, Patrick's brother, Joseph, was presented a new bicycle by his Agriservices Foundation bus group.

The Kenya We Saw

Kenya is about twice the size of New Mexico; religion—38% pagan (or no religious belief), 37% Protestant, 22% Roman Catholic, and 3% Muslim; main products—coffee, tea, cereals, cotton, sisal, dairy products, hides and skins, bark extract, timber, and minerals. Kenya is the world's largest producer of pyrethrum, a flower containing a natural insecticide, of which it supplies about one-half the world's output. Wild animals abound, especially elephants, lions, hippos, rhinos, giraffes, zebras, gazelles, leopards, antelopes, hyenas, and baboons, plus a great number of strange birds.

National Museum

We were particularly interested in the archaeological finds made in East Africa showing the earliest history of mankind. The find at East Rudolf in 1972 was written up in *Time* magazine last year. Ms. Silvester, a museum guide, narrated this story. Also, she told about the Animal Husbandry section.

From the museum's animal husbandry collection, we obtained the following information pertaining to the Masai tribe: Blood is a remedy for dysentery of the Masai. They shoot a blocked arrow into the jugular vein. Cattle can be bled once in about every two weeks. The Masai rarely eat meat. Blood is usually mixed with milk and drunk. Masai decorated milk gourds are washed out with cow's urine (a practice attributed to the scarcity of water) and fumigated with smoke. Sheep are fat-tailed or fat-rumped hair sheep (with little wool).

Gala Dinner, With Invited Guests, in Nairobi

Following the dinner, three of our distinguished guests addressed our group and answered questions; namely, Dr. Theodore R. Freeman, Agricultural Attaché, American Embassy, Nairobi; Prof. Dr. G. M. Mugera, Dean, Faculty of Veterinary Science, University of Nairobi; and Mr. Humphrey R. Were, Senior Animal Husbandry Research Officer, Ministry of Agriculture, Nairobi.

Leading Tribes of Kenya

The Kikuyu make up the largest tribe, with the Luo and Luhya nearly tied for a close second; but the Masai are the most colorful.

National Parks

A large part of the land area, about 5.7 million acres, has been set aside for national parks.

Farms

Out of the 1,047,000 farms in Kenya, only about

Dean G. M. Mugera, faculty of Veterinary Science, University of Nairobi; Mr. Humphrey R. Were, Senior Animal Husbandry Research Officer, Ministry of Agriculture, Nairobi; Dr. Theodore R. Freeman, Agricultural Attaché, American Embassy, Nairobi; and Dr. E.

5,000 have 20 acres or more, while more than two-thirds consist of 5 acres or less. Most of the coffee, tea, sisal, pineapples, wheat, and barley are grown on large farms, while small farms produce the bulk of the corn, pyrethrum (used in insecticides), and various vegetables. Corn is the principal crop grown on the small subsistence farms, totalling some 1.6 million acres. It is also the basic food for about 96% of the African population.

Livestock

Livestock constitute a very significant part of the agricultural sector. Cattle numbers range around 9.3 million head, while sheep and goat numbers are only slightly less, with about 8.0 million head each. The hog population is relatively small.

Nakuru Bird Sanctuary

Nakuru is known as the farming capital of Kenya. But the feature of Nakuru which has made it world famous is its alkaline lake and flamingos. The alkaline lake is ideal for the growth of minute plants know as algae. It is the algae that attract to Nakuru the incredible number of flamingos which make the lake edge such an awe-inspiring sight.

The flamingos form an incredible band of pink, many yards across, along the lakeshore. They feed on the algae that abound in these mineral-rich waters.

Report on the Cattle Feedlot Near Lanet

Michael Creek, DVM, project manager, gave the following report:

Foot and Mouth Disease

Dr. Creek stated that, by vaccinating, they live with foot-and-mouth disease, but that it has never been stamped out. Also, he stated that the disease is rather common among the wild cape buffalo of Kenya. Although the disease is not too severe in buffalo, they serve as a constant source of infection to cattle.

Water Rights More Important Than Land Title

Because of the scarcity of water, water rights are more important to a cattleman of Kenya than land rights.

The Masai Are Milk Consumers

They consume an average of one gallon of milk per person per day. To get this quantity of milk, the average family must have a herd of about 45 cows.

The Kenya Cattle Project

In 1968, the Government of Kenya, assisted by FAO and the UN Development Program, started the Beef Industry Development at Nakuru. Corn does well in this area; hence, corn silage is the basic feed. The Beef Research Station has been developed on 988 acres of crop land, with 4446 acres of marginal hill grazing. Yard facilities have been built to accommodate 2,400 animals in the feedlot at one time.

College of Veterinary Medicine, University of Nairobi, Kabete

This morning, we visited the College of Veterinary Medicine, University of Nairobi. The dean, Prof. Dr. G. M. Mugera, briefed us and showed us the facilities.

Professor, Dr. Mugera has his Ph.D. degree from Michigan State University, East Lansing, Michigan.

The Training of a Veterinarian

In sequence, it is: high school graduate, two years in junior college, one year in science at the University of Nairobi, and three years in the College of Veterinary Medicine, University of Nairobi, at Kabete.

Dr. G. M. Mugera, Dean, Faculty of Veterinary Science, University of Nairobi, Kabete, Kenya, showing Dr. E one of their laboratories.

Following graduation, veterinarians are required to enter government service for a period of three years. Anyway, there is very little private practice of veterinary medicine in Kenya.

College of Agriculture, University of Nairobi, Kabete

We also visited the College of Agriculture, where we were briefed and shown about by Prof., Dr. R. B. Contant. Prof., Dr. Contant earned his Ph.D. degree in Holland. Until recently, he was Dean of the Faculty of Agriculture.

The College of Agriculture of the University of Nairobi was established in 1970.

Nairobi National Park

The park boundary is only 15 minutes drive from the center of the city of Nairobi. It is relatively small as such parks go, being only 44 square miles in size.

Near the main entrance to the Nairobi National Park, there is an animal orphanage, which we visited. Its purpose: To give care and temporary sanctuary to young wild animals that have been found de-

Left to right: Dr. Contant, Trustee Art Solomon, Dr. E and one of our study-tour group members.

serted and without the means to fend for themselves, or that have been pets of departing residents and which need a good home.

In our rather hurried drive through the park, we saw rhino, giraffe, eland, waterbuck, warthog, Thomson's gazelle, Grant's gazelle, baboon, wildebeest, impala, bushbuck, and ostrich.

Maridadi Fabrics

We were taken through this business by Mrs. Martha Gikonyo, the manager. Maridadi Fabrics is a cottage industry which hand-screens fabrics in Nairobi, Kenya. It was started in 1966 for philanthropic and artistic purposes—to provide jobs for needy, unemployed women and to adapt and interpret traditional crafts and designs for contemporary use.

Today Maridadi Fabrics occupies an abandoned brewery made available by the Nairobi City Council. Most of the women are widows or deserted mothers.

Besides printing fabrics, Maridadi makes finished products: table mats, cushions, cushion covers, neckties, woven sisal baskets and mats.

The supervisors are on salary, but the workers are paid by the piece—which means that the latter are on an incentive basis.

The South Africa We Saw

The Union of South Africa was formed by act of the British Parliament, effective May 31, 1910. South Africa is about the size of Texas, Oklahoma, and New Mexico, occupying the southern portion of the African continent and includes the former colonies of the Cape of Good Hope, Natal, the Transvaal, and the Orange Free State, which became provinces. The nation was settled by emigrants from Cape Colony, mostly of Dutch extraction, in the Great Trek of 1831 and later.

Language

Afrikaans and English.

Main Exports

Diamonds 14%; fruit and vegetables 8%; wool 8%; copper 7%; iron and steel 7%; metal ores 5%.

Major Agricultural Products

Corn, cotton, wool, wheat, tobacco, sugarcane, citrus fruits, butter, and cheese.

Corn

Corn is South Africa's most important agricultural commodity in terms of value, volume of production and consumption, and area devoted to the crop. It is an important food item in the diet of the majority of South Africans and a staple food of the Bantus, who make up about 80% of the population.

Mohair

South Africa ranks third in mohair production, following the U.S. and Turkey. South Africa produces about 20% of the world's output of mohair.

Mineral Resources

With vast mineral resources, South Africa leads the world in the production of gold, gem diamonds, and antimony; it is among the top producers of platinum, chrome, uranium, vanadium, vermiculite, manganese, and asbestos. Coal and iron resources are large. Annual production of more than 50 minerals is estimated at over $2 billion.

Veterinary Research Institute, Onderstepoort

We were received and shown through the Veterinary Research Institute by Dr. Michael de Lange, Deputy Director, and Dr. Ian S. McFarlane.

Functions of the institute include applied and fundamental research into the diseases of domestic animals, production of veterinary biologicals, both vaccines and diagnostic materials, and teaching of graduate and postgraduate veterinary students.

Foot-and-Mouth Disease

In South Africa it is confined to Kruger National Park. This has been done by fencing. They have 500 miles of the following kind of fence: 8 ft high, 14 strands of barb wire, and three ½-in cables. It will even hold an elephant.

"The Ideal Cattle Herd Consists of about 125 Head"

Dr. McFarlane expressed the opinion that heat detection is much easier with this size herd.

Dr. Ian S. McFarlane *(left)*, Veterinary Research Institute, Onderstepoort, South Africa, noted animal scientist, showing Dr. E some of the institute's yearling heifers.

Gala Dinner, Boulevard Hotel, Pretoria

This evening, our guests of honor were: Mr. Harry Germishuis, Agricultural Attaché, American Embassy, Pretoria; Dr. and Mrs. Michael de Lange; Dr. and Mrs. Ian S. McFarlane; and Mr. and Mrs. Michael E. du Toit. Mr. du Toit operates a 15,000 head cattle feedlot.

Gala dinner in Pretoria with Dr. E presiding.

Rhys Evans (Pty) Ltd. Farms

This morning, we visited the Rhys Evans (Pty.) Ltd. farms, which consist of seven farm units, totalling 30,100 acres, located in the Western Transvaal and the Northwestern Orange Free State.

About Mr. Anthony R. Evans

He is 30 years of age, and single. Anthony took his undergraduate work in South Africa, went to Oxford (England), and earned a Masters Degree at Harvard (U.S.) in Business Administration.

Anthony started on the farm 4½ years ago; he has been managing director since the passing of his father last February.

Geldenhuys Bros. (Attie and Philip) Farms

We visited the Geldenhuys Bros. Farm, home of South Africa's largest and most noted Africander herd of cattle. In addition to seeing their show string, the Geldenhuys hosted a bountiful and delicious lun-

Left to right: Dr. E; Mrs. J. Rhys Evans; and Anthony R. Evans, Mrs. Evans' son. Mrs. Evans hosted a tea for us. Anthony Evans showed us their Suffolk cattle and farming operations.

cheon for us, in the home of Attie and Esther Geldenhuys.

Origin of the Africander

Mr. Koos Swart, a representative of the Africander breed registry, advised us that the Brahman and Africander descend from the same Zebu foundation. The only difference in their development is that the Brahman was developed in a hot, humid climate, whereas the Africander was developed in a hot, dry climate.

Beautiful Cape Dutch house on the Rhys Evans Farms in South Africa, headquarters of a 30,100 acre farm that we visited and where Mrs. J. Rhys Evans served a bountiful tea.

Africander bull owned by Geldenhuys Bros., Kroonstad, South Africa. This is the leading Africander herd of South Africa. In the background, left to right, are: Attie Geldenhuys, Dr. E, and Philip Geldenhuys.

General Reaction Relative to the Africander Cattle

They're good cattle, and, obviously, they're adapted to the area. In comparison with Brahman cattle, their hump sets further back—it's over the shoulders (withers). They are great walkers; they can outwalk most horses. Also, they strike me as a bit nervous and jumpy.

Springbuck Hide

After the bountiful and delicious luncheon, Esther Geldenhuys presented Springbuck hide to me. The Springbuck is the national emblem of South Africa.

Malabar Farm, Mr. and Mrs. Duke Jackson

This morning, we visited Malabar Farm, owned by Mr. and Mrs. E. F. Duke Jackson and their sons, Bruce Duke Jackson and Timothy Duke Jackson. In addition to showing us their good farm, the Jacksons hosted a tea for us, with their neighbors and friends present.

If a bus had to break down, it couldn't have broken down at a better place, for Duke Jackson towed it in to his shop where his expert mechanic repaired it while we looked over and discussed Malabar Farm.

This 30,800 acre facility produces primarily wheat, seed potatoes, cotton, lucerne (alfalfa), baby beef, fat lamb, pigs, timber, and grapes for wine and raisins.

Age of Operation

The present owner has had the farm for 35 years; his father acquired it during a great drought for the purpose of saving the sheep. The farm formerly belonged to Griqua Chief, Adam Kok, some of whose descendants are still working on the farm. Originally, the farm was called "Dry Hook." In 1944, following a big flood, the name was changed to Malabar Farm, after Louis Bromfield's Malabar Farm in the United States.

What's Unique About This Operation

The Jacksons have a highly successful, and very profitable, diversified operation in a predominantly sheep area.

Although the rainfall is low, the carrying capacity of the pastures is excellent, due to the conservation and range management methods followed.

Also, it's noteworthy that the two sons, Bruce Duke Jackson and Timothy Duke Jackson, are staying down on the farm.

Kimberley Mine, Kinberley

We visited the Kimberley Mine, near Kimberley, South Africa—the world's richest diamond center. Our guide was Ms. Jean Bothomley.

The Kimberley Mine ceased operations on August 4, 1914. By then, 22.6 million metric tons of ground had been excavated and 14,504,566 carats of diamonds had been recovered. Its Big Hole, which we inspected, has a 5,248 ft perimeter and is 1,312 ft deep. It is an impressive monument to the pioneers of the modern diamond industry. Alongside it is a museum, which we also visited, recording the early days of Kimberley.

Cyril Back, Fairview

This morning, we visited one of the most progressive farmers of the area—Mr. Cyril Back, Fairview. His 500-acre farm, including winemaking, was bought by his father in 1937. Crops include 250 acres of wine grapes, and 25 acres of figs.

Cyril Back (plaid shirt) showing Dr. E his battery type hog finishing operation (with each pig kept in a small individual pen).

Chickens

Mr. Back has 15,000 layers for egg production.

Swine

The swine unit, which has been underway for seven years, is strictly a finishing operation. The watering facility is a simple spigot, which the pigs turn on themselves.

The Dairy Beef (Heavy Veal) Program

The production of dairy beef (heavy veal) has been underway for two years. It consists of purchasing 3- to-7-day-old Friesian (Holstein) calves which are fed to a market weight of 400 lb, at which time they are marketed as heavy veals.

Following the tour-study of the farm, Mr. and Mrs. Back served refreshments, with many choices—all abundant and delicious.

Cape Town

Prof., Dr. F. J. Van der Merwe, Head, Department of Animal Science, University of Stellenbosch, Stellenbosch, South Africa, arranged our schedule in the Cape Town area. He also accompanied us in the study-tour for two days; and he and Mrs. Van der Merwe attended our dinner.

The port city of Cape Town, which has a population of one million, is dominated by Table Mountain.

Cape Point, the southern most point of the peninsula, is where the Indian Ocean meets the Atlantic. The Cape Peninsula is 32 miles long and 10 miles wide.

Nederburg Estate; The Stellenbosch Farmers Winery Ltd.

Because the Cape Town area is noted for grapes and fine wines, we were pleased to be able to visit the Stellenbosch Winery Ltd., and we were honored by their hosting a noonday barbecue.

Stellenbosch markets about 70% of the natural wines of South Africa. Also, it is noteworthy that they control the whole operation from the production of the raw material, the grapes, to the marketing of the bottled product.

Kind of Wine

Our host emphasized that there is no "best wine." The best wine is simply the wine you most like. It was pointed out, however, that some recommendations do make sense, provided it is remembered that they are purely intended as general guides. For example, a very good reason exists why white wines are recommended with lighter, more delicate foods such as egg dishes, fish and white meat; and red wines are recommended for richer fare such as steaks and venison. It is just that the wine should not dominate the flavor of the food, nor the food that of the wine. It is also true that a good, sparkling wine or a dry wine make an excellent aperitif (appetizer). It is also a proven fact that a white wine tastes much better if it has been slightly chilled (not too cold, since then it paralyzes the taste buds which cannot possibly appreciate the wine), and that red wine is at its best at a moderate room temperature.

Nederburg Estate, Stellenbosch Farmers Winery, near Cape Town, where they hosted a noonday barbecue for our tour-study group. Note the chunks of meat suspended on steel rods over the live coals. The heat causes the steel to bend and come closer and closer to the fire. Dr. E is second from left.

Wine Tasting/Lamb Barbecue

Following the tour through the winery, we participated in the traditional "wine tasting." Then we drove to the area where they hosted a very bountiful and delicious lamb barbecue for us.

Scenic Drive Around the Cape Peninsula

Following the barbecue, we took a scenic drive around the Cape Peninsula.

Secretary of Agriculture, Dr. W. A. Verbeek, Addressed Our Group in Cape Town

Dr. W. A. Verbeek, the distinguished Secretary of Agriculture of South Africa, addressed our group in Cape Town at our gala dinner. Dr. Verbeek, who is a

Left to right: Dr. W. A. Verbeek, Secretary of Agriculture; Mrs. Verbeek; Dr. E; Mrs. van der Merwe; and Prof., Dr. F. J. van der Merwe.

graduate of Cornell University, impressed us as both able and personable.

Range Improvement

Dr. Verbeek pointed out that range improvement has been achieved through a long-time program of providing certain compensation (or subsidies) for those who lessened their sheep numbers. This has been effective in avoiding overstocking.

Water Is a Problem

Dr. Verbeek emphasized that lack of water is one of their major problems. Accordingly, they are giving thought as to ways and means of providing more water, particularly from the standpoint of irrigation.

Groote Schuur Hospital

We visited Groote Schuur (which means, "the great barn") Hospital, where Prof., Dr. Christian Barnard, M.D., and his team, did the world's first heart transplant. Prof., Dr. Barnard, who was recovering from an auto accident, was not able to be with us. But Dr. J. G. Losman, M.D., a Frenchman and the third ranking member of Dr. Barnard's transplant team, took us through Groote Schuur Hospital.

Dr. J. G. Losman, M.D., a surgeon and member of Dr. Christian Barnard's heart transplant team with Dr. E.

His colleagues refer to Dr. Barnard as "Professor" Barnard, because he is on the Medical School staff of the University of Cape Town.

The University of Stellenbosch

We drove through the campus of the University of Stellenbosch, established in 1866, with Prof. F. J. van der Merwe serving as our guide and briefing us about the institution.

Classes are taught in Afrikaans (not English). The University has eleven faculties: arts, science, education, agriculture, law, theology, commerce, engineering, medicine, forestry, and military science.

About the Faculty of Agriculture

It is known as the "Stellenbosch-Elsenburg Agricultural College of the University of Stellenbosch." There are two agricultural buildings on the campus plus the Elsenburg Agricultural Farm which we visited.

Schoongezicht Farms (Jersey Cattle, Grapes, and Wine), Stellenbosch

Mr. Douglas Houston, manager, received us, and he and his staff briefed us and took us on a

Dr. E is presenting one of his books to Mr. Douglas Houston, Manager, Schoongezicht Farms.

Dr. E admiring a beautiful Jersey cow on Schoongezicht Farms, Stellenbosch, South Africa. This Jersey herd, which numbers 400, is based on U.S. and Canadian bloodlines.

study-tour of Schoongezicht Farms, following which Mr. and Mrs. Houston hosted us for tea.

The farm was first called Schoongezicht in 1810, although it was farmed under other names much earlier.

The total area covered by the Schoongezicht Farms is approximately 2,500 acres, the greater part of which is mountainous and used as a nature reserve—vegetation, birds and animals. Approximately 250 acres are under pine and gum forests, 120 acres under dryland vines, 250 acres under fodder crops grown in winter, 150 acres irrigable pastures and fodder crops, and 100 acres irrigable under various plum varieties.

Elsenburg Agricultural Farm

We made a tour of the Elsenburg Agricultural Farm. It began with refreshments and an interesting slide-seminar presentation by Prof., Dr. Van der Merwe, about the agriculture of South Africa. Then, staff members Erasmus, van Wyk, and Ferreira made presentation, either in the classroom or as we traveled over the farm.

Sheep

The Elsenburg Agriculture Farm maintains about 1,000 breeding sheep consisting of the following breeds: Dormer, (a Dorset Horn X German Merino breed; hence, the name "Dormer"), South African Merino (German Merino), and Merino.

Dairy Cattle

On the Elsenburg Farm, they maintain 100 Friesian (Holstein) females, and 50 Jersey females. Their Friesians are dual-purpose cattle.

Brood Sows

The Agricultural Farm keeps 50 brood sows of the Landrace breed.

Draft Horses

The Agricultural Farm maintains 25 head of Percheron horses, including two stallions.

Following our study-tour of Elsenburg Farm, Pikkie and Doreen Geffen were our special guests for dinner. Pikkie is a prominent lawyer in Cape Town. The Geffens are dear friends of my brother, G. A. "Buck" Ensminger.

Reception in the House of Parliament Building, by the Minister and the Deputy Minister of Agriculture, in Cape Town

This morning, both the Minister of Agriculture, The Honorable Hendrik Schoeman, and the Deputy Minister of Agriculture, The Honorable J. J. Malan, warmly received us in a reception room at the House of Parliament in Cape Town. Tea was served, the Minister spoke informally, and questions were answered. It was a pleasant experience.

The Rhodesia We Saw

Upon our arrival in Salisbury, Rhodesia, we were met by friends of the Ensmingers, Anthony and Ann de la Rue.

Throughout our study-tour of Rhodesia, we were most fortunate to have with us a fine and able government representative in the person of De. Cecil Rose, who was trained as a dairyman, and whom we found to be most knowledgeable about the agriculture of Rhodesia.

In South Africa, we were warmly received in the House of Parliament by the top government officials. Dr. E presenting a book to Hendrik Schoeman, Minister of Agriculture, at right is J. J. Malan, Deputy Minister of Agriculture.

Henderson Research Station

This morning, we visited Henderson Research Station, which is about an hour's bus ride from Rhodesia. We were received and shown over the station by Dr. Peter Thomas.

Dr. E being briefed on the Henderson Research Station by Dr. Peter Thomas (center), director.

Dr. Peter Thomas reported that by heavy nitrogen fertilization they can stock 7 to 8 cattle per acre during the 6 months rainy season; and, by irrigation, they can extend the grazing season to 8 months.

Up to 1,234 lb/acre of beef on yearling cattle grazing Star grass have been recorded.

Among the crops being studied on the station are: maize (corn), cotton, soybeans, groundnuts (peanuts), hybrid sorghum, sun hemp.

Mazoe Citrus Estates

We were served orange juice upon our arrival. Then we were briefed on and conducted through the Mazoe Citrus Estates by A. F. (Tony) Heberden, horticulturalist.

Mazoe Citrus Estates came into being in 1914 when it was owned by the British South Africa Company. The Charter Company (as it was known), which was founded by Cecil John Rhodes, pioneered citrus growing on a commercial scale in Rhodesia.

The estates embrace a total of 52,536 acres. Approximately 36,000 acres of this total can be classified as farming.

Citrus Trees

Today, there are nearly 330,000 citrus trees on the estates. Of these approximately 25,000 are lemon trees. The acreage under citrus at present is 3,500, with land available for an ultimate citrus acreage in the neighborhood of 6,500 acres.

A. F. (Tony) Heberden briefed, and conducted, us through the Mazoe Citrus Estates.

The Dam

Citrus trees required irrigating during the rainless winter and early summer months. To meet this need, construction of the Mazoe Dam was commenced in January, 1919, and completed in June, 1920.

Glenara Estate (Private) Ltd.

This estate is owned by Mr. H. G. Oppenheimer of South Africa, owner of DeBeers Consolidated Mines Ltd., of Kimberley, and Mauritzfontein—Thoroughbred horse breeding establishment.

We were briefed by Mr. R. Calmeyer, the manager, following which he and his son, Geffry, took us over the estate which totals 4,800 acres, of which 4,400 acres are under cultivation.

The dairy consists of 700 Friesians (Holsteins), of which 250 are lactating cows. The herd is dominantly of Canadian breeding.

The School

We visited the school, in which there are 271 students. The headmaster is Mr. G. K. Shaba.

We Visited the Sixth Grade

The teacher; Enos Nematombo. He has 60 children. We were impressed with the beautiful script on the blackboard.

Mr. R. Calmeyer *(left)*, Manager, Glenara Estate, showing Dr. E some of their famed Holsteins.

We visited the 6th grade in which there were 60 children, in a model school at Glenara Estate. The teacher, Mr. J. G. Masache, is standing back and to the left of Dr. E.

We also Visited the Music Class

The teacher was Mr. J. G. Masache. He instructed them in singing from large notes on a roll of paper displayed by sticking over the blackboard, with a crooked stick as his baton. The rhythm of these youngsters—about 80 of them, 8 to 10 years of age—was wonderful.

A Home

We visited the home of Mr. G. K. Shaba, the headmaster. It was plain, but adequate. Mrs. Shaba

The headmaster of the school, Mr. G. K. Shaba, is ushering Dr. E to his home. Mr. R. Calmeyer, manager of Glenara Estate, is standing on the lawn to the left.

was seated on the floor in one room, and she remained in this position as she folded her hands in front of her head and bowed. To remain seated on the floor is a mark of respect.

Mr. Calmeyer, manager of Glenara Estate, told about the "garden competition," through which the area around the African homes is kept attractive. They have a garden competition twice per year. A total of $40 is allocated from the student fee fund for this purpose each year. Twice each year there is a $10 first prize *plus* consolation prizes.

His Excellency Ian D. Smith, Prime Minister of Rhodesia

The Prime Minister received us in the garden near his office; and accepted a special leather-bound, gold embossed copy of *Animal Science*. In making the book presentation, Dr. E said of the Prime Minister: "He's a rancher and a cattleman, and he's an active member of the Rhodesian Branch of the South African Society of Animal Production." The Prime Minister stood with us for a group picture; shook hands with each of us; then responded briefly.

In a most sincere way, and with evident feeling, the prime minister referred to the present "unjust sanctions." Said he, "We do not have a thing to hide. See everything that you can, then tell your own story as you see it when you return home."

Prime Minister Ian D. Smith (right) of Rhodesia, received us in the garden near his office. Dr. E is shown presenting the prime minister a special leather-bound, gold-embossed copy of his book, *Animal Science*.

The prime minister expressed the fond hope that a settlement of the Anglo-Rhodesian dispute may yet be reached, so that trade relationships can return to normal and Rhodesia can again establish diplomatic relations with the free world.

The prime minister remarked that Rhodesia was in the "tragic position of fighting against our friends, rather than our foes."

Upon our return to Salisbury and the Jameson Hotel, on Saturday, March 3, I found the leather-bound copy of *Animal Science* in my room, along with a note stating the prime minister would like that the author autograph the book for him. Of course, I was pleased and honored to do so.

Gala Dinner in Salisbury; Address by David C. Smith, Minister of Agriculture

We had a number of distinguished guests at our gala dinner. The address of the evening was made by David C. Smith, Minister of Agriculture.

Head table at gala dinner in Rhodesia.

Marketing

They believe in orderly marketing controls; and when it comes to exports, they believe in one market channel.

Agricultural Production Doubled

In the past ten years, agricultural production as a whole has doubled in Rhodesia. A few commodities have been hurt by sanctions, especially the tobacco market.

Dr. E is shown introducing, and presenting one of his books to, David C. Smith, Minister of Agriculture, Rhodesia, who was our gala dinner speaker in Salisbury, Rhodesia.

Frank Goff, Padeswood Farm (Tobacco)

This morning, we visited Mr. Frank Goff and his diversified farm.

Acreage/Crops/Livestock

On this diversified farm, Frank Goff has 92 acres of Virginia tobacco, a cigarette tobacco; 150 acres of maize (corn); and 450 cattle (130 brood cows plus young stock). Sussex bulls are crossed with Africander cows. Mr. Goff has averaged an 84% calf crop for the past 3 years. He weans off 450-lb calves.

About the Goffs

He was educated in the U.K. Mrs. Goff teaches school. The Goffs have four sons. Frank Goff has operated this farm for 15 years.

Following the study-tour of the farm, we were served tea.

Claremont Orchards

We visited Claremont Orchards, of which Mr. J. Crosthwaite Eyre is the managing director.

There are 7,000 acres in the diverse farm. The enterprises embrace: fruit trees, consisting of 23,000 apple trees, 1,500 pear trees, and 500 nectarines; potatoes, 35 acres; maize (corn) and lovegrass rotated with potatoes (with potatoes planted on the same area only one year in four), 250 acres; nursery, 10,000 fruit trees, and 30,000 rose bushes; cattle, 350 head—mostly Angus.

Dr. E being briefed on Claremont Orchards by Mr. J. Crosthwaite Eyre, managing director.

Inyanga Trout Research Center

In keeping with the Foundation policy of seeing the type of operation for which each area is noted, it was appropriate that we should visit a Trout Research Center in an area where recreation and fishing are important. So, we made a tour-study of the Inyanga Trout Research Center.

At this Center, the following four pure species of fish are being propagated: American brook trout, Eastern American brook trout, Brown trout, and Tiger hybrid trout.

They breed 250,000 fish/year; put out 12,000 10-in. to 18-in. fish per year (these are catchables that are put in national park waters); and they sell eggs, fry, fingerlings, and catchables.

Films and Lecture on "Forestry in Rhodesia"

This evening, at the Troutbeck Inn, Mr. John Wiltshire, Director of Forestry of Rhodesia, lectured. Also, the following short films were shown: Man and His Forests—Rhodesia, Crocodile, and Portrait of A Lake.

The Middle Sabi Operating Division—a Resettlement Project for Europeans

The Middle Sabi Operating Division is part of a huge irrigation development which was created by Rhodesian legislative act in 1965. The region concerned comprises 26,000 sq mi in the southeast of Rhodesia, or 16% of the total area of the country.

When complete, the irrigation complex will support a population of 1¾ million people and will provide over 700,000 acres of irrigated land, growing both summer and winter crops and producing in annual value more than the present agricultural production of the whole of Rhodesia.

According to legend, this was the land of King Solomon's mines, yet even King Solomon can hardly have anticipated the true wealth offered by the hills, rivers and plains of this corner of Africa.

The Sabi Story

The Sabi Valley, a large area of low rainfall, has never been suitable for anything other than cattle and goats, yet the great volume of water which passes down the Sabi River and its tributaries each year, together with the presence of good soils, have suggested an enormous agricultural potential upon which the country might draw in the future.

The middle Sabi pilot project is located on the east bank of the river immediately below the Tanganda junction. Its basic purpose is to gain experience on the alluvial soils of the area and to assess the technical and economical problems associated with European farm settlement under these conditions.

A baobab tree on the Middle Sabi Resettlement Project, Umtali, Rhodesia. This tree is 150 ft in circumference, and is estimated to be 1,500 years old. In South Africa, this is a protected tree. The baobab tree is a broad-trunked tree that bears a gourdlike fruit.

To this end, a "parent" company estate of 800 acres was established by a wholly-owned subsidiary of the authority, the Middle Sabi Development Company, now know as the Middle Sabi Division.

Water is pumped or gravity-fed from the Sabi and Tanganda Rivers to irrigate crops of wheat, cotton, lucerne (alfalfa) and bananas. Beef cattle and sheep are also being produced on an experimental basis. In addition, the company has operated two adjacent experimental farms, each of 200 acres, one of which is sprinkler irrigated and the other flood irrigated.

At Middle Sabi, we were hosted by Mr. Howard Wicksteed, estates manager, and his staff. Mr. Van Rooyen, a South African who serves as settlement officer on the Middle Sabi project, served as spokesman. He told us that the reasons for the development were because the land is fertile and water abundant, and the area is inhabited by a large number of Africans, who are existing at the subsistence level.

The Chisumbanje Development Co.—an African Resettlement Project

We were briefed on this project by Mr. J. W. Van Tonder. This development is for Africans, whereas the Middle Sabi project is for Europeans. Moreover, sociological problems, stemming from deep-seated customs and traditions, make for mountainous problems in settling Africans on such a project.

This resettlement project is unique in two ways: it is on the Ndowoyo Tribal Trust Land, home of almost 37,000 Shangaan tribespeople; and the Ndowoyo, embracing 100,000 acres, is the largest single tract of black basalt-derived soils in the country. These soils are generally 3 to 4 ft deep, but areas more than 10 ft deep have been encountered. The Chisumbanje basalts are undoubtedly one of the most fertile and valuable irrigation soils in Rhodesia.

In the local Chindau or Hlengwe dialects, the word "Chisumbanje" means literally, "the place where marijuana is smoked." The reality is that Chisumbanje today—even at this early stage of its development—undoubtedly exceeds the wildest dreams of the early man who coined the name.

The Chisumbanje Development Company's irrigation scheme is being developed to harness the area resources of soil and water for crop production for the benefit of the country as a whole and the local African tribespeople in particular.

Sociologically, the effects of such a massive injection of capital and activity on a primitive population which had previously subsisted on an average of U.S. $40 per family per year can be imagined; after six years the project employs almost 500 local tribesmen on a full-time basis and during the cotton picking season provides work for almost 3,000 others—mainly women and children.

Also, the economics of the scheme are most satisfactory; a return on capital of between 14 and 20% is currently being obtained.

The Settler Scheme

Already a settler scheme is in operation whereby local African tribesmen (45 at present) lease up to five acres from the development company. Their farming activities are closely supervised and directed so that profitable levels of production of both cotton and wheat are obtained. A settler leasing up to five acres of land can show a net profit of U.S. $500 a year from cotton and wheat production, but there are additional labor-intensive crops, e.g. burley tobacco, vegetables, and flower seed grown on an individual basis which considerably increase this figure.

Chisumbanje has recently introduced a tenant training scheme, which provides laborers with sufficient skills to play their part in the long-term plan.

African Village

Contracts were recently awarded and construction commenced on the first "village" of some 4,000 housing units. In addition, a modern supermarket was built to serve the village and Chisumbanje area.

The full development of the Chisumbanje area offers an exciting challenge, which will involve considerable capital and human resourcefulness. The rewards will be measured not only in profits, but in social and human progress resulting from economic employment in the agricultural and industrial sectors for up to 500,000 African tribespeople.

Cotton and Wheat Production

At the present time, two primary crops are grown—cotton in summer and wheat in winter.

Crops Other Than Cotton and Wheat

As a necessary adjunct to cotton and wheat, a secondary area of some 50 acres has been set aside for the planting of other crops such as maize, repoko, groundnuts (peanuts), munga, rice, sorghum and, where possible, suitable legumes such as soybeans. The Chisumbanje Experiment Station has demonstrated that a range of crops such as these can be grown at reasonable levels of production, but which are unprofitable or only show marginal profitability within the national marketing system. In addition to the above, other crops include burley tobacco, citrus, bananas, linseed, sunflower, sugarcane, castor beans, and most vegetables in winter.

Ruware Ranch Field Day; Ian H. de la Rue and Tuli Cattle

We spent the entire day on Ruware Ranch, owned by Mr. Ian H. de la Rue, whom we found to be as colorful as he is able. Mr. de la Rue hosted us for morning and afternoon teas and for lunch, showed us Ruware Ranch and Tuli cattle, and presented a program by specialists following lunch.

History of the Ranch

Ian and Violet de la Rue, the present owners, acquired Ruware Ranch as virgin bushveld in 1936, when there were no bridges, roads or other communications. There was, however, an old wagon track. They lived much of the time on what they grew or killed, and they did without the rest of the time. At

Left to right: Ian H. de la Rue, Dr. E, Ann de la Rue (Mrs. Anthony), Audrey, and Anthony de la Rue.

the start of the rains, their four stored commodities were tea (or coffee), sugar, flour, and rice. African rations stored consisted of maize and salt. In one year, they were totally isolated for six months.

Wild Animals

Since 1936, they have killed 135 lions and over 600 leopards, which killed their cattle in large numbers. Buffalo carry tick-borne diseases, plus foot-and-mouth disease. Only in the last 10 years have they been able to keep cattle in paddock (pastures), due to ravages of carnivora and damage to fences by wild animals—especially zebra, elephant, buffalo, and hippo.

Size of Ruware Ranch

Ruware Ranch is 90,000 acres, of which some 7,000 acres are allocated to game. The count a short time ago was 200 zebra, 200 kudu, 300 impala, 75 each sable and eland, a few very rare hartebeest, and 11 species of buck including waterbuck, duiker, klipspringer, reedbuck, roisbuck and bushbuck.

Number of Cattle

Normal carrying capacity is about 4,500 head, giving a carrying capacity of about 1 cow to 17 acres.

Breed of Cattle

There was no good breed of cattle suitable for the tropics in the 1930s. Ruware's original stock was made up of Shorthorn, Hereford, Africander, native type, and a yellow type. Without calling it such, Ruware Ranch ran a "closed herd," because cattle brought in did not do as well as the homebred ones. They were hardy, functional animals, but they lacked beef quality. Said Mr. de la Rue, "We kept the pot stirred with the above breeds. About 13 years ago, I was persuaded by Conex (Conservation and Extension) to visit the Tuli Breeding Station 350 miles away. I was immediately struck with their beef qualities.

"In spite of foot-and-mouth hazards, we gradually got some 15 young bulls from Tuli, along with a few females. Today, our younger animals are about 75% Tuli blood; and they show quality. They are very productive, and early maturing, and have an exceptional slaughtering carcass—well fleshed with a light, even covering of fat.

The Ensmingers taking time out for a bountiful barbeque at Ruware Ranch. Ruth Stewart is holding the camera.

Irrigation

Mr. de la Rue reported that in the last few years 200 acres of overhead irrigation from the Government Manjerenji canal have been developed, and another 150 acres are in the process. Three crops of maize (corn) green chop can be grown per year per acre, at 25 tons per crop. Generally it does not pay to grow feed because such byproducts as molasses, cotton cake, and native beer residues can be bought cheaply.

Family Huts and Family Names

We visited the Tapera family (man, wife, and baby) and their two huts (one for living; the other for cooking).

They have a one-month-old baby boy, named Chimiso (which means "wait a bit," because the birth was a bit delayed). Africans only have one name; the name is prompted by some notable event surrounding the time of the birth—such as a delayed birth, the baby wasn't expected live, etc.; and the name bears no resemblance or relationship whatsoever to that of the father's name.

Mazipuchani, the "Boss Boy" Who Made It the Hard Way

An impossible dream! This best describes the true-to-life story of Mazipuchani, the boss boy on Ian H. de la Rue's Ruware Ranch.

Dr. E visited the Tapera family—man, wife, and baby (on back of mother).

Today, Mazipuchani is successful. He's a "boss boy" (which means that he's the head herdsman of a herd of approximately 50 cows and one or two bulls, and that he has a helper—an assistant boss boy); and he has two wives and four children (three boys and a girl). Other than walking with a slight limp, he appears to be healthy.

But anyone less resolute than Mazipuchani would never have made it. He began life as an abandoned child found in the bushes, without a known father or mother. He grew up fending for himself; by living on such berries as he could pick and on what food he could mooch. Malnutrition took its toll; as a child he developed rickets. He maneuvered, painfully and slowly, with the aid of two sticks—a long one held out in front to which one hand was clutched high up, and a short one behind. He shuttled along, pulling his coiled right leg behind him.

Mazipuchani, boss boy on Ian H. de la Rue's Ruware Ranch, in Rhodesia.

In 1939, at age 13, he trudged 20 miles to Ruware Ranch for the purpose of seeking employment. Impressed with Mazipuchani's perseverance, although doubting that such a hopeless cripple could ever earn his keep, Ian de la Rue rewarded his efforts and hired him. To spare him from much walking, for 10 years he labored as second boy looking after the ranch milk cows, and other odds and ends, kept near headquarters. Then he was advanced to boss boy of this little herd, which job he held for another 10 years. In the meantime, thanks to an improved diet, miraculously he outgrew most of the rickets of his childhood. Now only a slight limp of the right leg remains, and he's boss boy of a beef herd on the range, where he can outrun any critter.

Mazipuchani stood tall and proud, as his employer and benefactor—Ian de la Rue—conversed with him in his native tongue, to fill in the gaps of a life—his life. As we looked into his weather-beaten face, we saw positive proof that miracles do happen, and that Ian de la Rue helped make it so.

The Zimbabwe Ruins

We visited the Zimbabwe Ruins. This massive outer wall around the Great Enclosure or Temple is 827 ft in length and has a maximum height of 31 ft. The labor involved in building this single wall, estimated to contain 6,800 tons of stone, can only be imagined. The material for building was obtained from outcrops of granite which is the common rock which, when sufficiently heated, had water thrown on it, causing it to break off in great slabs which were then broken down by hand into suitable small blocks.

Victoria Falls

Victoria Falls is on the Zambezi River, one of Africa's mightiest rivers.

The Victoria Falls and zig-zag gorges are the biggest natural barrier to the Zambezi River in its struggle to reach the coast. Over a 350-ft drop of sheer black basalt cliff, 1¼ miles wide, surge 47 million gallons of water every minute of time, into the chasms below. Nature, too, has arranged a front-row view of this astounding feature from the great natural grandstand of the rain forest on the tongue of land immediately facing the falls, once part of the riverbed.

The Victoria Falls—the largest curtain of falling

water in the world—have a strange geological history. The sheer sides of the zig-zag gorges present in section, to a depth of about 300 ft, a solid wall of one single type of rock—black basalt—a rock which derives from age-old volcanic lava. From this natural display, geologists confirm their conclusion that millions of years ago lava oozed from the still-molten shells of the earth's crusts, through clefts rather than through craters, and spread over vast areas of central Africa, from east to west coasts, right down to Basutoland. This lava cooled and hardened into basalts which split up progressively into isolated patches by erosion.

The Niagra Falls, by comparison, are on softer limestone cliffs and are gradually being washed away.

A boat cruise on the Zambezi River.

High above the falls, the perpetual plunge and churn of water produces a stupendous cloud of mist, driving spray and "comets' tails" of vapor which constantly fluctuate and sway up to 200 ft into the sky.

Dr. David Livingstone was the first European to see the falls. It was on November 16, 1855, during one of his missionary journeys, that he first looked on the vast curtain of falling water and wrote in his diary "scenes so lovely must have been gazed on by angels in their flight."

A railway bridge, completed in 1905, spans the Zambezi River, below the falls. In 1930, the bridge was widened and reinforced to accommodate road traffic. Today, a line drawn halfway across the bridge marks the Rhodesia-Zambia border.

African Craft Village/Facilities for an African Man With Three Wives

We visited the African Craft village, where we saw the facilities for an African with three wives, witnessed a war dance by a group of African men—a dance designed to impart courage to the timid ahead of battle, and shopped.

Summary

In summary, I saw in darkest Africa the area that may be the world's trouble spot of the future. I saw a smoldering race problem.

1974
THE KING RANCH AND MEXICO WE SAW

The King Ranch study-tour was also a part of the January 1974 International Stockmen's School in San Antonio. The three days of lectures in the school ended with a banquet at which Mr. Robert O. Anderson, Chairman of the Board of Atlantic Richfield and a New Mexico rancher, was the speaker. This photo shows Dr. E introducing Mr. Anderson and presenting a set of the school books to him.

Many months in advance of the scheduled visitation, I contacted the officials of King Ranch and leading agriculturalists of Mexico, advising them of the things that the group wished to see and do. Also, a barbecue was arranged at King Ranch, and a gala dinner was arranged in Mexico City, as a means of meeting our counterparts and exchanging ideas—to the end that we could learn from each other.

The King Ranch, Kingsville, Texas, We Saw

The King Ranch visitation was the traditional livestock study-tour on the last day of the International Stockmen's School in San Antonio, Texas. A total of 310 enrollees boarded the seven chartered buses and visited King Ranch.

Richard King, founder of the ranch that bears his name, was born in New York City in 1824. He stowed away on a ship at an early age, and in 1847, after several years at sea, came to the Rio Grande to captain one of the river boats that supplied General Zachary Taylor's army during the Mexican War.

In 1852, Captain King rode horseback from Brownsville to Corpus Christi and first saw the area where the ranch is located. On July 25th, 1853, he made his first land purchase, the Rincon de Santa Gertrudis Spanish land grant, on which Kingsvillc stands. This area was then so sparsely populated that he had to go to Mexico to buy cattle to stock his land and persuade men to go to the ranch to work.

Prior to Capt. King's death in 1885, he had increased his land purchases to about 600,000 acres; begun the introduction of fine cattle and horses; been one of the prime forces behind the construction of the Corpus Christi-Laredo railroad; and taken other measures to develop the modern ranching industry and the area in which he operated.

After 1885, management of the ranch was carried on by his widow and her son-in-law, Robert J. Kleberg, Sr., who married Alice, the youngest King daughter. Mr. Kleberg's father was a young German lawyer who came to Texas in 1834, took part in the revolution of 1836, and was a close friend of Sam Houston.

The present day King Ranch, comprised of 823,403 acres, is owned and operated by a corporation of which Robert J. Kleberg, Jr. is president and general manager.

Outstanding in this period of the King Ranch history is the development of the Santa Gertrudis breed. Other major contributions have been the mineral feeding experiments, brush control equipment and methods, grass programs, soil conservation, range management practices, and wildlife conservation.

Santa Gertrudis sale bulls at King Ranch.

Santa Gertrudis Cattle

Necessity brought about development of the Santa Gertrudis breed of beef cattle. Until about 1880, hardy but low-producing Longhorn cattle grazed the King Ranch ranges. Hereford and Shorthorn bulls were introduced to improve these cattle, but this program met with only partial success, because they were not able to withstand the semitropical environment of South Texas and still produce good quality beef under what, at times, were very adverse conditions.

The Santa Gertrudis breed of cattle is the result of a Shorthorn-Brahman cross—representing five-eighths Shorthorn and three-eighths Brahman. The initial cross consisted of mating 52 three-year-old seven-eighths Brahman bulls to 2,500 Shorthorn cows. The very best red heifers and bulls from this mating were retained and interbred. Finally, after two or three years of the initial cross, a very superior first-cross bull was singled out. This bull was known as *Monkey*, and he marked the real beginning of the breed of Santa Gertrudis cattle.

The breed derived its name from the Santa Gertrudis land grant, first granted by the crown of Spain, on which the breed of cattle was evolved. The original land grant is now the headquarters division of King Ranch.

A herd of Santa Gertrudis cows at King Ranch.

Quarter Horses and Thoroughbreds

During its entire history, King Ranch has raised a great number of horses for use in its operations. Constant effort has been directed toward improving Quarter Horse and Thoroughbred stock.

The ranch developed a superior family within the Quarter Horse breed, made up of the progeny of Old Sorrel. This remarkable stallion was purchased by the ranch in 1915 and used in its program until his death in 1945. He had all of the attributes needed in a cow horse. He had the intelligence to learn and remembered what was expected of him. His temperament was alert without nervousness. He was strong muscled enough to carry good

A band of Quarter Horse broodmares at King Ranch.

weights, and agile under the saddle. At the same time he was speedy enough to outrun the fastest steer, yet compact enough to have an easy and ready maneuverability.

King Ranch is one of the charter members of the American Quarter Horse Association, organized in 1940. One of the ranch's stallions, a double grandson of Old Sorrel, was chosen by the association to receive registration number one. This was in recognition of the excellence of this horse's breed type.

Thoroughbreds have always been used on King Ranch. Serious efforts to establish a racing stable began in 1938 when the ranch purchased Bold Venture, winner of the 1936 Kentucky Derby. Bold Venture sired Assault, winner of the Triple Crown in 1946, and Middleground, winner of the Kentucky Derby in 1950.

Study-Tour of King Ranch

We were taken on a guided study-tour of King Ranch. We traveled in seven buses, with a King Ranch guide-narrator in each bus, and with stops along the way. The tour-study involved about 60 miles travel.

King Ranch had arranged for the cowboys to herd the cattle and horses near the roads along our route of travel. Additionally, the guide on each bus called attention to points of interest, including roads (the ranch has 500 miles of private roads), fences, pastures, prickly pear, windmills, mechanical feeders, mesquite brush clearing, working corrals, auction ring, Thoroughbred stable, colonies (homes of men employed on the ranch), equipment repair shop, and wild game.

Barbecue at J. K. Northway Exposition Center

At noon, we traveled to this large indoor arena, named after my longtime friend, the late J. K. Northway, DVM, who was for many years on the staff of King Ranch, and who appeared on the Stockmen's School program a number of years ago when it was held at Washington State University.

At the Northway Exposition Center, we were served a bountiful and delicious barbecue as guests of King Ranch. Following lunch, we were warmly welcomed by Mr. John Armstrong, Vice President of King Ranch. Also, Norman Parish introduced a number of the staff members of King Ranch, Texas A&M University, and Santa Gertrudis Breeders International.

Following lunch, we drove through a portion of the Laureles Division of King Ranch. This division embraces 254,000 acres, 16 pastures, 120 windmills, 100 employees, 29,000 breeding cows, and over 300 horses.

Performance Testing Santa Gertrudis Cattle at Edroy

Following the tour of the ranch, we drove to the King Ranch performance testing facility, where we saw 2,000 Santa Gertrudis bulls and 1,800 Santa Gertrudis heifers on performance test—without doubt, the largest number of cattle in the world on production test at one place, of one breed, and of one brand.

The Mexico We Saw

In addition to being our neighbor to the south and a fascinating country to visit, agricultural trade between Mexico and the United States is of vital importance to both countries. We had 41 delegates in our group.

Gala Dinner, Mexico City

Mr. Richard A. Smith, Agricultural Attaché, American Embassy, Mexico City, addressed our group at the gala dinner.

Agricultural Trade between Mexico and the United States

The total agricultural trade between the two countries has almost doubled during the past six years, reaching a record $770 million in 1972.

U.S. Exports to Mexico

Mexico is an important world market for U.S. agricultural exports.

U.S. Imports from Mexico

Although the U.S. imports a wide range of agricultural products from Mexico, most of this trade consists of three product categories: horticultural products, livestock and meat products, and tropical products—chiefly sugar and coffee.

Shrine of Guadalupe, Pyramids

This morning, we saw the Shrine of Guadalupe, a living tribute to the Mexican faith. Then, we continued on to the archaeological zone of Teotihuacan to see the Pyramids of the Sun and Moon. We walked among these huge and magnificent structures as we relived Mexico's early and fascinating history.

Luncheon at the Bullring Restaurant, La Morena, Mexico. *Left to right:* Audrey, Bill Finan, Agriservices Foundation trustee/ rancher, Musquiz, Coahuila, Mexico; Doris Osuna; Dr. E; Nellie Finan; and Guillermo Osuna, Agriservices Foundation trustee/ rancher, Musquiz, Coahuila, Mexico.

Bullring Restaurant and Bull Fighting

We had lunch at the novel Bullring Restaurant, La Morena, which is shaped like a small bullring. Following lunch, some of the intrepid among our group fought a bull.

Palace of Fine Arts Where We Witnessed the World-Famous Ballet Folklorico/Tour of Mexico City

Today we traveled to the Palace of Fine Arts where we witnessed the raising of the Tiffany Glass Curtain on the world-famous Ballet Folklorico. It presented the folk songs and dances from every province of Mexico; hence, it gave us a glimpse of rural Mexico.

In the afternoon we toured Mexico City. We visited the National Palace, with its frescoes by Diego Rivera depicting the history of Mexico; the Cathedral, Main Plaza, Chapultepec Park with its beautiful fountains; and the Museum of Anthropology where we saw the original Aztec Calendar, so accurate that no leap year was needed; Tlaloc, the 42-ton Aztec Rain God; Mixtec Tombs; a replica of Mexico City when Cortez landed; and many more historic items.

National Institute of Livestock Investigations, (Agricultural Experiment Station), Palo Alto

Dr. Raul Santibanez G. Jefe Del, Head of the Department of Scientific Information, warmly welcomed us to the institute and escorted us through it.

The institute was established in 1888. That year, it was the first laboratory on the American continent to produce vaccine against rabies. In 1900, it produced a vaccine against anthrax. From 1946 to 1952, the United States worked with the institute in stamping out foot-and-mouth disease in Mexico.

Presently, the institute is engaged in the production of biologics, drugs, and antigens; and in studies in the areas of nutrition, pastures, genetics, animal reproduction, bacteriology, and parasitology.

A Thoroughbred stallion at Rancho San Pedro Coxtocan, Corretera, Mexico. The sheep is the stallion's mascot (companion); it imparts a quieting effect.

Report by Dr. Hector Merino Z.

Dr. Merino, who is Head of the Institute's Nutrition Department and a graduate of Oklahoma State University, gave a brief report of their nutrition work. He mentioned their studies on the chemical analysis of feeds; grazing studies in the north of Mexico and in Coahuila; a breed of sheep without wool (on the peninsula of Yucatan); dairy cattle in the Central Plateau; sugarcane byproducts—especially molasses, of which they produce one million metric tons; and water lily as a livestock feed.

Visit to the Vaccine Production Laboratory

They produce enough vaccines to meet the nation's present demand, but they need to educate the country to use more vaccines. Mention was made of the institute making vaccines for use against equine encephalitis, foot-and-mouth disease, rabies, brucella abortions, Newcastle disease, and Marek's disease.

Rancho San Pedro Coxtocan (Thoroughbred Horses), San Martin Texmelucan, Corretera

Sr. Justo Fernandez A. lives in Mexico City. However, he was present for our visitation to his beautiful Thoroughbred horse farm, and he hosted a bountiful and delicious luncheon for us.

We were shown through the beautiful hacienda. The dining room is an exact replica of the dining room of El Greco, the famous painter of Spain. The kitchen features local made tile and pottery. Also, we saw the beautiful little chapel.

We experienced Mexican hospitality at its best. It was a case of wonderful people and good fellowship, fine horses, and wonderful food.

Rancho la Cotera (Holstein Dairy), Ixtapalupa

This, the most modern dairy in Latin America, was founded in 1929 by Emilio Fernandez Y., who came from Spain at age 17. The foundation animals were imported from the U.S. and Canada. It is dedicated to producing hygienically pure milk for Mexico.

Sr. Fernandez has had many national champions. He won over 50 trophies, including the gold

Holstein cows walking to the milking parlor at Rancho la Cotera.

medal for "Dairyman of the Year" in 1964, an award given by the President of Mexico.

The milk processing facilities are ultramodern, with much stainless steel. The bottling machine (made in Sweden) will fill 3,600 cartons per hour.

Later, we boarded a Braniff flight in Mexico City and returned to San Antonio; thus, ending our study-tour of King Ranch and Mexico.

Left to right: Guillermo Osuna, Agriservices Foundation trustee; Dr. E; and Sr. Fernando Senas, the foreman at Rancho la Cotera.

1974
THE JAPAN, SOUTH KOREA, AND CHINA WE SAW

There is much agricultural trade, and even greater potential, between the United States, and Japan, South Korea, Hong Kong, and China. So, it behooves the United States to be well informed about both our potential markets and our competition. On this study-tour of Japan, South Korea, Hong Kong, and China, I lectured and conducted seminars in each of the countries visited. I was accompanied by 22 delegates.

The Japan We Saw

Upon our arrival, at the airport in Tokyo, we were met by the following friends: Mr. and Mrs. Terry T. Hashida (Mr. Hashida, a noted consultant in Japan, is a longtime friend of the Ensmingers), who provided bus and tickets to the Kokusai Theater (Autumn Dance Review), with their compliments; Miss Taeko Soga and Miss Yakiko Soga, daughters of Mr. and Mrs. Tatsuo Soga, Soga-no-ya Swine Business, who, along with their father, visited the Ensmingers in 1973. We were in Nippon (the Japanese name for their country), meaning "Land of the Rising Sun," because the sun emerges from the myriad islands of Japan.

Japan! More than 108 million teeming people living on four major islands with a combined area slightly smaller than the state of California.

Japan! Whose "Tokyo Central Fish Market" is the largest in the world.

Japan! Artistic people, who have given the world exquisite pottery, embroidered silks, enamels, finely wrought mosaics, and beautiful pearls.

Japan! An industrious people, whose miracle is simply the hard work of a dedicated people pulling together.

Only 18% of Japan's total land area is agricultural. Consequently, intensive utilization of land is absolutely imperative. Of the total agricultural area, 86% is cultivated.

A briefing and slide presentation on the livestock inidustry of Japan was given by Karl Sera. He is a graduate of Iowa State University and an old friend of mine.

Soga-no-ya Swine Business

Mr. Sera threw pictures on the screen of the high-priced boars that Mr. Soga, of Soga-no-ya Swine Business, had purchased in the U.S. in 1973.

Soga-no-ya marketed 30,000 hogs last year. This was a low year, because of manure disposal problems that they had encountered. Now they are using solar energy to dry manure to 30% moisture. Soon the Soga-no-ya Swine Business will increase hog marketing to 70,000 head per year.

VIP Luncheon in Tokyo, with Invited Guests

Our 11 guests were: Mr. and Mrs. Tatsuo Soga; Mr. and Mrs. Terry T. Hashida; Mr. Karl Sera; Mr. Katsunori Yanagihara and his son, Yasufum (Yasufum was in the Ensminger's home in 1972, at which time he was a student at the University of Southern California); Dr. and Mrs. Yoshimasa Matsuo, Japan

Dr. E is presenting a book to Larry F. Thomasson, Agricultural Attaché, American Embassy, Japan, at a VIP Luncheon, in Tokyo. Mr. Thomasson briefed our delegation on the agriculture of Japan. Mr. Karl H. G. Sera, representative American Soybean Assn., is seated to Dr. E's left.

Racing Association, whom the Ensmingers had met during an earlier visit to Japan; Mr. Kazuo Fujii, who has a Thoroughbred breeding farm near Sanger, California; and Larry F. Thomasson, Agricultural Attaché, American Embassy, Japan. The Japanese do a great job in making visitors feel welcome.

The South Korea We Saw

We arrived in Seoul, South Korea with reservations at the Chosun Hotel. At breakfast, I briefed the group on Korea.

Korea is divided into two parts—Republic of Korea (South Korea), and Democratic People's Republic of Korea (North Korea)—at the 38th parallel. South Korea is about the size of Italy.

Korean Beef Cattle Feeding Demonstration

The Korean beef cattle feeding demonstration and pilot project was sponsored by U.S. Feed Grains Council (USFGC) in cooperation with the Daehan Livestock and Feed Company, Seoul, Korea. USFGC is a nonprofit trade association representing feed grain and seed producers, grain exporters, railroads, agricultural chemical companies, equipment manufacturers and other U.S. agribusiness firms that have a stake in seeing worldwide use of feed grains increase. The Daehan Livestock and Feed Co., Ltd. is a sister company to a broiler company and a flour mill. We were welcomed, briefed, and taken over the operation by Mr. Si Ho Kim, President.

The Daehan Project

On October 18, 1971, 264 steer calves were loaded into a DC8 "stretch jet" at Tinker Air Force Base, Oklahoma, to begin one of the longest cattle drives in western history. Some 7,717 miles and nine months to a year later, most of the steers wound up as beefsteaks on the dinner tables of Japan and Korea.

The cattle shipment was part of a pilot project designed to show that application of modern cattle feeding technology under Asian conditions could help fill the gap between the available supply of beef and the growing demand for steaks, roasts, and sukiyaki—and at the same time, show indications of financial feasibility. In these terms, the project was a success.

Left to right: Mr. Myung Boum Lee, Lot Manager, Daehan Project; Dr. E; Mr. Yang Sung Hoyk, Secretary General, Inchon Chamber of Commerce and Industry; and Mr. Si Ho Kim, President, Daehan Project.

The Daehan Project chalked up some important firsts. It was the first Asian airlift of U.S. feeder cattle, and the first U.S. feeder cattle ever fed out in the region. This was the first completely American designed beef cattle feedlot in Asia. Also, it represented the first attempt in Asia to put together a complete package of U.S. cattle feeding technology.

Korea-Cargill Co., Ltd.

We visited this commercial feed company, which is not far distant from Suwon. We were briefed on the plant, and taken on an inspection tour by Mr. Hin Sun Kim, feed plant manager.

Office of Rural Development (ORD)

We were warmly received by Dr. In Hwan Kim, Administrator, and his staff. The work of the ORD was first initiated in 1906. However, the organization and program has changed from time to time.

Research is being conducted at 11 research stations in order to implement three major goals of agricultural policy: increased food production, increased income for farmers and fishermen, and increased export along with market system improvement.

We were tremendously impressed with the program and work of the Office of Rural Development,

I was asked to sign the ORD guest book. Audrey is sitting behind me.

Dr. In Hwan Kim (right), Director General, Office of Rural Development, Suwan, Korea, making a presentation to Dr. E.

I presented my book *The Stockman's Handbook* to Dr. In.

Dr. E presenting a book to Mr. Gordon S. Nicks, Agricultural Attaché, U. S. Embassy, South Korea, at a gala. Mr. Nicks briefed our delegation on the agriculture of South Korea.

Our group at the Seoul airport.

especially with their program of getting the results of research applied on the farms. A lot of countries could take a page out of their book.

Gala Dinner

This evening, we had 15 dinner guests from South Korea. Mr. Gordon S. Nicks, Agricultural Attaché, U.S. Embassy, South Korea, addressed our group.

The China We Saw

At 8:00 a.m., we left the Hotel Miramar for the Tsui Sha Tsui Railway Station, Kowloon. Right on schedule, we boarded a train for the hour's ride to

Left to right: Mr. Chu Pao-Chen, interpreter; Mr. Tsu Kao-Pu, representative of Luxingsche (China travel service), Peking; and Dr. E. Mr. Chu and Mr. Tsu were with us during our entire China study-tour.

Shumchun, where we crossed the border and entered China. At the Chinese railway station in Shumchun, we were met by the two Chinese who were to accompany our group throughout China. Mr. Tsu Kao-fu served in a dual capacity; he represented both the Chinese Academy of Agricultural and Forestry Sciences and the Chinese International Travel Service. Mr. Chu Pao-chen, who served as our interpreter, represented the China International Travel Service.

Our train trip from Shumchun to Canton took us through the fertile and productive Pearl River Delta. In Canton, we checked in at the Tung Feng Hotel.

Fushan

Today, we traveled by bus to the two cities of Fushan and Shi Wan, where we visited the Fushan Art Pottery and Porcelain Factory, the Fushan Museum, the Fushan Folk Art Studio, and the Hungmien Silk Factory.

Fushan Art Pottery and Porcelain Factory

The town of Shi Wan, in which the Fushan Art Pottery and Porcelain Factory is located, is famous for pottery and porcelain—a fame which dates back 800 years. Before liberation, only plain pottery for family use was made. There was precious little artwork, except for some done in individual homes. After liberation, mass production of pottery and porcelain took place. Now there are 14 factories, similar to the one that we visited, in the area. They manufacture pottery for industry, engineering, daily use, and art.

Fushan Museum

At the Fushan Museum, we were met and welcomed by Mr. Sun Tai-lai, who escorted us through the museum. It is commonly referred to as the "ancestor temple." The temple was built 800 years ago, during the Sun Dynasty. There are five kinds of sculpture in the temple: Greek sculptures, lion sculptures, wooden carvings coated with gold, brick, and porcelain..

The Fushan Museum.

Fushan Folk Art Studio

Mrs. Lao Wei-ching met and welcomed us upon our arrival at the art studio, and escorted us through it. They produced many intricate works of art, including lanterns and scenes.

Hungmein Silk Factory

Mr. Ching Wen-ting met us upon our arrival at

the silk factory. He welcomed us, served tea, told us about the factory, and escorted us through the operation.

The Peking Area

Upon our arrival in Peking, we were welcomed by a delegation, following which we were escorted to the Nationality Hotel.

Peking, a city of more than seven million at the time of our visit, is the country's political, economic, and cultural center. The capital of China was moved from Nanking to Peking in 1420.

Tien An Men Square

This rectangular area, which is 2,625 ft. long and 1,640 ft. wide and embraces 99 acres, is in the center of Peking. It is the pride of the Chinese people. Here on October 1, 1949, Chairman Mao Tse-tung proclaimed the birth of the People's Republic of China. Here, too, on the same date every year the people come to celebrate with giant parades, fireworks, and singing and dancing far into the night.

To the north of the square stand Tien An Men (Gate of Heavenly Peace), with viewing stands for 20,000 people on each side. On the west is the Great Hall of the People, seat of the highest organ of China's state power, the National People's Congress. On the east stands the building housing the Museum of the Chinese Revolution and the Museum of Chinese History. In the southern part of the square is the Monument to the People's Heroes, with marble bas reliefs depicting scenes from different periods of China's revolution. On one side of the monument is a quote from Chairman Mao; on the other a quote from Premier Chou. South of the monument is an area of lawn, trees, and flowers.

In 1970, the square accommodated a crowd of 500,000 people. It is said to be the largest square in the world.

Audrey got separated from our group while photographing Tien An Men Square. She came across this group of curious people and wondered what they were watching. It was our group.

The Great Hall of the People

This hall stands on the west of Tien An Men Square, facing the Museum of the Chinese Revolution and the Museum of Chinese History on the east. The floor space of this building totals 42½ acres.

In the north wing of the building is the banquet hall seating over 5,000 people. This is where state leaders entertain visitors from other parts of the world.

On the average, about 14,000 workers are engaged on this site each day. This edifice, the most complex ever attempted in China, was built in only 10 months' time (11½ months, including all design work).

Tien An Men Square with the Great Hall of the People on the west side.

Peking Cotton Mill No. 2

Upon our arrival at the mill, we were met by Mrs. Chou Kan-hua, a secretary of the mill's revolutionary committee. Mrs. Chou ushered us into a reception room, where we were served the traditional green tea. Then, she warmly welcomed us and

Dr. E shaking hands with Mrs. Chou Kan-hua, Secretary of the Revolutionary Committee of Peking Cotton Mill No. 2.

briefed us relative to Peking Cotton Mill No. 2, followed by leading us through the huge mill.

Living Quarters

After going through the mill, Mrs. Chou took our group to the housing project where we visited the living quarters occupied by grandmother Chang Liau-sheng. Mrs. Chang warmly received our group.

Mrs. Chou advised that there are 10,000 people housed here.

Peking Cotton Mill No. 2 briefing.

Cotton fabric woven at the Beijing cotton mill.

Kindergarten

We visited the kindergarten, of which Mrs. Li Auei-jin is the teacher. Upon our arrival, the kindergarten youngsters sang in Chinese (which was interpreted for us), "uncle and auntie, how are you." Then a youngster took each of us by the hand and ushered us to a little stool, where we were seated. The teacher welcomed us to the kindergarten. Then, the 5- to 7-year-old kindergarten boys and girls, about 25 in number, proceeded with a program of song and dance numbers, accompanied by music (an organ, and some little instruments on which the youngsters kept time). At the close of their program, they sent greetings to all the children of the United States and invited them to come to see them. The visit to the kindergarten was most impressive—it got to the hearts of all of us.

Theater of Peking Exhibition Center

This evening we went to the theater. Thirteen numbers were presented—all very professional, with excellent costuming.

The Great Wall

I never cease to marvel at The Great Wall. Audrey and I visited it for the second time in 1974.

The Ensmingers at the Great Wall.

The Red Star Sino-Korean Commune

Statistics relative to the commune follow: Acreage, 162,000 mou (pronounced moo), or 26,776 acres; no. of families (households), 17,000; no. of people, 80,000.

The breed of dairy cattle here is known as Peking Black-and-White. They stem from Freisian cattle of the Netherlands, which were crossed on native cattle of the Pinchon breed, from the north of China. There are no bulls on the commune.

At the time of our visit to the Red Star Sino-Korean Commune, Dr. E presented one of his books to Mr. Liu Huai-teh, Leading Member of the Revolutionary Committee.

This commune also marketed 140,000 ducks in 1973.

Other Points of Interest in the Peking Area

We visited the Imperial Palace (Forbidden City); the Peking Roast Duck Restaurant; the Ming Tombs (Underground Palace); and Peking University.

At Peking University we met with some of the staff who had done graduate work at American universities.

The Tachai Area

Tachai, the mountain village that wouldn't stay dead! We boarded Train No. 80 at the Peking Railroad Station and traveled overnight to Yangchuan. Four of our people were assigned to each compartment, in the new and comfortable pullman car. Mr. Chia Teh-heng, Vice Director of the Revolutionary Committee, Tachai Production Brigade, met us upon our arrival at 5:38 a.m. Thence, we boarded a bus and traveled to Tachai, about 1 hour and 15 minutes by bus from the railroad station .

Before liberation, Tachai was very poor. In fact, most people of China did not know that it existed. It was almost inaccessible—there was no good road or railroad to it. With the coming of land reform and cooperative development, all the poor conditions have changed. Land has been reclaimed, water has been

Dr. E flanked by two Chinese guides, in Tachai.

brought in, and living quarters have been greatly improved.

In 1963, Tachai was hit by a seven-day rainstorm and flood. Seventy-eight of the 80 households were destroyed; and 80% of the cultivated land was devastated. The state offered aid following the flood, in both materials and money. But Tachai was too proud to accept aid. Thus, not one cent of state money was used in rebuilding Tachai. New stone houses were constructed.

Tachai—farming the hillsides.

Shih Ping Brigade

This morning, we visited Shih Ping Brigade, Hsi Yang County, Shanghai Province, People's Republic of China. Mr. Chen Yu-tang, Chairman of the Brigade Revolutionary Committee, met us upon our arrival, took us over part of the Shih Ping Brigade farming operations, served tea, and briefed us.

Size of Brigade

The Shih Ping Brigade embraces 1,900 people, 460 households and 534.4 acres of land. Before the revolution, the brigade was backward, with too many people and too little land. As a result, they sent people to the cities to work.

The Gully and Underground Tunnel

This area used to be an eroded gully with boulders, and without water. In the old days, it consisted of rock and barren land and a dry river.

Today, this area is producing good crops. There is an underground tunnel 4,704.2 yd long, and 53.4 acres of new farmland was brought into production in what was formerly a wasted gully area. The tunnel

The underground tunnel through which we walked.

and the benched terraces above ground were constructed in the winters of 1970 and 1971. The area is irrigated; and, of course, some moisture is derived from the underground tunnel below.

Nitrogenous Fertilizer Plant of Tachai

Upon our arrival at the Nitrogenous Fertilizer Plant of Tachai, we were met and welcomed by Mr. Chang Chi-chen, Chairman of the factory Revolutionary Committee. Mr. Chang took us through the fertilizer plant, then briefed us further aboard our bus.

Nan Nao Brigade, Tachai Commune

At the Nan Nao Brigade, Tachai Commune, we were met by Mr. Li Sho-shao, Chairman of the Revolutionary Committee, who took us on a walking tour of the brigade land, served tea, and briefed us.

In the past, there were 60 households scattered on three ridges—all of dirt construction. Today, the brigade has new houses, built in 1969. There are new stone cave dwellings and tile roof houses.

Kuo Chong Reservoir

We were taken on a walking tour of the Kuo Chong Reservoir by Mr. Chiao Chen-wu, Chairman of the Revolutionary Committee.

New stone apartments in Tachai Commune.

Signs on the Reservoir

There are two signs on the reservoir, which were translated for us as we approached. They are slogans from Chairman Mao reading as follows: "In agriculture, learn from Tachai," and "Water conservation is the lifeline of agriculture."

Construction

This dam was built in 1958. It took two years to construct. The reservoir serves three communes; among them, Tachai. Water from this reservoir is pumped a distance of 4.3 miles.

Fishery

In addition to irrigation, the reservoir is used for producing fish. It is stocked with approximately 150,000 fish.

Electricity

Electricity is generated from the reservoir, in the amount of 550,000 kilowatts.

Wu Chai Ping Production Brigade, Tachai Commune

Upon our arrival at the Wu Chai Ping Production Brigade, we were warmly welcomed by Mr. Kuo Lai-liang, who served tea and briefed us.

Our host cited the following accomplishments: The appearance of the village has greatly changed. In 1968, they started the construction of the new village. Three hundred twenty cave houses were built in the past nine years, and over 400 brick houses and three concrete buildings.

Peking Subway

We traveled in the Peking subway, boarding at Peking Railroad Station and getting off at the Military Museum of Chinese Revolution.

This particular stretch of subway was started in 1965 and completed in 1969. Its total length from east to west is 16.8 miles. It has 17 stations. We rode only one-half of its current length. Construction is still going on. When completed, there will be a north-south subway; in fact, it will cover the entire Peking area. Our guide told us that the subway is for public transportation in peacetime and for shelter in

At the Summer Palace, trustee Bill Farr (far right, wearing western hat) is surveying the architecture and Judy Farr is in the center (with sunglasses).

At the Summer Palace, Dr. E was delighted to pose with a little boy and his father.

Another group picture at the Summer Palace.

case of war. A unique feature of the subway is that different kinds of marble are used in each station.

Peking Veterinary Station

We visited the Peking Veterinary Station, primarily for the purpose of seeing a demonstration of acupuncture anesthesia used on a horse.

In the briefing by Dr. Ho Wen, we were told that the station is a county operated veterinary hospital. They have developed "acupuncture points" for use on animals. Since 1970, they have used acupuncture anesthesia in over 600 cases.

They reported 95% success in the use of acupuncture anesthesia on horses. Acupuncture anesthesia works better on females than on males (or geldings); the results are better on the Mongolian horse than on crossbred horses; and the results are better on gentle horses than on wild horses.

Herbs are extensively used in veterinary medicine. There are more than 2,000 medicinal herbs made from plants, animals, and minerals. They say that the combination of eastern and western medicine is best.

Chinese Academy of Agricultural and Forestry Sciences

We had the privilege and pleasure of spending an entire day with the distinguished members of the Chinese Academy of Agriculture and Forestry Sciences. Professors Chin and Cheng are old and dear friends of the Ensmingers.

In the forenoon, Professor Chin Shan-pao, who is age 79, presided. He introduced the rest of our Chinese hosts and extended a warm welcome to our group. In particular, he emphasized the value of exchanging ideas between the U.S. and Chinese counterparts.

Professor Chin welcomed our group to the Chinese Academy of Agriculture and Forestry Sciences. Chu, standing at left is interpreting, and I am seated between.

Prof. Cheng started out by saying, "Since liberation of the country, there have been great changes in Chinese agriculture." As examples, Prof. Cheng cited the following: in 1971, grain output was more than double the 1949 production. During this same period of time, cotton increased by four times and pigs by more than three times.

China's animal husbandry did not really develop until after liberation in 1949. In animal husbandry, the country is divided into two parts: the pasture area and the farming area.

Fish Farming in China, By Prof. Ching

This report pertains primarily to freshwater fish in China. We were told that, since 1949, freshwater fish culture has developed into big business in most provinces.

Mr. Ching stated that fish farming has a long history in China. Mention was made of an early handbook on fish culture and fish breeding. Later, in 618–917 A.D., people began to develop carp production.

My Invitational Lecture before the China Academy of Agriculture and Forestry Sciences

In the afternoon, at the International Club, I gave an invitational lecture entitled, "U.S. Agriculture 1974—production and research," before members of the academy and other Chinese agriculturalists. This was an illustrated lecture, involving more than 100 slides. Also, bound copies of the 151-page lecture, fully illustrated, were given to the academy and to both Professor Chin Shan-pao and Professor Cheng Pi-liu. Mr. Chu Pao-chen did an admirable job as interpreter.

In the entrance of the International Club, we saw these fabulous dahlias. Beverly Kyd is on the left and Lavell Andresen is on the right.

My lecture, with interpretation, took two hours. Then, a question and answer period followed.

Circus and Acrobatics by the Peking Acrobatic Group

We went to the circus at the Peking Workers Stadium, which seats 5,000 people, and it was full. The program was fast moving. The program alternated between animal acts and acrobatics. The animal acts, which were of particular interest to our group, included ponies, bears, camels, sheep, a goat, monkeys, and dogs. It was obvious to us that one horse was part Arabian; he was a beautiful animal. The most unique feature was a goat that walked a high wire. He turned at the end and retraced his footsteps. Then, he made a fantastic turn atop the wire on a little pedestal just big enough to accommodate two hoofs.

The next day we flew to Shanghai where we stayed at the Peace Hotel.

No. 2 Dairy Farm of Shanghai Milk Co.

We visited No. 2 Dairy Farm of Shanghai Milk Co., Shanghai. Upon our arrival, we were met and greeted by the manager, Mr. Chi, and eight of his staff. They escorted us to a reception room where they served tea and Mr. Chi briefed us. Then, they took us through the dairy, following which they served fresh, pasteurized milk.

From My Hospital Bed in Shanghai

The report reads as follows:

Date of Hospitalization: October 21, 1974.
Place: Hwa Tung Hospital, Room 715, Shanghai, People's Republic of China.
Patient: Dr. M. E. Ensminger.
Diagnosis: Acute infection of the gallbladder.
Surgery: Successful

I had gone on a prayer and sheer determination for some days. Prior to leaving the United States, I was completely exhausted because of having to assume a heavier than normal workload with the loss of one of my executive assistants. Also, leading a group and giving an invitational lecture before the academy are responsibilities that I do not take lightly.

The hard lump and the severe pain below my right rib had taken a toll. So, I asked to see a doctor. They took me to the Hwa Tung Hospital, in Shanghai, on the morning of October 21.

About 5:00 p.m., Dr. Huang Yu-wan, chief surgeon of Hwa Tung Hospital, joined the team of MDs for a high level conference. Their unanimous recommendation: that I be hospitalized. "But," I protested, "in visiting 50 countries since 1966, I have never been ill." I explained that I'm completely selfless—that I am more interested in the welfare of our group than in myself. "Moreover," I continued—mustering up all the courage at my command—"I have great stamina, so please give me a 'pain killer' and allow me to remain with my group." They were adamant. "We feel responsible for you," the MDs explained, speaking through interpreter Mr. Chu. Then, Mr. Tsu, for whom I have the highest esteem, looked me squarely in the eyes as he said in his halting English—"Please, Dr. Ensminger." That clinched it. I acceded, hoping the pain would subside and they would turn me loose the next morning.

Hwa Tung Hospital.

Within seconds, I was ushered to room 715, where I was put to bed. Soon, I experienced the most excruciating pains that I have ever endured. A team of surgeons arrived; in total, 12 doctors were involved in my diagnosis, surgery, and postoperative care. They made more examinations, took more samples, and held further consultations. Then, Professor Fu Bei-bin, whom they had summoned, arrived, and I was introduced to him. He is one of the most impressive persons that I have ever met. His very presence is that of greatness; he imparted great confidence. (Later, I learned that Professor Fu is Professor of Surgery, Shanghai Medical Institute No. 2; and, from authoritative sources, I was told that he is recognized as the finest surgeon in Shanghai, a city of 10 million.) The professor examined me, then left the room with the team of surgeons for a final conference. Soon, they returned to my room. Through interpreter Chu, they informed me that, "There is no alternative to immediate surgery."

"Proceed," I said. "I have full confidence in you, my Chinese friends. I have just one request: that Mrs. Ensminger, Mr. Tsu, and Mr. Chu must stay with the group, for I want that this tour-study of China be the best; and tell the group to go ahead and enjoy the trip and not to be concerned about me."

The Shanghai Surgery

Within minutes on the night of October 21, I was prepared for surgery and wheeled into the operation theater. Standing by the surgery table on which I lay, and dressed and masked like the surgeons, was that wonderful interpreter, whose sense of humor and hard common sense never failed. Said he, "Dr. Chu (referring to himself, because of his surgical attire) and your other surgeons are ready. Remember, Dr.

E., that you have the best of surgeons. Remember, too, that every cloud has a silver lining." "Thank you, Mr. Chu," I said.

Leaning over my exposed midsection and marking the line of the incision, I saw the great face of Professor Fu, the chief surgeon. I became relaxed and completely at ease. I had the finest surgeon in Shanghai, and I was a friend of China among my Chinese friends. I went to sleep.

The surgery started at 12:40 (midnight) and ended at 5:15 a.m.—4 hours and 35 minutes later. Back in Room 715, I was soon awake and fully conscious.

My Hospital Room 715

It was a pleasant room, with a view over the city. Its two unique features were an inlaid hardwood floor (warm in the winter and cool in the summer, I was told), which was kept spotlessly clean; and a beautiful colored picture on the wall to the front of my bed, of a mountain scene—terraced, with crops growing on each bench, and a reservoir. It reminded me of Tachai, which we had just visited.

There was a little buzzer attached to the top of my bed. Upon pressing it, a nurse appeared in seconds, day or night; and they were always cheerful. Also, on call around the clock there was an interpreter, provided by China Travel Service, to make my needs known in Chinese; and to assist the doctors and nurses in conferring with me.

My only problem was that I had so much time on my hands. I was being subjected to the supreme test theorized by England's great former Prime Minister, James Ramsay MacDonald. Said hc: "The test of an educated person is that he should enjoy his own company."

Never have I received such TLC (tender loving care) in a hospital, and never have I had such confidence in the professionals—the doctors and nurses—to whom I entrusted my life.

The Rest of Our Trip (by A. H. Ensminger and W. D. Farr)

We were only 13 strong when we left to visit the industrial workers' housing area. The rest were either staying in bed or hospital bound. It was the usual story: except for a few, most were either down, coming down, or just getting over a cold. On this trip, most of the group loved to go to the hospital to see the doctors. The prescription was usually herbal and the price was right: 35¢ and 5¢ for the medicine.

We traveled about 30 minutes through this industrial city of 5.6 million people and arrived at the housing complex. We entered one of the buildings through rows of children lined up along each side, and a sign saying "Warm welcome American friends."

They said that some of the women did not have enough to do, so they were organized into workers brigades. We visited one such group who were operating a flashlight bulb factory. We saw the process from beginning to end.

Then we visited a nursery school. Here we saw the students singing and dancing, an art class, another group chanted a story, one group of four-year-olds were packing the flashlight bulbs into the boxes. Once a week the classes all join the labor force. This teaches them both dexterity and a love of work.

We visited a home where a family of five lived. They had a parakeet. We have seen very few pets in China, so it was quite a surprise.

In the afternoon, we visited one of the 11 children's palaces in the Shanghai area. We were greeted by a large group of children, and a sweet little girl, named Yang Wei-min, took my hand and guided me throughout the afternoon.

In the evening, we attended a performance of acrobatic acts, which was held at a large theatre where we had seen songs and dances two years previously. It had been a dog race track, which they had made into a large theatre seating 20,000 people.

Our group at the light bulb factory.

Tuesday

This morning we visited the Lung Hua Hospital. As we walked into the building, we observed construction out front, so we asked what it was. They said it was a bomb shelter to be used in case of imperial aggression.

When we entered the hospital, we noticed sacks and sacks of what we thought was livestock feed, but they turned out to be herbs, as this hospital used the traditional Chinese medicine as well as the modern western medicine.

We were then taken into a briefing room and served the hot green tea. After a short briefing, we were taken to an observation room above a surgery room, where a goiter tumor was to be removed using acupuncture anesthesia. Soon after we got in, they made the incision, and we observed no reaction by the patient.

As the operation progressed, we asked Dr. Chen, the anesthetist, several questions. Then, when the operation was finished, we walked downstairs into the surgery room to speak to and photograph the patient as he sat up, drank water, and walked across the room.

In the afternoon, we went out to the Shu Hong People's Commune which we had visited two years before.

In front of the apartments were the same long tables of cotton spread out to dry. There was a canal running alongside the road, and we stopped to take a few pictures of some of the activity on the canal.

The canals and rivers in China are most important. They use the water for irrigation; they use the edges to grow their water hyacinths, which the pigs love to eat; they use the canals as one of their main avenues of transportation; and, of course, they build many ponds where they grow their fish. There must be more floating boats in China than anywhere else in the world. Many people live all their lives on a boat.

Lastly, we visited the basket weaving design center.

Wednesday

In the morning we visited the Shanghai Industrial Exhibition.

In the evening we attended a performance of the Peking Opera Company. There were three short selections. The first two had been written by local talent in Shanghai.

Ruth Stewart admiring the beautiful fabrics at the Shanghai Industrial Exhibition.

Thursday

When we arrived at the Hangchow station—having taken the train from Shanghai—we were met by the representatives of Luxingshe, and two agricultural experts.

After lunch we went by bus to the West Lake Banbooware Factory. Our briefing was in a room, completely furnished with bamboo furniture. Some of the bamboo is processed to produce a speckled brown.

The second stop was at the Hangchow Silk Brocade Factory. The most fascinating thing here was the way they design and weave the pictures on the cloth. Some of the designs require thousands of cards, which have been punched out according to the design. When framed and on the wall, it takes close inspection to tell whether it is a woven picture or printed.

Friday

The Yuanlung Production Brigade was located quite a distance off the road and through the fields. When we arrived at headquarters, we had a briefing and then proceeded to walk over hill and dale, through orchards and past towns. We saw their experimental mulberry plots, we passed fish ponds, and we crossed over water on little footbridges.

We saw a group harvesting jute, and passed by little housing areas where we saw children playing, chickens running around, and the mothers carrying on their day's work.

In the afternoon we walked down to the shore of West Lake, where we boarded a launch for a cruise around the lake. As we toured the lake, we passed the Pao Shu Pagoda and the Broken Bridge, then continued to the man-made island, on which they put some lakes—so it is described as "the island in the lake, with the lakes in the island."

We stopped first at the island known as Three Towers Reflecting the Moon. We got off the boat and walked across the island. There were bridges from one tower to the next, never in a straight line. We were walking over the lakes that they had made when they built the island.

On the other side of the island we boarded our boat again. After a short ride we disembarked at what they called the Fish Garden. We walked through the pretty gardens where there was a grass fish done in two different colored plants. There was a lake filled with gold fish, which we fed bread crumbs that Chu produced.

Later, we took our bus to the top of a hill, where there was a red wooden pagoda built in the Sung Dynasty, overlooking the Chientang River. Bill Farr, Chu, one of the local guides, and I climbed the 13 stories to the top. We said this was an international competition, two Americans vs two Chinese. We all made it in fine shape, so the competition was a draw—we all won.

West Lake.

Audrey on the island called Three Towers Reflecting the Moon.

Our last stop of the afternoon was to visit the Tiger Spring. It was another climb up the mountain. We saw the spring, then we sat in the tea house to sip Dragon Well (Longjing) tea made with the Tiger Well water.

Saturday

In the morning we visited a state experimental tea farm. We sat in their nice new building and sipped our tea.

We also went through the tea grading plant,

All the tea in China.

The little hand scale they used for weighing everything.

then out to the hills where the tea shrubs stood in neat rows, along each hillside. There were about six young women who gave us a demonstration of tea picking.

We returned to the hotel to finish packing for our return to Shanghai by train.

Sunday

Early the next morning, Jack Simplot and I went to see a large market with our interpreter, Min. The manager of the market and his assistant took us around the market explaining the various aspects.

By 8 o'clock I was ready to go the hospital to see Dr. E. We had a lot of things to go over, as the group was flying to Kwangchow that afternoon.

On arrival at Kwangchow, we were met by our old friends from Luxinghse, who took us once again to the Tung Fang Hotel.

Monday

We left for the Leh Liu Commune, Kwang Tung Province early, as we knew it was a long drive. We came to the river which we would have to ferry across. We all got off the bus, then the bus drove onto the ferry, followed by us. The whole procedure was reversed at the other side. While waiting to board, we saw several water buffalo by the side of the road. Everyone enjoyed the ferry ride.

We traveled to a little village and then walked along the dikes to watch them fish in a pond.

We then walked through a little town in order to see their silkworms. The townspeople were gathered in little groups and they clapped as we walked through. We saw newly hatched silkworms and the large ones that would be spinning their cocoons in a few days. At Hangchow we had seen only the cocoons.

In the evening the group attended the song and dance performance put on by a troop from Hainan Island.

Tuesday

In the morning we went to visit the Ping Chow People's Commune, which we had visited in 1972.

We were impressed with their progress. They had the statistics all printed for us (they said they have quite a few groups visit). When we arrived they had about 35 students from the foreign language institute at Kwangchow. These students are here for a couple of months for some grassroots experience, then they will return and eventually teach English in the schools of Kwangchow.

In the afternoon we visited the world-famous Canton Export Commodities Fair.

Wednesday

At last we had reached the final hour. Mr. Tsu and Mr. Chu accompanied us to the border. On the train we busily changed our Chinese currency and took care of other legalities.

We went through customs and finally the time came for us to say goodbye to our two very good friends, who had been with us all the way.

When we arrived in Hong Kong, there was no letup in the wind and driving rain. The airport was closed and the ferry boats were stopped. We could not see the harbor, but when the rain lifted later in the day, we observed the busiest harbor in the world was at a standstill. There were no small boats in sight, and the large boats were securely anchored. The water looked very rough.

After another day of rest and shopping in Hong Kong, we were on our last flight to San Francisco.

1976
THE GUATEMALA WE SAW

The Ensmingers in Guatemala City, standing in front of a garden. Note the ruins of an ancient aqueduct in the background.

Guatemala, a republic of Central America, is a beautiful tropical country. It is aptly called "the land of eternal springtime." Guatemala has one of the best climates in the world; the temperature throughout the year ranges from 50 to 70°F, with occasional extremes of a few days' duration.

Guatemala is about the size of Tennessee. Guatemala City is the capital and largest city.

The great Mayan civilization, which was the highest in the ancient western world, flourished throughout much of Guatemala before the Spanish conquest. Archaeologists have discovered much about these remarkable people, but mysteries still remain. There is evidence that the Maya had developed an advanced system of writing, a calendar of the solar year, and the mathematical concept of zero. These achievements predated Western Europe by a thousand years. Mysterious Maya cities flourished for 2,000 years. Yet, at the height of their civilization, they began to falter, and by the time of the Spanish invasion, they had been abandoned. Why the Maya left their magnificent temples, pyramids, and cities is still an unsolved mystery.

Pureblood descendants of the Maya Indians make up almost half of the population of Guatemala, with the remainder largely of Spanish or mixed Spanish-Indian descent. An estimated 30% of the Guatemalans are literate.

Exports

Coffee is Guatemala's leading foreign exchange earner, accounting for approximately one-third of the nation's total exports. Cotton ranks second. Other important exports are sugar, meat, bananas, and essential oils.

Cattle

The majority of the cattle are Criollo, which are high in resistance to ticks and other environmental handicaps of the region. However, there is an increasing interest in improved breeds, primarily Brahman, Indu-Brazil, and Santa Gertrudis.

The coastal area of Guatemala has been the ma-

Sr. Jorge Cordero is telling Dr. E about the Criollo cattle on his ranch.

jor center for fattening feeder steers brought in from Honduras and El Salvador. However, aware of the desirability of increasing its cattle numbers in order to take advantage of beef export possibilities, each country controls its live cattle exports more carefully each year. In Guatemala, live cattle exports are under license. By law (Decree 13-72), enacted in May 1972, over the strong opposition of the cattlemen, the country prohibits feeder cattle exports.

Guatemala is free of foot-and-mouth disease, as are the other countries from Panama north.

Gala Dinner

We had a group of distinguished and knowledgeable guests—our counterparts—for dinner at the Biltmore Hotel in Guatemala City. Following the dinner, we had a question-answer period, with both the hosts (the U.S. group) and the invited Guatemalan guests participating. This was scientific and cultural exchange at its best.

Hacienda El Caobanal

Unfortunately, Sr. Roberto Berger was ill and could not be with us. We were sorry to have missed him. However, his able son, Francois, who graduated from the University of Florida at Gainsville, with a major in animal husbandry, hosted us very nicely.

Francois Berger, age 30, married and the father of two children—a boy and a girl—is the manager. Francois lives in Guatemala City and commutes by plane—airplane or helicopter (he flies both).

Historical

This 13,000 acre farm was founded in 1888, by the great grandfather of Francois. So, Francois is the fourth generation Berger to operate it. Originally, it was a lumbering and grass fattening cattle operation. Many of the mahogany airplane propellers used by the U.S. in World War I were made of mahogany grown on this farm.

The Santa Gertrudis herd was founded in 1946. Only bulls (and semen) have been brought from the United States. No females have been bought. Thus, they have graded up the herd, and they have acclimatized the animals in the process.

Facilities

In addition to pastures and corrals, there are two scales and a modern feed mill.

Cattle

Presently, there are 15,800 Santa Gertrudis and crossbred cattle on Hacienda El Caobanal, of all ages. Of these, 7,000 are females of breeding age.

Horses

There are 600 head of horses on Hacienda El Caobanal, consisting of Quarter Horses, Thoroughbreds, and crosses.

The Uniqueness of This Operation

We were particularly impressed with the following: they have 16,000 head of cattle on 11,000 acres of grass, 85% of the ranch under is irrigation, the production of lumber for their own use, their stocking of wild game, an incentive basis for the help, the pasture rotation system—involving about 3 days grazing and 21 days rest. This system makes for a high carrying capacity and controls parasites.

They also produce grain sorghum for the cattle finishing operation, have a modern feed mill, and have an integrated operation—breeding, finishing, and very soon slaughtering-fabricating-marketing.

At Hacienda El Caobanal, steers are preconditioned by bunk feeding on pasture from 7 to 12 months of age, following which they are moved to the finishing (fattening) facilities. In this photo, Dr. E is examining the preconditioning ration.

Andalusian Horse Breeders Association

Today, we were guests of the Andalusian Horse Breeders Association, Guatemala City, where we saw their beautiful Andalusian horses—the mounts that they use for bullfighting, parade, dressage, jumping, and pleasure riding.

This was a special exhibition in honor of the Agriservices Foundation group. We were hosted by Sr. Rafael Aycinena, who is a Supreme Court Justice and President of the Asociacion Guatemalteca de Criadores de Caballos de Pura Raza Espanola.

The Horse Show

In opening the show, Sr. Rafael Aycinena Salazar first recited the history of Andalusian horses.

Next, Sr. Aycinena read a citation and made Dr. M. E. Ensminger an honorary member of the Asociacion Guatemalteca de Criadores de Caballos de Pura Raza Espanola. The citation reads as follows:

> LA ASOCIACION GUATEMALTECA DE CIRADORES DE CABALLOS DE PURA RAZA ESPANOLA, HACE CONSTAR QUE EN EL ACTA DE JUNTA GENERAL DE ASOCIADOS CELEBRADA EL 4 DE AGOSTO DE 1975 SE ACORDO EL SIGUIENTE PUNTO.
>
> SEPTIMO: POR UNANIMIDAD SE NOMBRA MIEMBRO HONORARIO DE ESTA ASOCIACION AL SR. DOCTOR M. E. ENSMINGER EN RECONOCIMIENTO A SU VALLIOSA CONTRIBUCION A LA ZOOCTECNIA A TRAVES DE SUS NUMEROSOS LIBROS, ARTICULOS, COLUMNAS, CONFERENCIAS Y SEMINARIOS EN UNIVERSIDADES DE DIFERENTES PAISES Y EN LA DIRECCION DE LA ESCUELA INTERNACIONAL DE GANADEROS.
>
> CIUDAD DE GUATEMALA, 18 DE ENERO DE 1976. (Signed by Lic. Rafael Aycinena S., Presidente and Sr. Jaime Vila S., Secretario.)

An Andalusian with a full flowing tail exhibited by the Andalusian Horse Breeders Association, Guatemala City.

An Andalusian fine harness class.

Then the 14 classes followed, with each class announced and described in both Spanish and English.

In all the classes, there was much dressage. The horses were well trained and the riders were superb. The army band played throughout the performance. Following the show, we were hosted to a luncheon provided by the club.

Finca San Rafael, Guatemala City

We visited this 700 acre farm, owned by John F. Whitbeck. All but about 75 acres of this farm has been put into a Guatemala City subdivision. So, very soon (perhaps within two months), the dairy at Finca San Rafael will be moved to Montecristo.

Montecristo Farm, Owned By Sr. John F. Whitbeck, Guatemala City

Montecristo is a 700-acre farm to which John Whitbeck plans to move his dairy herd in the next two months.

A new and modern dairy barn is being built. The milking parlor has provision for milking six cows at a time. Milking machines of a French make will be used. Also, there is a record room, a concentrate (feed) room, and a milk processing room (in which milk will be pasteurized and bottled).

It is noteworthy that John Whitbeck is going to pasteurize his milk despite the fact that government controls will not permit him to sell it for more than raw milk.

Finca San Sebastian, Duenas Antigua, Guatemala

We visited this diverse operation managed by Arturo Falla Cofino. He took training in the United States, on a scholarship. Sr. Falla has managed this farm for 25 years. We also met Arturo's aunt, Catalina, who is 42% owner of the operation.

The operation is Eighty-five-years old. It was started by the grandfather of the present manager. Arturo's father managed the place for 42 years.

The main products of the operation are coffee, fruit (oranges, avocados, pears, peaches, lemons, guavas), lumber (they grow timber and operate their own sawmill), flowers (roses), milk, and honey.

Coffee

There are 500 acres of coffee on this farm. It was being picked at the time of our visit. This coffee plantation has produced up to one-half million pounds of coffee.

Dr. E with Sr. Arturo Falla Cofino, Manager (right), and Catalina, 42% owner (left), of Finca San Sebastian, at Duenas Antigua.

Coffee plantation on Finca San Sebastian. Note coffee bushes in the background. Agriservices Foundation Trustee Bill Farr (white shirt) is asking the manager, Sr. Arturo Falla Cofino, a question while Dr. E is taking notes.

The coffee is processed on the farm. This means that the pulp is removed and it is washed, sorted, and dried (to 12% moisture). Thence, it is delivered to a plant in Guatemala, where it is roasted.

Fish

They produce carp, bass, bluegill, and other kinds of fish.

Macadamia Nuts

Some plantings of macadamia are now reaching bearing age.

Citrus

There are about 2,500 orange trees of bearing age (eight years of age). Also, there are lemon trees. Most of the oranges are navels.

Roses

They have been in the rose business since 1969. Presently, they produce and market about 375,000 roses per year. There are 10 commercial varieties, most of which are red. The roses are packed in boxes, which are iced; with 400 roses per box, in little packages of 25 each. Roses are marketed in Miami, Nicaragua, El Salvador, and locally.

1976 & 1978
THE CUBA WE SAW

The Cuba We Saw (1976)

In Cuba we met friendly people and we saw a beautiful country. Moreover, our hosts let us see everything that we requested. Our study-tour was a pleasant experience. Our trip to Cuba, the 52nd country that we have had the pleasure of visiting since 1966, lent further credence to the following statement, which we have repeated over and over again: *We find good people all over the world—only their faces differ.*

When we arrived in Havana Sr. Richard Darlington met us at the airport, checked us in at the Hotel Riviera, arranged our schedule. He also served as our guide-interpreter throughout Cuba.

The name *Cuba,* a relic of the original inhabitants (now extinct), is pronounced "kooba" by the islanders.

Poetically known as the Pearl of the Antilles because of its charm, beauty, and natural wealth, Cuba was formerly the vacationland of many Americans (Canadians still flock there—by the thousands). Cuba is also famed for sugar, fine cigars, coffee, and friendly people. Most Cubans enjoy singing and dancing, especially the lively folk music of the islands. I recently took a peek into this sugar bowl of the world.

The socialist republic of Cuba lies at the entrance to the Gulf of Mexico, dividing the opening into two channels. It is a mere 90 miles south of Key West, Florida; and Havana is only 1,197 miles from New York City and 597 miles from New Orleans.

Cuba is a tropical country, with an average temperature of 77.7°F. The average annual rainfall at Havana is 45 inches.

In this warm southern land, with soil so rich that almost anything will grow, vegetation is luxuriant. The royal palm is the most characteristic tree of Cuba. It attains a height of 50 to 75 feet, and sometimes more than 100 feet. Alone, or in clusters, or in long isles, towering above the plantations or its fellow trees in the forest, its beautiful crest dominates every landscape. Every portion, from its roots to its leaves, serves some useful purpose. Fields are covered with beautiful flowers and fragrant plants.

Historical

Cuba was discovered and claimed for Spain by Christopher Columbus in his first voyage in 1492. It is noteworthy, too, that the energetic Spanish explorer was responsible for getting sugarcane, which originated in New Guinea, to the new world. On his second voyage in 1493, Columbus took sugarcane to Santo Domingo and Haiti; thence, it was taken to Cuba a few years later.

Cuba served as the launching pad for Hernando Cortez's expedition for the invasion of Mexico, and for Ferdinando de Soto's expedition for the exploration of Florida—expeditions which very adversely affected Cuba, draining it of horses, money, and men.

The Spaniards began to settle the island in 1511. Soon, Cuba became one of the richest colonies in the West Indies. Most of the settlers took up sugarcane and tobacco farming, with the aborigines (Indians) serving as forced laborers in the fields. As the Indian population declined, the Spaniards filled the labor gap by importing slaves from Africa, beginning in 1517 and continuing until the abolition of slavery in 1886.

The Batista Era

In 1933, an army sergeant named Fulgencio Batista led a revolution that overthrew the government. Until 1940, Batista ruled Cuba as a dictator, with figurehead presidents serving in name only. In 1940, Cubans adopted a new constitution and elected Batista president. But, the constitution prevented him from seeking reelection to succeed himself in 1944. In 1952, Batista overthrew the government and again became dictator.

Then Came Castro

On July 26, 1953, Fidel Castro, a young lawyer who had grown up on a plantation, tried to start a revolution against Batista by attacking the Moncada Army Barracks in Santiago de Cuba. Castro and many of his followers were captured and imprisoned. After his release in 1955, Castro went to Mexico. There he organized the 26th of July Movement, a revolutionary group named after the date of his first revolt. Castro's forces landed in Cuba in December 1956. Most of the rebels were soon killed. But Castro and 11 others escaped to the Sierra Maestra Mountains. There, they formed a guerilla band to carry out surprise attacks against the Cuban government.

In 1957, Castro's forces began to attack army units and blow up bridges and railroad tracks. Attempts by the government to crush the revolution increased the people's support of the rebels. By mid-1958, many Cubans had lost confidence in Batista's government. On January 1, 1959, Batista fled the country. Castro's forces then took control of the government. Later, Castro became Premier of Cuba.

At first, the United States supported the Castro government. But very soon relations between the two countries declined sharply. Thereupon, Cuba turned to the U.S.S.R. for economic and military assistance.

There is a housing shortage in Cuba, but the government is building new apartments. Dr. E was shown this new apartment building by the guide.

Cuba Today

In our study-tour of Cuba, Mrs. Ensminger and I had the good help of Sr. Richard Darlington, one of the most dedicated interpreters-guides that we have had in any country. We apologized profusely to our ever-present and always cheerful Richard for our furious pace—including being up all one night traveling. His stock reply was: "It's my pleasure and my duty." Then there was Sr. Heriberto Fernandez Esquivel, Chief of the Press Department, whom we found to be as able as he was solicitous; and Sr. Raul Campuzano, another member of the Press Department, who knew all the best shopping places for Mrs. E., and without whose help I could have saved a lot of money.

Dr. E presenting one of his books to Professor Antonio Vargas, Nutritionist, at the University of Havana.

Livestock

Animals are of importance in the national economy. In the livestock programs, emphasis is on improved breeding (largely through artificial insemination), disease eradication (especially brucellosis), use of available feeds (chiefly grass, molasses, and bagasse), and improved facilities.

Sugar

Sugar has been the dominant crop in Cuba since the end of the 18th century. It is grown throughout the land, but the largest crops come from eastern Cuba. There are 152 sugar factories in Cuba, the majority of which are concentrated in the eastern provinces.

Tobacco

Tobacco, the second most important crop grown in Cuba, is noted throughout the world for its fine quality in the manufacture of cigars. It comes chiefly from the Vuelta Abajo district in northwestern Cuba.

Havana

Today, we saw the city of Havana and its people. We visited the Art Warehouse, Havana Libre Hotel (formerly the Hilton Hotel), and the Friendship Store. Also, we familiarized ourselves with Cuba's compulsory education, factory wages, apartment rental, and food prices.

Old Havana

This morning, we visited Old Havana. Among the historic places that we saw were the Cathedral of Havana, the first Cathedral of Havana, and Morro Castle—which was built by the Spaniards.

Hemingway Museum

Ernest Hemingway, who ranks among the most influential and famous Amcrican authors of his time, did much of his writing in Cuba. So, we asked to see Hemingway's old home, which is now a museum, located seven miles from Havana. We visited the Hemingway Museum on Friday, April 9.

Everything about the house (museum) reflects the colorful character of the noted author. Hemingway fought in and reported on wars, hunted big game, married four times, and survived several near-fatal accidents. He became as well known as his works, and his works seldom departed far from his life.

Hemingway was seriously wounded in Italy when he was 18. This event helps explain his enduring concern with physical and psychological violence.

Hemingway's last major work, *The Old Man and the Sea* (1952), the heroic story of an aged Cuban fisherman's lone expedition after marlin in the Gulf Stream, led directly to his receiving the 1954 Nobel prize in literature.

Hemingway was last in Cuba in 1960, at which time he became very ill. He went to the Mayo Clinic, Rochester, Minnesota. The diagnosis: Sclerosis of the liver (from drinking too much alcohol). In July 1961, at his home in Idaho, he shocked the world when he took his own life.

We were taken on a personally-conducted tour through Hemingway Museum by the Museum Director, Sr. Luis Puentes. It has been preserved just as the author left it, even to the dishes set on the dining room table and unopened mail in his bedroom.

The house occupies spacious grounds, with beautiful trees. Also, it is high on a hill, with a marvelous view of Havana. Hemingway bought the estate from a French family. The noted author lived there 6 to 7 months of the year. He divided the rest of the year between big game hunting in Africa and his home in Idaho.

His old Royal typewriter, on which he typed his writings, was on a shelf next to his bed. He wrote standing up, because of an old knee injury. Also, he worked very early in the morning (actually at night) and continued throughout the morning.

The four-story building (a square building four stories high, with one room on top of the other) was planned by Mary, with the thought that Hemingway would use the top floor for seclusion and writing. But the author never used it for the intended purpose. He preferred to stand up in his bedroom.

The four-story building next to the big house (called the "cat house") at Hemingway Museum. Some 40 to 50 cats occupied the bottom floor.

On the top floor of this four-story building, there is a telescope that Hemingway gave to Mary for her birthday. Rumor has it that Mary focused it on Hemingway when he was in Havana, in order to keep on eye on him.

The director of the museum also told how Hemingway would use the fourth floor for sessions with his pals when he wished to discuss things that he didn't want Mary to hear.

Ramon Castro and the State Cattle Breeding Station

This afternoon, we visited the cattle breeding station managed by Sr. Ramon Castro, older brother of Premier Fidel Castro. By car, it's a 1 hour and 20 minute drive from Havana. Upon our arrival, we were received by Sra. Castro, who serves as secretary to her husband.

Sr. Castro is a big man, with boundless energy—and very friendly. He is very proud of this cattle breeding farm, as well he should be, for he designed and supervised its development beginning in 1961.

Mrs. Ensminger asked Sr. Ramon Castro if he followed out the Cuban teaching of sharing in housework with his wife. His reply: "Yes, my wife and I go 50-50. I make the money, and she spends it; she cooks, and I eat the food; I dirty the clothes, and she washes them."

Left to right: Sr. and Sra. Castro and their daughter, Dr. E presenting his *Beef Cattle Science*, and Audrey.

Ramon Castro and Dr. E with the cattle breeding station in the background.

The Tropicana

Tonight, we were invited to the Tropicana for dinner and a dance review, as guests of the Cuban Press Department. The show started at 10:30 p.m. and continued until midnight.

The Tropicana is an outdoor theater, among the trees, with the moon and stars as the ceiling. It's a beautiful, natural setting.

An orchestra played throughout the dinner hour, until 10:30 p.m.

The dance review consisted of Cuban, Russian, Mexican, and African numbers—all beautifully costumed. Also, there were performers from outer space (who arrived on space needles) and acrobatics.

It was a fast-moving show, with plenty of variety—one of the best dance reviews that we had ever seen.

Animal Research Center, Havana

We spent half a day, including lunch, at the Animal Research Center. This station is responsible for the correlation of agricultural teaching, research and extension work with animals throughout Cuba. During our visit, we were hosted by Ing. Gustavo Crespo, a pasture specialist, and Dr. Miriam Ribas, a well trained animal geneticist with a doctorate de-

At the Animal Research Center, Havana, Cuba. Dr. Miriam Ribas (left) is showing Dr. E some Charolais bulls that were being production tested.

gree, who speaks perfect English. We plan to invite Dr. Ribas to appear on the program of the 1978 International Stockmen's School. She is receptive; and the U.S. Department of State has, in a preliminary way, reacted favorably. (I am happy to report that Miriam Ribas did serve as a guest professor on the program of the International Stockmen's School, in Phoenix, Arizona, January 9-12, 1978, and that her lectures were superb.)

Camaguey Province

Travel to Camaguey Province to visit Compania Ganadera Bacerra, the ranch owned by King Ranch of Texas, which was expropriated by Cuba when Fidel Castro came into power, was a mission on behalf of my King Ranch friends. From the time of expropriation until my visit—16 years later—King Ranch had no contact with, or report on, their Cuban ranch. So, I told my longtime friend, John Armstrong, President, King Ranch, that I would make every effort to visit the ranch. Fortunately, we were able to complete the mission. So, upon our return, John Armstrong called a meeting of the King Ranch board, owners, and other officials, before whom Audrey and I gave a slide presentation of the Compania Ganadera Bacerra that we saw. Tears streamed down the cheeks of many of those present as we presented the saga of their beloved ranch.

Camaguey Province, which ranks first in cattle among the provinces and second in sugarcane, is the "bread basket" of Cuba. As Castro put it: "The struggle for the economy is being decided in Camaguey." Thus, we wanted to see this fertile agricultural area. Additionally, in Camaguey we wished to visit Compania Gandera Bacerra, Inc., formerly owned by famed King Ranch of Texas. In Havana, we were told that we could see Compania Ganadera Bacerra, Inc., but that it would be a rugged trip; that we would arrive in Camaguey by air at 3:30 a.m., and that we would have to travel by jeep over rough roads in order to get to the former King Ranch establishment, on which they had Santa Gcrtrudis cattlc and Quarter Horses. Our reply: "Fine."

We were met by Sr. M. de J. Lefran, and Sra. Maria del Carmen Lapinel.

At breakfast, we were joined by Sr. Richard Darlington, our ever faithful guide, along with Sra. Maria del Carmen Lapinel, the cheerful little lady who had met our plane, Ingenerio Fredy Oliva Palomino, a livestock expert, and Sr. Juan Hernandez Machaco, who correlates visitations and programs, and who speaks very good English.

Ing. Fredy Oliva Palomino informed us that he knew the place that we referred to as formerly known as Compania Ganadera Bacerra. Presently, he informed us, it is known as the Coffee Plantation and used as a cattle fattening operation (pasture and molasses), and there are no Santa Gertrudis cattle or Quarter Horses there. Despite the inference of the name "Coffee Plantation," there is no coffee growing

Upon our arrival at Camaguey at 3:30 a.m., Sra. Maria del Carmen Lapinel presented Mrs. Ensminger with a beautiful bouquet of lilies and roses.

there now. Rather, they explained, it was so named for historic reasons, because many years ago some coffee was grown on this place. So, following breakfast, Richard (our guide), Ingererio Fredy Oliva Palomino, Sr. Juan Hernandez Machadeo, a driver, and Audrey and I started for the Coffee Plantation in a Ford car (made in Argentina).

First, we passed through the "Milk Triangle Area," a triangular-shaped area of 642,200 acres, on which they will eventually have 250 large, mechanized dairies. As we drove to the Coffee Plantation, Fredy briefed us on the agriculture of the area.

Newly constructed molasses facilities (designed for feeding molasses on pasture), consisting of a paved lot, two long bunks, and two long shelters—adequate for 600 cattle. In the Meat Triangle, 100 installations of this type are planned.

Meat Triangle Headquarters

We were advised that in order to visit the Coffee Plantation, two things were necessary: obtain the permission of the Director of the Meat Triangle, and transportation by jeep, because of the bad roads.

Eventually, we found Sr. Pedro Solas, Director of the Meat Triangle. He very graciously approved of our visiting the Coffee Plantation, lent us his jeep, and told Fredy how to get to the Coffee Plantation. Moreover, he said that he would be waiting for us upon our return; unfortunately, his schedule didn't permit him to accompany us.

Compania Ganadera Bacerra (owned by King Ranch of Texas, renamed the Coffee Plantation of Cuba following expropriation)

Within another hour, we arrived at the ranch. Here is what we found.

The Two Ranch Houses and the Caretaker

We visited the main King Ranch house, which Audrey photographed outside and inside. She also took pictures of the nearby house, where we understood the former manager lived.

The main house is well maintained as a museum or attraction, just like it was left by King Ranch. The library; TV; a table, the top of which is adorned by an American flag; beds; and other articles have been preserved just as they were left. On the shelves in the dining room were a number of familiar books, including *Feeds and Feeding* by Morrison, and *Animal Breeding Plans* by Jay L. Lush.

A caretaker (Sr. Alberto Cordovez) looks after the big house, but no one lives there. Sr. Cordovez, who knew the former personnel, had not heard of the passing of Robert Kleberg until I told him.

We were shown through the big house, consisting of a living room-dining room, a screened porch,

Dr E and Sr. Alberto Cordovez, visiting in the King Ranch Museum—the former King Ranch House. Sr. Cordovez is the caretaker of the museum.

The Ensmingers were served refreshments in what was the dining room of the King Ranch house.

four bedrooms, four baths, and a kitchen. The house is nicely maintained.

Then, Sra. Cordova invited us to have refreshments, consisting of a very sweet fudgelike candy plus plain soda crackers, a delicious homemade fruit ice cream, and coffee. The coffee was catered out from San Miguel.

Present Animals

The cattle presently on the place are of Zebu breeding—there are no Santa Gertrudis there. We saw a few ordinary native horses about the premises, but no Quarter Horses.

What Happened to the Santa Gertrudis Cattle and Quarter Horses?

We were told that these are being carried forward on Turiguano, a 19,760 acre island. This island, which has a land connection and can be driven onto, is about 100 miles from Camaguey, as we understood it.

Presently, Turiguano Island is the Santa Gertrudis cattle breeding center for all of Cuba. There are Quarter Horses there, too; but the island is not a Quarter Horse breeding center.

After a very pleasant and informative stop of an hour and a half at the Coffee Plantation, we started back.

Dinner Sunday Evening

We arrived back in the village where we met Sr. Pedro Solas, the able Director of the Meat Triangle. Mr. Solas had arranged for a delicious and bountiful steak dinner for us in the local restaurant. Also, he brought with him one of his engineers, Ing. Jose Luis Martin de Leon, who took his masters degree under Dr. T. R. Preston, a Britisher and friend of the Ensmingers. Dr. Preston spent seven years in Cuba, directing animal research and training students.

Sr. Solas has been in charge of this operation for seven years. Administratively, Sr. Solas has broken down his operation into 11 units, each of about 32,110 acres, with a manager in charge of each.

Horse Farm Supervised by Sr. Pedro Solas

Following dinner, Sr. Solas took us in his jeep to the horse headquarters, consisting of 9,800 acres which served as his source of cow ponies for the cattle operation.

Summary

Mrs. Ensminger and I were invited to visit Cuba for scientific and journalistic purposes, and the U.S. Department of State approved of our going. We found friendly people, good weather, and a beautiful country. It was a pleasant experience.

Dr. E looking over a Quarter Horse stallion on the horse breeding farm supervised by Sr. Pedro Solas in Camaguey Province, Cuba.

The Cuba We Saw (1978) by A. H. Ensminger

Due to pressures in the office, Dr. E was not able to take this trip, so I went accompanied by a study-tour group of 15. We met up in Mexico City and from there we flew to Havana. When we arrived, our guide and interpreter, Ronald Gonzalez, met us and helped us through customs and immigration. During our visit we covered the island from one end to the other.

1978. The Cuban study-tour group.

This is our story in capsule form:

We arrived at the Genetic Center in Guanabana and were greeted by the director, Dr. José Llanusa who briefed us and showed us through.

The next day, we boarded our bus and headed for the Island of Turiguano. This island was formerly owned by the King Ranch. We stopped first at the bull testing stations. This operation has 8,000 hectares and 10,000 head of cattle. Its main objective is grading up and maintaining the Santa Gertrudis breed of cattle.

We drove east to Camaguey and visited the dairy triangle project.

On our way back to Havana we saw fields of tobacco, banana plantations, teakwood trees growing wild, mango trees, papaya, and, of course, lots of cane sugar, and many other crops.

The next day, we visited the Instituto de Ciencia Animal, Miriam Ribas place of work. It is situated in the southeast part of the province of Havana. Dr. Ramón Ortiz is the director.

Audrey with the caretaker of the former King Ranch museum.

Audrey on the balcony of the Arabian restaurant where we had lunch one day, with the gorgeous view in the background.

Everywhere we went in Cuba we saw construction of new apartments and houses, construction of reservoirs for irrigation, and giant steps being made in their agricultural production.

I was so terrybly sorry that Dr. E could not make this trip because Dr. Miriam Ribas and the Cuban officials took us to all the places that we had heard about. Their hospitality knew no bounds.

1977
THE KING RANCH AND GUADALAJARA, MEXICO WE SAW

Time for class—not one minute late! Dr. E ringing his bell at the January 1977 International Stockmen's School, in San Antonio, Texas.

Following three days of lectures, on Thursday 200 (5 busloads) of the enrollees and staff of the International Stockmen's School visited famed King Ranch, Kingsville, Texas, the best known ranch in the world.

Following the King Ranch visit, Mrs. Ensminger and I led a small group of stockmen on a study-tour of the Guadalajara, Mexico area.

King Ranch

Stephen J. (Tio) Kleberg, board member and Secretary of King Ranch, arranged the schedule and directed the tour. The King Ranch staff met us in Kingsville, where two to three staff members boarded each bus and served as guides. Among the guides were two former staff members of the International Stockmen's School staff; namely, Norman Parish and Dr. G. L. Morrow. Also, John Armstrong, who joined us at the noon barbecue, had served as a staff member of the International Stockmen's School. Three King Ranch staff were enrollees in the International Stockmen's School of this week; namely, Peter McBride, Dirk Rhoad, and Scott Kleberg.

As we traveled through the ranch, the King Ranch staff told us about the operation—all very well done. Also, they had the cowboys herd the Santa Gertrudis cattle and Quarter Horses near the roads over which we passed.

Testing Quarter Horses for Cow Sense

Before being placed in the breeding band, all Quarter Horse stallions and mares are tested for "cow sense," which they must possess before being allowed to propagate. Also, it is noteworthy that each cowboy gets the offspring of animals that he has used to train and test. The evaluation is done by an impartial committee, however.

Roundup

Helicopters, rather than horses, are used for rounding up cattle. Normally, two helicopters work together, with a cowboy sitting beside each pilot.

Water

Most water is provided by wells, powered by windmills, located about 3 miles apart. Thus, on the average, cattle and horses do not walk more than 1½ miles to water.

Game

There is much wild game on King Ranch. Hunting is limited to King Ranch staff and their invited guests. Among the game that we saw were white-tailed deer, wild hogs, snow geese, Canadian geese, and ducks.

Cutting Horse Demonstration

At noon, we were favored with a cutting horse demonstration, under the direction of Joe Stiles, Quarter Horse division manager of King Ranch, at Kingsville. It was superbly done. All of the horses were good, but Mr. San Peppy, an eight-year-old stallion, whom we saw perform, is among the all-time greats. He is a two-time world champion cutting horse.

Presentation of Plaque—Dedication of Horses and Horsemanship

Prior to the barbecue, Dr. Ensminger presented a plaque—a replica of the dedication page that will appear in the new fifth edition of his widely used book, *Horses and Horsemanship*. (*Horses and Horsemanship* was recently translated in Spanish and published in Argentina).

Dr. Ensminger remarked that only an author's children are more a part of him than his book, and that the greatest honor that an author can confer upon anyone is to dedicate his writings to him.

DEDICATION

To

King Ranch

World-Famed

FOR QUARTER HORSES:

Major founder of the breed.
Charter member of the American Quarter Horse Association.
Breeder-owner of Wimpy P-1, a double grandson of Old Sorrel, chosen by the Association to receive registration Number One.

FOR THOROUGHBREDS:

Breeder of Assault, winner of the Triple Crown.
Breeder of Middleground, winner of the Kentucky Derby.
Breeder-owner of Bold Venture, Stymie, Rejected, High Gun, To Market, Better Self, But Why Not, Curandero, Bridal Flower, Scattered, Dawn Play, Too Timely, and Buffel.

FOR SANTA GERTRUDIS CATTLE:

Founder of first American-created breed of beef cattle, which was molded to perfection on the Santa Gertrudis Land Grant, from which it takes its name, now the headquarters division of the Ranch.

FOR THE GREAT PEOPLE BACK OF IT:

Captain Richard King, the founder, and the Klebergs—and their descendants, whose famous running W brand is a symbol of service, a pledge of integrity, a mark of courage, character, and wisdom, and indicative of the quality of the horses and cattle raised and the condition of the range.

The framed dedication page carries a line drawing of the Main House (The Big House) at King Ranch.

King Ranch Officials Present For the Luncheon

Among the King Ranch personnel present and introduced were James H. Clement, President and his wife, Illa; Mrs. Richard H. Kleberg, Jr., wife of the Chairman of the Board; Stephen J. (Tio) Kleberg, Director and Secretary, and his wife, Janell; John B. Armstrong, Director, and his wife, Etta; Joe Stiles, Quarter Horse Division Manager.

Dr. E presenting a plaque, engraved with a replica of the dedication page of the fifth edition of his book *Horses and Horsemanship*, to Stephen J. (Tio) Kleberg, King Ranch, following the tour of King Ranch and preceding the barbecue. Dr. Elvin Taysom (standing next to Dr. E), Trustee of Agriservices Foundation; and Joe Stiles, Quarter Horse Division Manager of King Ranch, look on.

Barbecue

Following the cutting horse demonstration, we were served a barbecue, which was as delicious as it was bountiful, by King Ranch. It consisted of barbecued beef, sausage, baked beans, coleslaw, potato salad, pickled onions, rolls, butter, and ice tea or coffee.

King Ranch of Cuba Story

At approximately 3:00 p.m., the 200 enrollees and staff boarded the buses and returned to San Antonio. Mrs. Ensminger and I stayed behind and met with the King Ranch officials for the purpose of telling our story and showing the slides of our April 1976 visit to Cuba, including Compania Ganadera Bacerra, Inc. (the Coffee Plantation), the King Ranch of Cuba, which was expropriated when Fidel Castro came to power. We met in the board room of King Ranch with the following King Ranch people present: James E. Clement, President, and his wife Illa; John B. Armstrong, Director, and his wife Etta and his son Stewart; Stephen J. (Tio) Kleberg, Director and Secretary, and his wife, Janell; W. B. Yarborough, Director; Don Archer, Comptroller for Foreign Relations; John Cypher, Public Relations; and L. A. Walker, Jr.; also, Trustee and Mrs. Guillermo Osuna were present.

The Guadalajara, Mexico We Saw

After visiting King Ranch, a small group of stockmen accompanied the Ensmingers on a study-tour of Guadalajara.

Guadalajara, Hotel Plaza Del Sol, VIP Dinner

Three of our hosts joined us for dinner this evening; namely, Sr. Lic. Enrique Dominguez, L., Jose G. Rochea Chavez, and Bruce Malkin.

Lic. Enrique Dominguez L., manager of the cattlemen's association, gave us the following information pertaining to the cattlemen's association of Jalisco: they have 45,000 members and 3,700,000 head of cattle. Breeds represented are Criollo, 65%; Zebu, 15%, Holstein, 20%; plus a few Angus, Charolais, and Herefords.

Report from Bruce Malkin, Commercial Officer, U.S. Consulate

Steel, hospital equipment, farm machinery, wheat, beans, and sorghum are all imported from the U.S., while Mexico exports oil and cattle to the U.S.

Sixty percent of the working force of Mexico is either unemployed or partially employed, which is frightfully high.

Granja Zapotiltic, Thoroughbred Horse Farm

Granja Zapotiltic is owned by Sr. Miguel Martinez. The buildings here are made of concrete and asbestos.

Dr. E presenting a book to Sr. Miguel Martinez Serrano, during the visit to Granja Zapotiltic, Thoroughbred Horse Farm.

They're fireproof, except for the wood shavings used as bedding.

Stall Floors

Building brick, unkilned, set on a 20 in. sand base, and with sand (not concrete) between brick.

Sr. Martinez paddocks.

Audrey giving Shooting Bill some sugar.

St. Joseph Farm (Loma Bonita Chapalita)

St. Joseph Farm (a Holstein dairy) is managed by Padre Francisco Orozco H.

In the planning stage, Padre Francisco visited top dairies in Mexico and in the United States and Canada (with mention made of California, Wisconsin, New York, and Toronto). The farm consists of 425 acres and has 600 lactating cows.

The padre bought some Holstein heifers from the United States. Then, he graded up some cattle of Mexican breeding.

This provides some resilience plus drainage for the urine. We liked it.

Senior Stallion

They have thity-four horses, of which the senior stallion is Shooting Bill, a 14-year-old brown horse—a son of Nashua, and out of Hyeriod dam. This horse ranks fifth place in the world for six furlongs, a record which he set at Santa Anita. Shooting Bill stands at a $10,000 stud fee, but Sr. Martinez lamented that few horsemen in Mexico are willing to pay this fee.

Health Program

They vaccinate against equine encephalomyelitis (sleeping sickness). Also, they administer a chembiotic once per year. The horses get wormed every three months.

Foal Crop

They get an 80% foal crop, which is very good.

We had lunch at Chapala Camino Real, a beautiful retreat on the shore of Lake Chapala, near the village of Chapala—a fishing village. We were guests of the cattlemen's association (Sr. Barragan and Sr. Dominguez).

Dr. E and Padre Francisco Orozco H., Director General, St. Joseph Farm, Guadalajara, Jalisco, Mexico, standing in a trench silo. This modern dairy, managed by the padre, has 600 lactating cows.

Mini-Bus Tour of Guadalajara/ Visit to the House of Arts and Crafts

Sr. Alberto Orozco Jimenez arranged our schedule for the day, and served as our guide.

Visit to the U.S. Consulate

This morning we made a brief stop at the U.S. Consulate. Bruce Malkin, the commercial officer, gave us some literature, then accompanied us throughout the day.

Union Ganadera Regional de Jalisco

At this second stop of the morning, we visited the headquarters of the cattlemen's association, of which Hugo Barragan is the president and Enrique Dominguez is the manager.

A total of 124 local livestock associations comprise the Union Ganadera Regional de Jalisco.

They have pens where cattlemen can bring their animals that are for sale by private treaty. Each cattleman using these facilities must pay a fee, bring his own feed, and care for and sell his animals.

There were a number of small demonstration grass-legume plots—all very good. Thus, when the cattlemen visit the headquarters of the cattlemen's association, they can study these grass and legume plots and obtain ideas for improving their own operations.

Enrique gave the following additional information pertaining to the cattlemen's association which he manages: every cattleman must belong to the association; each cattleman has a registered brand; each cattleman pays annual dues. This fund is divided as follows: half to the federal government, one-fourth to the city (local) government, and one-fourth to the state cattlemen's association.

Left to right: Lic. Enrique Dominguez L., Manager, Union Ganadera Regional de Jalisco, Guadalajara, Jalisco, Mexico; Pablo Barba Barba, Guadalajara, Jalisco, Mexico; and Dr. E.

Pablo Barba Barba's Farm

The third stop of the day was at the cattle farm owned and operated by Sr. Pablo Barba Barba, the recent past President of Union Ganadera Regional de Jalisco.

Rancho "El Pinto"

We visited the Rancho "El Pinto," the noted Zebu farm owned by Jose Guadalupe de Anda.

Before going to the farm, we stopped at Sr. de Anda's home in Tepatitlan, where we met the family and friends. Also, refreshments were served and we saw the room in which there were many trophies which the Zebu herd had won, in both Mexico and Texas.

The cattle operation was started in 1923, when the present owner's father imported the first Zebu bull from Brazil. In 1945, two more Zebu bulls were imported from Brazil.

Presently, Zebu cattle cannot be imported from Brazil. Neither can semen be brought in from Brazil. This restriction is due to the presence of foot-and-mouth disease in Brazil.

We were served a delicious barbecue in the shade of some huge trees in a pasture—a very beau-

During the luncheon at Rancho "El Pinto" Dr. E visited with the owner and the mayor of the nearby city, while a mariachi band played and sang.

tiful spot. The food included barbecued beef, refried beans, rice casserole, tortillas, fresh pineapple, apples, and tangerines, along with a choice of drinks. During the luncheon hour, a mariachi band played and sang for us.

For the luncheon, Sr. de Anda and his family had invited the mayor of the city, along with many other dignitaries. It was a gala affair.

Following the luncheon, fine horses and Zebu cattle were paraded before us.

This stop was characterized by great hospitality and equally outstanding Zebu cattle. Also, we were impressed with the gently rolling land and well-manicured pastures, and the raising of purebred cattle on little grain.

1977
THE CHINA WE SAW

Left to right: Dr. E, Audrey, Judy Farr, and cattleman/Agri-services Foundation Trustee William D. "Bill" Farr, Greeley, Colorado. This shows the Ensmingers and the Farrs on the Great Wall of China.

In May 1977, Mrs. Ensminger and I made our third study-tour of China, accompanied by a group of 20; and I gave a third invitational lecture before the Chinese Academy of Sciences. Also, throughout the study-tour, I lectured and conducted seminars.

Hong Kong to Shumchun/ Shumchun to Canton

At 7:00 a.m., we left the Hyatt Regency Hotel for the Kowloon Railway Station (Hung Hom). It's a new station and very modern. The train left right on scheduled time—8:18 a.m.—for the 75-minute ride to the border. The car in which we were seated was cooled by fans, along with raised windows, and there were no lavatories.

At the border, we went through the usual procedure required in leaving one country and entering another—passing through customs, having our passports checked and stamped, and taking our baggage through customs. There, too, we met our Chinese guides.

Our train departed from Shumchun promptly at 1:20 p.m., for the 95-minute run to Canton. The car was air-conditioned and very comfortable. We sipped green tea as we watched the countryside through which we traveled.

Chinese Export Commodities Fair

On the afternoon of our arrival, we were taken to the Chinese Export Commodities Fair, which was in progress. It is jointly sponsored by China's various foreign trade corporations. Each year, industrial products and manufactured goods account for a bigger share in China's exports.

There are 12 exhibition halls at the present session of the fair; among them, the Hall of Agriculture, the Hall of Industry, the Hall of Native Produce and Animal Byproducts, the Hall of Arts and Crafts, and the Hall of Machinery.

Sha Chiao People's Commune

The commune consists of 25 production brigades and 11,344 acres. On this commune, we were especially interested in seeing their fish farming and silkworms, in which they specialize.

Fish Farming

The commune has 9,000 fish ponds, on which 25 fishing brigades harvest the fish. They harvest 40 to 50 ponds per day, and they make an average catch of about 143,000 lb per day. We were also told that in terms of fish numbers that's about 13,000 fish per day. It takes about six months from the time fish fry are placed in these ponds until they reach the size that we saw them catching. Fish are harvested six times per year, with each of the ponds harvested about every 50 to 60 days.

Two kinds of fish are produced—grass carp and big fat carp. The fish are fed on mulberry waste from the silkworm operation, grass, sugarcane seedlings, vegetables, soybean cake, peanut cake, rice hulls,

We enjoyed a bountiful lunch at the Sha Chiao commune.

and silkworm pupae. It is noteworthy that most of the feeds used for fish are inedible for humans.

The fish are disposed of through two channels—two fish stations on the commune, and markets in Hong Kong.

Silkworms

The main feed of the silkworm consists of mulberry leaves, which they produce right there on the commune. Leaves in this particular area are harvested eight times per year. The silkworms are fed five times per day.

En route back to Canton, we stopped at the Foshan Pottery Factory. The ladies always enjoyed such visits.

It takes 25 days for silkworms to progress from the time they are hatched until they start spinning the cocoon.

Tibetan Performers

We went to a performance presented by The Song and Dance Ensemble of Tibet Autonomous Region. It was held in the Sun Yat-sen Memorial Hall. The hall is air-conditioned, so it was quite comfortable. The Tibetan performers were excellent. The program consisted of songs and dances; and the performers were dressed in native costumes. It made for a very interesting evening. The star of the show is a former serf—a lady soloist, whom the Chinese love. We were also told that she is in charge of the cultural program for Tibet. The next morning we boarded China Airlines for Hangchow.

Song and dance ensemble from Tibet.

Hangchow Area

Hangchow, the capital of Checkiang Province, is 710 miles from Peking and 100 miles south of Shanghai.

The name Hangchow (pronounced Hang-jo) was given to the city in the year 591. It is a famous scenic city as evidenced by the saying, "Up in heaven there is paradise, and down on earth there are Suchow and Hangchow." It is a city of pagodas and shrines, surrounded by mountains on three sides, lying on the banks of a huge lake dotted with man-made islands and lotus trees—renowned as a tourist and lakeside resort. There are four islands in

Our plane from Canton to Hangchow.

the lake, the most noted of which is Ku Shan, 47 acres in area.

Hangchow No. 2 Chinese Medicine Factory

We were received, briefed, taken through the factory, then accorded a question-answer session by Mr. Chi Hsin-yu, Chairman of the Revolutionary Committee, and Mr. Feng Keng-sen, Vice Chairman of the Revolutionary Committee.

Chinese medicine is very, very old. It has a history of over 3,000 years, going back to the 13th century B.C. Since the revolution, the quality of medicine has been greatly improved. Formerly, Chinese medicines were produced by hand—their factories were not automated.

Our host referred to a famous pharmacologist during the Ming Dynasty, Lie Shih-chen (1518-1593 A.D.), who recorded 1,892 drugs in his book. Today, more than 3,000 herbs are used to produce different Chinese medicines.

We were told that this particular factory produces about 70 different types of medicines. A display of these was in a case in the reception room where we were served tea.

Hangchow Silk Weaving, Dyeing, and Printing Complex

Hangchow is famous for silk; the city is known as the "home of silk."

In our visit to this huge silk factory, we were received, briefed, and taken through the factory by Mrs. Chuang Wei-ling, Secretary of the General Office of the Revolutionary Committee.

We were taken on a walking tour through the plant. Among the things we saw were cocoons being boiled for 15 minutes to kill the pupae (we were told that the killed pupae are used for oil extraction, then the residue is used for fertilizer); silk thread pickers in operation; warfing; reeling; thread tightening; screen printing (the highest quality silk is screened by hand): printing mechanically; color fixation; washing; and inspection.

Shangwang Production Brigade

We visited the Shangwang Production Brigade, Hungshan People's Commune, Shaohsin County, Checkiang Province.

We were received and hosted by Mrs. Chen Hsin-uo, Deputy Chairperson, Revolutionary Leading Group, and we were briefed by Mr. Wu Ark-sen, member of the Revolutionary Leading Group.

We were taken up on a high hill to see a tea planting that was started in 1958. Tea, an evergreen tree, which belongs to the Camellia family, is indigenous to China. In its natural state (untrimmed) trees grow 30 feet or more in height. The plant lives to approximately 100 years of age. It comes into production (that is, tea may be harvested) in 5 to 6 years. However, every 25 to 30 years, the bushes must be cut, and new growth produced from the old root stock. The stand that we saw was 19 years old at the time of our visit.

Barefoot Doctor

We visited with Mr. Han Jung-pao, one of the two barefoot doctors in the brigade. (The other barefoot doctor is a lady.) He is 30 years of age, married, and has two children. He has been a barefoot doctor for 12 years.

Mr. Han took 2½ years' training in a county hospital. At first, he attended classes. Later, he took care of hospital patients. His course work consisted of training in chemistry, physiology, anatomy, surgery, internal medicine, women's diseases, and acupuncture.

The main health problems handled by the barefoot doctor are colds, backaches, stomach problems, and minor injuries. Also, he takes care of deliveries and birth control. Both western and Chinese medicines are used. Antibiotics are rarely used.

Dr. E visiting with Mr. Han Jung-pao, barefoot doctor in the Shangwang Production Brigade, Hungshan People's Commune.

Dr. E thanked the kindergarten for their warm welcome, and told them that the American children sent their love to them.

When not busy with his doctoring duties, the barefoot doctor works in production.

Tea Processing

We observed black tea being processed. At the outset, it was made clear that both green and black tea come from the same plants, but the processing determines whether it shall be green or black tea.

Hangchow University

This morning, we visited Hangchow University. A number of the administrators and professors welcomed us and accompanied us through the university.

The main purpose of this university is to train teachers for middle schools. It has departments of chemistry, physics, history, geography, biology, Chinese literature, political science, foreign languages, physical culture, mathematics, and education. The department of political science is a two-year course, whereas the rest of the disciplines are three-year courses for a degree.

We were taken through the library, where they have 800,000 volumes. In addition, each department has a library room. Students are not permitted in the stacks. Instead, they have a card index in the downstairs room, where they decide what book or books they want. Then the librarian brings the book to the reading room.

We visited a number of kindergarten rooms. These were five and six year olds. They sang "Uncle and Auntie, How Are You" and "How Do You Do, Uncle and Auntie." Also, they held up a sign reading "Warm welcome to American Agriservices Foundation Group."

Seismograph

We saw a replica of the first seismograph machines used for measuring the intensity of earthquakes, the original of which was made about 2,000 years ago. It had a delicately balanced piece in the interior of an urn with arms protruding into the center. These eight arms were attached to eight dragons on the outside of the urn. Each dragon had a small ball in its mouth, which, when the lever was struck by the center pivot, would release the ball into a small urn. Thus, they could judge the extent of the earthquake by the number of balls released from the dragons' mouths.

Peking Man

We were given a briefing on the various stages of man's evolution, including Peking Man.

West Lake

In the afternoon, we took a boat trip on West Lake, followed by walking across to the islands. A brief about West Lake follows: it is 9.3 miles around the outside; it covers 2.5 square miles; it averages 5.9 feet in depth; and 1,100,000 lb of fish are harvested per year from the lake. The water lilies were at their height at the time of our visit. Enclosed by hills on three sides, West Lake, placid and glistening, mirrors the surrounding landscape to form a panorama of great beauty.

Liuhe Pagoda (Pagoda of Six Harmonies)

We visited this pagoda which was built in the Sung Dynasty. It was built in 970 A.D. and is one of the largest pagodas we have ever seen. An octagonal structure, it rises to a height of 196.5 feet.

Linyin Temple

This temple is 1,600 years old. It was under repair at the time of our visit; hence, we could not go inside the temple. However, we were fascinated with the carved shrines and statues in the caves and cliffs, which are along the road leading to the temple.

Shanghai Area

The name "Shanghai" means "on the sea." It was the center of the Western-controlled international business concerns before the revolution. Today, this populous city of 11 million is the nation's largest seaport and leading industrial and commercial city. It is located 12 miles south of the Yangtze River, on the Hwang Pu (pronounced Whang Poo) River.

Shanghai has long been a leading textile manufacturer. Also, the city is noted for shipbuilding, heavy industries like iron and steel, food processing, machinery, tools, chemicals, paper, fertilizer, and electrical and engineering plants.

Educationally, Shanghai is second only to Peking in facilities, boasting of more than 11 universities and technical institutions that offer a wide range of subjects including agriculture, textiles, pedagogy, medicine, and shipbuilding.

Sze-Ping Worker's Residential Area

We were taken through the Sze-ping Worker's Residential Area. Mrs. Wong Chung-hua, who is married and the mother of two children, warmly welcomed us. Tea was served, and Mrs. Wong briefed us as follows: This housing project accommodates 13,500 families, totaling 56,700 people; the living quarters have modern conveniences, including running water, gas range, electricity, and other modern conveniences; there are on the premises 7 nurseries, 6 kindergartens, 11 primary schools, and 7 middle schools; there is a hospital, along with 10 cooperative medical centers (one of which we visited).

Kindergarten

We visited a number of kindergarten rooms but prior to going through the various rooms, a very nice performance was staged for us by the children. The groups that we visited ranged from about three years to six years old.

Housing Unit

We were told that in 1960 two more stories were added to what had been three-story buildings, bringing the housing quarters up to five stories.

Medical Cooperative Service

We visited a medical cooperative service where we saw moxibustion demonstrated.

Electric Flash Bulb Factory

We visited an electric flash bulb factory that is operated by the women.

Shanghai Dairy Farm No. 7

We visited Shanghai Dairy Farm No. 7, one of the 11 state dairy farms of the Shanghai area, which was about an hour's drive from our hotel.

We were met by a large delegation headed by Chairman Chen Hsin-tsai. After being seated in the reception room, we were served tea, and Chairman Chen briefed us, then showed us through the dairy.

Shanghai Acrobatic Theater

This evening, we saw China's superb acrobatics in the Shanghai Acrobatic Theater, a theater that was constructed in 1964 and that has a seating capacity of 1,900.

Yimin No. 1 Foodstuff Factory

We were received by a welcoming committee headed by Mr. Chiu Hui-wu, Leading Member of the Revolutionary Committee of the factory, who has held this position since 1965.

In the reception room, we were served tea and warmly greeted by the Mr. Chiu.

Pertinent information relative to the factory follows: There are 3,000 workers; primarily, they produce three different kinds of products: canned goods, candy, and cold drinks.

Before going through the plant, we were required to put on clean rubber footwear and a laboratory coat, along with a cap or hat and a gauze mask over our mouth and nose (the latter had to be used when we were in the ice cream plant).

Pea Processing

We saw green peas being processed, from beginning to end. Also, we were told that peas are available only one time a year; and that the same machinery is used for processing corn and many other vegetables.

We were also told that the green peas, which incidentally were labeled "green peas" in English on the cans, are marketed in Southeast Asia, Europe, and Africa.

Candy

We saw different kinds of candy being made. In particular, we were impressed with the chocolate candies, which were being packaged in a most attractive can.

Ice Cream

We went through the ice cream factory, where we saw ice cream being made into small bricks coated with chocolate. We were told that the milk is pasteurized before making ice cream.

Shanghai Poultry and Egg Products Factory No. 5

We visited this poultry and egg processing plant. We were received by a large delegation headed by Mr. Huang Chi-chang, Chairman of the Revolutionary Committee of the factory. We were ushered to the reception room, served tea, and briefed.

Mr. Huang gave us the following information pertaining to this factory: The building was constructed in 1973; there are 38,736 square feet of floor space; and they process broilers entirely for export.

Visit With M.D. Friends

This evening, Dr. Fu Bei-bin, Dr. Hu Bao-hua, and Dr. Yaou Lu-ling, three M.D.s came to the Peace Hotel for dinner, as guests of the Ensmingers.

Dr. Fu, who was my chief surgeon when I had emergency surgery in Shanghai in 1974, teaches at Shanghai Medical College No. 2. He left China at age 12, studied medicine in Belgium, and remained in Belgium and France until 1945, at which time he returned to China. He is one of the finest surgeons in China.

Dr. Hu Bao-hua and Dr.Yaou Lu-ling were members of the medical team that looked after me during my stay at the Hwa Tung Hospital. They are former students of Dr. Fu.

Following dinner, we met informally with Doctors Fu, Hu, and Yaou, for a brief question-answer period.

Dr. Ensminger commented that China has done a marvelous job in health care and disease prevention. Hence, we would like to learn from them how this has been, and is being accomplished.

Dr. Fu stated that there is much difference in the health care that existed in the old China vs modern health care. Before liberation, medical attention was accorded to only the privileged few, whereas today they serve the masses.

After liberation, China developed its health care network to train new medical personnel, establish new medical colleges at the international level, and train, in the basics, barefoot doctors in the communes and the factories, with these practitioners serving in a dual role of barefoot doctors and laborers.

Since 1949, many infectious diseases have been practically wiped out. For example, cholera and smallpox, which were rampant in the old days, have been virtually eliminated.

Suei-Chin Hospital

This morning, we visited the Suei-Chin Hospital, where we were welcomed by a large delegation, headed by Dr. Chao Chiao-sen, Leading Member of the Revolutionary Committee.

In the reception room, we were served tea.

Then, Dr. Chao introduced the members of his staff. Following this, he briefed us relative to the hospital.

Stress of the Rural Area

Mention was made that stress is placed on the rural area. To the latter end, 20% of the personnel of this hospital go to the factories and communes each year.

Dr. Fu Bei-bin Greeted Us

We were taken through some of the wards prior to seeing acupuncture anesthesia used. At the outset, we were told that this hospital is attached to the Shanghai Medical College No. 2, where Dr. Fu Bei-bin is the Chief Surgeon.

We Saw Acupuncture Anesthesia Used in Surgery

We saw surgery for semilunar cartilage. This operation was being performed on a lady 28 years of age. Only four needles were being used—two needles in the back and two needles on the legs.

Advantages of Acupuncture over Regular Anesthesia

Our hosts at the hospital listed the following advantages in favor of acupuncture anesthesia over western anesthesia: there are few or no side effects, the patient is more comfortable during the operation, there is quick recovery following the operation, the patient can cooperate with the surgeon because of being fully conscious, there is a good appetite following surgery, the procedure is relatively simple, with the result that it can be used in rural and mountainous areas, and it may be used where there are complications, such as a bad heart, and so forth.

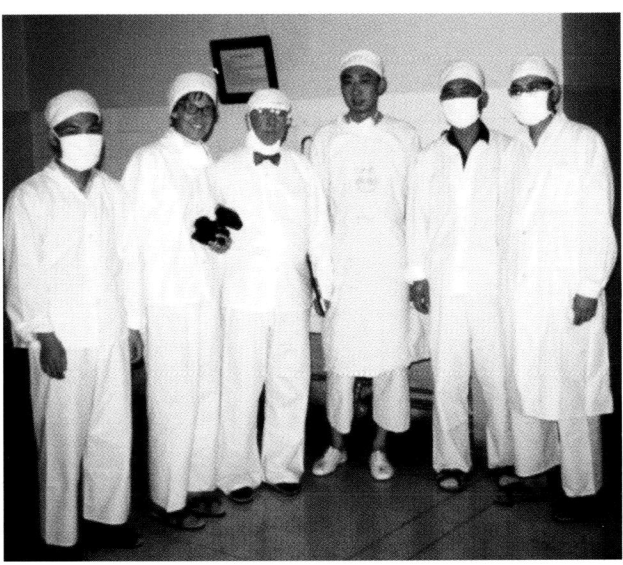

Dressed for surgery at the Suei-Chin Hospital, Shanghai. Audrey is second from the left, and Dr. E is third from left. We saw surgery for semilunar cartilage. While the surgery was underway, we visited with the patient.

Shanghai Jade Carving Factory

This afternoon, we visited the Shanghai Jade Carving Factory. They have five workshops: birds and animals, flowers and vases, incense burners and bottles, polishing and finishing products, and ivory.

Their jade is of many kinds, most of which comes from the northeast part of China. The rarest jade is called "emerald."

Tremendous labor goes into this type of work. We saw one jade piece approximately 10 inches high and 6 inches wide, on which there were 9 dragons, to which one man-year of labor has already been devoted. But another year will be required to complete the object.

Shanghai Carpet Factory

We visited the Shanghai Carpet Factory, which is very near to the Shanghai Jade Carving Factory. At this factory, we were received by Mr. Wu Chang-pa, Vice Chairman of the factory's Revolutionary Committee, who briefed us relative to the factory. The main products of this factory are wool carpet and wool rugs, along with tapestry.

They also make beautiful tapestry—mainly scenery, historical places and events, and revolutionary scenes.

Bank of China

Late this afternoon, we were taken to the Bank of China in Shanghai, where some of our folks exchanged currency; that is, gave U.S. currency for Chinese currency. It is a large, spacious building, set up much like many banks in the United States.

There are two main banks in China—the Bank of China, and the People's Bank. The standard interest rate on savings is 2.7 percent.

The Dance Drama (Shanghai)

We went to the Hu Tung Workers' Cultural Palace in Shanghai. This theater seats about 1,000 people. The two-hour performance began promptly at 7 p.m.

The dancing, the costuming, and the staging were all superbly done. The choreography was excellent. It was a performance that should receive topflight revues. Our interpreter, Mr. Huang, told us that this was one of the productions that had originally been banned. Now, they can perform it.

Shanghai Municipal Children's Palace

We visited the Shanghai Municipal Children's Palace. Pertinent information about the children's palaces in Shanghai, especially the Municipal Palace, follows: There are a total of 11 children's palaces in Shanghai. Each of the 10 areas or districts has a palace, then there is the Municipal Palace that we visited, which is the largest of all. The main building of the Municipal Palace was converted into its present use in 1953.

Upon our arrival, we were greeted by Mr. Tung Feng-di, a staff member of the Shanghai Municipal Palace. Also, several of us were hand-led by one of the children, who served as our special guides through the palace. My child guide was a pretty little 10-year-old girl named, Tan Li-li. Li-li told me that she was in the fourth grade in school, that her father and mother both work in a glass fabric factory, and that she has one younger brother.

We were told that 2,000 children come to the Municipal Palace each day for study.

We traveled by train through the beautiful and fertile agricultural area from Shanghai to Nanking. We had a new car with comfortable compartments.

Gala Dinner in Nanking

For dinner, we were hosted by Mr. Yueh Dia-hun, Leading Member, Luxingshe Head Office, Peking. Mr. Yueh is an old and dear friend of the Ensmingers. A several-course menu was served, along with Mao-tai and wine. Mr. Yueh toasted us. In his remarks, he warmly welcomed us and said that he felt that the Ensmingers' book, *China—the impossible dream*, had done much to improve the relationships between China and the United States. Also, he said that they were learning much from the great organizing ability of the Ensmingers.

City of Nanking

Nanking means southern capital. It has a proud history of being the capital of China as early as 229, through at least six dynasties. Nanking is the capital of Kiangsu Province.

The Dr. Sun Yat-sen Mausoleum is located on the southern slope of the Purple Mountain in the eastern suburbs. Beginning in 1927, and extending for 22 years, Chiang Kai-shek and the Kuomintang headquartered in Nanking. In April 1949, an army of a million, under the personal command of Chairman Mao Tse-tung, crossed the Yangtze River and liberated Nanking.

Kiangsu Provincial Agricultural Science Research Institute

We were received at the institute by a large delegation, headed by Mr. Yang Yun-sen, Leading Member of the General Office of the Revolutionary Committee, who briefed and hosted us. The research institute was started in 1949, although it operated under another name dating back to 1932. There are seven divisions, namely: grain, industrial crops, soils and fertilizers, plant protection, horticulture, agricultural physics and chemistry, and veterinary medicine.

We were told that Dr. Norman Borlaugh, Nobel Prize winner with the Rockefeller Foundation, visited this station in 1974. (Subsequent to the Ensmingers' 1972 study-tour of China, Dr. Norman Borlaugh requested a visa to visit China, but China turned him down. Thereupon the Rockefeller Foundation telephoned me from New York, asking if I could intercede and get Norman Borlaugh a visa to visit China. I answered in the affirmative, and I got Dr. Borlaugh permission to visit China. In foreign work, confidence and esteem are important!)

Dr. Sun Yat-Sen's Mausoleum

We visited the mausoleum, the tomb of Dr. Sun Yat-sen. He was born on November 12, 1866, and he died in Peking on March 12, 1925. In accordance with his wishes, he was buried near Nanking in 1929. The mausoleum is situated on the southern slope of the Purple Mountains in the eastern suburb of Nanking. The Chinese people revered Dr. Sun Yat-sen. He contributed richly to modern Chinese history.

Nanking-Yangtze River Bridge

En route to Yangchow from Nanking, we stopped to see the Nanking-Yangtze River Bridge at Wuhan, which is one of the three largest bridges in China. The construction of this bridge was started in 1960, and it was completed by the end of 1968.

Yangchow Area

Upon our arrival at the Hsui Yuan Hotel in Yangchow, we were warmly welcomed by a committee headed by Mrs. Chou Shui-yun, Leading Member, C.I.T.S., who briefed us. The area is primarily agricultural, with a population of 8 million.

Chiangtu Water Conservation Project

We visited the large and most interesting Chiangtu Water Conservation Project, located 8.7 miles from Yangchow. We were received by Mr. Huang Ming-sho, Leading Member of the Reception Committee, and Mr. Ku Si-chiang, technician. Mr. Ku told us about the project, using a beautifully prepared, illuminated relief map of the area as a visual aid. The project, which is primarily for irrigation and drainage purpose, covers 6,948 square miles and embraces 2,470,000 acres, and stretches across 15 counties; it makes for direct benefit to a population of 10,000,000; it is on the Hua River, which is on the northern bend of the Yangtze River.

In addition to irrigation, the project is designed to prevent flash floods, generate power, wash away alkalinity, and provide navigation and drainage.

They have on the drawing board plans for a really big irrigation project, to be completed by the end of the century, which will make it possible to divert irrigation water from Yangchow to Peking.

Kiangsu Provincial Poultry Scientific Research Institute

Several staff members of the research institute greeted us upon our arrival, and during our visit. We were welcomed and briefed by Mr. Tsai Kung-ji, Vice Chairman of the Revolutionary Committee of the institute, and Mr. Hsui Chu-yun, in charge of technical affairs.

The institute was set up in 1969, with three research areas being pursued: new breeds; feeding and management; and poultry diseases (their prevention and treatment).

Also, we walked through buildings. They are using bamboo quite successfully for slotted floors (being rounded, it is ideal both from the standpoints of the feet of the birds and of allowing the waste to pass through. Also, bamboo is in use for poultry fences. So, again and again, we marveled at the versatility of bamboo.

Yangchow Embroidery Factory

We were received by Mrs. Chang So-chen, Leading Member of the Revolutionary Committee of the factory, who served tea, briefed us, and took us through the factory.

Two girls were working (hand embroidery) on a beautiful double embroidery scene, which we were told would require 400 days for the two of them to complete.

Kiangsu Agricultural College

We were received by a large delegation of administrators, professors, and students—a total of 25 people—headed by Mr. Yang Chien-ming, Vice Chairman of the Revolutionary Committee. After serving tea, Mr. Yang briefed us relative to the college.

Nanking Museum

We visited this well organized museum which

Dr. E with four staff members of the Kiangsu Agricultural College, Nanking.

portrays the history of China beginning with Peking Man, 400,000 to 500,000 years ago, and extending to modern times. A few of the many significant events of Chinese history recorded in this museum are: primitive man grew rice, gathered wild fruit, caught fish, and ate pigs 5,000 years ago; all of China was first unified under the Chin Dynasty, 221–206 B.C.; a jade burial garment of the Eastern Han Dynasty (25–220 A.D.), which was used for burial of the emperors of the E. Han Dynasty, and which contained more than 2,000 pieces of jade sewn with silver thread and took one worker over 10 years to make; letter printing (block printing), the compass, and paper were developed by the Sui Dynasty (589–618 A.D.); blue pottery characterized by the Ming Dynasty (1368–1644 A.D.); the Ching Dynasty was the last of the feudal dynasties; in 1911, Dr. Sun Yat-sen became the Provisional President of China.

Peking Area

Upon our arrival in Peking we were taken to the New Peking Hotel where we had reservations. Because of earthquake warnings, temporary shelters lined the streets of Peking.

Summer Palace, Peking University, and Peking Zoo

We visited the Sino-Albania People's Commune, the Summer Palace, Peking University, and Peking Zoo.

Our group at the Summer Palace.

The Chinese Academy of Agricultural and Forestry Sciences (Peking)

I delivered my third invitational lecture before the distinguished Chinese Academy of Agricultural and Forestry Sciences. My old friend, Prof. Cheng Pi-liu, presided and introduced me. My lecture was divided into three parts: a general introduction,

I am delivering my third invitational lecture before the Chinese Academy of Agricultural and Forestry Sciences, Peking. My interpreter, Mr. Tung Ju-yung, is standing at the far left. My old friend, Prof. Cheng Pei-lieu, who presided, is seated to my left.

Prof., Dr. Y. Z. Tang and Mrs. Tang hosted a luncheon in a private dining room at the Summer Palace for the Ensmingers. Mrs. Tang (left) and Audrey are standing in front. Dr. E is in the back row second from the left, and Dr. Tang is third from the left. Drs. E and Tang are flanked by two of Dr. Tang's staff members. Prof. Tang is Head of the Animal Husbandry Department, Agricultural University, Peking. Dr. E and Dr. Tang are old friends; they first met at the University of Massachusetts in 1940.

about 100 slides, and answers to questions posed by the Permanent Mission of the People's Republic of China to the United Nations. Bound copies of my lecture were left with the academy.

At the close of my lecture, Professor Cheng Pi-Liu thanked me. A brief of his pertinent remarks follows:

> Dr. Ensminger has made a great contribution to scientific exchange between China and the United States—it will help the animal husbandry of our two countries. Now, allow me on behalf of all of those present to extend our thanks to Dr. Ensminger for his report.

National Agricultural Exposition

We went to the National Agricultural Exposition, a display of agricultural and other products produced by the communes throughout China. Howard Smith, Vice President of Kodak, who has great expertise in photography and visual aids, commented that it is one of the finest exhibits that he has ever seen, with its combination of small replicas of communes, pictures, and products.

Later, all of us went to the Peking Roast Duck Restaurant. We took our guides as our special guests.

At the dinner, we all complimented our guides on their superb performance. Also, Shu Chang, our head guide, made a beautiful speech. He told how pleased the guides were with our delegation and expressed the hope that all of us would return to the United States as friends of China and interpret the real China to the American people.

Chung Weimen Vegetable Market (Peking)

This morning, Mrs. Liang Hsiu-sha, leading member, took us through the vegetable market. Actually, this is what would be considered a food market in the United States. However, it did not have grain and noodles, which we were told are handled in separate shops.

In this market, they handled bean products, sauces and condiments, delicatessen items, vegetables, poultry (including dressed and live geese and ducks), meats, fish, canned goods, liquors, fruit, and milk products (including ice cream).

Jon Po Tsai (Studio of Glory and Treasure/Wood Block Painting)

Mr. Sun Chu-ming, Head of the Compiling Office, briefed us as follows: They are responsible for the reproduction of old Chinese paintings; their process is known as "wood block water printing"; this wood block printing process has a history going back 1,000 years; in the Ming Dynasty many colors were used; the present name of this studio was acquired in 1894; their specialty—to make reproductions very similar to the original painting.

Sightseeing Tourists

We visited the subway, the Imperial Palace (the Forbidden City), and we went to the circus.

The next day, we enyoyed visiting the Great Wall of China, the Ming Tombs, Tien An Men (Gate of Heavenly Peace), and the Great Hall of the People.

Dr. and Mrs. Ensminger Were Guests of Mrs. Huang Hua

This evening, Mrs. Ensminger and I were dinner guests of Mrs. Huang Hua, wife of the foreign minister of China, at a popular Peking restaurant. Mr. Huang Hua was out of the country at the time of our visit. The Huang Huas are old and dear friends of the Ensmingers, dating back to the time that Mr. Huang Hua served as China's ambassador to Canada and as China's ambassador to the United Nations.

The Ensmingers were dinner guests of Mrs. Huang Hua, wife of the Foreign Minister of China. Minister Huang Hua was out of the country at the time of our visit.

Peking Internal Combustion Engine Plant

This morning, we visited a large internal combustion engine plant in Peking. We were received by Mr. Li Ke-yin, Vice Chairman, Revolutionary Committee of the factory and chief engineer (who graduated in engineering from the University of Minnesota, which he attended from 1945 to 1948) and Mr. Ku Ching-hsien, Leading Member of the General Office of the factory. Mr. Li has been chief engineer in this plant since 1952.

In the briefing, Mr. Li presented the following information relative to the factory: It was set up in 1949. From 1949 to 1964, the plant manufactured farm machinery, such as horse-drawn plows and reapers, primarily for peasant farmers. They started manufacturing internal combustion engines in 1964, and they started manufacturing diesel engines for combines in 1965. Their chief products are diesel and gas engines. Mr. Li said that he works 11 to 12 hours per day, then he added the following beautiful statement: "Life is limited, but serving the people is unlimited."

Dr. E and Mr. Li Ke-yin, chief engineer of the Peking Internal Combustion Engine Plant. Photo taken in front of the factory. Mr. Li Ke-yin graduated from the University of Minnesota. When Dr. E asked Mr. Li if he attended those great football games at the University of Minnesota, he responded loud and clear: "Go Gophers."

The Temple of Heaven

En route to the airport, we saw the Temple of Heaven, which is 667 acres in area and was completed in 1420 A.D. as a ceremonial place for the Ming and Ching emperors to worship heaven and pray for bumper harvests.

A Fond Farewell

We bade a fond farewell to our guides—all old friends now, and each a part of us, as we departed from Peking via Japan Airlines for Tokyo, thence home.

1983
THE CHINA WE SAW

In order to understand China's agriculture, it is important that one be knowledgeable relative to its history and culture, for they are inseparable. For this reason, significant historical and cultural places were visited.

China's strengths are its immense population and area. Its challenge is that it must grow sufficient food for its huge population and provide raw materials for the expansion of industry, from a land of limited and already extensively exploited agricultural resources.

China is the most populous country in the world with more than 1 billion people. Just 7% of the world's cultivated land sustains a fourth of the world's population.

Tokyo, Japan

En route to China, we made an overnight stop in Tokyo, Japan. Mr. Terry T. Hashida, Director, Soga-no-ya Swine Business Group, and a longtime friend of mine, met us upon our arrival and stayed with us until our departure. In our informal visit with Mr. Hashida, we were told that Soga-no-ya, which is the largest swine operation in Japan, markets 11,000 hogs per month.

Dr. E with Mr. Terry T. Hashida, consultant, Tokyo, Japan, seated next to him. Terry Hashida, a longtime friend of Dr. E, met us upon our arrival in Tokyo, hosted a dinner for us, and saw us off following our overnight stop in Japan.

In Hong Kong, before entering China, the Farrs and the Ensmingers had dinner at the famed Peninsula Hotel. *Left to right:* Dr. E, Audrey Ensminger, Judy Farr, and William D. "Bill" Farr.

Beijing (Peking)

Mr. Cheng Runming met us upon our arrival in Beijing and served as our guide throughout China.

As the national capital, Beijing is the focal point of communications and transportation in China. Railroads and air services radiate to all major provincial capitals and industrial cities.

Prof., Dr. Cheng Peilieu, Director, Institute of Animal Science, Chinese Academy of Agricultural Sciences, and an old friend of mine, was our guest for dinner this evening, at the state guest house.

We visited the zoo (to see the pandas), the Summer Palace, and the Temple of Heaven.

The Forbidden City (Palace Museum)/Travel to Harbin

We visited the Forbidden City and then traveled to Harbin.

Upon our arrival in Harbin, we were met by Mr. Chin Chih-yung, who served as our guide in the

Our group at the Summer Palace.

In the Forbidden City (Palace Museum) Dr. E posed with this cute little girl.

Harbin area. Harbin is the capital of the northernmost province of China, Heilongjiang.

Daqing Area

We traveled from Harbin to Daqing on Train No. 273. It was a pleasant trip through the country. The train was diesel powered and ran over ties made of concrete, rather than wood. It was a smooth ride. We were able to see the crops, the animals, and the countryside. The crops consisted primarily of corn, soybeans, millet, rape, and sorghum. We also saw considerable pasture land devoted to cattle, sheep, and horses.

Daqing Oil Field

We were taken to the site of one of the 5,000 oil wells in this great Daqing oil field. This particular well was started on October 1, 1960. It produces 37 barrels (5 tons) of crude oil per day. This well has been in operation for 22 years. During this time, it has produced 3,958,200 barrels (540,000 tons) of crude oil. It is 3,150 ft deep.

There are approximately 7.33 barrels of crude oil per metric ton. Note, too, that an average oil well in the United States produces about 19 barrels a day.

In answer to our inquiry, we were told that there are about 80 drilling machines in operation throughout the Daqing oil field.

Mr. Li told us that they started geological oil surveys in 1950. However, they did not start drilling until 1959, and they opened the first well in 1960.

Greenhouses

From the oil field, we traveled to where they had greenhouses. The person in charge was Mr. Tung Hongzang. The total area of the greenhouse is 15 acres.

Tomatoes

Fourteen people are employed in growing tomatoes. The tomato plants that we saw growing were set out in January. On the average, they expect

Left to right: Mr. Tung, Mr. Cheng, our interpreter, and Dr. E in the tomato greenhouse.

a production of 52,800 lb per acre. After growing tomatoes, they plan to rotate to cucumbers, and then to green peppers.

All of the produce of this greenhouse is consumed in Daqing.

They have been using oil for heating the greenhouses, but they are converting to gas, because the latter is cheaper.

Cucumbers

They have 10 acres of cucumbers, and there are four varieties of cucumbers being produced (two European varieties and two Chinese varieties).

No. 1 Daqing Dairy Cow Farm.

Green Peppers

They have one-third acre of green peppers. Green peppers can be expected to yield about 13,200 lb per acre.

Reasons for the Greenhouses

The manager, Mr. Tung, emphasized that the operation is not profitable. Rather, it is subsidized so that the people may have fresh vegetables in the winter time.

Children's Park

This facility was opened in 1981. Twenty acres are devoted to the Children's Park. It consists of the following parts: recreation, games, such as electronics, artificial lake, landscaped garden, and flowers, birds, fish, etc.

Daqing Animal Husbandry, Industrial, and Commercial Complex

This complex includes both the No. 1 Dairy Cow Farm, and the Daqing Dairy Factory.

No. 1 Dairy Cow Farm

We visited the No. 1 Dairy Cow Farm. Pertinent facts about this operation follow. The following were the head people at this farm: Mr. Ying Yi, manager; and, Mr. Huang Guo Ching, dairy specialist. They refer to the cows as the "Black-and-White" breed. There are 1,200 dairy cows on this farm, 82% of which are in lactation.

Daqing Dairy Factory

Next we visited the Daqing Dairy Factory. It is under the directorship of Mr. Wong Xing Zai.

The milk is received in stainless steel tanks, which are not refrigerated. After unloading, the milk proceeds through the following steps in the process of being dehydrated and packaged (remember that they are processing whole milk, not skim milk): purification, storage, pasteurization, drying, further drying, and packaging.

Dressed for seeing the Daqing Dairy Factory. Dr. E is on the center, Judy Farr is on his left, and Bill is behind Judy.

New Apartments in Daqing

We learned the following about the new apartments in Daqing: Most of them are five stories high. If they are only five stories high, there are no elevators. There are both two- and three-bedroom apartments. All of them have individual kitchens and individual toilets, and they are heated by steam. A very few families have refrigerators, and a very few have laundry facilities. Most of them rely on a sink in the kitchen for doing their laundry.

Daqing Petro Chemical Works

Mr. Wu Jiu Cheng, Assistant Director, Daqing Petro Chemical Works, met us upon our arrival, briefed us, and took us through part of the plant.

This petro works is one of the largest in China. The part that we visited covers 741.3 acres. It produces 36,650,000 barrels (5 million tons) of crude oil annually. It produces 600,000 tons of chemical fertilizer per year, consisting of 46% urea and 24% ammonium nitrate. It produces 3,000 tons of synthetic fiber—namely, acrylic, annually. We saw blankets and sweaters that they manufacture.

Prior to seeing part of the huge Daqing Petro Chemical Works we were served the traditional tea and briefed by Mr. Wu Jiu Cheng. *Seated back of the table right to left:* Dr. E, Mr. Wu Jiu Cheng, and Mr. Cheng Runming, our interpreter.

Harbin Area

When we returned from Daqing to Harbin, we were met by our local guide, Mr. Chin Chih-yung.

Harbin, which is the capital of the northernmost province of China, Heilongjiang, has a population of 2,360,000. It is an important industrial city (noted for mechanical and electrical industries) in Northeast China, as well as a rail junction linking China with Russia and Inner Mongolia.

Exhibition of Products

The Exhibition is what the name implies—an exhibition of the products produced in the province of Heilongjiang. We saw displays of many of the agricultural products of the country.

Xiangfang Provincial Experimental Farm

This morning, we visited the Xiangfang Provincial Experimental Farm and were warmly welcomed by Mr. Wang Ke Bin, the director, and his staff.

The provincial experimental farm is suburban, It consists of 2,100 acres, with a population of 1,500 people. Its main enterprises are agriculture, animal husbandry, and small industries. Also, it has forestry and fishing. Its main crops are: wheat, sorghum, maize (corn), soybeans, and fodder (green chop of corn or sorghum).

The animals consist of 500 Black-and-White milk cows, 300 Harbin White pigs (breeders), and 10,000 White Leghorn chickens (layers).

There are five industries or factories on this farm; namely, agriculture, brewery (hard liquor), repair shop (tractors and trucks), printing, and ice cream factory.

We were told that each family has 726 sq ft of land assigned per family member; so, a family of four would be assigned 2,904 sq ft of land, as their individual plot. On this plot, they grow whatever they wish, either for their own use or resale.

Soybeans being cultivated on the Xingfang Provincial Experimental Farm. I am in front of the tractor.

Harbin Zoo/Return to Beijing

We went to the Harbin Zoo for the purpose of seeing the Northeast China Tiger, of which we saw five. They are huge beasts which almost became extinct due to hunters. Presently, they are protected.

Overnight In Beijing

We celebrated July 4 by having a party followed by special guests for dinner.

The Gallo Party

Prior to dinner, Joe and Pat Gallo, two of our delegates, invited the group to their suite in State Guest House No. 10 for a Fourth of July celebration. Delicious tidbits, along with champagne and other drinks, were served. Imagine such a celebration in Beijing, China!

Mrs. Ke An-Lin Came to Dinner

Mrs. Ke An-Lin, and her son, Chen Li Chung, were our special guests for dinner at the state guest house. An-Lin was the Ensmingers' national guide in 1972. Also, she was a visiting scholar at New York University in 1979-80. She teaches English at Beijing University. Her son is a sophomore at Beijing University, where he is majoring in chemistry.

Urumqi Area

We flew from Beijing to Urumqi, where we were met by Mr. Ki Changhui, who served as our local guide. Urumqi is the capital of the Xinjiang Uygur Autonomous Region, China's most western province. It is 2,050 miles from Beijing. The city is a green-blanketed oasis amidst Xinjiang's barren and uninhabited deserts, loess (windblown) highlands, and the snow-capped peaks of the Tianshan Mountains.

Urumqi has about 800,000 inhabitants belonging to 13 different nationalities. The Han Chinese are now the majority nationality. There are about half a million Kazakhs, most of whom live a nomadic life in the Northwest, in the Junggar Basin, a region that borders the Soviet Union. There are many more (7 to 8 million) Kazakhs just across the border in the Soviet Union than in China, where they are better known by the Slavic term, "Cossack." They are renowned horsemen.

The ancient Silk Road passes through Xinjiang; one route to the north leading to Europe, the other route to the south leading to India.

Xinjiang Livestock Breeding Farm

We visited the Xinjiang Livestock Breeding Farm, in a suburb of Urumqi. First, we were served tea and briefed by Mr. Meng Fu Cheng, the director. The barns are of permanent construction, with large, roomy stalls, concrete floors, and heavy steel fronts.

Urumqi Carpet Factory

Mr. Yang Ming Shen, the manager, briefed us. From 1958 to 1972, the factory produced felt. Since 1973, it has produced Persian or Oriental carpets.

Left to right: Audrey, Ke An-Lin, Dr. E, and Chen Li Chung, son of Ke An-Lin.

Turfan Area

We traveled by bus from Urumqi to Turfan, a four-hour drive—112 miles, part (37 miles) of which was through the Gobi Desert. Except for an occasional oasis, and a bit of sparse grazing land prior to reaching the desert, it is a pretty barren area. However, we did pass a large factory where they were producing urea, using coal; and we saw a few animals along the way.

About Turfan

As early as 2,000 years ago, Turfan was

Sheep watched over by herders on horses in the Gobi Desert/Turfan area.

Here I am shown inspecting Karez (underground irrigation) on the Five Star People's Commune.

an important town, for it once stood on the Silk Road where the northern and southern routes separated; the northern route wound its way to Southern Europe, and the southern route led to India.

Turfan lies in one of the world's great land depressions, 505 feet below sea level—the lowest area in China. It is an oasis that gets all of its water from an underground irrigation system called *Karez*, developed in Persia in ancient times. The tunnels begin at the foot of the mountains and rise nearer and nearer the surface as they get further from the source, finally emerging into open channels. The tunnels connect to wells at regular intervals. Fine crops are produced, including seedless grapes, sweet Hami melons, long-staple cotton, wheat, soybeans, and tomatoes.

Turfan is known as the "furnace town," its summer temperature soars to 117.5°F., while the desert rocks are said to reach 170°F.

This is the lowest and hottest place in China. The Aydingkol Lake is 604 ft below sea level. Trees and high walls are used as protection against high winds.

Karez (Underground Irrigation)/ Five Star People's Commune

We inspected the marvelous underground irrigation system, known as the Karez, on the Five Star People's Commune. This system requires considerable labor for construction and maintenance, but it does not require any energy—for it relies entirely on gravity. Without irrigation, the oasis of the Turfan area would not exist.

The Ruins of Jiaohe

Jiaohe, built in the 2nd century B.C., was a strategic point on the ancient Silk Road. The ruins of Jiaohe stand on a loess mound (windblown soil) surrounded by two small rivers. It is oval in shape; 3,281 ft from north to south, and 985 ft from west to east. There are no walls.

Traces of streets and lanes of the ancient town are still discernible. The houses were half underground. There was a dungeon, which had better quarters for prisoners who received preferential treatment. Also, there are old wells, and a city gate with a lookout post.

Jiaohoe was destroyed by the Mongols in the 13th century, and abandoned during the Ming Dynasty.

New Town Mosque

We visited the New Town Mosque, the front of which was newly finished and painted in bright colors. In addition to taking pictures, we went inside. One Moslem was praying at the time.

Turfan Museum

We visited Turfan Museum. Three very old mummies and silk fabrics of the Silk Road era were of much interest to us. We were told that one of the mummies was from the South-North Dynasty,

426–518 A.D., and that two were from the Tang Dynasty, 618–900 A.D.

Suliman's Minaret

We stopped to see Suliman's Minaret, the tower of which is of beautiful design. It was built in 1776 by the Khan of Lukqun in memory of his father. The tower is 144 ft tall.

Valley of the Grapes

We drove to the Valley of the Grapes, which is near the Flaming Mountain. This is a productive grape area, devoted to white seedless grapes (which are like our Thompson Seedless grapes in the U.S.), growing on high trellises, so that people can walk beneath the vines. Because of the cold winters, they must cover these grapes in the winter.

Urumqi Area Again

We returned from Turfan to Urumqi. Then we drove to the Dong Feng Commune (a Kazakh commune) in the Valley of the White Poplars (the mountainous summer pastures) for a superb horsemanship demonstration, commonly referred to as the "horse games." In order to accommodate our group, the Kazakhs opened the season one day early.

The Kazakhs live in yurts (tents) and move from place to place, according to the season, herding (on horseback) sheep, goats, and cattle.

Horse Games by the Kazakhs

The horse games were staged by the Kazakhs on a plateau (or ledge) on the side of the mountain, on grass. Approximately 30 Kazakhs, including eight women, participated. With the exception of one Ili horse, they were mounted on tough little native ponies about 12-hands high (about the size of Welsh Ponies). The saddles used by the Kazakhs are of their own design; they are sturdy, but much lighter than our U.S. western saddles, and without horns. Snaffle bits were used on the horses. The following three games were staged: horse race, the girl pursues, and the goat tussle (called *buzgashi*).

Obviously, these horse games are a source of great enjoyment for the Kazakhs; they're a test of horses and horsemanship, plus a social event.

Our hosts, Mr. and Mrs. Nulan, entertained us in their yurt, a superbly built tent-like abode, which was carpeted and warmly padded for their cold winters.

The "goat tussle" (*buzgashi*) consisted of the riders dashing madly about trying to keep possession of a headless goatskin.

Following the horse games, we washed our hands in Kazakh style, which consisted of Mrs. Nulan pouring water on our hands from a teakettle three times, without shaking hands (shaking the hands after washing may bring bad luck, and is to be avoided), then drying on a towel. Mr. Nulan presided over the main meal, which consisted of lamb (boiled), shish kebab, bolsak (a deep-fried bread), nang (with sesame), and meat soup.

We were pleased that two Kazakh traditions were omitted at the dinner; namely, asking the guest of honor to eat the eyeball of the sheep—which is considered a delicacy, and throwing the sheep's head through the central hole in the roof of the yurt.

The above foods are typical of the diet of the Kazakhs, which consists chiefly of meat, milk, wheat, and tea. There are a few vegetables. In answer to Audrey's question, we were told that they do eat some fruit, which probably provides a minimum of vitamin C.

Following dinner, Dr. Ensminger presented a replica of a U.S. western saddle to Mr. Nulan and made him an Honorary American Cowboy; and presented Mrs. Nulan a set of writing tools (a spike and a hammer) and a stained-glass bird. Also, an Agriservices Foundation knife and an Agriservices Foundation fountain pen were presented to Mr. Han Fuyou, of the Foreign Affairs Office, as our "thank you" to him for arranging the horse games.

I am standing at the entrance to our yurt on the Dong Feng Commune, in the Valley of the White Poplars. After seeing the horse games, we were served a Kazakh-style meal in this yurt.

The Valley of the White Poplars is operated by the Dong Feng Commune, Kazakhs tribesmen, who raise sheep, goats, and cattle. It is a rather narrow valley nestled between mountains on both sides.

The animals consist of sheep, goats, cattle, and horses; with sheep ranking first in numbers, followed by goats.

Two kinds of sheep were seen. The most numerous were fine wool sheep of Merino breeding. However, we saw a few fat-tailed sheep, which are used for mutton and the production of coarse wool for carpeting.

I am inspecting the Biological Factory on the outskirts of Urumqi.

Biological Factory

We visited the Biological Factory, located on the outskirts of Urumqi. We were warmly welcomed by Mr. Lang Yu Min, Director, and his administrative staff. Mr. Lang briefed us relative to the factory, following which he took us through the plant.

We were taken on a walking tour of the laboratory, where we saw the following vaccines being processed: Newcastle vaccine for poultry (a dry virus vaccine), blackleg vaccine, egg embryos being used to produce vaccine, and sheep pox vaccine. We also saw glycerol being processed for use as a carrier, and bottles being hand-cleaned and disinfected for reuse.

More About Urumqi

The following information was obtained from Mr. Li Changhui, China International Travel Service, Urumqi.

Incentive for Population Control

Although the legal ages are 22 for male and 20 for female, young people seldom marry before 25 years of age. If there is only one child, and the couple agree to have no more children, a bonus of 1,000 yuan is to be paid. This bonus is prorated and paid on a monthly basis, with payments starting at the birth of the child and completed when the child is age 14. Should the couple have another child, thereby breaking their agreement, they must refund whatever bonus payments have been made.

Tax Incentive to Factories

Effective June 1, 1983, a tax scale, graduated downward on factory profits, was instituted. Prior to this date, a factory paid a set tax rate on profits, regardless of how large or how small the profits. Presently, the tax scale is graduated downward; that is, with higher profits, the percentage taxes is lowered, and, conversely, the lower the profits, the higher the taxes.

Barefoot Doctors

Today, they are called medical workers, reflecting an upgrading in training and work.

Sian Area

Of all the cities in China, Sian and its history most vividly portray the continuity of Chinese civilization.

The Wei Valley and middle Yellow River area of Shaanxi Province have been inhabited since the Neolithic Era—and before; it was the cradle of Chinese civilization.

Once the largest city in the world, Sian served as the capital of 11 dynasties. Also, it was the starting point of famous "Silk Road" that led westward. Today, Sian, with a population of 2.5 million, is the capital of Shaanxi Province, and the largest city in northwest China.

The Underground Army (Qin Shi Huang Tomb)

The report pertaining to the Qin Shi Huang Pottery Figures of Warriors and Horses is based on what we were told by Mr. Yu Chang Ming, our local guide, and Ms. Wu, who briefed us at the site, along with my subsequent library research. Pictures of the Underground Army were not permitted.

The important discovery of Vault No. 1 was made in March 1974 by peasants digging a well in a sweet potato patch to cope with a drought. Subsequently (in 1976), Vaults 2 and 3 were discovered. It now consists of three underground mosques, described as follows:

- **Vault 1**—Rectangular in shape, 755 ft long and 203 ft wide, 3.52 acres, is the main body, in which there are 6,000 soldiers.
- **Vault 2**—Arrow-shaped, 1.48 acres in size, is an auxiliary force of 1,500 warriors.
- **Vault 3**—0.13 acres in size, is the command post, consisting of 68 soldiers.

In total, there are 8,000 life-sized horses and soldiers, with a breakdown of 7,900 soldiers and 100 horses. Four horses were hitched to each chariot. The soldiers are 5.9 ft in height; and the horses 6.6 ft long (from muzzle to root of tail) and 14-3 hands high at the withers.

This is the mausoleum of Emperor Qin Shi Huang (259–210 B.C.), the founding emperor of the Qin Dynasty. Emperor Qin Shi Huang is credited with two notable accomplishments during his reign: He linked up the various sections of The Great Wall, and his mausoleum was started when he was enthroned at age 13.

This museum was erected over the tombs to facilitate working and restoration. When completed, it will be one more wonder of the world.

Upon completion, it was covered with earth and seeded to grass to make it resemble a hill. Traps were set inside the passageway to kill anyone who entered. Historical records suggest that upon completion of the tomb, all those who had worked on the structure were entombed alive so that no one could reveal its secrets.

But Emperor Qin Shi Huang did more—he unified China; he unified the language and money system; and he established a national government.

Huaqing Hot Springs

According to historical records, the hot springs (which are no longer hot) were found 2,800 years ago. The water, which contains nine kinds of minerals, is said to be efficacious for skin and rheumatoid diseases.

Tombon Mountain

This is the mountain that some of us climbed. The reward: A magnificent view of the region's agricultural communes.

Sian Cloisonne Factory

We visited the Sian Cloisonne Factory, which is one of three in China; the other two are in the Beijing area.

Judy Farr at Huaqing Hot Springs.

Our group was privileged to stay at one of the state guest houses. Audrey and I had luxurious accommodations and we were told that Henry Kissinger had been housed in the same rooms when he accompanied President Nixon.

Dayan (Big Wild Good) Pagoda

The Dayan Pagoda was completed in 652. It is 240 ft high. It was built to store the Buddhist scriptures which Xuan Zang, a renowned monk, brought back from India. Xuan Zang was made abbot of the temple, where he translated the scriptures into Chinese.

Beihai (North Lake) Park

We visited this beautiful park, which is said to date back to 300 A.D. It is named for one of three imperial lakes on its grounds. The Bridge of Perfect Wisdom, one of the park's famous landmarks, links Qionghua Island on the North Lake to the southeast shore. On this island stands the prominent Tibetan-style White Pagoda, built in 1651 to commemorate the visit of the Dalai Lama. We were told that Beihai Park is now one of Beijing's most popular spots for recreation and, increasingly, for romance.

Minister He is nearest the camera.

Minister He Kang, the Minister of Agriculture, Hosted a Dinner for the Ensmingers

Mr. He Kang, Minister, the Ministry of Agriculture, Animal Husbandry, and Fisheries, hosted a dinner for the Ensmingers at the Beijing Hotel. Eight of the minister's staff were present. Mr. He is an old friend of the Ensmingers; he visited us and Agriservices Foundation in 1978.

Chinese Academy of Agricultural Sciences

Upon our arrival at the entrance gate to the Chinese Academy of Agricultural Sciences, we were met by Professors Cheng Peilieu and C. H. Liu, and ushered to a reception room where Professor Lu Liang Shu, president of the academy, was waiting for us.

My Invitational Lecture Before the Chinese Academy of Agricultural Sciences

I gave an invitational lecture before the Chinese Academy of Agricultural Sciences. This was my fourth lecture before this distinguished body; similar lectures were given in 1972, 1974, and 1977.

My subject: "United States-Canada Agricultural Research Update–1983." The following is taken from my introduction:

> Research can determine only what is, not what should be. Man largely determines his own destiny through futuristic research, which he focuses, interprets, and applies.
>
> Directly or indirectly, current United States-Canada research is focused primarily on food, hunger and malnutrition. Producing enough food of high nutritional value to meet the demands of an ever expanding world population is the world's greatest challenge in the decades ahead.

I briefed much of my lecture and used 82 slides in order to minimize the language barrier.

Delivering my fourth invitational lecture before the Chinese Academy of Agricultural Sciences, with Dr. C. H. Liu serving as my interpreter.

Left to right: Dr. E, Audrey, Dr. Cheng, Bill Farr, Judy Farr, and Dr. Cheng's daughter, Dr. Chin Cheng.

Bound copies of the 78-page report, including 74 pictures depicting different types of research, were presented to the library of the Chinese Academy of Agricultural Sciences.

Luncheon Hosted by Prof., Dr. Cheng Peilieu and Prof., Dr. C. H. Liu

Following my lecture, Professors Cheng Peilieu and C. H. Liu hosted a luncheon in the Academy Club for Bill and Judy Farr, whom they had met on their previous visits, and the Ensmingers.

Wang Tsomin and Duan Liancheng Had Us for Tea in Their Home

This afternoon, we were invited by Mary Tsomin and Duan Liancheng to tea in their home. It was an interesting visit, with a choice of several drinks and goodies served. They have a three-bedroom apartment, plus a sitting room, kitchen, and bath. Also, they have gas, refrigeration, and running water.

Both Mary Tsomin and Duan Liancheng are doing important work in China. Mary Wang is writing a book on the United States, for the Chinese; it's the counterpart to the Ensmingers' book on China. Duan Liancheng is in charge of the New World Press,

In the Mary Tsomin and Duan Liancheng home. *Standing left to right:* Dr. E, Mary Tsomin, and Duan Liancheng.

The Ensmingers were dinner guests of their old and dear friends Mr. and Mrs. Huang Hua, at Diaoy State Guest House No. 18. Mr. Huang Hua was the recent past Foreign Minister of China. At the time of our 1983 visit, he was Vice Chairman of the Standing Committee of the National People's Congress. Preceding the dinner, Mr. Huang Hua (left) and Dr. E had a visit in a relaxed atmosphere.

which handles foreign language publications, and which has 4,000 employees.

Dinner Hosted by the Chinese Academy of Agricultural Sciences

The Ensmingers were hosted for dinner by the Chinese Academy of Agricultural Sciences, at the Henan Restaurant.

Dinner for the Ensmingers Hosted by Vice Chairman and Mrs. Huang Hua

The Ensmingers were guests at a dinner in Diaoyutai State Guest House No. 18, hosted by Vice Chairman and Mrs. Huang Hua.

Mr. Huang Hua was the recent past Foreign Minister of China. Presently, he is Vice Chairman of the Standing Committee of the National People's Congress. Mrs. Huang works in the office of the Ministry of Foreign Affairs. The Huangs are old friends of the Ensmingers.

It was a warm and friendly visit, with a beautiful floral centerpiece, palace lanterns, and many courses of delicious food. Mr. Huang Hua toasted the Ensmingers as old and warm friends of China, with mention made of the Ensmingers' book, *China—the impossible dream*, and with expression of best wishes in going to Tibet.

Dr. Ensminger's toast follows: "To Mr. and Mrs. Huang Hua, for their great contribution to the peace and understanding between nations for the benefit of mankind."

Evergreen People's Commune

We checked out of the State Guest House and traveled to the Evergreen People's Commune, in the suburbs of Beijing. We were received and briefed by Mrs. Wang Shuen Ying, who took us to three divisions of the commune; namely: art, Peking ducks, and fruit.

The Ensmingers climbed The Great Wall for the fourth time.

Dr. E being briefed on the Evergreen People's Commune by Mrs. Wang Shuen Ying (center).

The commune operates three factories: boilers, plastic ware, and screws.

We also saw the breeders, baby ducklings, and ducks being grown for market.

Following the visit to the Evergreen People's Commune, we flew to Chengdu. We were met by Mr. Chen Wang, who checked us in at the Jinjiang Guest House.

Chengdu Area

Chengdu is the capital of China's most populous and richest agricultural province, Sichuan. Chengdu produces more rice than any other province in China. Also, it is a major producer of wheat. Two crops per year are produced—rice and wheat.

Sichuan Province also produces corn, barley, fruit, potatoes, sugarcane, cotton, tobacco, jute, and tea. Although industry is not as important as agriculture, Sichuan produces oil, natural gas, coal, iron ore, and rock salt.

Chengdu is more than 2,000 years old. Marco Polo visited it in the 13th century, a short time after the region had been ravaged by the Mongol hordes of the Great Khan. He reported that the province and its surrounding areas were inhabited by lions, bears, and other wild beasts. Travelers who slept outdoors used to place green sugarcane on their campfires. The noise of the cane bursting open frightened off predatory animals.

Dujiang Yan Dam

We drove to the Dujiang Yan Dam. Situated about 24 miles northwest of Chengdu, this engineering marvel dates back to 250 B.C. Designed as a mammoth irrigation project, Dujiang Yan Dam checks the Min River which flows down from Green City Peak. A trunk canal was cut through the mountain, and a water distribution network set up to irrigate 3.2 million acres of land. Since 1949, irrigation has been expanded. Today, the whole system irrigates well over 16.5 million acres, including the Chengdu region.

Near the Ming Tombs, we visited the famous *Avenue of the Animals,* 12 statues line both sides of the road, alternately standing and reclining. I am shown here with a horse.

Also on the *Avenue of the Animals* was this statue of an elephant.

Taoist Temple, Fulongguan

We visited this temple, which commands a superb view of the river valley.

Arrival in Tibet/Travel to Lhasa

We arrived at the Lhasa airport, more than two hours drive from Lhasa over rough roads. Mr. Teng Zhiping, our local guide, reported that the population of Tibet is 1.8 million, and of Lhasa, 120,000.

Tibet Area

Tibet, the roof of the world (12,000 ft), is the most coveted, most extraordinary, most unobtainable, and most remote tourist spot in the world.

The awesome Himalayas form Tibet's southern boundaries with India, Nepal, Bhutan, Burma, and Pakistan. Most of Tibet is mountain wilderness.

The Tibetans are a branch of the Mongoloid race. The people are short and sturdy. They live a primitive life. Nomads (shepherds and herdsmen) roam about in the northern uplands, tending their yak, sheep, and goats, and living in tents of yak hair. Once a year they travel to the lower levels to sell their produce and buy necessities.

Getting to Tibet is a problem! Recently, the Chinese resumed construction of a railroad which was started in 1951, but which will take years to complete. The mountain roads are slow and tortuous. (It takes 10 to 13 days via truck to travel from Chengdu to Lhasa.) Air flights are uncertain due to weather; and the landing strip at Lhasa is 80 miles from town, over a dusty, rough road.

Yak on the outskirts of Lhasa.

Tibetan winters are fiercely cold. Much of Tibet has less than 10 in. of rain annually. Violent winds are common.

The yak is a multipurpose animal in Tibet. It provides butter, cloth, cheese, meat, milk, and transportation. It is also used as a beast of burden. Its hair is used for tents, and its hide for shoe leather and boats.

Why the allure of Tibet? As a scientist, I wanted to study the possible effect of such a high altitude on the fertility, longevity, and well-being of people and animals. Also, Tibet is beautiful; no pollution mars the magnificent, jagged mountain peaks or darkens the deep, clear lakes. Until 1950, no cars or trucks were permitted on the few dirt roads for fear their wheels would scar the earth and thereby release the evil spirits. Then, too, Tibet has a mystical charm, stemming in part from the Dalai Lama, the spiritual head of the Tibetan Buddhist religion. Finally, getting to Tibet satisfies the Marco Polo in each of us.

Jokhang Temple

Jokhang Temple, the first principle Buddhist temple in Tibet, is located in the center of old Lhasa. It was built in the mid-7th century A.D., more than 1,300 years ago. Jokhang Temple is still one of Tibet's holiest shrines. Throughout the day, prostrate pilgrims fingering prayer beads and murmuring sutras are a common sight.

The small, crowded chambers of Jokhang Temple are saturated with the fumes of fermented yak butter, burned as a ritual.

Norbulinka (Summer Palace)

The Norbulinka, meaning jeweled garden, was first built in 1755. It is located in what is now the People's Park, about two miles west of Lhasa. It was formerly the Summer Palace of the Dalai Lama.

Tsa Lalupa

Tsa Lalupa was built in the 8th century. It is commonly referred to as "The Cave Temple." The trail to it from the street leads by pig pens, shacks, and small caves.

Drepung Monastery

The Drepung Monastery is located six miles

Judy Farr and Audrey Ensminger at the Drepung Monastery, near Lasha.

north of Lhasa, on a high cliff, its many tiers leaning into a steep mountain face. Founded in 1416, it is financially supported by a noble from Liuwu Zong named Sangbu. The Drepung Monastery is 1 of only 10 remaining monasteries in Tibet. Before the reform of 1959, over 10,000 lamas were housed here. Today, there are 400.

Najing People's Commune

We visited the Najing People's Commune, a short distance from Lhasa. During the briefing, followed by a walk and a drive, Kashopa Jamyang, Li Yung Feng, and Lhawang Ngodu gave us the following pertinent information,

The word Najing means "big nose," taken from the shape of the nearby mountain.

The Tibetan barley wine, which was served during the briefing, and which is so highly esteemed by Tibetan people, is made by fermenting highland barley. It is grown only in Tibet. To us, it more nearly resembled a beer than a wine. Our hosts emphasized that each family can make Tibetan barley wine—that a big brewery isn't necessary.

I talked with the Najing People's Commune staff during our visit.

Potala Palace

Florence Wheeler, one of our delegates, became very ill soon after arrival in Tibet, due to the high altitude. So, rather than risk Florence Wheeler dying in Tibet, I made special arrangements to get her back to Chengdu a day earlier than the rest of the group. Florence Wheeler, Dr. David Brown, Mr. Cheng, our national guide, and I flew back to Chengdu.

Potala is a Sanskrit word meaning "Buddha's Mountain." The Potala Palace was originally started in the 7th century; it has a history of over 1,300 years. The palace was burned down in the 8th century, after being struck by lightning; and the second palace was destroyed in a war during the 9th century. The present Potala really consists of two palaces—the White Palace and the Red Palace, each built in the 17th century by the fifth Dalai Lama (1617–1682). The Potala Palace comprises a series of magnificently decorated prayer rooms, sutra libraries, hallways, and antechambers; and it houses priceless treasures of gold, silver, and precious stones.

The Potala Palace.

At the top of the Potala Palace.

In Chengdu, I visited a "free" meat market. The cuts of meat are suspended by hooks attached to a rail.

Chengdu Area Again

En route from the airport to the hotel, we stopped at the Gui Hu Restaurant, located in the county seat.

Following lunch we went to the Chengdu Zoo, where we saw the pandas and the lesser pandas. We were told that this is the native habitat of the pandas, and that, presently, pandas are protected as an endangered species. Along the way, we saw the city of Chengdu.

Du Fu's Thatched Cottage

This morning, we visited the Du Fu Cottage Shrine—a shrine in memory of the famous Chinese poet, Dr. Du Fu, 712–770 B.C., which was during the Tang dynasty.

Chengdu Bamboo Factory

Following the visit to Du Fu's Thatched Cottage, we visited the Chengdu Bamboo Factory, where they were making woven bamboo wares with porcelain body, marketed as "the three companions brand." Three types of bamboo are used; hence, the word "three" in the brand name.

Jinma (Gold Horse) Commune

We were briefed and shown this commune by Mr.Yu Zai-Shan and Mr. Luo Guo-Chie.

Their main crops are paddy rice, winter wheat, and rapeseed. They also have pigs, layers, silk worms, a silk reeling factory, and they fabricate concrete for buildings.

Silk Worms

They showed us 25-day-old silk worms, to which they were feeding mulberry leaves eight times daily.

Briefing at the Gold Horse Commune.

At the Gold Horse Commune.

At the Gold Horse Commune in Chengdu, we visited the home of the Liu Hui Ying family. Mrs. Liu, a retired teacher, is shown with Dr. E.

I did a little fishing at the Jinma (Gold Horse) Commune.

Silk Reeling Factory

After seeing the silk worms, we were taken to the Silk Reeling Factory. It takes the spun thread of eight silk worms to make one thread—3,281 ft long.

The Liu Hui Ying Family

We visited the home of the Liu family, where we were welcomed by Mrs. Liu, a retired teacher. The Liu home consists of a living room, three bedrooms, a kitchen, and a toilet.

Shu Embroidery Factory

Mr. Bai Huai Liang, leader of the factory, briefed us. The Shu Embroidery Factory is one of the four famous embroidery factories in China. Embroidery in China has a history going back 2,000 years. There are 360 workers in the factory, 60% of whom are women.

There are two kinds of production in this factory: The fancy work, like double embroidery, made primarily for export; and the practical, like blouses and scarfs.

Dr. E persuaded Bill Farr to model a robe.

Shanghai Area

Upon our arrival in Shanghai we were met by Mr. Wang Guo Xian, who served as our local guide. We registered at the Shanghai Hotel, following which we had a luncheon at the hotel.

Shanghai is the leading industrial and commercial city of China. Lying on the Whangpoo River on the east China coast, it is one of the world's great ports. About half of China's foreign commerce passes through the city. The expanded city has a population of 13 million.

Shanghai is China's pacesetter, both in politics and fashion. Shanghai is probably the most prosperous city in China. The women appear to be better dressed and more clothes-conscious, they wear smarter jackets and more colorful floral skirts than elsewhere in China.

July 1st People's Commune

Upon our arrival at this commune, we were met by Mr. Yuan Yi-Xing (a college graduate, and former teacher) and Mr. Chang Fa-geng. Mr. Yuan briefed us; and the two of them took us through the commune. It is noteworthy that both of these men are elected for a period of three years.

There are 24,000 people in the commune, and 4,200 households. The total area of the commune is 5,263 acres.

We visited their dairy, swine operations, and kindergarten, following which we enjoyed a bountiful and delicious lunch on the commune. All the food served, except the pineapples, was produced on the commune.

Briefing at the July 1st People's Commune.

Research Institute of Livestock and Veterinary Medicine

Following lunch, we visited the Research Institute of Livestock and Veterinary Medicine, where we were warmly welcomed by Mr. Zhao Zhi Long and his staff.

The Institute is largely devoted to animal husbandry research pertinent to the Shanghai area, although they do some research for the state. They work primarily on diseases in pigs, dairy cattle, and poultry (chickens and ducks).

Dinner at Jingan Guest House, With Dr. Fu as Special Guest

We had a banquet at the Jingan Guest House, with Dr. Fu Bei-bin, famed surgeon as our special guest.

Dr. Fu is Superintendent, Department of Surgery, Shanghai Medical College No. 2. He received his medical training in Europe, following which he returned to China at a very low salary, dedicated to serving his people.

Dr. Fu supervises a staff of 200 in the hospital, 45 of whom are in surgery. They are doing many kidney transplants, but liver and heart transplants are limited and on an experimental basis.

At the end of the banquet, I presented Dr. Fu with a copy of my lecture before the Chinese Academy of Sciences; a gold pen-and-pencil set; and a saddle, making him an Honorary American Cowboy.

Dr. Fu arranged for a fabulous baked Alaska for dessert. It's one of the Ensmingers' favorites.

Jia Diang Swine Breeding Farm

We visited this farm for the specific purpose of seeing the Meishan breed of swine, without a doubt the most prolific breed of swine in the world. This breeding farm is under the direction of Mr. Zhao Zhi Long. Meishan means "plum mountain," after the mountain. They have 200 sows of the Meishan breed.

Chengong People's Commune

We obtained the following pertinent information from Mr. Chen Fu-ming, a staff member of Jia Diang County, relative to this commune. The commune embraces 10.8 sq miles, 17 production brigades, 165 teams, 7,000 families, 26,000 people, and 4,199 acres of cultivated land. The main crops are wheat, rice, cotton, and rapeseed.

In the last couple of years, many new houses have been constructed. Approximately 237 sq ft of housing is allowed each person. They are building duplexes, at a cost of 20,000 yuan for the duplex. Because the workers own their own homes, there is no rental. Also, they have free water, and they have their own vegetable garden.

Mr. Gam Si-chan, Chief of the Director's Office of the Chengdong People's Commune, led us on a tour of the commune.

We saw the dairy and the mink. On this commune, they also produce fresh-water oysters, which are used for two purposes: Pearls for ornaments, and, as a traditional Chinese medicine, ground pearls are used to treat insomnia and hypertension (about 80% of their production is used in medicine).

It takes seven years to produce pearls. This commune has 170 oyster ponds, in which it produces 440,000 lb of oysters per year.

Suzhou Area

We traveled by train from Shanghai to Suzhou. In Suzhou, Mr. Yu served as our local guide. We had breakfast and lunch at the Suzhou Hotel, opened in 1979, which is large and modern.

Suzhou, meaning "plentiful water," is one of China's oldest and most beautiful cities. There is a Chinese proverb which says, "In heaven there is paradise, on earth Suzhou and Hangzhou." The Grand Canal is located on the west side of the city. It was originally constructed to carry grain from the Yangtze Plain to the capital. Marco Polo, who visited Suzhou in the 13th century, wrote: "The great Khan . . . has made a huge canal of great width and depth from river to river and from lake to lake, and made the water flow along it so that it looks like a big river. . . . By this means it is possible to go . . . as far as Beijing *[called Khan-balik at that time]*."

Grand Canal

The Grand Canal, started in 589 A.D., located immediately west of the city, is the largest man-made waterway in the world. It was originally built to transport rice from the Yangtze Plain to Beijing. The segment of the Grand Canal near Suzhou is heavily traversed by long lines of cargo barges carrying agricultural products and raw materials. The canal's embankments have masonry towpaths which are still in use. The canal averages 100 ft in width, but narrows at the numerous picturesque stone bridges that arch gracefully above it. The average depth is 7–10 ft, which is adequate for small river craft.

The Grand Canal.

National Embroidery Institute

Following lunch, we visited the Embroidery Research Center.

Embroidery is recognized as an art in China. In order to preserve and perpetuate it, the National Embroidery Institute was established in Suzhou in 1957.

Briefing at the National Embroidery Institute. The lady at the center and far end of the table is doing the briefing.

Humble Administrator's Garden

This garden, which is also known as "Plain Man's Politics Garden," was laid out in 1513 by Wang Xianchen, a censor of the imperial court. A not-so-humble administrator, Wang retired to Suzhou to "tend his garden"—but only after he had extorted enough money from court officials to build it. Upon Wang's death, the garden passed to his son, who lost it gambling. Through the centuries, it passed from hand to hand, until it was made a public garden in 1952.

Because the garden was built on marshy grounds, three-fifths of the 12-acre area is water. Bridges zigzag at right angles across the many ponds. It is recognized as one of the four best gardens in China.

Tiger Hill

This artificial hill is located two miles northwest of Suzhou. It reaches a height of 117 ft. Tiger Hill includes all the traditional elements considered essential to an aesthetically perfect Chinese hill: stones, plants, trees, pagodas, waterfalls, and a multitude of legends.

The Yunan Pagoda at the summit was built in 961 A.D. It is about 150 ft high, and is constructed entirely of brick and stone. Over the centuries, it began to tilt (it is 7.6 in. off center), a process recently halted by reinforcement with concrete and steel.

Lingering Garden (Tarrying Garden; Liu Garden)

This garden, located about a half-mile northwest of town, is one of China's four protected gardens (the other three: Humble Administrator's Gardens, The Summer Palace in Beijing, and the Imperial Mountain Resort in Chengdu). It covers about 10 acres. Lingering Garden was first laid out during the Ming Dynasty. The first man to acquire it when it was sold was a man by the name of Liu. It was rebuilt as a public garden in 1876, and it was fully restored in 1953.

Children's Palace, Changning District

Mrs. Wang Hongying, teacher, along with three of the children (two boys and a girl), escorted us through the Children's Palace.

In our guided tour through the palace, we saw the following activities: sports, amusement park, piano (a six-year-old boy, who will be a concert pianist some day), music using Chinese traditional instruments, painting, singing, computer instruction, dancing, bicycle racing, and Chinese chess.

At the Children's Palace, Changning District, Shanghai. *Left to right:* Mr. Cheng Runming, our guide/interpreter; Mrs. Wang Hongying, teacher at the Children's Palace; and Dr. E. Mrs. Wang Hongying briefed us before showing us through the Children's Palace.

Shanghai No. 1 Silk Printing Mill

In the briefing, and during the tour through the mill, Mr. Chen Guang Sing, staff member in charge of reception told us this plant was started 30 years ago; it specializes in printing silk and rayon; there are more than 1,000 workers; they turn out 54,700 yd of printed material per day.

Boat Trip on the Huangpu River

This afternoon, we took a 3½-hour trip on the Huangpu River on the Pujing, a triple-deck tourist ship that makes daily trips to the mouth of the mighty Yangtze River. Aboard the boat, seated in comfortable chairs, we saw diesel-powered Chinese and foreign freighters, along with occasional junks and sampans.

Dr. T. C. Huang's Relatives

Two brothers and a niece of Dr. T. C. Huang met the Ensmingers at the Shanghai Hotel, where we had refreshments and visited for an hour with T. L. Huang, T. C.'s elder brother; T. Y. Huang, another brother of T. C., who studied horticulture at Michigan State University; and T. D. Huang, daughter of T. L. Huang. (Dr. T. C. Huang took his doctorate degree at Washington State University under Dr. Ensminger. He lives in the United States.)

Rui Jin Hospital/Acupuncture Anesthesia Used in Surgery

We went to the Rui Jin Hospital, Shanghai, where Dr. Fu Bei-bin had made arrangements for us to see acupuncture anesthesia used in surgery. At the hospital, we were received by Dr. Lin Yen-Tchen, and Mrs. Zao Yucheng, head nurse, who stayed with us throughout our visit. Dr. Lin has officed and worked with Dr. Fu for more than 30 years. Dr. Lin also reported that Dr. Fu has been in charge of surgery since 1947.

This morning, we witnessed a thyroidectomy under acupuncture anesthesia, with the surgery performed by Dr. Chiang Lu Ping. Only four needles were used, two in each hand. A sedative was given to the patient before she was wheeled into the operating room. Dr. Lin also mentioned that acupuncture is used primarily where surgery is from the chest up, and that the patient must be of a calm disposition.

Ready for surgery! *Left to right:* Dr. Lin Yen-Tehen, Dr. E, and Dr. Fu Bei-bin, at the Rui Jin Hospital.

In Shanghai, we had a gala dinner at the International Club in honor of our superb guide and interpreter, Mr. Cheng Runming, at which time there were many well-merited gifts and accolades for him.

Shanghai Community Church

Following the visit to the Rui Jin Hospital, we drove by the Shanghai Community Church, a Protestant church. According to our local guide, Mr. Wang Guo Xiang, there are 15 Protestant churches in Shanghai at the present time, and people are free to worship at the church of their choice.

Canton (Guangzhou) Area

Mr. Zhang Zhi Lin, our local guide, met us upon our arrival in Canton and checked us in at the White Swan Hotel, a luxurious joint-venture hotel between Hong Kong and Canton.

Canton, with a population of 5,000,000, is the largest and most important city in southern China. Canton is an English name. The Chinese name is Guangzhou. The city is located on a bend of the Pearl River. The delta, with its hot, humid summers and mild winters, has a growing season that is almost year-round.

The rich alluvial soil of the Pearl River Delta makes the Guangzhou region highly productive. In

Dr. E and Mr. Chan Hon Sang (center) at the Ping Chou People's Commune. Mr. Chan welcomed and briefed us before showing us the commune.

addition to three rice crops a year, the area produces wheat, fruit, vegetables, sugarcane, and oil-bearing crops.

Ping Chou People's Commune

This morning, we visited the Ping Chou People's Commune. Mr. Chan Hon Sang welcomed and briefed us, then led us over the commune.

Ping Chou Commune has a population of 70,000 people, and 18,000 families; and it has 11,115 acres of cultivable land. The chief agricultural products are: rice (9,880 acres), wheat, taro, fruit, vegetables, sugarcane, rape, pigs, chickens, ducks, and fish.

Also, the Ping Chou Commune has factories for producing brick, hardware, farm machinery, cement, lime, and clothing.

Tour of the City of Canton/ Farewell Banquet

We were taken on a tour of the city of Canton and shown the following: the Trade Fair, which is open in spring and in autumn, Sun Yatsen Memorial Hall, and Monument to the Martyrs in the Sha Kee incident.

We were told that the city of Canton is noted as the southern gateway to China, for tropical climate and vegetation, and for distinctive cuisine cooking.

Tonight, we went to the Canton Restaurant for a farewell banquet, where roast pig was served. It was about a 35- to 40-lb pig, served without the U.S. traditional apple in the mouth.

Exit China

Today, we traveled by train from Canton to Hong Kong. The first part of the travel was through the fertile Pearl River Delta.

We crossed the border at ShumChun, which has changed so much since our 1972, 1974, and 1977 visits, that we scarcely recognized it. Today, it is a city of factories and multistory office buildings and apartments.

1984
AG-TECH SCHOOLS IN CHINA

Because of my long friendship with China and expertise in conducting international schools and seminars, I was invited to conduct the first extensive schools in animal science in China in more than 30 years. Following two years of planning, along with a personal visit and much correspondence with Chinese friends, the schools were scheduled for June 18–July 11, 1984. Twenty-five agriculturally oriented people participated in, or provided the very considerable support for, the schools.

At the outset, I recognized that a prerequisite to successful schools in China was a thorough understanding of China's agriculture, along with the history and culture of the country, for they are inseparable. For this reason, historical and cultural places were visited along the way.

The Beijing Area We Saw

During our five days in the area, we stayed at the Great Wall Hotel. It's a very new and luxurious hotel infused with the mystique of China. While we were there, they had the official opening celebration.

Beijiano Farm

We visited the Beijiano Farm (a state farm). Mr. Sun Yefu, Director of Management Office, welcomed us and briefed us relative to the operation.

Madame Chen Haiging, deputy director and animal technician, briefed us relative to the animals on the farm.

There are a total of 5,300 dairy cattle on the farm.

The pig farm's breed of swine is known as the Peking Black, which was developed here. It is a rather fat (lardy) pig; hence, they have crossbred them with animals of the Duroc, Landrace, and Hampshire breeds.

This farm supplies 80,000 ducks to the state each year.

Maliendian Village

Mr. Sun Yefu gave us the following information relative to this village:

They have three main businesses: a dairy of 1,040 head, a lamp factory, and a woolen coat factory.

We also visited the nearby dairy that is operated by this village.

We walked along the cattle corrals in which the animals were confined. Only a high shade was provided for shelter. The cows were clean, their hair was glossy, and they were contented.

We also walked by the calf corral. Calves are removed from their mothers immediately following birth, after which they are fed colostrum for six days. The heifers are used for replacements, and the bull calves are sold to family farms for beef production.

Bull Station

This is a state operated bull stud, which means that it is under the Ministry of Agriculture.

After inspecting the bulls, Audrey and I, along with our son John and his wife, Jane, left for a luncheon engagement with Mr. He Kang, Minister of Agriculture, Animal Husbandry, and Fishery.

Beijing Municipal Poultry Breeding Company

Five units of the company were visited.

■ **Farm 1**—This is a turkey breeding farm. We did not enter the buildings because of the disease risk.

■ **Farm 2**—This farm has 200,000 laying hens. We viewed birds through the windows.

■ **Farm 3**—This is a quail breeding facility.

■ **Farm 4**—Approximately 400 mink are kept for breeding.

■ **Farm 5**—This is an incubator facility. About

50,000 eggs are set per day in large incubators with temperature control and an automatic egg movement system.

Mr. He Kang, the Ministry of Agriculture

Mr. He Kang, an old and warm friend of the Ensmingers, hosted a luncheon in honor of Dr. and Mrs. M. E. Ensminger and Mr. and Mrs. John Ensminger, at the Beijing Hotel. Those present in addition to the Minister and the Ensmingers were Mr. Xiang Chongjang, Vice Minister of Agriculture, Animal Husbandry, and Fishery; Ms. Xu Jing, Chief of Division, Department of Foreign Affairs, Ministry of Agriculture, Animal Husbandry, and Fishery; and Ms. Jin Yunziu, Translation Officer, Department of Foreign Affairs, Ministry of Agriculture, Animal Husbandry, and Fishery.

This was primarily a visit between old friends. Mr. He Kang led the group of 28 high level Chinese (there were seven governors in the group) that visited the Ensmingers and Agriservices Foundation at Clovis, California in 1978.

Mr. He Kang received the Ensmingers very warmly. In addition to his kind accolades to the Ensmingers, extolling the contributions of the Ensmingers and Agriservices Foundation to China and the Chinese people, he presented me with an autographed copy of the Chinese edition of my book *Animal Science*.

Audrey and I met with Mr. Xu Weizeng, Greater Encyclopedia of China Publishing House, Beijing.

The Greater Encyclopedia of China Publishing House

Prior to traveling to China in 1984, I made an appointment for Audrey and me to meet with Mr. Xu Weizeng, Greater Encyclopedia of China Publishing House, Beijing. This was prompted because Encyclopaedia Britannica, U.S.A., was marketing the Ensmingers' two-volume human nutrition book, *Foods & Nutrition Encyclopedia* and they were eager for us to visit Mr. Xu. We subsequently became warm friends with Mr. Xu.

Mr. Xu warmly welcomed us. He reported as follows relative to the Chinese edition of *Encyclopaedia Britannica*: In 1980, the government of China entered into a contract with Encyclopaedia Britannica of Chicago, to publish a Chinese edition of *Encyclopaedia Britannica*; about 500 people were involved in the translation, which has been completed.

Mr. Xu mentioned that there is much interest in human nutrition in China, the subject covered in the Ensminger's *Foods & Nutrition Encyclopedia*. Subsequently, China published a Chinese edition of *Foods & Nutrition Encyclopedia*, in 5 volumes, 10,000 sets of which were sold in four months' time.

Left to right: Dr. E; Mr. He Kang, Minister of Agriculture, Animal Husbandry and Fisheries; Audrey; and Prof., Dr. Cheng Peilieu.

School in Beijing

We conducted a school in the Science Hall, Beijing. China Association for Science and Technology (CAST) had invited representatives of several organizations to attend.

The general chairman, President An Min, Beijing Agricultural University introduced me.

I made a 30-minute illustrated (slide) presentation before the entire group of 150 people on the subject, "Ushering Animal Science into the 21st Century." Following this, the enrollees were divided into three groups.

- **Room No. 1**—Animal nutrition and management.
- **Room No. 2**—Animal breeding and management.
- **Room No. 3**—Veterinary medicine and tropical diseases.

Each of our school professors made a 30-minute presentation, following which there was a question-answer period between Chinese and Americans in each room. A total of a half day was devoted to each presentation. An interpreter was used in each session.

There was an excellent enrollment of 150 people, with representatives from the several organizations that were invited to participate.

John and Jane Ensminger Conducted Seminars

My son, John Ensminger, a lawyer, presented a scholarly legal seminar at Beijing University; and his wife Jane Ensminger, a graduate of Julliard in New York, presented a professional dancing and choreographic seminar at the Beijing Institute of Dancing.

John also met with the leaders of the Beijing Association of Lawyers at their invitation.

Mr. and Mrs. Huang Hua Hosted a Dinner for the Four Ensmingers

The four Ensmingers were honored guests at a dinner hosted by Mr. and Mrs. Huang Hua, in State Guest House No. 7.

Mrs. Huang has retained her maiden name, He Liliang, as is a rather common practice in China.

The Huangs have a son who is enrolled at Harvard; and a married daughter.

Other guests at the dinner party were: Mr. Xiang Conghyang, Erwin Engst, and Joan Hinton.

The dinner party made for a pleasant evening, with bountiful and delicious food, and a warm and friendly visit with old and dear friends. Toasts were given by Mr. Huang and me.

Dr. E and Mr. Huang Hua (right) at a dinner hosted by Mr. and Mrs. Huang Hua, in State Guest House No. 7, Beijing, for the four Ensmingers.

The four Ensmingers, *left to right:* John, Jane, Audrey, and Dr. E. Photo taken at the dinner hosted by Mr. and Mrs. Huang.

Institute of Animal Science

We visited the Institute of Animal Science, where we were briefed by my old friend, Prof., Dr. C. H. Liu, Director of the Institute.

The institute is concerned with the application of techniques, and theoretical studies essential for the development of livestock production. The institute is also engaged in the key national projects and in coordination of national projects, and is responsible for the academic exchanges, the international

On a walking tour of the facilities and equipment of the Institute of Animal Science, Beijing. *Left to right:* Dr. James R. Carlson, Chairman, Animal Sciences, Washington State University, Pullman; Dr. E; and Prof., Dr. C. H. Liu, Director, Institute of Animal Science, Beijing.

cooperation in animal science, and the training of graduate students in three subject areas; feedstuffs, poultry reproduction, and breeding.

Following the more formal presentation, the group was divided, then taken on a walking tour of the facilities and equipment. Professor Liu Chin-Hsu led one group, and Professor Cheng Peilieu led the other.

Summer Palace

Our group had lunch in the Oriole Restaurant at the Summer Palace, followed by sightseeing and boating on Kunming Lake. The following guests joined us for lunch: Ms. An-Lin Ge, Mr. Chen Lichong, Mary Wang, along with members from the academy.

Church in Beijing

At my request, our guides arranged for us to visit a church. It was Sunday, and the church was packed full. We visited the Nangtang Cathedral, founded by Brother Ricci, an Italian Jesuit. The cathedral was built in 1904.

The Inner Mongolia Area We Saw

Inner Mongolia is a vast territory on China's northern frontier. Its proper name is the Autonomous Region of Inner Mongolia.

The Mongol territories came under Chinese control in the 17th century; the first section (Inner Mongolia) in 1635, and the remaining portion (Outer Mongolia) in 1697. Outer Mongolia became autonomous in 1912, and became the People's Republic of Mongolia in 1924. Inner Mongolia continued under Chinese control and, in 1949, became the first autonomous region created by the new China.

Inner Mongolia is a plateau with an average altitude of 3,200 feet. It has a population of 8.6 million. The region stretches along China's northwestern border with Russia and is considered strategically vital to China.

Inner Mongolia is famous for the great grasslands, which cover about two-thirds of its area, and is one of China's main centers for animal husbandry.

In the grasslands, many Mongols still live in yurts—cylindrical shaped tents with dome roofs; the entire structure is supported by collapsible lattice work of wood, and the outside is covered with cloth and skins to keep out the cold winds. The yurts that we visited were modernized by having a small attached metal building in which there was running water, a shower, and a toilet; on the top of which was a solar energy system. Today, 74% of the herdsmen have permanent dwellings.

The great grasslands, as far as the eye can see, are in the background of this photo of me with our Chinese friends in Mongolia.

Inner Mongolia Academy of Animal Science

At the Inner Mongolia Academy of Animal Science they conduct research—there is no teaching. They have three institutes: Animal Science, Veterinary Medicine, and Range Science.

Inner Mongolia College of Agriculture and Animal Science

The teaching facilities consist of laboratories, which are augmented by one crop farm, and an animal husbandry and veterinary station. In animal husbandry, students may specialize in either ruminants, or nutrition of feeds.

The Center for Cultural Education of Inner Mongolia

Ten members of our group accompanied Jane Ensminger to the Dancing Center for the Cultural Education of Inner Mongolia. Audrey Ensminger's report on this activity follows:

The director is a former famous dancer by the name of Si Chim Tarha.

Jane Ensminger performed two dances, after which they performed some of their traditional dances including one dance called the Chopstick Dance.

Sightseeing in Huhehot

Huhehot means "green town" in Mongolian. It is an ancient town, with a long history outside the Great Wall. The city covers 2,346 sq mi with a total population of 1,200,000 people.

Five-Pagoda Temple

The Five-Pagoda Temple was built in the Ching Dynasty. In ancient times, it was called the 1,000 Monk Temple. Buddhist temples served three purposes: as places of worship; as safe places to preserve what few books had been written, most of which recorded the history of the church; and as places to bury very famous people.

In times of celebration, they placed lamps at the four corners on the roof.

Grave of Wang Zhaojun

We traveled about five miles from Huhehot, into the lush green of the countryside. There, with a high knob of ground to mark it, is the grave of Wang Zhaojun, who was the beautiful wife of the king of Mongolia.

About 33 B.C., the story goes, the Hans and the Mongolians were at war. In order to bring peace between the nations, the emperor of the Hans promised to give the prince of Mongolia a young girl from his court. When the emperor asked to see Zhaojun, he found that she was very beautiful and he wanted to keep her himself, and Zhaojun wanted to stay. However, the emperor had made a promise which he felt he had to keep.

When she arrived, and the prince of Mongolia saw how beautiful she was, he fell in love with her.

The fall games, which are still held in Inner Mongolia, originally started as a celebration of the wedding anniversary of Zhaojun and the king of Mongolia.

Museum (or Factory) for Native Handicrafts

This place was built in 1969. It employs 300 workers, produces 29 kinds of products, and represents three minority groups.

We saw them making several different knives. Also, they were making several different kinds of leather boots. All of the products that they were making are used in Inner Mongolia.

School in Huhehot, Inner Mongolia

We conducted a seminar in Huhehot, Inner Mongolia. We followed the same pattern as in Beijing. That is, I addressed the general session. Then, we divided into three different sessions.

By actual count, there were 170 people in the general session. This was a larger attendance than we had in Beijing. The veterinary/horse section was packed—with standing room only.

Following my lecture in the general session, I met with a group of the high-ranking staff officials of CAST in Inner Mongolia. They advised me that CAST of Inner Mongolia has 80,000 to 90,000 members. The delegation was headed by Professor Liu Zhong-Ling, a biologist. Professor Liu is the highest ranking officer of CAST in Inner Mongolia.

Visit to the Exhibition/Shopping/ Visit to a Kindergarten

Twelve of our group visited the exhibition, or museum. The museum houses many fossil bones of dinosaurs that were dug up in Mongolia. There was one skull that is 10,000 years old. There were many artifacts from the more recent dynasties, including some clothes. Also, Genghis Kahn and his grandson, Kublai Kahn, were depicted.

Next, we visited one of the department stores, where some of the group did some shopping.

Finally, we visited a kindergarten, where the precious children performed for us.

The Great Grasslands

This morning, we traveled northward from Huhehot, crossed the Daqing Mountains, and traveled to the great grasslands in the Wulantuge area.

Liu Zhong-Ling, Vice Chairman of CAST, met us upon our arrival at the commune and stayed with us during our visit there.

The great grasslands in the Wulantuge area, north of Huhehot. Note the sheep, horses, and herdsman's house.

Nadamu

We visited a nadamu, a rock structure on a high hill, which is used for the following purposes: A yearly (usually July) gathering place to the celebrate the harvest, and to make a sacrifice to heaven; to tell directions, through the stone arrangement; and as a place for courting.

Herdsman's House

We visited a herdsman's house. It was comfortable. They served us milk-tea, millet, and other tidbits.

After lunch, I made Dr. Liu an Honorary American Cowboy.

Boiled Mutton Luncheon

At noon, we were served boiled mutton, along with other traditional Mongolian foods.

Dancing and Singing

Following lunch, a Mongolian troupe staged superb dancing and singing for our entertainment.

Horse Races/Camel Races/ Wrestling/Riding

For our entertainment, our hosts first raced four Mongolian ponies on a reasonably level area around a mile track.

Next, they raced three camels. One camel was "barn sour, without a barn," for he didn't want to keep on the track—he wanted to return; so, they herded him with the riders mounted on Mongolian ponies.

The third activity consisted of wrestling.

Following the exhibitions, our people were invited to ride the camels and the Mongolian ponies (small, tough horses about 13 to 14 hands high).

Banquet Hosted by CAST

CAST hosted a banquet for our group at the Huhehot Hotel. Professor Liu Zhong-Ling, the ranking officer of CAST for all of Mongolia, headed the host group. Also, Professor Lan Gianfu (Veterinarian, friend, and classmate of Dr. T. C. Huang who took his Ph.D. with me) and other Chinese friends were pres-

On Wednesday evening, CAST hosted a dinner in our honor at the Huhehot Hotel. *Left to right:* Yang "Kevin" Zhijian, interpreter; Dr. E; and Prof. Liu Zhong-Ling, the ranking officer for CAST for all of Mongolia.

Left to right: Prof., Dr. Lan Gianfu, veterinarian; Audrey; and Dr. E. Photo taken at the dinner at the Huhehot Hotel.

ent. It was a bountiful and delicious banquet, with many courses. The boiled lamb was superb.

Mao Memorial Hall

Upon our arrival in Beijing, we visited the Mao Zedong Memorial Hall. Foreigners were not allowed to go through the hall at that time, but our good friends the Huang Huas made the arrangements.

Few men in world history have had greater impact than Mao Zedong. Without him, there would not have been a New China.

The building was opened on September 9, 1977, the first anniversary of Chairman Mao's death.

In the entrance hall is a white marble statue of Mao Zedong seated. Inside the mausoleum itself, Mao's body lies in a crystal sarcophagus, draped with the red flag of the Communist Party of China.

When visiting, hats are removed, there is silence, and photos inside the building are prohibited. A visit to the Mao Zedong Memorial Hall is both moving and memorable.

Chongqing Area

We traveled by plane from Beijing to Chongqing. Our reservations were at the Renmin Hotel.

Chongqing, the largest city in Sichuan Province, is the most important industrial city in southwest China, and a key regional transportation hub. The city owes its early development and rapid recent growth to its location at the juncture of the Jialing and Yangtse rivers.

Chongqing's climate is one of the least appealing in all of China, as indicated by the local nickname "furnace of the Yangtse." Summers are hot and humid. From May to September, heavy rain falls 4 days out of 10. Of course, warm temperature, rainfall, and humidity make for a lush growth of vegetation. However, the climate is favorable for varied agricultural development, including the production of rice, edible crops, oil crops, citrus fruits, tea, silkworm cocoons, vegetables, hogs, hog bristles, sausage casings, and poultry eggs and feathers.

Sechuan College of Fine Arts

We visited the Sechuan College of Fine Arts,

Briefing at the Sechuan Art College.

which is the only major art school in Southwest China. Our guide and narrator during our visit was Ms. Liu Landing Danielle, who teaches English in the college. She has excellent command of the English language.

We were much impressed with the art that we saw. The oil paintings of famed Luo Zhang Li were outstanding.

They have an enrollment of more than 400 students; and they have more than 200 teachers.

Hot Springs

Our group traveled to the Northern Hot Springs, located in a large park overlooking the Jialing river. Here, visitors can soak for hours in one of the 40 baths filled with mineral water maintained at 100°F, or swim in one of the three olympic-size pools fed by the hot springs.

Yangtse Gorge

We boarded our ship, East Is Red 49, at Chaotian Men Dock for a 2¾-day cruise downstream on the Yangtse river from Chongqing to Wuhan, a distance of 850 miles.

The pagodas located below almost every town were built in the belief that they would prevent the wealth of the towns from being swept away by the rapid current. Many Daoist temples are also visible.

Wanxian

Situated in rich and beautiful country, Wanxian is an old river city. Our East Is Red steamer pulled into Wanxian on the evening of the first day and remained there until 4:30 a.m. of the second day, to enable the ship to reach the gorges by sunrise. Following Wanxian, we saw the splendor of the gorges. The passage through them was relatively calm and peaceful. They are outstanding for their natural beauty.

Qutang Gorge (5 miles)

It is the shortest, the narrowest, and also the most magnificent of the three gorges. In ancient times, it was said that if the gate were locked by an iron chain, no boat could pass; hence, the name "Qutang Pass."

Three beautiful Yangtse River gorges.

While our "East Is Red" steamer was docked in Wanxian, we climbed these steep stairs to see a free market high over the Yangtse.

Xiling Gorge (9.3 miles)

In this gorge lies a whole range of large stone reefs and dangerous shoals. The slopes along the Xiling gorge are covered with orange trees.

As we cruised down the Yangtse, we were aware that what we were seeing would soon be under water due to the giant dam they are building to supply water for the ever-increasing agricultural production needs of their billion-plus population.

The three gorges have always been famous for their beauty. But, in the past, they were also infamous because boats on the zigzagging river course were endangered by the innumerable reefs and shoals. The hazardous waterway was best described by Bi Bai, a talented poet of the Tang Dynasty who la-

Our cruise ship.

Yangtse river locks.

mented, "Traveling to Sichuan is as difficult as climbing to the sky."

The local people along the Yangtse, in and near the gorges, are engaged mainly in agriculture. Poor transportation hampers advanced farming, which remains hand-operated by and large.

Wuhan Area

We arrived in Wuhan, following our boat trip down the Yangtse River. Upon our arrival, we were met by a large delegation, including Drs. Qin, Peng, Sun and Chen, from Huazhong Agricultural College, and Ms. Wang Shan, dancer, Hubei Singing and Dancing Troupe (she came to meet Jane Ensminger).

Following a drive through the city, we checked in at the Qingchuan Hotel, Wuhan's newest, largest, and most modern hotel. We had the honor of being the first American group to occupy this new hotel; and we were there before the official opening.

Banquet

We were honored with a banquet at the Qingchuan Hotel, hosted by Mr. Chang Kuangho, Vice Chairman of Hubei Technical and Science Association; which also included other invited guests.

About Wuhan

Wuhan, the capital of Hubei Province, is the collective name given to three closely linked municipalities—Wuchang, Hankou, and Hanyang. Wuhan, meaning "Witches Mounting," is thought to have been inhabited by demons. Wuhan is situated at the confluence of the Han and Yangtse rivers.

Wuhan is synonymous with iron and steel production in China. It also produces a substantial array of chemicals, fertilizers, construction materials, and rolling stock, as well as cotton fabrics and a number of other light industrial products.

Wuhan is a major cultural and political center in China. Among its 21 institutions of higher education are the prestigious Wuhan University, the Central China Engineering Institute, and the Central China Teachers' College.

Wuhan University campus consists of traditional-style pagoda structures, which overlook the Yangtse River and the city of Wuhan. The university was established in 1913.

Huazhong Agricultural College

Upon our arrival at Huazhong Agricultural College, we were briefed by Vice President Jin Kaizhu.

The college experimental station is on the campus, including four substations, specializing in crops, horticulture, livestock, and fisheries. There are also a workshop of agricultural machinery, a factory of microbial products, and a veterinary clinic.

In addition to teaching duties, a fair proportion of the academic members engage in research activities on national and provincial projects.

We all proceeded to their largest lecture theatre where the Huazhon Agricultural Collge made me an Honorary Professor of the college, the details of which are in the chapter entitled "Awards."

Tour of Huazhong Agricultural College

Following the conferring of the title of honorary professor upon me, Vice President Jin Kaizhu led us on a tour of the campus, especially the new library.

School at Huazhong Agricultural College

Our third Ag-Tech School in China was held on the campus of Huazhong Agricultural College.

I gave my presentation immediately following the ceremony in which I was made an honorary professor.

There were 150 enrollees in the school that was held on the campus of Huazhong Agricultural College, and there was great interest. Also, we were pleased with the quality of the enrollees.

English Language Instruction

While the three separate schools were in progress, Vice President Jin took me to see their English Language Institute, which is the best of its kind that I have seen.

The main objective is to teach English so well that the graduates are superbly prepared for advanced degree studies in English speaking countries abroad.

Students spend six months in the course, during which time only English is spoken. They live in dormitories on the campus; and they speak only English when eating, playing tennis, in classes, or what not. They use cassettes, movies, and other modern language teaching tools and techniques.

At the completion of the course, students are examined by four teachers and must pass both a written and an oral examination.

Following our visit, I placed 12 of their students on graduate assistantships at universities throughout the U.S.

Acupuncture Program

In 1980, at the International Stockmen's School in Tucson, Arizona, we were privileged to have three veterinarians (Drs. Sun Yongcai, Chen Cilin, and Peng Hung-ze) who gave a demonstration of acupuncture anesthesia. At Huazhong Agricultural College, Drs. Sun and Chen briefed me on their animal acupuncture program, involving both anesthesia and treatment for certain diseases. They plan to institute a training program on the campus primarily for enrollees from Asia, Africa, and Latin America. This will involve 16 enrollees who will take two to three months training.

Also, Mr. Sun and Mr. Cheng reported that soon they will travel to Sri Lanka where they will give an acupuncture demonstration. They also reported that cattle are the easiest class of animal on which to apply acupuncture anesthesia and dogs are the most difficult.

John Ensminger Met With the Lawyers of Wuhan University

John Ensminger met with 10 of the lawyers on the staff of Wuhan University. He conducted a seminar, using slides. He considered the meeting productive and rewarding.

Jane Ensminger Met With the Dancers

Jane Ensminger, dancer, accompanied by Audrey, met in a new studio with Ms. Wang Shan, dancer, and the Hubei Singing and Dancing Troupe, Wuhan, China. Jane gave a dancing demonstration, and the Chinese dancers did likewise. Jane was enthusiastic about the exchange.

Banquet at the Qingchuan Hotel, Wuhan

The Huazhong Agricultural College hosted a bountiful and delicious banquet, of many courses, for us at the Qingchuan Hotel. Vice President Jin Kaizhu was the master of ceremonies for the evening.

Guilin (Kweilin) Area

Upon our arrival in Guilin via train from Wuhan we checked in at the Banyan Lake Hotel, where we had very nice accommodations, and where we ate our meals.

About Guilin

From a lush green plain laced with rivers and

lakes, suddenly there is a range of peaks, all of which has caused Guilin to be immortalized in Chinese paintings and poetry. The celebrated Tang Dynasty poet, Han Yu (768–824), described the region as follows: "The river forms a green silk belt, the mountains are like blue jade hairpins."

Today, Guilin produces nitrogen fertilizers, spun silk, cotton cloth, tires, medicines, rubber, machinery, electronics, and a wide range of other industrial items. Also, the area produces an abundance of grain, rice, bamboo, pomelos, and cassia byproducts (tea, herbal medicines, fragrant oil, and flavorful local wine). Fishing and river commerce are also important to the local economy.

Reed Flute Cave

This cave is located in the northwestern suburbs. It is the most famous cave of the area. Its name is derived from the reeds at its entrance which were once used to make flutes. First discovered in the Tang Dynasty (618–907), the cave was a frequent refuge for the local population to escape bandits and the ravages of war. Since 1959, it has been transformed into a tourist attraction.

Another Ag-Tech School

Upon our arrival in Guilin, we learned that they wanted us to conduct a school. As the day progressed, we also learned that they could muster up only one interpreter—our national guide-interpreter, Ms. Tai Weidong. So, we changed the format of the school to have only one session, at which I presided. A total of 70 people attended.

Following the introductory remarks by Mr. Ar Peixin, Vice Chairman of the Animal Associations of Guilin who chaired the seminar, we presented a condensed-combined school.

School in Guilin.

Dr. E introduced the American staff at the Guilin school.

The school was well presented by our staff, and well received by the Chinese. Again and again, they asked that we return.

Banquet

We were guests at a special banquet given by our hosts of Guilin at the Banyan Lake Hotel. The banquet was chaired by Mr. Shi Rude, Vice Chairman of the Science Association of Guilin. Among the delicacies served at the multi-course banquet were: frog legs, weanling roast pig, and masked civet, which looks like a mouse but eats only fruit. There were the usual toasts, along with a choice of drinks and bountiful and delicious food.

Li River Cruise

We boarded a pleasure boat for a spectacular six-hour cruise on the winding Li River. The boat traveled approximately 15.5 mi down the river, then docked at Yangdi, a small village at the foot of two mountains (said to resemble the horns of a sheep). When we docked at Yangdi, we were met by many local peasants, all eager to sell their wares. Also, there were many shops in the village. We returned to Guilin by bus.

Guilin Pig Breeding Farm

En route back from Yangdi, we stopped to see the Guilin Pig Breeding Farm, a state-operated pig

Our visit to the pig breeding farm.

breeding farm, directed by Qin Qiuseng and Tao Liangkai.

Guangzhou (Canton) Area

We traveled by plane from Guilin to Guangzhou. Upon our arrival, we registered in at the Dongfang Hotel, which is located directly across the street from the trade fair complex.

Guangzhou (Canton), with a population of 5,000,000, is the largest and most important city in southern China, and the capital of Guangzhou Province.

The city is located on a bend of the Pearl River. The delta, with its hot, humid summers and mild winters, has a growing season that is almost year-round.

Sightseeing in Guangzhou

Our group went sightseeing in Guangzhou, visiting the following four places: Sun Yatsen Memorial Hall; Temple of the Six Banyan Trees; Tower Overlooking the Sea (Zhenhailou) and the Guangdong Historical Museum; and Qing Family House.

Visit With Four Livestock Specialists

While the rest of the group was sightseeing around Guangzhou, I met with the following local livestock specialists, accompanied by an interpreter: Mr. Wu Hui Lun, Director and Deputy General Manager, Canton American Flower Lounge Livestock Co. Ltd., Xin Tan Farm, Dong Pu, Guangzhou; Mr. Zhu Shang Xiong, Senior Engineer, President, China Association of Mechanization in Pig Farming, Bai Yun Mechanization in Pig Farming Factory, Bei Jiao Jia He, Kwangchow; Mr. Wu Tin Xiao, Lounge Livestock Co., Ltd., Kwangchow; and Mr. Wang Wan Zou, Veterinarian Service, Kwangchow.

Meeting With Mr. Chan Hon Sung and Mr. Chen Yungguang

These two old friends, whom the Ensmingers have known since 1972, also came to the Dongfang Hotel for a visit: Mr. Chan Hon Sung, Nan Hoi County Ping Chow District Office, Ping Chow People's Committee Office for Importing Foreign Economy and Techniques, Ping Chow Hui, Nan Hoi Yuen, Kwang Tung Province; and Mr. Chen Yunguang, Vice Chairman, People's Prosecutional Office of Nanbai County, Guangdong Province.

Dinner at Pan Hsi Restaurant (Banxi [Friendship] Restaurant)

We had dinner at Guangzhou's largest restaurant, the Pan Hsi Restaurant, which employs 400 people and seats 1,000. The dinner was hosted by Mr. Shen Zhongfan, Vice Chairman, Secretary General, Guangzhou Science and Technology Association.

Depart China/Return to San Francisco

We traveled via train from Guangzhou (Canton), to Hong Kong, and from there returned to San Francisco, thus ending a memorable visit to China, along with conducting the first schools in China—four of them—with a total enrollment of 560.

1993
AG-TECH SCHOOLS IN UKRAINE AND RUSSIA

In 1989, I first received "smoke signals" from my longtime friends in the U.S.S.R. that they desired that I conduct International Ag-Tech Schools over there and I reacted favorably.

From November 10 to 17, 1991, we had the pleasure of hosting eight agricultural scientists from the U.S.S.R. They were proposing three schools in Ukraine, Moscow, and Vladivostock.

Enter Iowa State University

Due to the unrest that culminated in a coup, our Russian co-sponsors requested that the schools be postponed to August 1992. Then a long silence from Ukraine and Russia ensued. At this point, Dr. Bruce W. Menzel, Iowa State University, entered the picture in a most innovative and unique way. In a telephone call to me, he reported that he and three of his colleagues at Iowa State University would be traveling to Ukraine and Russia in May 1992, to discuss cooperative research with Iowa State University; and offered his services in ferreting out information relative to the status of the schools.

Thereupon, I briefed Dr. Menzel relative to my concerns, and asked that he contact Dr. G. A. Bogdanov in Ukraine, and Ms. Elena Polouchkina in Russia, in my behalf. Dr. Menzel returned with a message, along with a letter, from Dr. Bogdanov and Ms. Polouchkina. Loud and clear, the message requested that the schools be postponed a second time.

When telephoning the message, Dr. Menzel must have sensed my despondency (three years hard work, mountainous expenses—but no schools). So, he suggested that Iowa State University and Agriservices Foundation join forces in conducting these much needed International Ag-Tech Schools. I snapped up the offer.

The eight U.S.S.R. scientists surround Audrey and me in our conference room.

Persistence, Meetings, Time, and Money Followed

There was a wide chasm between desire for and conducting the schools, which required all the persistence and patience that I could muster up, plus much time and money.

The following important meetings, along with files of correspondence and mountainous costs, and (to paraphrase Sir Winston Churchill) no small amount of "blood, sweat, and tears," preceded the schools in Ukraine and Russia.

Three Iowa State University Staff Members Came to the Foundation

June 13–16, 1992, the following three Iowa State University staff members met with the Ensmingers at the Agriservices Foundation Headquarters, Clovis, California: Dr. G. E. Klonglan, Dr. B. W. Menzel, and Dr. M. Douglas Kenealy.

Left to right: Dr. E, Dr. Klonglan, Dr. Menzel, and Dr. Kenealy.

Trustee Elvin Taysom and I visited Russia, Kazakhstan, and Ukraine on a Fact Finding Mission.

October 15–26, 1992, Dr. Elvin Taysom, Trustee of Agriservices Foundation, and I made a fact finding mission to Stavropol, Russia; Alma Ata, Kazakhstan, and Kiev, Ukraine. *Our message:* "No more postponements. Now or never." Also, we met the personnel and checked the facilities. We decided that Kazakhstan wasn't ready for our type of school at this time. But the personnel and facilities at Stavropol, Russia, and Kiev, Ukraine, were good.

Because of the great importance of the fact finding mission which Trustee Taysom and I made, it is detailed in the sections that follow.

Jerry Perkins

Jerry Perkins, who represented the governor of Iowa in cooperative work in the Stavropol area, proved to be the right person, at the right place, at the right time, from the standpoint of the school. He arranged for us to meet with the three key people who will make the school happen in Stavropol; namely, Prof., Dr. Ludmila N. Petrova, General Manager of the Niva Stavropol Research and Production Compltex; Victor M. Pupov, Deputy General Director, Niva Stavropol Research and Production Complex, and Anatoly Tartychev, Stavropol Executive Committee, International Affairs.

Agriservices Foundation Representatives Visited Iowa State

September 16–18, 1992, the Ensmingers and Agriservices Foundation Trustees Art Solomon and Dr. Robert E. Walton (and Jan Walton) met with concerned Iowa State University staff members at ISU, Ames, Iowa.

At Iowa State University, Ames, Iowa, Sept. 17, 1992. *Left to right:* President Martin Jischke, Dr. E, and Dean David G. Topel. Dr. E has just presented a miniature western saddle to each President Jischke and Dean Topel and made them Honorary American Cowboys. In this meeting, Iowa State and Agriservices Foundation finalized the joining of forces to conduct International Ag-Tech Schools Abroad. Dr. E was accompanied by Audrey, Trustees Arthur Solomon and Dr. and Mrs. Robert Walton.

Prof. Petrova and Victor Pupov, the Facilities and Equipment

Prof. Petrova is one of the most impressive, able, and electrifying lady administrators that I have ever met in my worldwide travels. She supervises 2,500 people. At the time of our arrival, she was on the telephone discussing the school with the Russian Minister of Agriculture, Moscow.

Victor Pupov has a pleasant smile, and he speaks and understands English. So, he was a great help in showing us the meeting rooms.

After exchanging greetings, I briefed Prof. Petrova, Victor Pupov, and Jerry Perkins relative to the International Ag-Tech School.

Prof. Petrova would prefer that the school be held in the following order (month): March, October, June, August. However, a June school is quite acceptable.

Prof. Petrova estimates that they will have an enrollment of 300 in the Stavropol school.

They will have sufficient interpreters. I urged that all interpreters study the papers, and familiarize themselves with the technical terms, in advance of the school, which they can do as the papers should be published in a *Russian Handbook of Ag-Tech School Lectures*.

Prof. Petrova indicated that they will borrow some equipment, but that they will meet these needs.

I asked if they would like to have, for showing one evening during the school, a video tape portraying U.S. agriculture, made by Iowa State University. The answer was an enthusiastic "yes."

Also, I asked if they would like that Iowa State University make a video tape of the school in progress, along with some views of Russian agriculture—perhaps with the latter taken immediately preceding, and during, the school; when the guest professors are being shown Russian agriculture. The answer was an enthusiastic "yes."

Meeting With Anatoly Tartychev

Anatoly Tartychev, who is an impressive person and a good operator, invited us to meet in a nice tearoom in his department. At the suggestion of Jerry Perkins, I briefed Mr. Tartychev relative to the International Ag-Tech School.

Summary Relative to Stavropol

Jerry Perkins, Prof. Petrova, Victor Pupov, and Anatoly Tartychev were thinking positive and acting positive relative to the school.

Kiev, Ukraine

Because of shortening our stay in Kazakhstan, Dr. Taysom and I arrived in Kiev a day earlier than scheduled. However, we were unable to make a telephone call from Moscow to Kiev; so, we arrived in Kiev without anyone to meet us and without hotel reservations. We took a taxi to the Dnipro Hotel, where we secured our reservations.

In the morning, I telephoned Professor Olexiy O. Sozinov, President, Ukrainian Academy of Agricultural Sciences. I apologized to Dr. Sozinov for our arriving a day earlier than scheduled without giving him advance notice, explaining that we had been unsuccessful in getting a message to him by telephone or fax, and that we felt that it would be mutually helpful to have an extra day together. Dr. Sozinov was very understanding. He asked that we remain in our hotel room, and indicated that we would be picked up in another 30 minutes. Soon, two of Dr. Sozinov's staff members. Dr. Ivan V. Shabliz and Margaret Dieztar, knocked on the door of our room.

Meeting With Prof. Olexiy O. Sozinov

We were escorted to Prof. Sozinov's office, where Dr. Taysom and I visited with Dr. Sozinov for about 40 minutes. Although we had interpreters, Dr. Sozinov does very well with English.

I urged that the Ukrainian Academy of Agricultural Sciences make the *Russian Handbook of Ag-Tech School Lectures* available to Russia (Stavropol) on a cost of printing basis only, *and that this book be off press well ahead of the schools* so that each enrollee and each interpreter will have a copy.

In the meantime, Dr. G. A. Bogdanov arrived, and entered into the discussion.

At this point, I explained that benefiting the enrollees is the primary objective of the school; hence, there should be a goodly number of enrollees. Thereupon, Dr. Sozinov estimated that they would have about 250 enrollees.

Time to Conduct the School

It was agreed that the school in Kiev should be conducted in June 1993. I emphasized that a third postponement is unthinkable for two reasons: the staff can no longer be held together, and I will be age 85 in 1993—hence, I must get along with other work before I sleep.

A Successful School Can Be Conducted in the Academy Building

Although some rooms are a bit small, we feel that the meeting rooms in the Academy of Agricultural Sciences building are adequate. We were particularly impressed with their largest room, in which my lecture and the dairy group (estimated to be their largest group) will be scheduled.

Summary of Visit With Dr. Sozinov

We were much impressed with Dr. Sozinov. He presented the several problems that he must overcome (such as a shortage of paper for the *Handbook of International Ag-Tech School Lectures*), but Dr. Taysom and I left with the feeling that Dr. Sozinov is equal to the task ahead, and that he and his staff will overcome.

I invited Dr. Sozinov to come to see Agriservices Foundation and the Ensmingers during his next visit to the United States, at which time we shall show him the fertile and productive San Joaquin Valley.

Tour of Kiev, and Hospitality of Dr. and Mrs. Bogdanov

Following the meeting with Dr. Sozinov, Dr. and Mrs. Bogdanov extended the following hospitality which was greatly appreciated by Dr. Taysom and me. They took us to their attractive and comfortable apartment for morning refreshments, followed by a tour of Kiev, accompanied by Anna, the interpreter, and a professional guide.

I urged that they get the Russian edition of *Feeds & Nutrition Digest* off press not later than May 1993, in order that it may be used in the Kiev and Stavropol schools next June.

They served a bountiful and delicious 4:00 p.m. dinner at the Bodganov's apartment. Tamara (Mrs. Bogdanov) is an excellent cook; not only that, she prepared some special Russian foods that she had observed that I liked.

Prof. Olexiy O. Sozinov and the Bogdanovs made it a great and unforgettable day in Kiev!

Meeting the Minister of Agriculture and Food of Ukraine

Dr. Bogdanov and Anna, the academy interpreter, joined us for breakfast at the Dnipro Hotel, following which we went to meet the Minister of Agriculture and Food of Ukraine, Yuri M. Karasyk.

It is noteworthy that the minister returned to Kiev late Saturday night. Yet, he received Dr. Taysom and me (accompanied by Dr. Bogdanov and Anna) in his office on Sunday morning in keeping with the schedule that Dr. Bogdanov had arranged.

Mr. Karasyk Was Made an Honorary American Cowboy

After exchanging greetings, we made Minister Karasyk an Honorary American Cowboy, presenting him the Agriservices Foundation miniature Western saddle.

Next, Minister Karasyk pulled from the library back of his desk the following books that I authored: *Beef Cattle Science* and *Feeds & Nutrition Digest*.

We learned that Minister Karasyk is trained in animal breeding. Moreover, he told us that for more than 10 years he has been engaged in improving the quality of the native dairy and beef cattle of Ukraine by infusing Holsteins in the dairy cattle and Angus in the beef cattle.

1,300-Cow Dairy, Bokhroma

Following the visit with Minister Karasyk, Dr. Bogdanov and the academy interpreter, Anna, arranged for us to see a 1,300-cow dairy, out toward the airport. About 680 of these cows are located in the dairy complex that we visited.

After seeing the dairy, Dr. Bogdanov and Anna took us to the airport. Dr. Taysom and I departed from Kiev confident that Prof. Sozinov, Dr. Zubets, Dr. Bogdanov, and Mr. Karasyk, Minister of Agriculture and Food of Ukraine, will make the school successful.

Three Russian/Ukrainian Delegations Visited the Foundation

Subsequent to 1989, when the schools were first requested, three different Ukrainian and/or Russian delegations came to Agriservices Foundation, Clovis, California, for instruction on their role in Schools of such magnitude.

The Two Schools Became a Reality in June 1993

Following my briefing at the JFK Airport Hilton in New York City, 21 guest professors and delegates departed for Kiev, Ukraine, where they were joined by 11 more staff members from abroad. At the request of Ukraine and Russia, the staff of 32 conducted an International Ag-Tech School in each of the republics of Ukraine and Russia.

The volunteer staff came from throughout the

United States, and from Germany, Austria, Ireland, Yugoslavia, and Saudi Arabia. It was the most distinguished group of agricultural experts ever to visit Ukraine and Russia. The schools were conducted jointly by Iowa State University and Agriservices Foundation in cooperation with each of the respective republics—Ukraine and Russia. Both Iowa State University and Agriservices Foundation have a long and impressive history of working with the former Soviet Union, dating back to the 1950s and 1960s.

The first school was conducted in cooperation with Ukraine and held in Kiev June 18, 19, 20, 1993. The second school was conducted in cooperation with Russia and held in Stavropol June 23, 24, and 25. The primary purpose of the schools: Increased food production and improved economy, along with reclaiming radiation-contaminated soils, and lessening radiation in food and water.

The Ukrainian co-sponsors reported more than 400 enrollees (students) in the opening session; and Stavropol, which is in a less populous area, reported more than 270 enrollees in their opening session. However, enrollment was not limited to Ukrainians and Russians. A Texas rancher and his wife were among the enrollees. Also, seven Chinese scholars, members of the Xinjiang Academy of Animal Science, along with their English and Russian interpreters, were in attendance.

The Schools Had a Heap of Good Help

The Schools were a team effort. I especially wish to acknowledge the great contribution of the following who made these Schools happen:

Our U.S. co-sponsor, Iowa State University, especially Dean David G. Topel, Dr. Gerald E. Klonglan, Dr. M. Douglas Kenealy, Dr. Paul O. Brackelsberg, Dr. Bruce W. Menzel, and Ms. Elena Polouchkina. They were great!

Our Ukraine co-sponsors: the Ukrainian Academy of Agricultural Sciences, especially Dr. Olexiy O. Sozinov, Dr. M.V. Zubets, and Dr. G.A. Bogdanov; and the Ministry of Agriculture and Food of Ukraine, Minister Yuri M. Karasyk.

Our Stavropol, Russia co-sponsors, especially Prof., Dr. Ludmila N. Petrova and her great staff; and Governor Kouznezov and Lieutenant Governor Scheeyanov.

The great guest professors and supporting study-tour delegates.

The trustees of Agriservices Foundation, especially David McGlothlin and the late Clair Pollard, the two nearby members of the Executive Committee, for their unswerving support; Mrs. Ensminger and the dedicated loyal staff members of Agriservices Foundation; Jerry Calvin and his staff at Jostens, Visalia, California, who printed gratis the *Book of Slides* and the final report entitled The International Ag-Tech Schools in Ukraine and Russia 1993; Michael R. Jaeger, Lab 1, Fresno, for preparing gratis the 2" x 3" prints that were used in the *Book of Slides*; Alex and Ann Swiridoff, Swiridoff Photography, Fresno, who provided invaluable counsel and assistance throughout the four years in making the schools happen; Victor Reimer, who served as interpreter when called upon; the Bank of America, Dr. Sam Vathayanon, and Mr. and Mrs. Elmer Peterson, and others, who provided financial assistance; and United Air Lines, without whose help Mrs. Ensminger and I could never have gotten the six projectors and the "school office" transported from Fresno to JFK Airport, New York City, and return.

Kiev, Ukraine, School

At the airport, a delegation from the Ukrainian Academy of Agricultural Sciences met us upon our arrival and presented flowers. Following check-in, we had lunch at the Hotel Russ—our place of stay in Kiev.

Upon our arrival at the Academy of Agricultural Sciences Building in Kiev, we were warmly welcomed by Dr. O. O. Sozinov, the president.

Staff Orientation in Ukrainian Agriculture

We departed for a very special day in the country. We were accompanied by the following: Dr. M. V. Zubets, Vice President, Ukrainian Academy of Agricultural Sciences; Valery P. Burcat, General Director, National Livestock Breeding Association of Ukraine; Natalia I. Vasilchenko, Ministry of Agriculture and Food of Ukraine; and Dr. G. A. Bogdanov, Ukraine Academy of Agricultural Sciences.

Poloskovsky Cattle Breeding Facility

This was our first stop. In answer to our question, the manager said that there are many more collective farms than state farms in Ukraine.

Following the tour of the farm, we were served a bountiful luncheon on the state farm. At the luncheon, I made Valery P. Burcat and Peter Fedose-

The school staff being warmly welcomed upon their arrival at the Academy of Agricultural Sciences Building in Kiev. Facing the audience, left to right are: Dr. O. O. Sozinov, President, Ukrainian Academy of Agricultural Sciences; Elena Y. Zharkikh, interpreter, Dr. E; and Dr. G. A. Bogdanov, Academician, Ukrainian Academy of Agricultural Sciences. (Photo by David DeSilva)

Holstein dairy cows on Poloskovsky Cattle Breeding Farm, Poloskovsky, Ukraine, an 8,000-acre farm on which there are 3,800 head of cattle. The foundation cows for this herd were imported from Canada in 1973. This dairy farm is about 40 miles from Kiev, Ukraine, where the first of the two schools was held. Ukraine is the "bread basket" and the leading dairy country of the former U.S.S.R.

jerick "Honorary American Cowboys" and presented to each of them a miniature Western saddle.

Living History Museum

En route from Poloskovsky Farm, we visited the historic Ukrainian village known as the "Living History Museum." Dr. Garth Boyd's report pertaining to it follows:

Our stop at the Living History Museum was most educational relative to Ukrainian culture and their

Among the historic treasures in the Living History Museum, Ukraine, is this ancient windmill mounted on a sled so that it could be positioned to take full advantage of the wind.

agricultural heritage. Sculptures dating about the time of Christ's birth were on display, and life-size replicas of homes from different eras of the past were visited.

Central Pedigree Facility (CPF)

The CPF is primarily an artificial insemination (AI) establishment, which has been ably directed by the following person for 32 years: Irina S. Volenka, general manager.

The CPF has more than 200 bulls, and both beef and dairy cattle. The dairy cattle consist of black and white, and red, Holsteins. Several beef breeds are being started; however, Ukraine farmers favor the Angus breed. They bought 480 head of animals, 7 to 8 months of age, from Mr. Houston, of Denver, Colorado. These animals were shipped by boat to Odessa, then trucked to CPF.

Following the very excellent guided tour of the CPF, we were served a bountiful and delicious supper, hosted by Irina S. Volenko and prepared by her staff. I made Irina an "Honorary American Cowgirl" and presented her with a miniature Western saddle. Irina presented me with the following gifts: table runner, silk hanging of their famous poet; and an embroidered shirt.

Kiev School

The Kiev School was in the traditional format that I followed in conducting all my schools. It was a three-day school, with 60 lectures, given by more than 20 guest professors, with a choice of up to six

Irma S. Volenko, General Manager, Central Animal Breeding Enterprise, Khmelmitzsky, Ukraine, is shown presenting a linen shirt to me. (Photo by Jack and Terry Wilkinson)

lectures each hour, and run on time—not one minute late.

I opened the school promptly at 9:00 a.m. by ringing my bell, followed by playing the national anthems of the United States and Ukraine, with the Ukraine flag on the left and the U.S. flag on the right.

The group was welcomed, and I was introduced, by Minister Yuri M. Karasyk, Ministry of Agriculture and Food of Ukraine, and Dr. Olexiy O. Sozinov, President, Ukrainian Academy of Agricultural Sciences.

The opening ceremony of the school in Kiev with more than 400 enrollees. Standing and facing the audience left to right: Dr. O. O. Sozinov, President, Ukrainian Academy of Agricultural Sciences; Minister Yuri M. Karasyk, Minister of Agriculture and Food of Ukraine; Dr. G. A. Bogdanov, Academician, Ukrainian Academy of Agricultural Sciences; and Dr. M. V. Zubets, Vice President, Ukrainian Academy of Agricultural Sciences. Dr. E is shown at the podium, with Interpreter Elena Y. Zharkikh on his right. (Photo by David DeSilva)

There were more than 400 people present for my opening lecture, the first part of which was on TV. Because of the overflow crowd, I excused our guest professors and support school delegates following my introduction of them. I used slides, with Russian captions, to minimize the language barrier; and Dr. Elena Y. Zharkikh did a wonderful job as my interpreter. At the close of my lecture, I invited Dr. Sozinov, Dr. Zubets, and Dr. Bogdanov to join me for the question-answer period (Minister Yuri M. Karasyk couldn't stay because of the demands of the ministry).

Dinner Hosted by Ukrainian Academy of Agricultural Sciences

The Ukrainian Academy of Agricultural Sciences hosted a dinner at the academy in honor of our group, along with the seven scholars from China. It was a great evening, enhanced by good food, appropriate toasts, good fellowship, and singing by four Ukrainian scientists. Dr. Sozinov chaired the meeting. As souvenirs, everyone was given a tablecloth and napkin. Additionally I was given a shirt.

Dinner Hosted by U.S. Group With Invited Guests

Our group hosted a dinner for our Ukrainian friends in the Phoenix Room of the Russ Hotel. Minister Karasyk and Dr. Sozinov were made "Honorary Life Members" of Agriservices Foundation, and each of them was presented with a beautiful plaque so indicating.

The seven Chinese scholars were our guests at the dinner party.

Iowa State University showed a 15-minute video tape of Iowa farming, with the narrative in Russian. It was well received.

Kiev School Closes

On the afternoon of June 20, the school closed with a special ceremony beginning at 4:30 p.m., the first part of which was covered by TV. After thanking our Ukrainian co-sponsors, the school closed by singing Auld Lang Syne in Russian for the first time

This is a view of the staff headquarters of the Ukraine School. Dr. E is shown working at the table; and his sister, Aileen, is facing the camera.

ever in Eurasia. In addition to singing with gusto, I asked each person to give a bear hug to the person on his or her right.

Several of the top officials of the Ukrainian Academy of Agricultural Sciences asked for a certificate with their name thereon, to which I readily complied and accepted as a high compliment.

Fond Farewell to Ukrainian Friends

The Kiev, Ukraine school was a tremendous success, with more than 400 enrollees (students) representing all segments of Ukrainian agriculture.

Following a fond farewell to our Ukrainian friends, we departed for Moscow, with overnight reservations at Hotel Salyot.

Dr. E with seven Chinese scholars from the Xinjiang Academy of Animal Science, Urumqi, China, who were enrolled in the Kiev, Ukraine School.

Stavropol, Russia

Upon our arrival in Stavropol, we were met by a large delegation headed by Prof. Petrova, flowers were presented to the ladies and Dr. Ensminger, and a police escort was provided. A police escort was provided for all our travels in the Stavropol area. It made for greater traffic safety and speeded up our travels.

After freshening up, we ate a light luncheon at the Intourist Hotel, inspected the facilities for the Stavropol School, and were hosted by Prof., Dr. Petrova to a tasty lamb barbecue.

Staff Orientation in Russian Agriculture

Today, Prof. Petrova arranged for us to travel to the great Arabian Stud Farm No. 169, a state farm, near Pyatigorsk, a distance of over 100 miles. Aboard the bus were Prof. Petrova and several agricultural experts from the Stavropol area who told about the agriculture along the way. It was a wonderful drive through a great farming area, and

Three of the officials of the Stavropol, Russia, School. *Left to right:* Prof., Dr. Ludmila N. Petrova, General Manager, Niva Stavropolya Research and Production Complex, and co-sponsor of the School in Stavropol, Russia; Dr. E, who directed the School; and Dr. Gerald E. Klonglan, Assistant Director, Iowa Agricultural Experiment Station, and Assistant Director of the School. Dr. E said of Dr. Petrova: "She is a top administrator—superbly organized." (Photo by J. E. Oldfield)

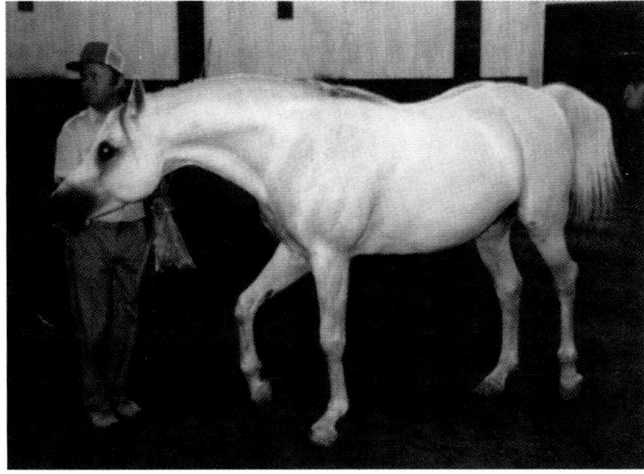

Arabian stallion at famed Stud Farm No. 169, Mineralnye Vody, Zuejka, Russia, with horseman, Vladimir Strakhov. At this state farm, they have an annual Arabian horse auction in which prices have ranged up to U.S. $1,000,000.

through hilly or mountainous areas used for grazing of sheep, goats, and cattle.

Arabian Stud Farm No. 169

At the Arabian Stud Farm No. 169, we were met by the deputy director of the farm, Grigory Niouzha, and by Vladimir Strakhov, a son of the late Peter Strakhov, the former head of the horse division and my longtime friend from the time of my earlier visits in 1966 and 1972. Vladimir did a superb job of exhibiting their great Arabian stallions, which were well trained. After each stallion was exhibited, he "reported" to Vladimir for his reward consisting of sugared bread. Their Arabians have a bit more height and bone than most Arabians in the United States.

At the end of our visit to Stud Farm No. 169, I was interviewed by the Pyatigorsk TV station.

This horse breeding establishment was founded more than 100 years ago.

Following the visit to Stud Farm No. 169, we made a short trip into the forest, and partook of a 2:00 p.m. luncheon at a nearby local restaurant.

Stavropol School

The Stavropol school was a repeat of the school that we conducted in Ukraine.

We were apprehensive when classes started because we were unable to have a "dry run" upon our arrival, due to our plane from Moscow to Stavropol being delayed by four hours. But our Iowa State University co-sponsors—Klonglan, Kenealy, and Brackelsberg—departed from the hotel at 7:30 a.m. in order to get the big room ready for my opening lecture.

I rang the bell promptly at 9:00 a.m., opening the school, with the local TV station covering the historic event.

At the close of the opening session, Prof. Petrova invited me, along with Mrs. Ensminger and my sister Aileen, to her office. Also, she had invited the Lieutenant Governor, Alexander Csheeyanov, and other officials to be there. Coffee and cookies were served and we had a get-acquainted visit.

While in Prof. Petrova's office, I was told that several of the people present would like to have one or more of my books. So, I promised to send them gratis as soon as we could find a way to assure their delivery. To the latter end, I alerted Iowa State University and Phil Leino, the Stavropol representative of the governor of Iowa.

Dr. Douglas Kenealy, Iowa State University, lecturing to students in the Stavropol School. (Photo by David DeSilva)

Church music choir in Stavropol, showing Conductor Valery Korothov taking a bow. They are world class. (Photo by Norm Wright)

Church Music Choir Performance in Stavropol

In the evening, Prof. Petrova arranged a cultural event. It was a singing group from one of their churches. The 19 church choir singers were marvelous.

Dinner Hosted by U.S. Group With Invited Guests

This dinner was held at the Intourist Hotel. We had a total of 51 people present for the dinner; 26 of our group, and 25 guests. We had a very brief program consisting of Dr. Ensminger welcoming the group and Prof. Petrova being made an Honorary Life Member of Agriservices Foundation, and being presented with a handsome plaque.

An Eisenhower silver dollar was presented to each of our 25 guests. Jerry Klonglan told about Iowa State's programs in the republics, and about the video film which couldn't be shown due to equipment failure.

Closing Ceremony

Prior to the closing ceremony of the Stavropol school, our Iowa State University co-sponsors arranged to show the video film to the enrollees in Room 1 in each of the two afternoon sessions.

The closing ceremony was held in the same big room as the opening ceremony. I rang my bell promptly at 4:30 p.m. Then, I thanked our Stavropol co-sponsors, especially the governor and lieutenant governor, and Prof. Petrova (including her great staff).

Retirement of My Bell

I reported that several people had asked that I leave my bell, symbol of 42 International Schools. So, I decided to retire my bell in Stavropol for posterity, in the custody of Prof. Petrova; and Prof. Petrova volunteered to have it engraved (with a statement prepared by me).

I rang the bell for the last time, and passed it to Prof. Petrova.

Boris Plyasov and Prof. Petrova thanked the group once again.

Dr. E is shown ringing his bell, symbol of 42 successful International Schools, calling the Stavropol, Russia school to order for the closing ceremony. Seated, left to right, are: Valentin Mezin, interpreter; Boris Plyasov, Representative of the Governor; and Ludmila N. Petrova, General Manager of the Niva Stavropolya Research and Production Complex, and co-sponsor of the Stavropol school.

Auld Lang Syne in Russian, Followed by a Russian Song

Next, we bade a fond farewell to our Russian friends by singing Auld Lang Syne.

The school closed with the singing of a Russian song that Prof. Petrova had arranged, which all the Russians knew and sang well.

At the close of the school, the Stavropol group asked for our American flag; hence, we were happy to leave it with them. I greatly enjoyed working with Prof. Petrova, who is a good administrator, extremely well organized, and a detail-type person.

Farewell Party Hosted by Prof. Petrova and Her Staff

This evening, Prof. Petrova and her group hosted a farewell party for our group at the Experimental Horticultural Farm, which is under Prof. Petrova's supervision and managed by Vitaly G. Ermolenko, Director of Horticultural Experimental Farm.

Following our tour of the Horticultural Experimental Farm, our hosts (Prof. Petrova and her group) had a bountiful and delicious banquet for us. The dinner was enhanced by an accordion player, who played and sang for us.

After the dinner, we moved to a patio outside the dining room, where it was a bit cooler. Then, Prof. Petrova and her staff entertained us by singing and dancing, accompanied by the accordion.

Following the dancing and singing, we moved back to the dining room for cold drinks. At that time, Prof. Petrova gave each member of our group a souvenir of fine china made near Pyatigorsk (where we visited Stud Farm No. 169).

Thus, a memorable school, followed by a memorable dinner party, closed.

Fond Farewell to Russian Friends

At the airport, several of our friends from Prof., Dr. Petrova's staff came to see us off; among them,

Dr. Petrova danced with Victor Popov. Victor was the "Master of the Table" at the farewell dinner on the evening of June 25, which meant that everyone had to do as he told them.

Staff of the Ukraine and Russia Schools, including our interpreters. Photo taken on the steps of the Intourist Hotel, Stavropol, Russia. The volunteer staff of 32 came from throughout the United States, and from Germany, Austria, Ireland, Yugoslavia, and Saudi Arabia. Dr. E said of the staff: "It was a very distinguished group of agricultural experts."

Ivan Neshin; Nikolai Petrova, son of Prof., Dr. Ludmila Petrova; and Nikolai I. Atamanichenko and his M.D. wife, Vera; along with several people to handle our baggage. They conveyed the regrets of Prof. Petrova, who was ill. We sent our best wishes for good health to Prof. Petrova, along with our everlasting appreciation for a job well done.

Stavropol to Moscow

At the Moscow airport, we were met by Natalia Yu Zhilina, a representative of Amscort. After getting our baggage, it took another hour to get from the airport to the Hotel Rossia. Then, it took more than an hour for me to turn in our passports and secure our room assignments. We unloaded our baggage and checked in at Hotel Rossia.

Moscow

Following breakfast, we saw historic Moscow, with Tanya Savotchkina serving as our head guide.

Kremlin

The Kremlin is surrounded by a high wall, 65 ft high and 12 ft thick, which was built many years ago. Inside the Kremlin, the main activities of the government of the former U.S.S.R. were conducted. Presently, the many great buildings in the Kremlin house

The Kremlin and the high wall that surrounds it. Inside the Kremlin, the main activities of the government of the former U.S.S.R. were conducted. Presently, the many great buildings in the Kremlin house the government of Russia.

the government of the republic of Russia. Additionally there are glittering palaces, churches, museums, and beautiful cathedrals.

Armory Museum

The Armory Museum houses the "finery" of former Russian czars. As an animal scientist, I was fascinated by the ornate carriages, saddles, and other tack. Some of these royal stables had as many as 20,000 horses. Of course, the czars lived in a horse and buggy era. They had no other method of transportation. Imagine having trappings—everything from saddles and blankets to carriages—covered with precious stones!

Lunch at McDonalds

We had lunch at McDonald's first unit in Moscow. We met the following two officials: Alexei Abramov, Manager, and Oxana Savkina, Assistant Manager. They reported that they employ 700 people, feed more than 10,000 people per day and produce their own food.

The service was fast, the McDonalds' staff smiled, and the place was clean (including the rest rooms). Through other sources, I learned that it took McDonalds 15 years to get this first unit in Moscow in operation; it was necessary that they produce their own food, have a year-round supply available, and teach the personnel to smile.

Red Square

Red Square is the place where they have their great parades. The centerpiece of Red Square is St. Basil's Cathedral, built by Ivan the Terrible to commemorate his victories. On the east, Red Square is bordered by GUM, the big department store. At the north end of the square is the History Museum.

The focus of Red Square is the Lenin Mausoleum, containing the embalmed body of Lenin. Behind the mausoleum is the burial place of many leading Soviet politicians, including Stalin, Kosygin, Suslov, Brezhnev, Andropov, and Chernenko. Urns set in the Kremlin wall contain the ashes of Gorky and others. It was from the balcony of the mausoleum that former Soviet leaders watched the great Moscow parades.

Dinner in Moscow With Invited Guests

At our dinner this evening we were delighted to have the presence of Dr. Nicolay G. Pervov, my longtime friend; and Dr. Michael Kuzhetzov, a friend of Jerry Klonglan.

St. Petersburg

Our guides met us in St. Petersburg. Elena Silina

Dr. E with a Russian guide in front of St. Basil's Cathedral.

Moscow University, an impressive structure of 31 stories. It's the country's largest university.

narrated the sightseeing along the way from the airport to Hotel Helen.

Today, St. Petersburg is a major industrial center with a high standard of production.

St. Isaac Square

In the southern part of the square, stands St. Isaac's Cathedral. This, the largest church in the city, took forty years to build. No expense was spared to glorify Peter's patron saint, and some 200 lb of gold went into gilding the dome.

St. Isaac's Cathedral, which faces onto the square.

Today, the palace houses the St. Petersburg City Council.

Peter-and-Paul Fortress

It was here that St. Petersburg was founded when Peter laid the foundation of the first fortress on an islet in 1703 to protect the mainland and to secure Russia's outlet to the sea. This has become the chief monument to St. Peter's reign.

From the early 18th century, the Peter-and-Paul Fortress served as a prison, reserved for some of the most important state prisoners. Today, the fortress is a museum and memorial to its former inmates.

Smolny Convent

The site chosen for the Smolny Convent had in Peter's day been a tar yard (smolny dvor; hence, the name). His daughter, the pleasure-loving and yet deeply-religious empress, commanded the future designer of the Winter Palace to build a nunnery for orphan girls. The cathedral, the framework of which was completed in 1764, is in the shape of a cross with adjoining living quarters, forming an open square in the same shape. Small churches stand at the four points of this internal square.

Shopping/Lunch in St. Petersburg

This morning, our group went shopping. The articles at the first stop were too high. So, we went to an open free market where the prices were more reasonable. Nevertheless, all the vendors were great bargainers.

We had lunch at the Universal Restaurant.

Following lunch, we returned to Hotel Helen where Roy Rauschkolb and his interpreter, Dr. Daniel Wolfberg, boarded our bus.

Research Institute of Farm Animal Breeding and Genetics

We visited the Research Institute of Farm Animal Breeding and Genetics which is located at Pushkin—about 25 miles from Moscow.

En route to Pushkin, Dr. Daniel Wolfberg narrated along the way, telling about the areas through which we passed—especially the historical.

Dinner in St. Petersburg With Invited Guests

We had a dinner with the following invited guests: Victor A. Zubkov, Vice-Chairman, City of St. Petersburg, Office of the Mayor; Prof., Dr. Albert I. Beach, a noted dairy cattle breeding specialist on the staff of the Research Institute at Pushkin, accompanied by his daughter who also has a Ph.D. degree; Prof., Dr. Igor B. Uskov, Director of Institute, Head of Modeling Agroclimate Laboratory; and Mrs. Uskov; Roy Rauschkolb, U.S. Department of Agriculture, Farm Privatization Project; and Dr. Daniel Wolfberg, who served as our interpreter.

Dr. E is shown presenting Victor A. Zubkov, Vice-Chairman, Office of the Mayor, City of St. Petersburg, a miniature Western saddle, making him an "Honorary American Cowboy."

Dr. E is shown receiving a book from Dr. Pyotr N. Prokhorenko, Director of the Research Institute of Farm Animal Breeding and Genetics, at Pushkin, which is about 25 miles from St. Petersburg. Dr. A. I. Beach, noted dairy breeding specialist, is standing on Dr. Ensminger's right. Dr. Ensminger and Dr. Beach are old friends. Dr. Beach first appeared on an International School program in Phoenix, Arizona, in 1978.

At the dinner, Jerry Klonglan told about the work of Iowa State University in the republics.

Dr. Ensminger made Mr. Zubkov, Vice Chairman, City of St. Petersburg, Office of the Mayor, an Honorary American Cowboy; presented bolo ties to Dr. Beach, Dr. Igor Uskov, Roy Rauschkolb, and Dr. Daniel Wolfberg; and presented writing tools to Dr. A. I. Beach's daughter, and Mrs. Uskov.

Victor A. Zubkov, Vice Chairman, City of St. Petersburg, Office of the Mayor, indicated interest in having a school conducted in St. Petersburg. My recommendation for consideration by Iowa State University is that the schools be rotated among the Republics and the Baltics about every two or three years.

Dr. E Met With Dr. Albert I. Beach

Dr. E met with his longtime friend, Dr. Albert I. Beach, followed by bringing his Master Host List and report up to date; and Audrey brought her records of the travels up to date. So, Dr. E asked Dr. Klonglan to serve as leader of the group for the day.

Dr. Beach told Dr. Ensminger that he now has about 30,000 cows in his dairy improvement work, most of which are Holsteins. Also, it is noteworthy that Dr. Beach is continuing his dairy improvement work in other republics and in the Baltics; and that Dr. Beach served as Chairman of Mr. M. V. Zubets' committee when the latter completed his Ph.D. degree.

After the dinner, Dr. E visited with Dr. Beach and his daughter, who is also Dr. Beach.

Summer Palace (Peter's Home/ Petrodvorets/Grand Palace)

This palace is located about 20 miles west of Leningrad. Its construction was started in the first quarter of the 18th century when, after the victory of 1709 in the Northern War, Peter I ruled that a gala summer residence be built on the coast of the Gulf of Finland. The work and art of several generations of craftsmen went into the development of Petrodvorets.

Summer Palace of Peter the Great.

Winter Palace (Hermitage)

The Winter Palace (Hermitage) and the various Hermitage buildings are now known as the "State Hermitage." The setting is magnificent and lavish; malachite, jasper, agate, and marble provide a fine backdrop to the treasures. The Hermitage was started by Catherine II who wanted to have a home for the art collection which she was beginning to acquire abroad, and a retreat (hence, the name) connected to her private apartment in the Winter Palace.

This was the former residence of the czarist family. This huge building is one of the masterpieces of the famous architect B. Rastrelli. It was built in 1754–1762.

It has ceilings ornamented with stucco molding, walls covered with murals; and its floors, inlaid with precious woods, are works of art. A walk through all its halls would mean covering a distance of nearly 18.6 miles.

Today, the Winter Palace and the buildings adjoining it, house the Hermitage. There are 2½ million exhibits on view in this museum, among them works by Leonardo da Vinci and Titian, Rembrandt and Rubens; sculptures and art objects of Ancient Egypt, Greece and Rome. It is the richest and largest of St. Petersburg's museums.

Following dinner this evening at Hotel Helen, St. Petersburg, on behalf of the group, Dr. Robert Walton presented a small bell to me, and admonished me to keep on keeping on. My sister Aileen, gave an even smaller bell to me. Since both bells are much smaller than the bell that I retired at Stavropol, they must convey a message!

Swan Lake Ballet

This evening, we saw the Swan Lake Ballet in three acts, which we were told ranks second only to the Bolshoi. It was superb. There was a full house.

The history of this theatre dates back to 1756. It was once named Alexandrinsky, in honor of Tsar Nicolai I's wife. Today, it bears the name of the National Pushkin Theatre, after the great Russian poet A. Pushkin.

Depart From St. Petersburg for New York City

This morning, we left Hotel Helen at 6:00 a.m., with a box breakfast—including a cucumber. We checked in at the airport easily and quickly and boarded Aeroflot flight 319 for New York City. Our plane was a new Russian-made wide bodied Aleutian 8B, which was very, very comfortable, smooth, with generous baggage space above. The food and service aboard the flight were excellent. The front (a large first class section of about 50 seats) of the plane was empty. So, I asked the head stewardess for permission for our group to move forward to the first class section. She approved. This made for a comfortable return to New York City, with just our group in first class.

In New York City, our 20 remaining members bade a fond farewell to each other and departed for their respective homes across the United States.

Dr. E and Dr. Sozinov are standing in front of the Olympic-size pool at the Harris Ranch.

Visit from Dr. Zozinov

In the fall of 1993, we received a call from Dr. Sozinov, President of the Ukrainian Academy of Agricultural Sciences. He said he was at a motel in the San Francisco Bay area and could we pick him up. We said we would do so. We took him to our favorite tour places and we had a dinner party for him. It was so wonderful to have him as our guest.

1995
AG-TECH SCHOOLS IN HAVANA AND CAMAGUEY, CUBA

United States relations with Cuba were severed in 1961 and, in 1962, a complete trade embargo was imposed. Thus, the June 1995 schools, sponsored jointly by Cuba, Iowa State University, and Agriservices Foundation, were the first schools of this kind and magnitude conducted in Cuba in more than 30 years. The following seven U.S. Land Grant Colleges provided one or more of the guest professors: Auburn University, Auburn, Alabama; University of California, Davis; University of Florida, Gainesville; University of Illinois, Urbana; Iowa State University, Ames; Louisiana State University, Baton Rouge; and New Mexico State University, Las Cruces. Also, the staff of 27 was enhanced by successful farm and ranch owners and managers.

I saw a country which, because of its natural beauty, is known as "The Pearl of the Antilles." But Cuba is noted for much more than its beauty. It is famed for its sugar, seafood, distinctive rum, and fine cigars. Cuba is also the world's largest exporter of sugar. As a result of our recent visit, we can add that Cuba is noted for beautiful, warm, and friendly people.

I saw a country which, by necessity, is leading the world in sustainable agriculture—in reducing off-farm inputs of pesticides, herbicides, and fertilizers; and maximizing the use of forages. Soon after the year 2000, I predict that more and more countries will follow the lead of Cuba in sustainable agriculture. We can learn from each other.

I Saw A Dream Come True

Agriservices Foundation/Ensmingers and Cuba have a long and pleasant history of working together in scientific and educational programs. Mrs. Ensminger and I first traveled to Cuba in 1976 at which time we visited the Institute of Animal Science (ICA), Carretera Central, KM 47½, San Jose de las Lajas, Havana, Cuba, where we inspected the research in progress and participated in a seminar in which we exchanged research information with the staff. Here, we met Cuba's outstanding animal scientist, Dr. Miriam Ribas. We also visited the Camaguey Area, which ranks first in cattle, and second in sugarcane, among the provinces.

Dr. Miriam Ribas, Cuba's great animal scientist and treasured friend of the Ensmingers, lectured in the 1978 International Stockmen's School in Phoenix, Arizona. Also, Dr. Ribas submitted papers that were published in the handbooks of the 1987 International Stockmen's School.

During my 1976 visit, I promised the people of Cuba that, if invited by Cuba and approved by the United States, one day I would return and conduct schools. Thus, the two International Ag-Tech Schools in Cuba in 1995 marked the fulfillment of a commitment that I made nearly 20 years before. It's a dream come true following 20 years of relentless effort by Dr. Miriam Ribas and me.

Leadership of the Cuban Schools

The Cuban Schools were organized by, and conducted under the joint leadership of, the following staff members:

For Cuba

Dr. Miriam Ribas and Director Liberty Garcia, Institute of Animal Science (ICA), Havana, along with the great help of Rector Omelio Borrato; and Rector Carlos Diaz Barranco, Dr. Arnold del Toro, and Ing. Wilfredo Marshall Stewart, in Camaguey; and with the help of a host of other people in both schools.

For Iowa State University

Dr. David G. Topel, Dean and Director, College of Agriculture; Dr. Gerald E. Klonglan, Assistant Director, Agricultural Experiment Station; Dr. Dennis N. Marple, Head, Department of Animal Science; Dr. M. Douglas Kenealy, Department of Animal Science and Assistant Director Cuban Schools; and Dr. Paul O. Brackelsberg, Department of Animal Science and Assistant Director Cuban Schools.

For Agriservices Foundation, Clovis

The distinguished trustees of Agriservices Foundation, with the following serving as Cuban school staff members: Audrey H. Ensminger, certified human nutritionist, in charge of the ladies' program; and Guillermo and Doris Osuna, Coahuila, Mexico. Sr. Osuna gave three lectures in each Cuban school and provided invaluable support to me. I directed the Cuban schools.

Enrollment

There were 239 enrollees in the school held at the Institute of Animal Science (ICA), Havana, and 254 enrollees in the Camaguey school—making for a total of 493 enrollees. Four enrollees came from Panama. Additionally, there were more than 100 enrollees in a special sugarcane course who received a special certificate. Thus, the total enrollment was 600. But many more Cubans and our staff interacted through U.S. school staff members meeting with their Cuban counterparts in biotechnology, veterinary medicine, beef production, dairy production, sheep production, pig production, poultry production, horses, and sugarcane; by the ladies visiting hospitals, schools, and the biotechnology and cultural centers, and by great press, TV and radio coverage.

It is noteworthy that the above figures were achieved in a country of only 11 million people.

The Staff Made the Schools

A top notch U.S. staff of 27 blended perfectly together for top performance. We had six Spanish-speaking staff members; and Cuba provided expert interpreters for the rest of us.

The Cuban Friends Were Great Hosts

Our Cuban friends were hosts *par excellence*. They provided fellowship, food, and a 50-passenger air-conditioned bus equipped with a microphone for our transportation—including travel through the beautiful countryside to and from Camaguey, a distance of 300 miles from Havana. We also visited and enjoyed a barbecue luncheon at King Ranch in the Camaguey area—formerly owned by King Ranch in Texas, the most famous ranch in the world.

Three Ministers and Their Staffs Cared For Our Every Need

This included the Ministry of Agriculture; the Ministry of Science, Technology and Environment; and the Ministry of Higher Education. Additionally, many other high government officials of Cuba joined us for dinner and/or one or more sessions of the schools.

Flags, National Anthems, and Tears

Both Cuban Schools were opened in the traditional Agriservices Foundation way by playing the national anthems of the host country (Cuba) and the United States while standing and facing the flags of the two countries. This brought many tears of joy.

I Was Highly Honored

The following honors, which came as a complete surprise, were conferred upon me:

- Jose Nuvez made me an Honorary Member of the Cuban Association of Animal Production, and presented a resolution and a certificate to me so signifying.

- Director Liberty Garcia, Institute of Animal Science, presented a gold medal and a beautiful leather hanging to me.

- Rector (President) Omelio Borrato, Agricultural University, ISCAH, Havana, conferred an Honorary Guest Professorship upon me, and presented to me a scroll and other documents, and a medal so signifying.

- Rector (President) Carlos Diaz Barranco made me an Honorary Guest Professor of the University of Camaguey, and presented a resolution and a scroll to me so signifying.

The Two Greatest Schools

I have conducted 44 successful international schools worldwide. All factors considered, I rate the two Cuban schools as greatest of all. In recognition of Dr. Ribas' untiring efforts, I conferred upon her Honorary Life Membership in Agriservices Foundation, and presented to her a handsome plaque.

Closing Ceremony

At the closing ceremony in each school, I retired a bell, world-famed symbol of the school. In the ICA Havana school, the bell was retired in the custody of Director Liberty Garcia; and in the Camaguey school, the bell was retired in the custody of Rector Carlos Diaz Barranco.

We closed each school by standing, joining hands, and swinging and swaying (many people with tears of joy) as we sang Auld Lang Syne.

The Cuba That We Saw

Because Audrey got a multitude of good pictures of "The Cuba That We Saw," the rest of my story is told in the pictures and captions that follow.

Our comfortable 50-passenger, air-conditioned bus, equipped with a microphone, in which we were transported during our entire stay in Havana; including the 300-mile trip from Havana to Camaguey, and return.

Upon our arrival at the Biocaribe Hotel, Havana, well past midnight, a welcoming delegation was there to greet us. *Left to right:* Dr. Omelio Borrato, Rector of the Agricultural University (ISCAH) of Havana; Dr. Miriam Ribas Hermelo, Institute of Animal Science (ICA), Havana; Director Liberty Garcia, Institute of Animal Science (ICA), Havana; and Dr. E. (Photo by Dr. Paul O. Brackelsburg)

The staff seated in one of the new classrooms at the Institute of Animal Science (ICA), being briefed by Dr. E and meeting the ICA staff.

Dr. E briefing the staff at the Institute of Animal Science (ICA), Havana. *Left to right:* Dr. E, Dr. Miriam Ribas, and Director Liberty Garcia.

At ICA, Havana, where the first Cuban School was held. The sign reads: "Republic of Cuba, Institute of Animal Science." *Left to right:* Dr. Julian Rodriguez, Vice Minister of Higher Education, Dr. Miriam Ribas, Dr. E, and Director Liberty Garcia.

In my office at the Institute of Animal Science (ICA).

A herd of water buffalo at Los Naranjos Enterprise, kept for milk and meat.

The guest house at which we sampled 13 different cheeses and enjoyed a bountiful and delicious barbecue luncheon of beef, broiler, and many other foods; hosted by Director Liberty Garcia.

Prior to the luncheon at a big stone house in the country, Dr. E presented the symbolic miniature western saddle and made each of the following distinguished Cubans Honorary American Cowboys: In front of Dr . E and nearest the camera: Jose Gonzalez Torres, Vice Minister, Ministry of Agriculture in charge of livestock production; on Vice Minister Gonzalez's right: Oscar Basulto Torres, First Vice Minister of Agriculture, Ministry of Agriculture.

At the Biocaribe Hotel, Havana. We returned to our rooms in the evening to find our towels artfully arranged on the bed to look like swans around a lake. I enjoyed it. The maid got a good tip!

A bounteous luncheon in a dining room near the old stone house; hosted by the Minister of Agriculture and Los Naranjos Enterprise.

We had a fabulous day at beautiful Veradero Beach, arranged by Raul Hernandez and Sylvia Hernandez. The Beach is a two-hour drive from Havana. It was Director Liberty Garcia's birthday. She is shown blowing out the candles on her birthday cake. We sang *Happy Birthday.*

Dr. E is shown giving the opening lecture to a capacity crowd in the theater at the Institute of Animal Science. Dr. Miriam Ribas, who served as interpreter, is seated next to Dr. E, and Director Liberty Garcia, Institute of Animal Science, is on the right. A full set of the Ensminger books, which Dr. E presented to Director Garcia, is shown at the front of the stage.

We met with Dr. Fernando Vecino, Minister of Higher Education, who told us about Cuba's educational system. Following the minister's presentation, Dr. E presented a miniature saddle and made him an Honorary American Cowboy.

Because of its beauty, Cuba is known as the "Pearl of the Antilles." Cuba's beauty is enhanced by royal palms.

A street scene. Note the horse-drawn vehicle, bicycles, and automobile. There are many more automobiles than horse-drawn vehicles or bicycles.

A vintage car, followed by a horse-drawn vehicle and a bicycle. All these methods of transportation are in vogue in Cuba.

The U.S. Staff of 27 shown in Havana, Cuba, following completion of the first School at ICA/Havana, and just before departure by bus to Camaguey. The picture was taken in front of the Biocaribe Hotel, Havana, where the staff stayed during the Havana School. In the background is the new state-of-the-art Biotechnology Building in Havana. (Photo by Paul O. Brackelsberg)

Dr. E and Agriservices Foundation Trustee, Guillermo Osuna, shown visiting during a bus stop.

En route from Camaguey to King Ranch we stopped for this herd of cattle that was being moved across the road to another pasture. We were told that there were 432 head in this herd.

At King Ranch, we were welcomed by a colorful cowboy flag-carrying brigade.

Dr. E is shown standing at the front entrance to King Ranch House, Cuba. On the wall is the *Running W,* brand of world famed King Ranch of Texas.

Entrance to King Ranch House. Note the *Running W* brand of King Ranch.

Dining room of King Ranch House. Dr. E is shown holding a table in which an American flag is inlaid.

In a rodeo at King Ranch-Cuba, a bull rider suffered a broken collar bone when a bull fell on him. Later, the smiling cowboy, with shoulder and arm in a cast, came by to let us know that he was O.K. At that time, Dr. E presented a miniature western saddle to him and made him an Honorary American Cowboy. Dr. Ernesto Hechavarria, Manager of King Ranch (near cowboy), and Dr. Arnold del Toro look on.

Preceding the luncheon, Dr. E is shown with Antonio Valido Guiterrez, Director of the Cattle Breeding Enterprise, Rescate de Sanguily Farms, Camaguey. This enterprise has 32,100 acres of land and employs 740 people. They have cattle, horses, and sheep, and an embryo transfer center. They have 4,000 cattle and 120 brood mares—mostly Arabians.

At Rescate de Sanguily Farms, the embryo/AI staff briefed us, in which they effectively used a number of charts.

Our staff looking over a herd of Zebu cows at Rescate de Sanguily Farms, Camaguey.

Dan and Sheila Banke reach for bananas at a banana plantation near Camaguey. Sheila is a daughter of Ron Baker, one of my former students of whom I am very proud.

Dr. E holding the beans on a coffee bush, in a 15-year-old plantation.

This huge coffee cup at Villa Tayabito, where we stayed while in Camaguey, and where we had most of our meals, evoked a broad smile from Dr. E—a true coffee lover. Coffee is actually made in this huge cup.

The attractive building in which the Camaguey School was held. Three of our staff are standing in front: *left to right:* Dr. Louise Giamalva, M.D., Dr. Mike Giamalva, and Heather Will.

Dr. E shown drinking strong Cuban coffee from a huge metal coffee cup. The coffee is made in a cloth filter that drips into the metal cup.

During the School in Camaguey, Dr. E was assigned a spacious office. Dr. E is shown seated at his desk. *Standing, left to right:* Ing. Wilfredo Marshall; Rector Carlos Diaz Barranco, Dr. Miriam Ribas; and Iris Cruz Gomez, Director of the School of Political Sciences, Camaguey University.

At the closing session of the school in Camaguey, Dr. E introduced the U.S. staff, which prompted a standing ovation in the theater room.

Mario Santiesteban, Delegate of the Minister of Agriculture in Camaguey, is shown presenting a miniature Cuban saddle to Dr. E following dinner this evening. Ing. Wilfredo Marshall served as interpreter.

Rector Carlos Diaz Barranco is shown presenting Dr. E a beautiful carved wood art object at the closing ceremony in Camaguey.

Julian Rizo Alvarez, the highest ranking government official in Camaguey Province, joined us for dinner and extended a warm welcome. Following dinner, Dr. E presented Julian Rizo Alvarez a miniature western saddle and made him an Honorary American Cowboy. That same evening, Cuban friends presented a Cuban saddle to Dr. E and made him an Honorary Cuban Cowboy. So, Dr. E suggested to Julian Rizo Alvarez that they ride the range together, and that Dr. E drink the strong coffee, and that Mr. Julian Rizo Alvarez drink the rum.

The Manager of the Hotel Villa Tayabito where we stayed, 60 employees of the hotel, a band, and many of our Camaguey friends bade us farewell when we departed.

En route from Camaguey to Havana, we stopped our bus in order to get a picture of these oxen. Oxen consume forage instead of fuel!

From the penthouse where we had dinner, we could see the dome of the capitol building of Cuba, which was patterned after the United States capitol building in Washington, D.C.

Penthouse dinner in Havana, hosted by the Minister of Science, Technology, and Environment on our last night in Cuba. *Left to right:* Director Liberty Garcia, Dr. Miriam Ribas, Jose Gonzalez Torres, Vice Minister in Charge of Livestock Production at the Ministry of Agriculture, Dr. E, and Audrey.

Ramon Castro, brother of President Fidel Castro, whom the Ensmingers met during their 1976 visit, came to dinner at the House of Scientists to renew acquaintance with the Ensmingers and meet the U.S. group. Presently, Ramon Castro serves as consultant to the Ministry of Agriculture.

Sheila Banke, Audrey Ensminger, Rusty Armstrong, and Heather Will, enjoying a refreshment break.

A portrait of the ladies in our group when they visited the Camaguey Ballet Company.

One of the old houses at the Jesus Suarez Gayol Cooperative.

The new houses at the cooperative.

1996
AG-TECH SCHOOL IN KIEV, UKRAINE

Dr. E did not write a report after the Kiev, Ukraine Ag-Tech School in 1996, because Iowa State University (ISU) agreed that they would do this. This was the first school for which ISU assumed the greater responsibility, but Dr. E had promised to give the opening lecture.

In preparation for the opening lecture, Dr. E contacted all the land grant colleges for their latest research. It was a mammoth project, as were all our projects. It took us many hours of follow-up, then organizing, writing captions, securing Russian translations, and having the typesetting and printing done. ISU kindly made the slides for the lecture.

On August 27, we left San Francisco and arrived in Frankfurt early the next morning. We got some sleep, then went to a briefing with the other staff members who had been arriving from various parts of the world. Fortunately, at the Frankfurt airport, there is a very good hotel nearby—just a short walk on an overpass.

The title of the 95-page book was *Ensminger's World Book—state of the world's people, animals, and food.*

August 29

At the Kiev airport, the faculty of the school was met by the first vice rector of the National Agricultural University of Ukraine (NAUU), Dr. Surduk. We were transported to the NAUU and checked into our rooms.

The university had just transformed a section of apartments into a hotel for their visitors because the downtown hotels were too far away. It made it convenient for us to walk to the cafeteria for our meals, and to the classrooms.

Rector, Dr. D. Melnichuk (NAUU) and Dr. G. A. Bogdanov (Ukrainian Academy of Agricultural Sciences) greeted the party at a reception in the evening. For most of the party, this was their first opportunity to enjoy Ukrainian food.

August 30

In the morning we departed in buses and vans for a day in rural Ukraine. We were accompanied by Dr. Reznichenko (vice rector, NAUU) and Dr. Bogdanov.

Anatoly Danilenko, the Chairman of the Agricultural Committee of the Parliament of Ukraine, had arranged a tour of the collective farm some 80 miles from Kiev. Mr. Danilenko is also the manager in charge of an exemplary farm with a very well-developed infrastructure. We had the opportunity to view its combines (for wheat), hog facilities and new orchards. A visit to a newly built church and to its hospital was also a nice touch.

Then we went to see the monument to the famous Ukrainian writer and poet, Taras Schevchenko. The monument is located in the region

The monument to Taras Schevchenko.

south of Kiev (Cherkasy), Kaniv town. The monument is impressive. It is built on the bank of the Denpro River,the largest river in Ukraine.

On the way back, we had dinner at the local fancy restaurant, where the hosts served us traditional Ukrainian meals. It was interesting that the restaurant is a business venture of the local semi-professional soccer team.

While the rest of the faculty enjoyed a day of agriculture, culture, and fellowship, Dr. E and Dr. Elena Zharkikh worked on the opening presentation.

August 31

During the morning we toured a large dairy farm located adjacent to the Kiev airport. This large dairy farm is involved in genetics research to enhance the dairy industry by improving the quality of bulls available for AI programs. We observed some of the cows in an alfalfa pasture with irrigation equipment nearby in the pastures and corn fields. The corn is planted after the winter wheat has been harvested. The corn is cut for silage production because it does not have adequate time to mature before the expected frost in early October.

Our afternoon visit was to the State Pedigree Poultry-Breeding Farm "Polesskiy" west of Kiev. This poultry genetics farm system consists of nine farms used to produce grandparent broiler breeding stock.

The farm system spans two communities and produces much of the grain used to feed the broiler breeders. The system includes a feed processing center, a hatchery, and a premix manufacturing center in which feed additives were blended and prepared for distribution to feed processors.

Dr. E and Audrey returned early from the farm tours to do a "dry run" on the opening presentation. Doug Kenealy, David Acker, and Colin Scanes worked with our Ukrainian colleagues in setting up the auditorium, stage, and projectors for Dr. E's opening presentation and then assisted with the dry run.

September 1

The faculty of the school was invited to NAUU's Knowledge Day. This is held at the beginning of each academic year with students, parents, faculty, administrators, dignitaries, etc. Among the dignitaries were Vice Prime Minister Zubets, Mr. Horuschko (Minister of Agriculture), Mr. Danilenko (Chairman of the Agricultural Committee of the Parliament of the Ukraine), and from the United States Dr. E, Dr. Kozak (Provost, Iowa State University), Dr. Topel (Dean, Iowa State University), and Dr. Caffee (Chancellor, Louisiana State University).

Knowledge Day is really an orientation for the incoming freshman students. The students declare their majors and stand in the appropriate section. There are demonstrations by the upper classmen showing the sports available, the music and dancing

Dr. Melnichuk (President of NAUU) and other faculty and dignitaries march into the athletic field as the band plays.

group, and the other facets of life at the university. It gives the freshmen a feeling of belonging to a very special group of people. It is a fine introduction to their future college life. Even we experienced the warm welcome, and we weren't even students!

After President Melnichuk made his introductory comments, he introduced Dr. E. With only a few minutes for preparation, Dr. E made an excellent five-minute speech. He urged the students to not only excel academically, but to consider some philanthropic work. He said to remember that we now live in one world and we must maintain the peace by helping those less fortunate. Afterwards, Dr. Melnichuk said he wished that the whole student body could have heard Dr. E's talk.

President Melnichuk presented the honored guests with beautiful engraved cut-glass vases and other appropriate gifts.

As a finale, they had some horse events. Dr. Douglas Kenealy, ISU, represented our group by dressing in traditional Cossack attire and riding a horse around the track, as well as taking a ride in a horse-drawn vehicle.

Dr. E speaks to the students and faculty at Knowledge Day.

The NAUU folk dancers.

Dr. Kenealy in a carriage.

Dr. Kenealy, ISU, in Cossack attire.

In the evening, they had a special dinner party with many toasts in the traditional Russian manner.

September 3

At 8:50 a.m., Dr. Zubets, President of the Academy of Agricultural Sciences, and Rector Melnichuk introduced Dr. E. Promptly at 9:00 a.m., Dr. E rang the bell to open the school. This was a general session with all staff and enrollees. There were over 500 in attendance.

After the national anthems for both countries were played, Dr. E commenced his lecture. His special interpreter was Dr. Helen Zharkikh from Odessa.

She had been Dr. E's interpreter for the 1993 school. She was formerly head of the Language Department at the University of Odessa, and currently was working on a big government project.

Dr. E is waiting at the podium to start the school.

Dr. E is at the podium and in the process of giving out the Russian translation of *Feeds & Nutrition*. Standing left to right: Dean Topel, Dr. Scanes, Dr. Acker, Dr. Marple, and Dr. Kenealy, all from ISU.

Dr. Bogdanov was instrumental in setting up a corner in honor of Dr. E. He had Dr. E's portrait, his books, and other items that told of Dr. E's activities. President Melnichuk is shown here with Dr. E and Audrey.

Before starting his lecture, Dr. E presented copies of the Russian translation of his book *Feeds & Nutrition* which had just come off press.

Dr. E finished his lecture on time and received a standing ovation.

Along the way we were informed that the president of Ukraine wished to meet us. At the appointed hour, we were taken to his office building and, after being checked by numerous guards along the halls and doors through which we passed, we finally came to the president's office.

He greeted us warmly and we sat at a large conference table.

We had a very nice visit and President Kuchma invited Dr. E to return in 2002 for a very special anniversary of the country. Alas, it was not to be.

That evening, the interview was shown on the local television station.

We attended some of the classes. Dr. Zharkikh is sitting to Dr. E's right.

Dr. E is shown here making President Kuchma of Ukraine an Honorary American Cowboy. It was something he liked to do all over the world, because it broke the ice.

1997
THE TIANSHAN MOUNTAINS, URUMQI, CHINA WE SAW

On April 18, 1997, we received a telephone call and a long fax letter from Liliang He, wife of former foreign minister Huang Hua, in Beijing, China. Mrs. Huang described in detail a large livestock project in the Tianshan Mountain area in the autonomous region of Xinjiang. Located on the Silk Road, Urumchi is the largest city in the region. Xinjiang borders on the west with Kazakstan. We had visited Urumchi previously in 1983.

It was an extremely fascinating project. It had been partially developed to help the Cossacks who live in the Tianshan Mountains. Because of the two compelling reasons—the government of China's request (which came by way of the former foreign minister, Mr. Huang Hua) and the fact that it would help the people of that area—It was impossible for Dr. E to turn it down.

As we would be going in July, we proceeded to make our plans and reservations.

Meanwhile, in May, the Huang Huas came to Fresno for a visit. They arrived on May 10, in time for lunch, and left on May 11 after lunch.

We ate lunch at the Ramada Inn, then went to the foundation headquarters for an afternoon meeting.

The Huang Huas came to see the Ensmingers as a result of their son, Bing, a Harvard graduate, who is interested in the mammoth sheep/cattle/horse project in Xinjiang province. Bing had visited the Ensmingers in 1986 after finishing his degree at Harvard.

During our afternoon meeting, we learned the details of the project. It was to be a cooperative venture between the government of China, the China Carrie Corporation (which had received a low-interest loan from the Spanish government), and the Xinjiang Academy of Animal Sciences in Urumqi.

The Huang Huas stated that the proposal calls for the production of 700,000 sheep/cattle/horse skins per year. The reason for production of animal skins was for a factory that would be making leather coats to be exported to foreign markets.

Gala Dinner

We had a gala dinner in honor of the Huang Huas on May 10, with 32 invited guests. Both Mr. And Mrs. Huang Hua addressed the group. At the close of the meeting, the Huang Huas and the Ensmingers exchanged gifts. The Ensmingers gave the Huang Huas a framed copy of "Home on the Range" and several of their books. The Huang Huas gave the Ensmingers a limited copy (100 only) of a

At the Harris Ranch with Bing Huang in 1986.

On left, Dr. E (standing); Justice Larry O'Neill; Clovis City Manager, Kathy Millison; on the right Huang Hua; Pastor G. L. Johnson; Marilynn Dunn; Sheriff Steve Magarian; and Audrey (standing).

Luncheon for Mr. & Mrs. Huang Hua.

1,500-year-old painting. The Ensmingers air mailed their gifts to the Huang Huas in China.

We spent their last morning at the foundation headquarters working on the schedule for our visit to Beijing and Xinjiang and various other items relating to our trip in July. Then, we had a farewell luncheon in our home before we took them to the airport.

We Arrived in Beijing

Mrs. Huang Hua, Zhao Yue (Mr. Huang Hua's secretary), and Mr. Yao met us upon our arrival at the Beijing airport. They took us to the Minzu Hotel, where we had a very comfortable room and good food from July 16 to July 20, when we departed for Urumqi.

Gala Dinner

Mr. And Mrs. Huang Hua hosted a fabulous 12-course dinner at the Beijing Hotel in our honor, with 24 of our friends in attendance. At that time, Mrs. Ensminger and I made a 45-minute slide presentation on the worldwide work of the Ensmingers and Agriservices Foundation. The evening was characterized by many toasts and many pictures. During the evening, we made an appointment to meet with the Minister of Agriculture upon our return from Urumqi, for the purpose of arranging a realistic and workable China policy on the importation of semen and fertilized embryos, thereby giving China access to the greatest animal genetic material in the world, which is in the United States.

Dinner party at the Beijing Hotel. *Left to right, seated:* Mrs. Cheng Pielieu; Prof. Cheng Peilieu; Dr. E; Mr. Huang Hua; Audrey; Dr. Lu Liang Shu, former President of the Academy of Agricultural Science of China (Dr. Lu also spearheaded the movement recommending Dr. And Mrs. Ensminger for the World Food Prize). *Left to right, standing:* Xing Zheng, daughter of Dr. And Mrs. Cheng Pielieu; Prof. Suo Ying, Chief Dietitian Xuanwu Hospital Affiliate of Capital Medical University, Beijing; Hua Yun, Carrie Enterprises, Deputy Division Chief, Property & Engineering Department; Mr. Yao Hongwen, Assistant to General Manager, China Carrie Enterprises, Property & Engineering Department; Mrs. Huang Hua; and Mr. Wang Pingwa.

The Beijing That We Saw

Audrey and I had visited China five previous times, the last time in 1984. In the meantime, Beijing was transformed into a beautiful and modern city with wide streets and many 20 to 25 story buildings—most of which have the unique Chinese artistic touch. China is retaining its identity, but increasingly embracing American customs in clothing and food (there are now 30 McDonald's in Beijing, along with

Audrey and I are eating lunch at McDonald's in Beijing.

Kentucky Fried Chicken and other fast food services). One day in Beijing, we heard the song "You are My Sunshine."

We Traveled to Urumqi

We flew from Beijing to Urumqi on a Russian-built airplane in the company of Zhao Yue. Mr. Yao had left earlier. It was a comfortable 3 hour and 10 minute flight, with the plane departing and arriving right on time. In flight we were served a good luncheon.

We arrived in Urumqi where we were met by a delegation consisting of Mr. Yao and his group and taken to the Holiday Inn, a four-star hotel managed by Jan Hilhorst, a very personable Hollander.

Following dinner one evening the pianist in the hotel lobby made us feel at home by playing "Home on the Range" and "Auld Lange Syne," I threw the pianist a kiss!

The Holiday Inn restaurant was located to the left of the white marble foyer. The centerpiece of the buffet area was changed every three or four days, but this horse rearing was the most appropriate one according to Dr. E (barely visible on the left).

Xinjiang Academy of Science

The staff of Xinjiang Academy of Science showed us their laboratories and their modern equipment, followed by a luncheon, after which we returned to the academy for a briefing relative to the project.

That evening, the academy and Mr. Yao hosted

At the Xinjiang Academy of Animal Science they gave us a briefing. There was a large black conference table laden with fresh fruits and drinks. There were about 20 staff members involved.

Typical scene in the Tianshan Mountains in Xinjiang Autonomous Region, which borders on Russia. This is at an elevation of 10,000 feet. They get 50 inches of snow and it is bitter cold. Audrey and I were the first foreigners ever permitted in this area. It is the last great frontier in the Orient. The yurt is the "home on the range" for the Cossack family, each family of which owns and operates about 400 sheep. A lesser number of Cossacks raise cattle, Mongolian ponies, yak, and camels.

They presented Audrey and me each with a beaded hat similar to the Moroccan fez.

At the animal breeding center in Urumqi. *Left to right:* Prof. Guo, Dr. E, and Jian Zhang, the academy staff member who acted as our interpreter. He had spent some time in Australia, so his English was good.

a dinner in our honor at a four-star hotel. About 20 members of the academy, as well as Mr. Yao and his staff, were present. The dinner was characterized by many toasts and many pictures.

The next day we visited the animal breeding center where they showed us their stud bulls. There, we also saw pictures of Mr. He Kang and Prof. Cheng Peileu made during their earlier vists.

Tianshan Mountain Area

Our caravan to the Tianshan Mountain area consisted of 5 cars and 18 people, including an M.D. (Dr. Fong Ourbr) and oxygen for the higher altitude (which the Ensmingers didn't need); nevertheless, we appreciated their precaution.

The Tianshan Mountain area is the last great frontier of the Orient. Its beauty is breathtaking. The valleys, which are often between steep snow-capped mountains (in July) are devoted to stock raising, primarily sheep, cattle, and horses, along with some yak and camels. It is an especially great sheep country, with few trees and short grass in the valleys.

Dr. E is listening to the Chinese interpretation of his having made Governor Bao and another Chinese government official Honorary American Cowboys.

We arrived at the Hejing Hotel in Hejing County, where Governor Bao hosted a dinner in our honor, featuring an entire roasted lamb.

The next day, Governor Bao showed us an abandoned lamb slaughtering operation, and some of the irrigation of Hejing County, plus many poplar trees, Red Deer, and a lamb fattening operation. We had a late lunch in a partial cave house (for winter warmth) and used nature's bushes and trees as toilets.

The following morning we started up the Tianshan Mountains over very rough roads. En route, after a barbecue at the side of the road and beside a beautiful stream, we stopped in the mountains to see a synthetic pasture (an experimental seeded pasture).

We arrived at the White Swan Yurt Motel in the evening. After moving into our individual yurts, (where we spent two nights without running water and trying to keep warm under a pile of blankets) we went to dinner in the largest building. It was a festive meal.

White Swan Lake

Some 10,000 to 20,000 white swans (according to Mr. Huang Hua) come to the White Swan Lake Wildlife Preserve to mate and nest each year. Also, there are many cranes in the area. The white swans winter in the Indian Ocean.

En route back to the White Swan Yurt Motel we stopped at a horse farm consisting of two yurts and 10 or 12 mares which were producing milk. The milk is fermented and very good; it tastes like buttermilk. The mares are milked two times daily, and each mare produces 2 to 4 liters of milk daily. The Ensmingers sat on a blanket in a yurt as they enjoyed the mare's milk.

We also stopped at a view spot on a promontory where a tourist group was having lunch. The lamb was freshly slaughtered (on grass) and then boiled in a nearby iron kettle. The slaughterer used a large, sharp knife in cutting up the lamb. He was a master slaughterer!

The next morning we stopped at a yurt for breakfast in a large pasture, with goats in the foreground and a beautiful view of the mountains be-

White Swan Lake Breeding Preserve. Audrey is standing on a viewpoint with the White Swan Lake marshes and river in the background.

yond the yurt door. Following breakfast, they gave me a real live horse, which they suggested be named after me; which they would keep for my return. The horse was a spirited, beautiful light gray (almost white) six-year-old Mongolian pony standing about 12.2 hands high.

Following the horse ceremony, documents creating a three-way cooperative agreement for development of the project were signed on a portable covered table out on the pasture. The order of the three signatures: Governor Bao, Mr. Yao, and President Guo, Xinjiang Academy of Animal Science.

At the end of the ceremonies on the pasture, Audrey and I gave an Eisenhower silver dollar to

In the Tianshan Mountain area, the Cossacks (the greatest horsemen of the area) presented to Dr. E a beautiful Mongolian pony which they named "Dr. E." In this photo, Dr. E is shown anointing the pony traditionally by putting mare's milk on his forehead, which means "he is mine." Dr. E said, "They also promised to take care of my pony until I return."

Signing the agreement in the Tianshan Mountains. At the table *left to right:* Mr. Yao, Governor Bao, and President Guo, Xinjiang Academy.

each of the 18 Tianshan Mountain Club members, plus about 12 or 15 to the local Mongolian people who had assembled—we made certain that each of the several children got a souvenir dollar (one mother wept with joy).

Return to Urumqi

We then drove to Urumqi, stopping for a picnic lunch at a memorial beside the road, and arriving in Urumqi very late (about 1:30 a.m.). The next day was declared a day of rest.

The next day the Academy of Animal Science staff and Mr. Yao detailed the Tianshan Mountain project and showed an excellent video tape of our travels in the Tianshan Mountain area.

The following day we visited a state dairy farm where we saw one barn with 200 Simmental cows and another barn with 147 Holstein cows. The manager of the dairy, along with his two assistants, favored the Simmentals because, as they put it: "They provide both milk and beef for the local people."

The next day we visited a carpet factory, where souvenirs were available, and beautiful all-wool carpets were being made.

In the afternoon, we were told that Minister He Kang, China's newly retired Minister of Agriculture happened to be visiting Urumqi and requested to see us. We were picked up by President Guo and a driver and traveled quite a distance to an army base, where Minister He was staying. He welcomed us warmly and we had a good visit.

In the evening we had dinner at the Hall of the People, with the dinner hosted by Mr. Yao and the Xinjiang Academy of Animal Science.

The visit with Minster He Kang. *Left to right:* Dr. E, He Kang, Audrey, President Guo.

Return to Beijing

We flew from Urumqi to Beijing. President Guo and several of his staff saw us off. In order to spare the Ensmingers from standing in line, they arranged for a special car to take us directly to the plane for boarding, which we appreciated.

Soon after we registered at the Minzu Hotel, Zhu Baochen called, whom we had not been in touch with for more than 25 years, wanting to take us out to dinner (which we accepted).

The following day Prof. Cheng Peilieu and his daughter, Xing, came to the Minzu Hotel and took us to lunch in the restaurant off the lobby. It was most enjoyable.

The next day Audrey went shopping with Zhao Yue, Mr. Huang Hua's secretary, at the palace open air shops. The prices for all the quality items were unbelievably low.

The farewell banquet was held at the Hall of the People. Everyone is allowed to have a dinner or other activity in one of the many, many rooms in the hall. The table was laid with fine crystal and elegant candelabra.

The day after that, the Ensmingers (accompanied by Zhao Yue) had an appointment with the Ministry of Agriculture for the purpose of getting a workable change in protocol so that China could import semen and fertilized embryos from the United States.

The Ensmingers were later hosted for dinner at the Peking Roast Duck Restaurant. Those present were Mr. and Mrs. Huang Hua and their son Bing, Zhao Yue, and Mr. Yao.

The following morning we departed for the Beijing airport where we boarded a flight to San Francisco, changed planes, and flew home.

My Conclusion

The "musts" for this project are water, a railroad for low-cost and reliable freight transportation, improved roads for access, good laborers and superior management. Water in the project area is in abundance, and a new railroad and improved roads will be completed within another two years.

AWARDS

This book would not be complete without recording for posterity the numerous honors and awards that Audrey and I have received. Thus, a chronological listing follows. Although I am deeply grateful for these honors, in listing them I am reminded of what Golda Meier, the outspoken prime minister of Israel from 1969 to 1974, used to admonish her friends under similar circumstances. Said she: "You need not be humble, because you are not that great."

Actually, I *am* humble because I received more awards than anyone is entitled to. I was always surprised and delighted that I would get an award for doing something that I loved.

■ In **1926**, at age 18, I was awarded the *Missouri Ruralist* trophy for 4-H Club leadership.

■ In **1955**, the FFA made me an Honorary State Farmer.

■ In **1958**, the animal science students at Washington State University hung my portrait in the Lariat Club Hall of Fame

■ In **1960**, I was the recipient of the *Distinguished Teachers Award* of the American Society of Animal Science.

Chancellor Schooling presents me with Faculty-Alumni Gold Medal in 1975.

■ In **1972**, I was made an Honorary Member of the Indian Council of Farmers, New Delhi, India.

■ In **1975**, I received both the Faculty-Alumni Gold Medal and the Citation of Merit from the University of Missouri.

■ In **1975**, I received the Distinguished Teacher Award of the National Association of Colleges and Teachers of Agriculture (NACTA).

Dr. Robert A. Alexander, President of NACTA, presents me with their Distinguished Teacher Award in 1975. Audrey is in the center.

■ In **1976**, I was made an Honorary Member of the Association of Spanish Purebred Horse Breeders of Guatemala.

■ In **1984**, Washington State University named its new Beef Cattle Research Center after me.

■ In **1984**, I was made an honorary professor of Huazhong Agricultural College at Wuhan, Hubei Province, China.

Preceding the ceremony, an elaborate formal announcement and invitation was passed out to the members of our group. It read as follows:

The Huazhong Agricultural College
requests the honor of your

Huazhong Agricultural College, Wuhan, conferred upon Dr. E the title of "Honorary Professor." *Left to right:* Robert Price, El Paso, Texas; the interpreter; Dr. E; and Vice President Jin Kaizhu. Note the sign above the head table.

presence at the ceremony to confer
the title of Honorary Professor upon
Dr. M. E. Ensminger, President of
Agriservices Foundation, U.S.A.
on Wednesday, the fourth of
July, nineteen eighty-four
at eight o'clock a.m.
in the Reporting Hall

This was the first honorary professorship ever conferred by Huazhong Agricultural College. Addresses were made by the following: Professor Sun Jizhong, President, Juazhong Agricultural College; Mr. Chang Kuangho, Vice Chairman of Hubei Technical and Science Association; and Professor L. R. Qin, DVM, Department of Animal Husbandry and Veterinary Medicine, Huazhong Agricultural College.

Dr. Sun wrote:

> Dr. Ensminger also has a deep feeling toward the Chinese people. Since 1972, he has traveled to China five times to give lectures, which have been beneficial to the production and development of Animal Science in China, and to the teaching and researches of our college. Also, Doctor Ensminger has played a positive roll in promoting the friendship between the peoples of the United States and China, and in communications in science and technology between the two countries. I wish to take this opportunity to express our gratitude to Dr. Ensminger.
>
> In view of Dr. Ensminger's academic attainments, his contributions to science as well as his concern, help and support to Huazhong Agricultural College, the Academic Committee of the college, with the approval of the Ministry of Agriculture, Animal Husbandry & Fishery, is pleased and honored to confer upon Dr. Ensminger the title of *Honorary Professor of Huazhong Agricultural College,* and to award him his Honorary Professor Certificate.

I am giving my response.

Response by Dr. M. E. Ensminger following conferment of title of Honorary Professor:

> Mr. Vice President Jin, distinguished faculty, Chinese and American friends.
>
> I am humbly grateful to you for the high honor that you have bestowed upon me this morning. I accept it on behalf of all those who have helped make me what I am, including Mrs. Ensminger and my many Chinese and American friends. I also accept it as a symbol of the increasingly close working relationship between the scientists and all other peoples of our two great nations.
>
> On July 4, 1776, the United States was an unfinished miracle. Today, we are still an unfinished miracle—for the best is ahead. Today, too, China is an unfinished miracle, for your best is ahead.
>
> The world owes much to China.

■ In **1985**, an oil portrait of me was placed in the 300-year-old Saddle & Sirloin Club Portrait Gallery of Louisville, Kentucky, which is recognized as the highest honor that can be bestowed on anyone engaged in the livestock industry. The portrait was painted by the noted artist, and my longtime friend, Tom Phillips.

The program participants were: Dr. Leo K. Bustad, Dean Emeritus, College of Veterinary Medicine, Washington State University, Pullman, Washington; Dr. Elvin D. Taysom, Professor Emeritus, Arizona State University, Tempe, Arizona; Dr. Joseph P. Fontenot, President, American Society of Animal Science/Department of Animal Science, Virginia Polytechnic Institute & State University, Blacksburg,

Dr. Leo K. Bustad, Ph.D., DVM, Dean Emeritus, College of Veterinary Medicine, Washington State University, Pullman, Washington, and one of Dr. E's former students of whom he is very proud, presided when the portrait was placed in the famed Saddle & Sirloin Club Gallery in 1985. Dr. E (left) and Dr. Bustad (right) are posing with the portrait, which had just been unveiled. The portrait was painted by superb animal artist Tom Phillips. I figured because he does animals so well, he would do a good job on a maverick like me.

Among those attending were most of the trustees of Agriservices Foundation. *Left to right:* Cabot Sedgwick, Judy Farr, Art Solomon, and Paula Sedgwick.

Virginia; Dr. Clair E. Terrill, U.S. Department of Agriculture, Beltsville, Maryland; Dr. Stewart H. Fowler, Professor & Head, Department of Agriculture, Berry College, Mount Berry, Georgia; W. H. (Bill) Stuart, Jr., Chairman of the Board, W. H. Stuart Ranch, Inc., Bartow, Florida; Dr. Hilton Briggs, President Emeritus, South Dakota State University, Brookings, South Dakota; Dr. W. T. (Dub) Berry, Jr., Consultant, Overland Park, Kansas; John Armstrong, Executive Vice-President, King Ranch, Inc., Kingsville, Texas; Dr. Robert Walton, President, American Breeders Service, DeForest, Wisconsin; Dr. L. S. (Bill) Pope, Director, The International Stockmen's School, Texas A&M University, College Station, Texas; William D. Farr, President, Farr Farms Co. and Farr Feeders, Inc., Greeley, Colorado; Clair Pollard, President, Sunland Ranch, Fresno, California; and Robert C. Crosby, Kentucky Fair Board, Maysville, Kentucky.

In my response, I ended the program by saying: "Now, I must be about "my father's business," for there is much to do and I have miles to go."

■ In **1987**, Mrs. Ensminger and I were the recipients of the *Humanitarian-of-the-Year Award* of the Academy of Dentistry International, which had organizations in 45 coun-

A photograph of the original oil portrait of Dr. E, by the noted artist Tom Phillips. The original painting is now in the Saddle and Sirloin Club Gallery, Louisville, Kentucky. When doing the painting, artist Tom Phillips remarked: "I want to capture your 'I've got a secret smile'—your Mona Lisa smile."

The Ensmingers with Dr. Clifford Loader (right), CEO, of the Academy of Dentistry International, at the time of the 1987 award.

tries at that time. The Ensmingers were cited for "giving freely, unselfishly, and without salary to the cause of World Food, Hunger, and Malnutrition."

■ In **1991**, I was the recipient of the *Outstanding Achievement Award* of the Regents of the University of Minnesota. I opened my address by saying that Sir Winston Churchill, the great Prime Minister of England, expressed my innermost feelings when he said: "We make a living by what we get, but we make a life by what we give."

■ In **1993**, Mrs. Ensminger and I were the recipients of the American Medical Association (AMA) Distinguished Service Award. Excerpts from the citation follow:

May 9, 1991, at the University of Minnesota. *Left to right:* Dr. E; Dr. C. Eugene Allen, Vice President of the Institute of Agriculture, Forestry, and Home Economics; Dr. Richard Goodrich, Head, Department of Animal Science; and Dr. Robert M. Jordan, Professor Emeritus. Dr. E is shown wearing the medallion of the *Outstanding Achievement Award of the Regents of the University of Minnesota.*

Immediately preceding our award, Mrs. Hilary Clinton addressed the 5,000 M.Ds. assembled at their annual meeting in Chicago.

> Dr. and Mrs. Ensminger have dedicated their lives to lessening world hunger and malnutrition . . . Their work includes the monumental books, *Food and Nutrition Encyclopedia* and *Food for Health* . . . Their creativity and energy have contributed to the health and well-being of people everywhere.

Dr. John Lee Clowe, American Medical Association (AMA), is shown presenting the AMA's prestigious *Distinguished Service Award* (plaque) to Dr. and Mrs. M. E. Ensminger before the house of delegates, AMA, 142nd Annual Meeting, Chicago, Illinois, June 13, 1993. This is the highest award that the AMA bestows on nonphysicians.

The Ensmingers are shown here with U.S. Surgeon General, Antonia C. Novello, M.D. at the annual meeting of the American Medical Association, Chicago, June 13, 1993, when the Ensmingers received AMA's prestigious Distinguished Service Award.

Donald Palmisano, M.D. and his wife Robin spearheaded our nomination. They spent a weekend with us and Donald videotaped an extended interview to show to the committee.

Conferring the Doctor of Laws (LL.D.) upon Dr. E. On March 27, 1994, the prestigious Ukrainian State Agricultural University, Kiev, Ukraine, conferred upon Dr. E. the Doctor of Laws (LL.D.). For the first time ever, the university officials flew to the United States to confer the degree. The ceremony was held at the Agriservices Foundation Headquarters, Clovis, California.

Left to right: Dr. V. I. Vlassov, Agricultural Attaché, Embassy of Ukraine; Dr. G. A. Bogdanov, Academician, Ukraine Academy of Agricultural Sciences, Kiev; Rector (President) D. O. Melnichuk, National Agricultural University of Ukraine; Kyle Bennet, Stillwell, OK (Dr. E's grandnephew); Dr. E; Audrey; and Aileen Bennett, Stilwell, OK (Dr. E's sister).

■ In **1994**, The Ukranian State Agricultural University, Kiev, Ukraine, conferred the Doctor of Laws (LL.D.) upon me. Rector (President) D. O. Melnichuk's kudos follow:

> Marion Eugene Ensminger—professor/doctor/scientist/educator/author/innovator/humanitarian. Dr. Ensminger is the best known animal scientist in the world; he is as well known throughout the former Soviet Union as in the United States. Dr. Ensminger is also the world's leading author of classic agricultural books in the 20th century; he is the author of 21 books which are in many languages and used all over the world. The whole world is his classroom. Dr. and Mrs. Ensminger have dedicated their entire lives to world food, hunger and malnutrition.

■ On **September 10, 1994**, Iowa State University made the following announcements:

- That Iowa State University will carry forward the International Ag-Tech Schools abroad that the Ensmingers started 40 years ago.
- That Iowa State University will carry forward

the Ensmingers' books in the field of animal science and human nutrition.

- That a specially designed international conference room on the campus will be named the Marion Eugene Ensminger and Audrey Helen Ensminger International Room (with a mural 8 feet high and 24 feet wide depicting the life and legacy of M. E. Ensminger), and that it will serve as a beacon for international work for the decades to come.

■ In **November 1994**, Audrey and I received an award from the American Medical Writers Association for our *Foods & Nutrition Encyclopedia*, second edition.

Audrey has just received the citation from the Executive Director of the AMWA. She addressed the 500 members at their annual meeting.

■ On **May 11, 1996**, I received the Doctor of Humane Letters from Iowa State University at their commencement exercises. In the morning, I was asked to address the animal science graduates.

Preceding the commencement, Dr. Marple and my sister Aileen assisted me with my robe.

Dr. E addressing the ISU animal science graduates.

President Jischke has just put the ISU Doctor of Humane Letters hood over my Ph.D. hood. I felt extremely honored to receive this prestigious award.

■ In **1996**, I received the American Society of Animal Science International Animal Agriculture Bouffault Award, sponsored by Roussel UCLAF, Paris, France. I was indeed honored to receive this prestigious award.

■ In **1998**, Belton High School, which I attended, started a Hall of Fame, so that students would have some role models. I was pleased and honored to be chosen in the original five.

However, the greatest awards that I ever received weren't accompanied by a plaque, trophy, medal, certificate, or any other emblem. It came straight from the heart of one of my former students of whom I am very proud, now a distinguished Trustee of Agriservices Foundation. In a letter dated September 15, 1993, W. H. (Bill) Stuart, Jr., Bartow, Florida wrote:

> Your vision, energy, and tenacity are marvels. Had your calling been the ministry, you would have exhausted sinners to repentance!

Dr. E's posthumous award was perhaps the "crown jewel" of all his awards. It was the dedication of the Marion Eugene and Audrey Helen Ensminger Room which contains the mural entitled: "The Life and Legacy of M. E. Ensminger." Dr. E had been in on all of the plans for the room and the mural, and he had seen the photos when the mural was 50% complete. We all prayed that he would be able to go to the dedication, but alas, it was not to be.

M. E. Ensminger passed away on July 5, 1998, and the dedication at ISU was held on October 31, 1998, four months later.

I am including here the ISU news release of the dedication. It tells the whole story.

AHE

W. H. (Bill) Stuart, Jr. (right), Chairman of the Board, W. H. Stuart Ranch, Inc., Bartow, Florida. Photo taken when Dr. E's portrait was presented to The Saddle and Sirloin Gallery, Louisville, Kentucky in 1985. Bill Stuart's address that evening was entitled, "Dr. E, My Professor and Student Counselor."

International Room Honors Marion Eugene Ensminger & Audrey Helen Ensminger

A highly respected international educator has been honored by Iowa State with the dedication of a conference room on campus. The dedication of the Marion Eugene Ensminger and Audrey Helen Ensminger International Room was held at 2 p.m. Saturday, October 31, in Kildee Hall. The room is in the new addition to Kildee Hall and the Meats Laboratory that houses ISU's animal science department.

For more than 30 years, Ensminger conducted international agricultural technology schools to improve livestock management practices. His relationship with ISU began in the early 1990s, when he teamed with ISU officials to conduct schools in Russia, Ukraine, Cuba and China. "Gene" Ensminger died this summer at his home in Clovis, California, at age 90. He is survived by his wife Audrey, who attended the dedication ceremony.

In 1996, ISU awarded Ensminger an honorary doctorate of humane letters to recognize his lifelong achievements in animal science, education and international agriculture.

Dr. Ensminger is highly respected in the nation, said Dennis Marple, professor and head of the animal science department. He was an excellent

There was a standing room only crowd for the dedication.

teacher and author. Marple said Ensminger excelled in teaching, writing and sharing knowledge with others. He said the dedication of the room is a way for ISU to honor Ensminger.

The new conference room will be used primarily for educational programs for international visitors and livestock groups. Every student and visitor who uses the room will have the chance to be inspired by the legacy of Dr. Ensminger and his wife Audrey, his partner in service to humanity, said David Topel, dean of the College of Agriculture.

The Ensmingers' son John, former students and colleagues and many friends attended the ceremony, as well as ISU dignitaries and foreign academicians, including Dr. G. A. Bogdanov, Academician, Secretary and Professor, Ukrainian Academy of Agricultural Science. Dr. Bogdanov presented a large portrait of Dr. Ensminger that had been created by Ukrainian artists. The large portrait is very attractively and accurately "painted" with native Ukrainian seeds.

Other guests were Elvin Taysom, Arizona State University; Rodney Bertramson, retired Dean of Agriculture, Washington State University; Bill Farr, Greeley, Colorado area cattle feeder; artist Tom Phil-

At the podium, Dr. Marple, Head of Animal Science, was M.C. for the dedication proceedings. To his left are Audrey Ensminger, and Leonard and Barbara Vanderhoop, sponsors of the mural.

Left to right: Audrey Ensminger, Dr. Bogdanov, Dean David Topel, and Dr. Dennis Marple.

lips; Robin and Donald Palmisano, nutritionist and surgeon, respectively, from New Orleans. Former students included cattleman Ron Baker and Richard Johnson of Cal State and an ISU animal science graduate. Those who had known him best lovingly shared their stories of Dr. E. They agreed that "that's the way I see it from my end of the log," was a favorite saying of Dr. E.

Another guest of honor was Vernie Thomas, president of Interstate Publishing Company, an Illinois firm originally founded by Russell Guin. Thomas related that Guin and Dr. E first signed a book contract August 13, 1949. According to Thomas, to date there have been 750,567 copies of Ensminger books in print. The best-selling title, he stated, is *The Stockman's Handbook* at 226,000 (English-only version), a fair number in textbook sales. Thomas presented copies of the original contract to Mrs. Ensminger and the University. Interstate, under an agreement with ISU, still publishes Dr. E's books.

A large mural 8' x 24' entitled *The Life and Legacy of M. E. Ensminger* dominates the room. The original idea for a mural had the approval of Dean Topel. The oil painting is the work of New York City artist Jason Gaillard. It was commissioned by a former student of Ensminger, Leonard Vanderhoop and his wife Barbara of Azusa, California. Gaillard and the Vanderhoops attended the dedication.

Gaillard told the audience that he and Dr. E had visited about the commission, but, when it came time for him to meet with Dr. E and Audrey, he was not sure he would have the necessary time to devote to the project. Dr. E encouraged him to come anyway and they would visit. Gaillard went.

Gaillard immediately sensed a bond with Dr. E when they met. Mrs. Ensminger had already gathered together an extensive collection of old photos and organized them. It was Mrs. Ensminger who early on determined the title and subject of the mural, after Dr. E broached her repeatedly about an art project.

Gaillard said Dr. E called the mural "the Silk Road to the rest of the world." That idea stayed with him as he began to work on the picture and re-

"The Life and Legacy of M. E. Ensminger"

Leonard and Barbara Vanderhoop commissioned the mural.

mained with him throughout the project. It took him twelve months to complete. The mural itself begins with a classroom in which Dr. E is teaching, the key to his life work. This education process progresses to the "Silk Road" to developing countries emphasizing crops and animals. "Dr. E," Gaillard explained, "was husband, father, teacher, educator, student who worked hard at these roles. I worked hard, too. As a son or proud grandson, I had a conscience over my shoulder: could I do this better?" Dr. E's personal integrity inspired him to paint it the very best he could. He recalled Dr. E telling about his books and the editing process, and how the publishers finally practically had to pry the manuscript from him, he just kept working on it, fine-tuning it, improving it. "They nearly had to do the same with me and this picture. I regret Dr. E didn't get to see it," he ended.

Dr. Martin C. Jischke announced at the conclusion of the event that an Ensminger Professorship in honor of David G. Topel, Dean of the College of Agriculture, will be established and that Dean Topel will be asked to be the first Chair of that position. Dean Topel has announced he will be stepping down as Dean next spring. He will return to teaching in the animal science department in the meat science area.

The meeting room is an archive for many of Ensminger's papers, memorabilia and collected works of art. Oil paintings by their friend Tom Phillips adorn the walls. Wood, ceramic terra cotta and metal animal sculpture, housed in modern glass showcases, that has been collected by the Ensmingers during their world travels adds genuine excitement. A backdrop of maple paneling and a high ceiling create warmth. State-of-the-art media equipment has been incorporated into the planning of the room. Indeed, it is a room that will well meet the needs for which it has been designed.

Jason Gaillard, the artist, and his wife, Michelle.

EPILOGUE

BY AUDREY ENSMINGER

From time to time, my closest friends would wonder how we could keep what to them seemed such a frantic pace; or in fact, why I married Gene. Let me count the ways!!!

We Both Loved the Frantic Pace

Dr. E regularly worked 18 hours a day, 365 days of the year. When we were first married and Dr. E was head of animal science at Washington State College, he worked night and day to elevate the low esteem for the department around the state. This meant attending livestock meetings, extending a helping hand to stockmen who needed an association for their animals, and letting everyone know that he was there to help. Some of his friends became concerned that he would burn himself out by the age of 35. Well, let me tell you, he went on burning himself out for another 55 years. His modus operandi never changed. He had more stamina than anyone I have ever known.

We Both Loved a Challenge and There Were Lots of Them

The challenge that is most vivid in my mind is the assignment Gene gave me one day. He said that the first least cost ration charts in his books had been worked out by some graduate students and that they used a formula. He told me to take my calculator into another office, away from the telephone and other interruptions, and try to figure out the formula. He did not know how long it would take me, but he thought it might be as long as a month.

After about two weeks of running formula after formula, I started to get a few ideas and eventually worked out the three charts. There were a dozen feeds on each chart. I knew how to check them by working them backwards. The first two worked out correctly, but the third chart did not. I realized I must still have a mistake, so I had to keep working another week. When I found the error, I ended up running all three charts again. It's too bad I couldn't have discovered the computer while I was at it!

Speaking of computers, I want you to know that when we started our business activities in the 1940s we had no computers, no copy machines, no faxes, no cell phones, no answering machines, no typesetting equipment, and electric typewriters were still relatively rare.

The method we used for multiple copies up to 10 was onion skin paper and good carbon paper. When we needed more than 10 copies, we had a thin sheet of gel in a pan, then we typed a purple stencil. We laid the purple stencil face down on the gel and smoothed it out. We removed it and then put each sheet onto the imprinted gel. Gradually, they developed a machine that we cranked to do somewhat the same process. It is hard to believe that so much technology has come in the last 50 years and that equipment for which we paid thousands of dollars can now be bought for hundreds.

We Both Loved Our Home and Our Offices Within It

When we moved to Clovis, Dr. E told me to draw up the house plan, as we needed to start building our permanent abode during the winter months, when the cost of building dropped. I had two weeks to plan it. I asked him what he wanted. He said one office for him at the back of the house, where it was quiet, and an office for me (the secretary) across the hall. So that is where they were in the original plan, which entailed 3,700 sq ft.

As the business grew, we needed more and more rooms, and we finally ended up with around 10,000 sq ft. It was a good, workable plan, with all of the offices in one area. Murt Sullivan and Gerald Lassley built the original 3,700 sq ft, but Gerald continued adding each room as we needed it. He saved us a lot of money because we recycled every window that we had to take out of the original house, and used it over again. Usually our square footage cost was about half the current rate.

We Both Loved the Books Dr. E Wrote

He loved writing them, and I loved designing the covers, finding pictures and photos for illustrating them, proofreading them, etc. Our publishers, both Russell Guin and later Vernie Thomas, allowed us to design our own covers. Not many authors are accorded that privilege.

Also, I was the "reader." Dr. E said that if it was not clear to me, then it would not be clear to the reader. Sometimes I would ask him, "Did you mean this, or that?" Then he would change it so it was crystal clear. One of the best compliments Dr. E received was from an M.D. who said that he was not really interested in livestock, but he found reading Dr. E's books very pleasurable.

We Both Loved the Schools

At our schools—Horse Science Schools, the International Stockmen's Schools, Ag-Tech Schools abroad—we operated with volunteer help. We recruited former students or former staff, along with relatives. We always took some of our current office staff to the schools. We made all the meal tickets ourselves, all the signs that were needed, etc. We operated on a tight budget.

Some of our volunteers *left to right:* Frances Johnson (my sister), Myrtle Taysom, Dr. Elvin Taysom, and me.

We Both Loved the Travel

We jokingly said that we worked our way around the world, but it was true.

It was amazing how each facet of our program helped the other facets. Because the books were known around the world, many people knew Dr. E's name. As we traveled, Dr. E inquired about, and met, outstanding animal scientists. Then, these people would be asked to be on the staff of the schools. In addition, we got some good pictures that were used in the books.

We Both Loved Good Art

We were fortunate to know three very excellent artists.

First, there was Richard F. Johnson. He was a graduate student at Washington State College, and later became Head of Animal Science at California Polytechnic University-San Luis Obispo. His proportions in drawing livestock were infallible. I once heard him say that when he asked the students to draw livestock, if the proportions were right, he knew that individual would be good at judging livestock. I knew right then, I would never have made the judging team. He did countless drawings for Dr. E's books.

Second, we used Tom Phillips of San Francisco, whose animals were also perfectly proportioned. In addition, he was superb at animal psychology. He painted several large pictures for us, which are now hanging in the Ensminger Room at Iowa State University.

Our third fine artist was Jason Gaillard of New York City, who painted the mural entitled "The Life and Legacy of M. E. Ensminger" that is in the Ensminger Room at ISU. It is a masterpiece.

We Both Loved to Entertain

As soon as we received word that we were going to have out of town guests, we would get out our mailing list of cards, and go through them to choose the guest list. Then, it was a case of sending out the invitations and keeping record of the replies, planning the menu, and, when the time came, setting up the tables and cooking the meal.

We had staff who had been through the

Margret Fox, shown sitting in her office, was also in charge of book sales.

Esther Lowery, a perfectionist, kept everything in superb condition.

routine many times. Besides Margret Fox and Esther Lowery, Greg Rivera, our gardener, helped people park their cars, then poured the wine and helped with the serving and the dishes. Greg's wife Mela was

Christmas 1994

1995, The People's Church group.

1995. The People's Church group.

Christmas 1996

also part of the regular dinner staff, and we sometimes called on other members of the Rivera family.

Besides the dinners in honor of out-of-town guests, each year we had an early Christmas dinner, as well as dinners for the staff and friends from the People's Church.

We Both Loved Animals

We loved animals so much that they were dominant fixtures of the décor.

This parade horse pranced above the fireplace.

This Trojan horse resided on the large conference table.

We had a flock (three) of sheep in the conference room.

We Both Loved Our Dogs

Dr. E mentioned the cocker spaniel dogs John grew up with earlier in this book. When we moved to California in 1962 and built a house in the country, Gene was a little apprehensive about the security for the files and materials and pictures we were collecting, so he asked the Fresno County Sheriff for suggestions. They sent out Steve Magarian who was

1972. King, Bonnie, and Happy.

assistant sheriff at the time. He suggested floodlights, as there were no streetlights, a woven steel fence, and guard dogs. We started out with German Shepherds. First there was Bonnie, followed by Butch, Happy, and King. We finally had four at one time. The more we had, the safer Dr. E felt. We then became acquainted with Rottweilers and got a pair. Gene felt even safer with Duke I and Duchess I, followed by Duke II and Duchess II.

1991. Duke II and Duchess II with Margret Fox, Dr. E, and me.

Of an evening, when Greg was working at pruning the shrubs, Duke II used to get a mouthful of the podocarpus and run for cover. He thought this was a great game, because we always chased him to retrieve it.

Last, and Most Important, We Both Loved and Were Proud of Our Son John

John was an excellent student. Although we had dinnertime activities, such as one evening when we spoke only French, or another when we listened to classical music, we never helped John with his homework. He did it all by himself.

After he graduated from the University of California-Berkeley, he spent a year at the University of British Columbia on an assistantship in zoology. He graduated from Hastings Law School, San Francisco, and went east to New York City.

John was with Warren, Gorham & Lamont, a New York publisher of tax specialty products from 1987 to 1995 where he became a senior managing editor. When Warren, Gorham & Lamont merged into the Research Institute of America, John became the director of the new organization responsible for the journals and international tax divisions. He held those responsibilities until 2000, when he founded and became the first president of Delta Hedge Publications, a publisher of tax and finance specialty journals.

1992. At the Harris Ranch Restaurant. *Left to right:* John, his lovely wife Joan, Dr. E, and me. (Joan and I share the same birthday, December 30.)

Five Girls from Canada

I did not know where to put this anecdote, but I felt it was unique. I do know that Gene did not, and John does not, keep in touch with very many friends from college days.

This is a story of five girls who have been close friends for over 60 years. In 1936, we met at the University of Manitoba, Canada as students in the Home Economics department. There were a total of 50 girls in the class of 1940. For four years, we all took the same required courses for a Bachelor of Science degree. We were not allowed to skip any of the tough courses.

For one of the courses, we lived in the Home Management House. Our group was the first group to live in the brand new house. Because we had been in every class together, we had bonded like sisters. There were Audrey, Frances, Eleanor, Ruth, and Georgina. Can you imagine that for 60 years we have met together in Vancouver, Canada as often as we can, which was every few years? Most of our class of 50 who still survive are in touch with others of our class. What a wonderful experience it has been. I do not know of many college graduates who have had such a delightful friendship.

1939. Our group in the brand new Home Management House—now the Alumni House.

1993. *Left to right:* Audrey, Frances, Ruth, Eleanor, and Georgina.

One Last Anecdote

In 1962 when we bought 20 acres on Sierra Avenue with an old farm house on it, the land was considered a farm in Fresno County, with a Fresno *County* address. Because Clovis was the nearest town, we received our mail with the address being 3699 *East* Sierra Avenue, Clovis.

As we gradually started marketing our own books, when there was a telephone order, we asked where they learned about the book. The answer was usually either "at the library" or "through a friend." As one of our guiding principles was to try to make life easier for all, we reasoned that, if we put the address and phone number in the books, it would facilitate their ordering the book.

The day soon came when the city of Clovis needed to incorporate the surrounding areas, and our location was one of them. Our address then changed from *East* to *West* Sierra: 648 *West* Sierra. The address change meant that, as we revised our books, we used the new address. When people commented on our moving, we had to explain that we were still in the same place, but the address had changed.

Due to the books being around the world, to the end of our business we were still receiving mail addressed to 3699 *West* Sierra. Fortunately, almost everyone at the Clovis post office knew where the Ensmingers could be located.

About one-half mile from our house was a small Clovis cemetery, which had been out in the country when established. We heard that only people living in Clovis at the time of purchase could buy a plot there and that they were running out of space. We decided it was closest to our beloved home at 648 West Sierra, so, in 1991, we purchased two plots to avoid trauma when the time came that they were needed.

After Dr. E's funeral, I had to decide on the lettering for his headstone. It was not difficult, because Dr. E had finished many speeches with what he wanted as his epitaph: He was a maverick who made his dreams come true.

As I wanted the design and lettering to match on my headstone, I was ordering mine at the same time. I had thought that I wanted as my epitaph: She died laughing. Somehow I didn't think most people would appreciate that, so I opted for: She was a maverick who made *his* dreams come true.

Our headstones in the Clovis cemetery.

This is goodbye until we meet again!